" ___ The ESTIMATED COST IS MORE IMPORTANT THEN THE ACTUAL COST "

AN ESTIMATE IS A FACT UNTIL ACTUAL COSTS NEGATE IT.

AM COST ESTIMATOR

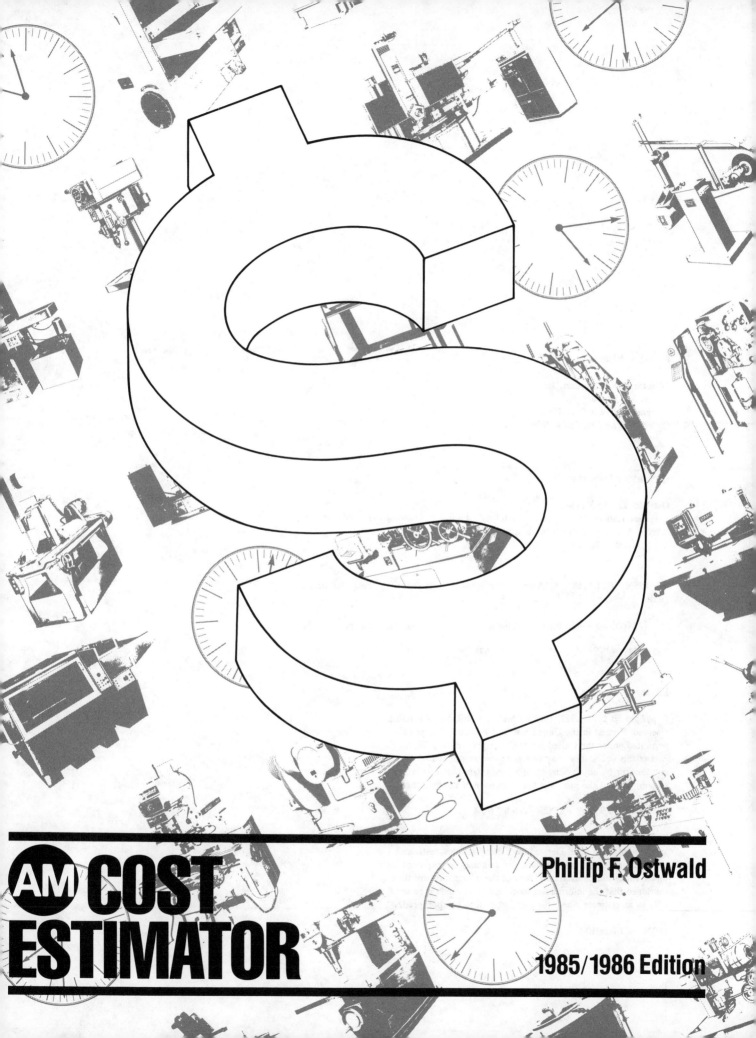

AM COST ESTIMATOR

Phillip F. Ostwald

1985/1986 Edition

Publisher: Richard H. Larsen

Director: W. M. Stocker, Jr.
Editor: Jeff McCartney
Designer: Roberta Rezk-Plesko
Cover Designer: Marianne Johnston

LIBRARY OF CONGRESS

Ostwald, Phillip F., date
   American machinist cost estimator / Phillip F. Ostwald — 1982 ed.- —
[New York] : American Machinist, c1981-
      v. : ill. ; 28 cm.

   ISSN 0731-5368 = American machinist manufacturing cost estimating
guide.

   1. Metal-work—Estimates—Collected works.   I. American   machinist.   II.
Title.
TS213.087   671   81-83792
                                                 AACR 2   MARC-S

Library of Congress   [8401]

The publisher and author make no statement regarding the
accuracy of these data. Derived from many sources, tests, and
manufacturer's recommendations, the data may be inappropriate
under various circumstances. Users of the information are thus
cautioned that the information contained herein should be used
only as an estimate where the user judges it to be appropriate.

ISBN 0-07-606910-9

Contents

Preface

With this edition of the *1985–1986 AM Cost Estimator,* history is being made. For the first time a manual providing manufacturing estimating information has been available for several consecutive editions. In the construction industry, of course, estimating manuals have been in existence for more than 50 years. This has not been the situation in manufacturing until *American Machinist* of McGraw-Hill undertook this important task.

Changes and improvements are a result of this renewal. Growth in pages and content is obvious to those that remember the first edition in 1982. This information provides a valuable service for the many businesses that require time and cost values for manufactured parts, services, and products.

The *1985–1986 AM Cost Estimator* continues to provide estimating information for the professionals who work in this important occupation. While the material is directed to the "estimator," this may not be your title or responsibility within your organization. However, it is our observation that many titles and types of backgrounds do this work, and for sake of simplicity, we address these remarks to an estimator, one who needs to appraise the time or cost of manufactured products. The reasons for this business appraisal are also equally diverse.

New to this edition are additions to the Operation Costs and Element Estimating Data sections. The Instructions section has been revised and simplified. Those using this *Estimator* for the first time will find it easy to use.

Operation Costs, included in Section IV, have been expanded to include electronic fabrication and pack-

aging, two new items that provide costs for setup and cycle or "run time." These direct labor wages are estimated by Items. The time values are condensations of the Element Data provided in Section V. The Item direct labor costs are based on the central part of the United States and use Productive Hour Costs. This information has been found to be broadly applicable to other regions; however, a method is provided which allows the estimator to change location and time period. These details, along with specifics on how to complete an estimate, are found in the Instructions.

Most estimators will use Section V, Element Estimating Data, which is the largest part of the *Estimator.* This section has been increased by twenty-five new technologies. Many of these technologies are recent, while others are divisions of older technologies. This reflects two objectives of the new edition: to expand the cutting technologies and to provide better coverage of existing and well known machining, processing, or bench work. There are twelve new technologies within the Electronic Fabrication section. All are suitable for the many job shops and product manufacturers who provide services, parts, or products that require estimating data. This follows our desire to provide information as we develop it. Manufacturing is diversified, especially when one considers the variety of ways to produce a product.

Our attention to "coverage" suggests that some information should be divided into greater detail. Numerical controlled turning lathes is an example of this expansion. We have divided this section into turning and chucking. Automatic screw machines are now segregated into single and multispindle types. The notion of coverage implies that data for older equipment are necessary for many shops that still find ways to use older equipment in primary or secondary service.

With this expansion of data, a total of 135 cost numbers are new in the Operation Cost Section. We have also added new numbers for time estimating in Section V, Element Estimating Data. This time section has over 15,000 time values specified for over 100 machine, process, and bench identifications. We plan to continue it as the most comprehensive and authoritative work of its kind. The research and technical effort to expand the *Estimator* is considerable, and the many contributions by practitioners, machine tool builders, associations, and others interested in the art and science of manufacturing estimating are appreciated.

Despite these impressive numbers, we recognize the unending requirement for more coverage. Some have asked us to consider technologies that are considered "rare" by others. Their inclusion remains a long-term objective. Despite the shortcomings of incomplete coverage, an experienced estimator understands that estimating data are always incomplete. An accurate, complete, and broad data base for the *Estimator* remains our goal.

The 1982 Material Cost Section considered only "mill" quantities, which was not practical for small requirements. In the 1983 edition, however, we provided a range of quantities from one unit of bar stock, for example, to mill quantity. The cost due to quantity alone, for example, can decrease over 200 percent, a significant amount. The reduction depends upon the material specification. This type of material cost reporting is a regular feature of this book. Job shops, moderate lot manufacturers, vendors and fabricators, and proprietary product companies have special needs. Field reports on this presentation have been favorable and useful for designers, buyers, estimators, etc.

The Productive Hour Costs (PHC) have been expanded for the new technologies added to the 1985–1986 edition. The PHC considers distinctions for area and increases in wage rate. Differences of wage rate in an economic catch-basin can wander as much as $4 for each of the values listed. The PHC is targeted for the in-between winter period of the 1985 and 1986 years. The estimator is able to use this information for estimates. It is also possible to "backcast" or "forecast" with this information. Once again, methods are suggested that allow the estimator a choice of using this information or making modifications. These methods are easy and are presented in detail in the Instructions.

The *Estimator* has been used for cost estimating of direct labor cost and time, material cost, break-even, make-vs-buy, and return-on-investment types of analysis for equipment purchases, operations, parts, and manufacturing technologies. The *Estimator* aids in the pricing decision. Reports from estimators indicate that the *Estimator* was indispensable for this work. The variety of business applications for which it is being used is impressive.

Both large and small companies, the government, and colleges are using the data. Some firms which have extensive information already developed are finding that the *Estimator* helps to "complete" their data base requirements. Sometimes it is used as the only opinion. Small companies, which do not have sufficient or trained staff available to obtain these data, are relying upon the *Estimator* for their estimates. Irrespective of company size, the estimator, after a brief period of self study, will find it is easy to use for estimating manufacturing time and costs.

"How long should an estimate take to prepare?" Speed in estimating, along with accuracy, is important. But it should be apparent that this book does take more time than the old-fashioned "guesstimate." One of the advantages of this guide is that speed is emphasized along with the ever-present insistence on accuracy. There are many tricks to encourage speed. For example, selecting the next higher range in the table, rather than making a time-consuming and not particularly effective interpolation speeds the estimate. Other time-saving ideas are discussed in the Instructions. You will see that these practices are easy to learn and develop the ability to increase speed and accuracy. But while the *Estimator* does require more time, as compared to the typical "guesstimate," there are many advantages over personal opinion. Repeatability, confirmation, and proven accuracy in long-term tests and field results substantiate the importance of spending a little more time in constructing an estimate. It has been gratifying to hear that the time required to estimate with this *Estimator* was a small price to pay for its advantages.

A new software package that emulates this book has been developed, with particular application for the information in Section V. This software will make your cost estimating practices more effective. The software package is independent of this book, but can be used with it. The price of this book does not include the floppy disk and the specially developed manual.

As with the former editions, I am dedicating this new book to all cost estimators.

Phillip F. Ostwald
Boulder, Colorado

A Letter from the Publisher

American Machinist is pleased to introduce the author of our 1985–1986 *AM Cost Estimator,* Dr. Phillip F. Ostwald. He is Professor of Mechanical and Industrial Engineering in the Department of Mechanical Engineering at the University of Colorado, Boulder. A respected authority, he is the originator of the popular "Manufacturing Cost Estimating Seminar." Dr. Ostwald is the author of many papers, technical reports, and several books including *Cost Estimating,* 2nd ed., published by Prentice-Hall, which provided the first unified textual treatment of the topic. He edited *Manufacturing Cost Estimating* for the Society of Manufacturing Engineers and is the co-author of *Manufacturing Processes, Seventh Edition,* published by John Wiley & Sons.

Dr. Ostwald is a member of many national and professional panels and committees. The Work Measurement and Methods Division of the Institute of Industrial Engineers, citing the *American Machinist Manufacturing Cost Estimating Guide,* selected him for the 1983 Phil E. Carroll Award. The Society of Manufacturing Engineers selected him for the 1982 Sargent Americanism Award, which honored him for his writing and development of the importance of profit and free enterprise—two democratic ideals. He is a consultant and President of Costcom Inc.

Richard H. Larsen, Vice President and Publisher
American Machinist
McGraw-Hill Publications Company
New York, NY 10020

Instructions

INTRODUCTION

Using the AM Cost Estimator

The *Cost Estimator* provides estimating information for direct labor and direct material. Estimators, engineers, accountants, financial analysts, foremen, superintendents, office managers, controllers, and other professionals who regularly do this work will find that estimating with this guide is a simple process.

The book is composed of five sections:

I Instructions
II Productive Hour Costs
III Material Costs
IV Operation Costs
V Element Estimating Data

This section is a "how-to-do-it" discussion which explains how to use the guide. By using the information in Section I, the estimator can determine the current or future cost or time for operations, parts, products, or fabrication services. Cost and time are vital to thousands of firms in the United States. Companies depend upon estimating information for pricing, vendor-cost studies, planning, value-engineering, evaluation studies, and performance checking. With intelligent application, this information can be used for wide-ranging cost determination.

Productive Hour Costs (referred to as PHC) are presented in Section II. This information is time-based to mid 1985–1986. Adjustments to these Productive Hour Costs are possible. Multiplying by indexes will change these values to other time periods or locations. Section II consists of 113 machines, processes, and bench identifications for 23 cities or cities and regions. There are a total of 2600 entries.

Material costs are listed in Section III and are also time-based to mid 1985–1986. Some 55 different ma-

terials prices, or estimates, are provided. Each material has a quantity and price value. These weights and prices range from the cost for a single bar, for example, to a mill quantity.

Section IV gives operation estimates for direct labor cost. The information is presented in dollars ($) for mid 1985–1986. Information is given for 110 machines, processes, or bench work identification. There are 144 entries for setup. Over 750 operational cost estimates are given.

Element estimating information is provided in Section V, which includes time dimensions. Setup work is listed in hours while cycle work is listed in minutes. The 1985–1986 edition has increased coverage to 113 machines, processes, and bench work. Over 15,000 individual time values are available for selection by the estimator.

Sections IV and V estimate identical machines, processes, and bench work but differ in units and detail. The operation method of Section IV provides the answer in dollars. The element approach of Section V gives the answer in time. For example, there may be a job that requires milling. The operation costs approach will provide the productive hour cost to perform the work. The result of the estimate will be a cost, for example, $725.50. The same work can be estimated in units of time, as provided by Section V, and the final answer could be expressed in lot hours, for example, 60 hours. This guide allows the estimator a choice in how the job can be estimated.

This book provides estimates for direct labor and direct material. We define direct labor as "touch labor," which assumes that the machine operator is working on parts that are sold to customers. An example of direct labor is an NC machine operator. The material cost section also provides information useful for direct materials. An example is the part that is being sold to a customer. Direct material is the raw material required for the part.

The price that a company bids for work includes direct labor, direct material, overhead, and profit. Since overhead costs are specific to each company, this *Estimator* does not provide information for overhead. There are various kinds of overhead calculation, and the *Estimator* will accommodate any style of overhead determination.

Figure 1 shows the composition of a total product cost estimate. Direct labor and direct material are important because they form the foundation of much of the bid and price analysis. Overhead is frequently related to direct labor. Since the other cost elements are internal and specific to a company, this book is only concerned with information for labor and material.

PRODUCTIVE HOUR COST (PHC) ESTIMATING INSTRUCTIONS (SECTION II)

The information listed in Section II is identified by a number and a machine, process, or bench description. A typical entry might read, "3.4 Turret punch press." A total of 23 locations are shown across the top of the pages. For example, the PHC for the turret punch press, 3.4, is $8.89 and $10.80 for Atlanta and Baltimore respectively.

The information listed in Section II is arranged by machine, process, or bench number. These numbers correspond to the data found in Section V. The turret punch press PHC is the labor necessary to operate a similarly titled machine given in Section V. Thus, it is simple to multiply total time of the operation by the PHC and find the cost for a production operation. Suppose that the lot time for a turret punch operation is 7.62 hr, and the job is in Baltimore. The productive

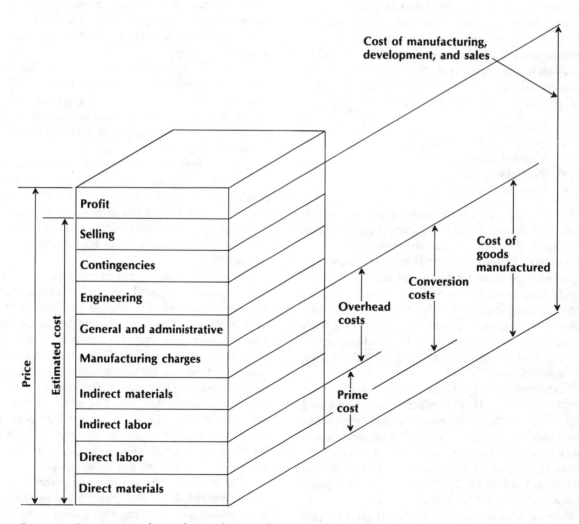

FIGURE 1.   Composition of cost element for a product cost estimate.

cost, then, is calculated as 7.62 × 10.80 = $82.30. Other locations, with different factors, could be used as well.

A city, or city and state area, location is listed across the top of the PHC tables. These locations correspond to the Bureau of Labor Statistics' Standard Metropolitan Statistical Areas. The area includes contiguous counties if there is an economic catch-basin relationship, and it may cross state bounderies. Each city's data may also be valid for other cities within a limited radius.

The source of data is the Bureau of Labor Statistics (BLS), U.S. Department of Labor. The BLS data are derived from industrial surveys of companies with more than 100 employees. The BLS data are already out of date when they are published. They are inappropriate for estimating future costs. Therefore, these data are analyzed and projected to the 1985–1986 period. Time-adjusted values are given in Section II.

The PHC data do not include shift differential, overtime, paid holidays and vacations, health insurance, and retirement plans. These costs are part of the overhead of direct-labor cost estimating. Bonuses and end-of-year profit sharing are also not considered. However, cost-of-living adjustments, as they are reported in earnings, are included. Time and incentive methods of payments are averaged in the analysis and are not separated for the Productive Hour Cost (PHC).

The PHC is cross numbered to a machine, process, or bench rather than to a job description. The two are not exactly identical. A job description, turret lathe operator for example, may have A, B, and C classes. Class A is able to set up the turret lathe, while Class C is only capable of routine and lower-quality work. Furthermore, a class may have various wage steps and may overlap other classes. Thus, earnings of identical job descriptions vary within a company and an area. A specific job description can show a spread of $4 or more within an area. Oftentimes, estimators do not know which class will perform the work or the specific wage step. An estimator may be estimating for cities outside of his or her own company's experience, which is another example of the usefulness of nationwide PHC values. The PHC, when multiplied by the lot hours, gives productive direct-labor cost. This quantity is eventually adjusted to reflect the productivity. This relationship can be expressed as

$$\text{Direct labor cost} = \text{time} \times \text{PHC}$$

The rules for using the Productive Hour Cost section are given in Figure 2. From the operations sheet, the machines, processes, or benches are selected to do the routing of the part. Each machine has a number. That number, 3.11 Ironworker, for example, corresponds to a PHC. The estimator may use his or her own labor wages, but in the absence of that information the PHC is selected for the nearest like city.

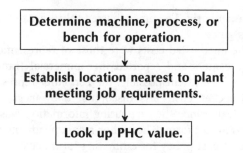

FIGURE 2. Rules for using Productive Hour Costs.

Consider this example: A resistance spot welding operation is estimated to require 2.84 min for the cycle, and with a setup of .35 hr, a lot of 8 units will result in a total of .73 hr. Now, our estimator knows that the work will be done in Pittsburgh, for example, and the PHC number for resistance spot welding is 16.3. The PHC, as copied from the tables on page 32, is $10.19. Then, $7.44 (= 0.73 × 10.19) is direct-labor cost for this operation and location.

MATERIAL ESTIMATING INSTRUCTIONS (SECTION III)

Section III lists mid 1985–1986 costs for selected materials of manufacturing. These costs are expressed in various units. Specifications describe the particular material.

Unfortunately, it is too large a task to provide a complete list of materials, which would number in the tens of thousands. Complications of differing sizes, tolerances, grades, and quantity cause a number of reporting difficulties. The estimator should adjust the values in Section III to his or her particular design.

Involved in the development of these material costs are assumptions of a base quantity, dimension of the shape and length, and specifications for the material. Various arrangements exist for delivery. In some cases protection is specified for special-finished materials. Some materials are identified by chemical composition. The material specification and the quantity are the principal cost-effecting factors.

An example of a material specification for steel strip is: "Strip, cold-rolled, carbon steel; coils, No. 4 temper, No. 2 finish, No. 3 edge, base chemistry, 6 × .050 in., in quantity of 10,000 to 20,000 lb, mill to user, FOB (free-on-board) mill, per 100 lb."

Sources for the data are commercial service centers, Bureau of Labor Statistics (BLS), U.S. Department of Labor, and special inquiry. The sources are believed to be reliable, and the data, as received, were current or of recent date. Standard forecasting methods were applied to update each material to the 1985–1986 period. Each material was analyzed separately for future cost-price competition, since various materials do not behave similarly. The time-adjusted values are reported in this guide.

The unadjusted costs were those of representative service centers and reported in commercial transactions. To the extent possible, the *Estimator* represents out-of-pocket cost, less discounts, allowances, and other deals, since the originating information was requested in this form. The author recommends the out-of-pocket cost policy for estimating future cost. Other cost estimating policies may be inconsistent with this practice.

Costs are generally free-on-board (FOB) service center or warehouse or central marketing point, to avoid the effect of transportation costs. However, delivery prices are presented when the customary practice of the industry is to quote on this basis.

Estimating of materials is done for direct materials, *i.e.,* materials appearing in the product. Customarily, the weight, volume, length, or surface area is determined from drawings. This theoretically computed quantity is then increased by losses such as waste, scrap, and shrinkage. A general formula for material estimating is

$$C_{dm} = W(1 + L_1 + L_2 + L_3)C_m$$

where C_{dm} = cost of direct material for a part in dollars, \$;

W = theoretical finished weight of a part in pounds, lb;

L_1 = percentage loss due to scrap which is a result of errors in manufacturing or engineering;

L_2 = percentage loss due to waste which is caused by manufacturing process such as chips, cutoff, overburden, skeleton, dross, etc; and,

C_m = cost per pound, lb

L_3 = percentage loss due to shrinkage (or theft and physical deterioration).

These three losses (L_1, L_2, L_3) are determined by measurement or historical information. Once these losses are computed and the decimal added to 1, a material estimate is possible using the formula.

The value for C_m would be taken from the tables given in the Material Cost Section or from company records or special inquiry.

Material estimating practices are summarized in Figure 3. The materials, as reported in the guide, are classified as ferrous and nonferrous, the principal classifications used for manufacturing. They are organized as follows:

Ferrous Products
Structural shapes
Plate

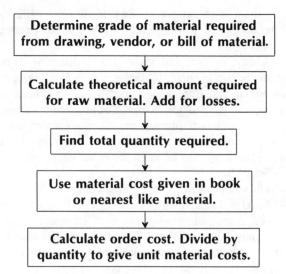

FIGURE 3. Rules for using Material Costs.

Ferrous Products (*Continued*)
Bar
Sheet, strip, and bands
Pipe, tubing, and wire

Nonferrous Products
These materials are arranged in order of increasing cost within the above categories.

The small requirement's cost is a feature of this book. The estimate may only require one bar, sheet, tube, etc., instead of a large mill run. In many cases, weight range starting with a minimum order and extending to a base quantity is given. In the case of ASTM A-36 plate, for example, the reduction between one plate and a base quantity of 10,000 lb is 17%, while for hot-rolled bar, 1-in. OD, AISI 1020, the increase is 247% from one bar to the base quantity. Usually the reduction is significant.

The amount of material is important to the estimate, since the estimator must know whether one lot run, one order, one year's requirements, or a model life is selected as the quantity upon which to base an estimate. We recommend that the estimator use the anticipated out-of-pocket material volume purchase for the material as the more significant factor in choosing a quantity.

Material unit cost, cutting or shearing charges, delivery of material in a single or consolidated shipment, and terms of the purchase agreement influence the cost estimate. These are the values expressed in \$100 per lb, etc. and reported in the *Estimator*.

Practices vary among suppliers of these materials. They are too numerous or minor to mention. However, shipping costs are an important part of the cost. In some cases, a service center may allow the combining of orders, while another may limit the consolidation of different materials for purposes of weight rate determination of shipment costs. In almost all cases, the

6

guide indicates the freight cost stipulations. FOB mill, FOB service center, or FOB shipment point is exclusive of costs to ship, while FOB destination implies that freight costs have been included in the estimated values. In this latter situation, obviously the distance from the supplier to the destination is a factor in the values presented here. It is the practice of the nonferrous industry to provide information in terms of FOB destination.

The base quantity is that weight at which price is no longer sensitive to additional amounts of purchase order. Usually, a single base quantity is given by the data. Any exceptions noted are due to base amounts which vary among suppliers, and in some cases, base quantities are indeterminant.

OPERATION COST ESTIMATING INSTRUCTIONS (SECTION IV)

Direct-labor costs for manufacturing can be estimated using the operation cost data given in Section IV. Two ways to estimate direct labor costs are provided. One method deals in productive hour costs. A second way considers "time" for the operations.

The methods for estimating operations are simple. Of course, one must know the machine, process, or bench that will be used to make the part. An operations sheet, formal or informal, should be available.

Introduction to operational cost data

Information for operation estimating was derived from element estimating and PHC data. Section IV, Operation Costs, uses dollars for setup and dollars per 100 units ($ per 100 units) for repetitive cycles.

Direct labor costs, of course, vary throughout the United States. Historically, wages have been increasing, although most recent advances have been nearly flat. In the *Estimator,* we have chosen Chicago as the location base since it is considered the industrial heartland and its wages are average for the United States. Regional or plant-determined productivity factors can adjust estimated costs of a part, lot, job, or product to any other location in the United States.

The time base is mid 1985–1986. Labor-inflation indexes make it possible to adjust the estimated costs of a part, lot, job, or product to any other time period. The total estimated value can be accommodated to your own plant for a particular time. The following techniques demonstrate how to compute an operation estimate.

Features of operation estimating

Operation estimating is a faster process than element estimating. Overall, the error of application for operation estimating is similar to element estimating. However, for any one operation or part, the detailed estimates are more accurate. Thus, the estimator has a choice to use either operation or element estimating. This choice may depend upon your capture ratio (estimates won to estimates made). If this ratio is relatively low, it means that many estimates are made for jobs that are won, and it is important to keep the estimating costs controlled while maintaining high output. Operation estimating can fulfill this requirement. Often, preliminary estimates are made before sufficient marketing information is available or before engineering drawings are final. In these instances, since there is a shortage of information and time, operational estimates are preferred.

If the capture ratio is high, estimating tends to be for company products or for job shop work which is highly successful. There is more certainty that the work will follow. Element estimating, then, is recommended for high-capture ratio estimating where detailed knowledge of time or costs is more essential.

Estimating data are given in Section IV for 110 machine, process, or bench operations. This information is suitable for most manufacturing estimating requirements. However, because estimating data are seldom complete, the estimator may select operational costs from similar machines in this book if there are operations for which data are unavailable. A qualified opinion ultimately may be necessary if measured information is unavailable.

Procedures for using operational cost data

In a normal situation, operational estimating can proceed once engineering drawings, quantity, materials, and marketing information are available. Preparation of the operations sheet that defines the sequence of manufacture is done simultaneously with the estimating of direct labor. With the operations and the machine, process, or bench selected, the estimator refers to the corresponding Section IV item. In this section each operation, process, or bench is referred to as an "Item." The numbering system specifies an item number, which is identical to the PHC. For example, the number for a turret lathe machine is 6.2, which is also the number for the PHC cost for a turret lathe machine (6.2). The PHC for the turret lathe in Chicago is found by looking up 6.2 and reading Chicago across for the figure, which is $12.08.

Consider Item 3.6, press brake. (Refer to page 52 and follow these instructions.) Each setup occurrence costs $3.55. The variables, shown in the next column, are used to determine the cycle or run cost. In this example, the blank length (L), blank width (W), and any additional (add'l) lips are the variables. The results of your calculation will be dollars per 100 units ($ per 100 units). The press brake is estimated with the Item relationship of

$$[.831 + .060(L + W)] +$$
$$[.942 + .035(L + W)] \text{ (add'l lips)}$$

Here's an example: "A sheet metal part having a flat blank size of 16 × 24 in. has two 4-in. folds along the 16-in. dimension. A lot of 756 units is required."

The first number in the item is .831, which represents the constant cost for the operation. Next we multiply .060 by the sum of the length (L) and width (W), or 40. This means that .060 × 40 = 2.40. This subtotal of .831 + 2.40 = 3.23, which takes care of the first lip brake. The second lip requires that we use the second term in the item. The constant in the second term is .942, and we use that. This value covers the rehandling. Next we multiply the $L + W$ by .035, or 40 × .035 = 1.40. This subtotal of .942 + 1.40 = 2.342 is the cost for the second lip brake. If there had been a total of four brakes, we would have multiplied by 3.

The total of $5.57 is the estimated productive hour cost to produce 100 units. If the lot quantity is 756, we multiply by 7.56 to find the cycle cost. After that we add the setup cost of $3.55, which results in a final lot cost of $45.68 for the press brake operation. At this point it is possible to find the unit cost. To find the unit cost, simply divide the $45.68 by 756 ($45.68 ÷ by 756 = $.060). Therefore, the operation cost or unit cost for one part is $.06.

This informal method of finding the operation cost can be tabulated by using a simple preliminary operation sheet. The three-column format includes the item number, description, and the cost. Each operation (making a part or assembly) is estimated in this fashion.

Item	Description	Cost
3.6	Setup subtotal	$ 3.55
3.6	Constant cost for first lip	$ .831
3.6	Blank size factor, .060 × 40	2.40
3.6	Constant for second lip	.942
3.6	Second lip factor, .035 × 40	1.40
	$ per 100 units subtotal	$ 5.573
	Lot cost for 756 units	$45.68
	Unit cost	$ .060

Similar examples are found throughout this book. In fact there are over 100 examples of operation estimates using the items of Section IV. For instance, turn to page 123 and note Example B for the press brake.

Note that many operational estimate items correspond to the linear equation

$$y = a + bx$$

where a = intercept and is the constant portion of an operation; for example, .831. These constant costs are always used in an estimate.

b = slope of the operation, expressed as so many dollars per 100 units of x; for example, .060.

The variable portion, or slope, relates to an easily understood cost driver. These cost factors are multiplied by a number relating to the machine or the part. This multiplication product is then added to the constant. Remember, the items are added after multiplication.

The explanation for using the operation cost item follows advice given for element estimating, and there is corresponding numbering. Sawing and cutting is identified as Item 1 for operation estimating, while 1.1, 1.2, and 1.3 identify power bandsaw, abrasive saw cutoff, and oxygen cutting processes in element estimating. This easy cross identification allows the estimator to examine additional data if necessary.

A discussion of how to use operation estimating items is given in the *Estimating Data Discussion* throughout Section V.

The advice for making operation estimates is similar to that of element estimating. Once element estimating is understood, the extension becomes obvious, since the principal cost driver for item estimating is identical to major time drivers. Many of the example estimates dealing with an element time approach are also re-estimated using operational costs items. These solutions for estimating items are found in the *Examples* part of *Element Estimating Data* in Section V.

Adjusting Operation Estimates to Your Situation

The sum of operation estimates is the cost for trained operators to perform predesignated operations. The optimum estimating procedure will estimate for a normally efficient plant performance and adjust this cost for differences in PHC, location, time, and productivity.

In the *Estimator,* operation estimating items are based upon average Chicago PHC for mid 1985–1986. The method of pinpointing one city as the base area has several advantages. It permits a comparison of various vendor cost / price values in different locations, relates your plant cost to other areas, allows for inflation indexing, and formalizes a method for measuring productivity.

Adjustments to your cost estimates are improved if overall productivity factors are used instead of separate adjustments for each operation. For example, adjust a product, or lot, or a part having many operations, rather than adjusting each operation.

One method to make this adjustment involves gathering actual plant costs and comparing them to the estimated cost for the same operations, parts, lots, or products. An overall productivity factor would have the following relationship:

8

$$OPF = \frac{\Sigma AC}{\Sigma EC}$$

where OPF = overall productivity factor, dimensionless number

ΣAC = sum of actual direct-labor cost total for operations, parts, lots, or products

ΣEC = sum of operational costs from the *Estimator* for operations, parts, lots, or products

For instance, if ΣAC = \$5,157.58 and ΣEC = \$4,715.00 then $OPF = \frac{5157.58}{4715.00} = 1.094$. If the plant OPF data were considered representative of future work, total estimated costs would be increased or multiplyed by 1.094 to anticipate total future cost. Also if AC = \$492.82, and EC = \$502.95 for a unit of product, future product estimates would be multiplied by $\frac{492.82}{502.95}$ or .98. This overall adjustment factor is simple to develop if the actual data are available. In some plants and companies, direct-labor cost totals cannot be accurately determined, and calculation of OPF is not possible.

Conversion of $ per 100 units to other cost units

Operational data are given in dollars for setup and dollars per 100 units for cycle time. If a lot has multiple setups, then the number of setups is multiplied by the setup value. The \$ per 100 units is chosen because of convenience for the number of decimals, though the national average lot size is about 75. The cycle time can be converted to other denominations, although it is better practice to estimate using the data directly from this book.

Convert \$ per 100 units to:

\$ per 10 (\$/10) units by dividing the total value by 10

\$ per 1 (\$/1) unit by dividing total value by 100

\$ per 1000 (\$/1000) units by multiplying total value by 10

If a prorated unit cost is desired use

$$\text{Unit cost} = \left(\frac{SU}{N} + RT/1\right)$$

where SU = setup cost, dollars (\$)

N = lot quantity associated with setup

RT = cycle time, dollars per unit (\$/unit)

Let's look at the press brake example again. The cycle cost for 100 units was calculated as \$5.573.

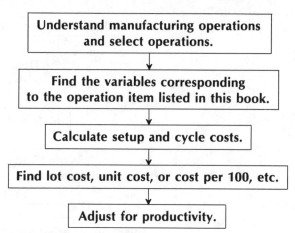

FIGURE 4. Rules for using Operation Costs.

Therefore, one unit will cost $\frac{\$5.573}{100}$ or \$.05573, and the setup, which is for the lot quantity of 756 units, is prorated, or distributed, over the 756 units. This means that we divide the setup cost of \$3.55 by 756, or \$0.0047. This is then added to the cycle cost for a total of \$0.06. Notice that we round for decimals at the last step. This is preferred to earlier rounding.

The steps for estimating operation items are summarized in Figure 4. This is a simple process, and it is a quick way to supply costs.

ELEMENT ESTIMATING INSTRUCTIONS (SECTION V)

The information for estimating direct-labor time is given in Section V. It has been constructed so that the estimating procedure is simple to complete, while it is sensitive to minor differences in manufacturing. This sensitivity is made obvious by various selections of the element for a specific machine, process, or bench.

Figure 5 lists the rules for using the element estimating data.

Sources of Information

The methods of measurement used to first uncover the information for Element Estimating include time study, predetermined motion time data systems, laboratory investigation, manufacturer's recommendations, and judgment. One or more methods may have been adopted for any one set of element estimating data. If an abundance of data were available, consensus analysis was used for consolidation.

Dimensions of the Information

The information provided in Section V, Element Estimating Data, uses the units of time: hours for setup and minutes for the elements of the operation. This type of presentation is unaffected by inflation or PHC

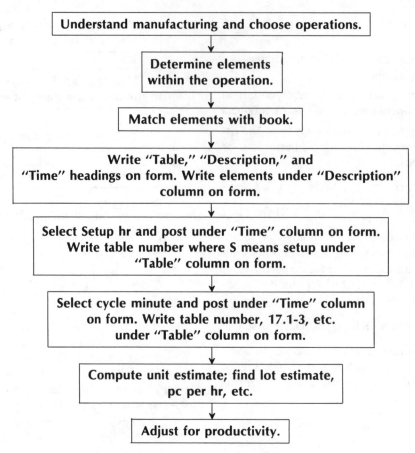

FIGURE 5. Rules for using Element Estimating Data.

changes. Hours (hr) are appropriate for setup because this is the customary expression for setup operations in the United States. Morever, decimal minutes (min), rather than seconds (sec) or hours, are adopted for the elements of an operation because they are more easily understood. Estimators relate to the "minute" more easily than with other time dimensions.

Universal Information

The approach used in this book assumes that plant differences for trained operators of a specific machine, process, or bench are minor for the purposes of estimating. However, differences, say for handling, are significant for different classes of machines. For instance, the time it takes to move and load a part on the punch press is significantly different for an open-back inclinable punch press than it is for a turret punch press. But, the operator time needed to load a turret punch press is similar for different plants or regions. Also, the element estimating time for handling a part for a bed milling machine is about the same for plant A in city Z as it is for plant B in city Y.

The Operations Sheet

The operations sheet is fundamental to manufacturing planning. It may also be referred to as a "route sheet," "traveler," or "planner." There are many styles and each plant usually has its own preferred form. The purpose of the operations sheet, however, is the same:

● To select the machine, process, or bench which is necessary for converting the material into other forms

● To provide a description of the operations and tools

● To indicate the time for the operation.

The order of the operations is special too, and this sequence indicates the various steps in the manufacturing conversion.

Each operations sheet has a title block indicating the material nature, part number, date, quantity, and other features that may be essential to the company. For cost estimating purposes, consider the following: Suppose that we want to machine a stainless steel block by drilling two holes, tapping one hole, milling a step, and hand deburring the milled edge. Parts and assemblies are more complicated than this, but we only want to illustrate the estimating process. A typical and simple operations sheet is shown in Figure 6.

Completing the Operations Sheet

Beginning in the upper left-hand corner of the sheet, the estimator fills in the *part number* (1) and *part name*

OPERATIONS SHEET

① Part No.: 512-2042
② Part Name: BLOCK
③ Plant Location: BALTIMORE
④ Lot Quantity: 185
⑤ Material: BAR, HOT-ROLLED, TYPE 304 STAINLESS STEEL, 15 lb.
⑥ Unit Material Cost: $26.70

⑦ Operation No.	⑧ Machine, Process, or Bench	⑨ Estimator Table No.	⑩ Description	⑪ Setup Estimate, Hr	⑫ Unit Estimate, Min	⑬ Lot Hr	⑭ Productive Hour Cost	⑮ Total Operation Cost
10	DRILL PRESS	9.3	DRILL 2 HOLES / TAP 1 HOLE	.34	3.91	12.396	10.62	131.65
20	BED MILL	7.3	MILL STEP	1.25	1.82	6.862	12.59	86.39
30	BENCH DEBURR	18.4	HAND DEBURR EDGE	.10	.93	2.968	8.65	25.67

⑯ Total Operational Productive Hour Cost: $243.71
⑰ Unit Operational Productive Hour Cost: $1.32
Unit Material Cost (from above): $26.70
⑱ Total Direct Cost: $28.02

FIGURE 6. A typical operations (or route) sheet.

(2). The estimator then indicates the *plant location* (3), *lot quantity* (4), and the *material* (5) specification. The *unit material cost* (6) required by the design should include material costs to cover losses for scrap, waste and shrinkage. Multiply by the cost-per-lb rate of the material, as given by the material costs shown in Section III, Material Costs, of the *Estimator*.

The sequence of the *operation numbers* (7) and the selection of the *machine, process, or bench* (8) to manufacture the part are made next. The column titled *Estimator table number* (9) corresponds to the table numbers indicated by the *AM Cost Estimator*. For example, Table 9.3 refers to the upright drilling machine class. The operations sheet column titled *description* (10) is an abbreviated instruction that the shop will follow in making the part or subassembly. For operation number 10, the instructions to the shop are "Drill 2 holes, and tap 1 hole." The description could be expanded to list all elements that are pertinent to estimating the operation. This operation will be estimated later, and you'll see how this list of elements could be repeated instead of the abbreviated list.

The columns titled *setup estimate, hr* (11) and *unit estimate, min* (12) are very important. The instructions that follow describe the methods and selection of the elements and time that are necessary to manufacture the part for that operation. All of the tables in Section V pertain to the determination of the values that are listed in these two columns.

The column titled *lot hr* (13) is a computation that is shown on the operations sheet. It is explained in the discussion dealing with the Appendix. The calculation is made using the setup, unit estimate, and the lot quantity. This lot-hr quantity varies, and it is an important fact found on the operations sheet.

The *Productive Hour Cost* (14) column is completed using information that is obtained from the book or from the company's internal records. For example, this part number, 512-2042, is to be manufactured in Baltimore. The Productive Hour Cost (PHC), corresponding to upright drilling machine for that area is listed by Section II and number 9.3, and is $10.62. Or, the estimator may use his or her plant's wage rate that corresponds to this machine. The estimator may be dealing with operations that are outside the local plant area or may have no knowledge of the machine, process, or bench. In this case, the estimator will need systematic information that can be verified, and the Productive Hour Cost fills this very real need.

The column titled *total operation cost* (15) is found by multiplying the lot figure by the Productive Hour Cost for each operation. The sum of all total operation costs gives the direct labor cost or the *total operational Productive Hour Cost* (16). When *unit material cost* is added to the *unit operational Productive Hour Cost* (17), the *total direct costs* (18) are found. From this point onward a variety of accounting and estimating practices become possible, and we leave that development to the individual plant.

This operations sheet can be altered to consider simple or complicated assemblies and products, but the approach remains the same. The purpose of this book is to provide time or cost for the direct labor or material component of the product. The preparation of the operations sheet is important for finding the part operational costs. Notice that the part cost is the sum of the operational costs, and this fact allows us to concentrate upon the important steps that are necessary for estimating operations. Henceforth we will not show the entire operations sheet. Instead, we will provide only that information necessary for estimating. This example points out that operations planning precedes cost estimating. This *Estimator* does not provide the logic that goes into the planning process. After all, cost estimating is difficult enough. Once the operational sequence, the selection of the machine, process, or bench, and a basic description of the work has been roughed out, cost estimating begins.

Breaking Down an Operation into Elements

Detail estimating requires that the operation be "detailed" or reduced to its elements. For example, the drill press operation of drilling two holes and tapping a third could be visualized in details, or as we choose to call them "elements."

The selection of these elements vary, and their choice depends upon the particular machine, process, or bench being used. Element estimating, as advocated here, balances the number of elements that are eligible for selection, since too many choices increase the estimating cost. Although there is no proof that excessive details, beyond those provided here, reduce estimating errors, it is certain that extensive details increase estimating costs.

Before elemental estimating can begin, one must have:

- Engineering drawings
- Marketing quantity
- Material specifications
- A list and specifications of the company machines, processes, and benches
- An operations sheet.

Of course, the preparation of the operations sheet may occur at the same time as direct-labor estimating. Once the operations have been listed on the sheet, the estimator can refer to the machine, process, or bench in this book that coincides with the ones designated by the operations sheet. The operation is broken down or detailed into elements which are described by the estimating table. These elements may be listed on a standardized company form. Marginal jottings on the operations sheet or even scratch-pad calculations may suffice. The purpose of the formal or informal elemental breakdown is identical: a listing of elements that will do the work is visualized and this listing is coordinated with the estimating tables of Section V.

Setup and Operation Elements

The various machine, process, and bench tables provided in Section V list setup and cycle elemental times.

Setup includes work to prepare the machine, process, or bench for product parts or the cycle. Starting with the machine, process, or bench in a neutral condition, setup includes punch in/out, paperwork, obtaining tools, positioning unprocessed materials nearby, adjusting, and inspecting. It also includes return tooling, cleanup, and teardown of the machine, process, or bench to a neutral condition ready for the next job. Unless otherwise specified, the setup does not include the time to make parts or perform the repetitive cycle. If scrap is anticipated as a consequence of setup, the estimator has the option to increase the time allotment for the unproductive material.

Setup estimating is necessary for job shops and companies whose parts or products have small to moderate quantity production. As production quantity increases, the effect of the setup value lessens its prorated unit importance, although its absolute value remains unchanged. Setup values may not be estimated for some very large quantity estimating. In these instances setup is handled through overhead practices. Our recommendation is to estimate setup and to allocate it to the operation since it is a more accurate than costing by overhead methods. This recommendation applies equally to companies manufacturing their own parts or products and vendors bidding for contract work.

Some operations may not require setup. Flexible manufacturing systems, continuous production, or combined operations may not need to consider setup time. Nonetheless, even a modest quantity may be appropriate in these circumstances. Discussion of the details regarding setup is given for each machine, process, or bench.

Cycle time or run time is the work needed to complete one unit after the setup work is concluded. It does not include any element involved in the setup. Each typical example in Section V provides a unit estimate. Besides finding a value for the operational setup, the estimator finds a unit estimate for the work from the listed elements, which are called "estimating minutes." The term "estimating minutes" implies a national norm for trained workers. These times include allowances, in addition to the work time, that take into account personal requirements, fatigue where work effort may be excessive due to job conditions and environment, and legitimate delays for operation-related interruptions. Since the allowances are included in the time for the described elements, and therefore part of

the allowed time for several or many operations, then the allowed time is considered fair. The concept of fairness implies that a worker can generally perform the work throughout the day.

Organization of the Information

Section V includes 111 sets of estimating information which are presented in a similar way. Each set provides a *description, estimating data discussion, examples* and *tables.*

The *description* discusses the machine, process, or bench which is to be estimated. Sometimes a photograph is included for instructional purposes. The *description* is intentionally brief because the estimator is usually familiar with the equipment being estimated.

The *estimating data discussion* describes most of the elements listed in the *table* in language that is simple and easily understood. Though misinterpretation is possible, awareness of manufacturing language is a requisite to estimating. The estimator must know the machines, processes, benches, and their associated elemental language.

In some cases, discussion is expanded in another estimating set. For example, the *estimating data discussion* provided for knee and column milling machines, page 191, is also appropriate for other milling machines. Consistency of terms and practices in describing the elements is followed throughout the book.

Each set gives several *examples* of typical estimates that show how the data are selected and how the estimate is made. A typical problem describing material, special tooling, quantity, and circumstances affecting the work asks one to find and estimate the unit estimate, lot time, prorated unit time, hr per 1 unit, hr per 100 units, pc per hr (pieces per hour), etc. Following the problem statement there are three columns labeled *"table," "description,"* and *"time."* Each is explained below.

The *table* column head is the listing of the estimating data. Various setup possibilities are given. Estimating minutes are provided for a variety of work elements. The estimator using the elemental breakdown selects elemental time from the many possibilities. For an example, look at Table 9.3 on page 234. This table number, of course, is what is posted on the estimating summary.

The table column identifies the estimating table and element number. For example, if a sheet metal operation of braking were necessary, the number "3.6" would first be posted. Similarly, for a drill press operation, the number "9.3" would be written on the row corresponding to the machine selection. Notice for any estimating table that clusters of elements also have a number, starting with "1," "2," etc. These clusters are generally related. The element "handle" may have many possibilities and be listed as element no. 1. Following the machine number is the element number, which is preceded by a dash. For example, "3.6-1" is a power press brake element called "brake." Also, "9.3-2" is a cluster of elements for "clamp and unclamp" for the upright drilling machine.

The *description* lists the elements of the operation. These correspond to the element description listed in the estimating tables. This is an elaboration of the description that is given in the operations planning sheet (described above). There is little difference, except that the number of lines or elements is greater for estimating than for planning. The description may also indicate additional information such as the length of cut, tooling used, type of NC manuscript order, etc.

The *time* column is a listing of the numbers removed from the table corresponding to the value listed for the element. The time units for setup is hr (hour). The time units for cycle elements is min (minute). These values are listed under the heading "time."

The examples conclude with a summation of the elemental time, and gives a unit estimate, expressed in minutes, for the cycle time of one part for one operation. The lot time includes a setup time, and is calculated using: $SU + N \times RT$, where N is the lot quantity and SU(setup) and RT(cycle time) are in equivalent dimensions of hours.

Let's return to the stainless steel block problem described earlier for constructing a simple operations sheet. To add the additional and important estimating features we have just discussed, examine the drill press operation, op. no. (operation number) 10.

It is necessary to add the column heading *table* and *time*, as *description* already exists.

There are many ways to estimate parts like the ones shown in our example. The expertise in estimating stainless steel parts is left to the estimator. Notice that the columns titled "operation number" and "machine, process or bench" often are not included because of space limitations. Henceforth, for our typical example estimates, they are dropped. Though they are vital in operations planning, they are less important in detailed estimating.

Notice the variety in the table numbers. We used several tables in constructing this estimate, such as 9.1, 9.3, 11.2, and 11.4. In many cases the estimating data are used in a variety of circumstances. Drilling machine time is necessary for several machine tools, and this information is collected in a centralized point, *i.e.,* Table 11.2. In many cases the data are universal and can be used for a variety of circumstances.

The examples that are provided for each of the element estimating sets are composed of the three columns and are useful guides for constructing other estimates. You'll need some self study here.

Rules for Using the Elemental Tables

Published estimating data as presented in the tables of Section V are of two types:

1. A listing
2. Row and column tabulations.

There are suggested rules for using the tables. The *listing* identifies the element. You should jot down the exact number without alteration. If the value of the time driver falls between two neighboring numbers for a row-and-column table, adopt the higher value. Do not interpolate or select the lower value even though it may be closer. Interpolation is time consuming, and using the higher value usually does not introduce any significant error to the application total. Of course, these rules may be adjusted in unusual cases.

Operation Number	Machine, Process, or Bench	Table	Description	Time	
10	Drill press	9.1-S	Setup upright machine 2 spindles; Vise;	.34	hr
		9.3-1	Handle, 15 lb	.17	min
		9.3-2	Clamp, unclamp vise full turn	.09	
		9.3-4	Start and stop, 2 × .03	.06	
		9.3-4	Raise tool, hole-to-hole, 3 times, 3 × .11	.33	
		11.2-4	Power drill in stainless, 3 holes, .44 min per in. of length. Each hole is 2 in. deep. 3 × .44 × 2	2.64	
		11.2-8	Tool wear, 2.64 min	.26	
		11.4-3	Tap 10 threads for 3/4 in., .48 × .75	.36	
			Unit estimate	3.91	min
			Setup	.34	hr
			Lot hr for 185 units	12.396	hr

If the value of the time driver is smaller than any of the row-and-column numbers available, use the initial value, as it may represent the threshold time for the element. If the value of the time driver is above the range of the table, a tendency exists to extrapolate. An "add'l 1" (meaning additional 1) may be provided, and the extrapolation slope is provided. The "add'l 1" provides the slope of the data or equation at the maximum value. The extrapolated quantity is added to the maximum listed value of the table. In some cases, an "add'l 1" is not listed, as there may be a natural manufacturing barrier, or our data sources may not have extended into those regions. Extensions in these cases may require slope extension or judgment by the estimator.

Consider this example. A part is handled with occasional repositioning during the handling. The data for the element is given as:

$L + W + H$	15.0	15.5	16.1	17.4	18.2	Add'l 1
Min	.07	.08	.09	.10	.11	.013

The $L + W + H$ refers to the box dimensions of the length, width, and height of the part. They are added. For instance, suppose that a part had a $L + W + H$ girth dimension of 13.7 in., then the time posted in the "time" column is .07 min. We use the minimum initial value. Suppose that the part girth is 15.6 in., then the practice is to go to the next higher time value and adopt the time of .09 min for the estimate. Suppose that the value of the girth is 19.1 in., the trick is to take .11 and add that to (19.1 − 18.2) .013, for an answer of .122.

These rules encourage speed in application and consistency. It is important to be able to reconstruct an estimate with a minimum of paperwork. Consistency becomes more possible if two or more estimators derive an equal or similar estimate for the same operation. This can be aided by crosstalk within the estimating team. Following the suggested procedures for using the Section V tables can substantially improve your estimates.

Unfortunately, estimating data are seldom complete. If the element description of the operation uncovers requirements not included in the estimating data, you may choose elements from other similar data that meet the requirement. As a final resort, and oftentimes a necessary action, use individual judgment to estimate missing elemental times.

Adjusting Elemental Estimates to Actual Times

Variations in plant productivity have an effect on the times. Productivity must either be measured against the estimated values of these data or estimated for each plant. Consistency in estimating time is achieved by using simple productivity factors. The overall adjust-ment of a part(s), lot(s), or product(s) time by the productivity factor yields the consistency. Bulk adjustments, meaning an overall productivity factor adjustment, are superior to individualizing and adjusting each estimate.

An estimate represents the time which is determined to be necessary for trained operators to perform given operations. For the best results, you should estimate operations, parts, lots, or products for normally efficient plant performance using the national norm data included in this book. For the purpose of direct-labor estimating out-of-pocket or actual time, the estimated total for operations, parts, lots, or products is adjusted by a productivity factor. The productivity factor is found by using the relationship

$$PF = \frac{\Sigma AT}{\Sigma ET}$$

where PF = productivity factor, dimensionless number
ΣAT = sum of actual time total for operations, parts, lots, or products
ΣET = sum of estimated times from the guide for operations, parts, lots, or products.

The AT can be determined from time-keeping records, reports, time and production studies, dropoff counts of parts from production equipment, or qualified opinion. Of course, the AT is matched time-wise against the ET. The productivity factor can be determined from a single sample or it may be periodically evaluated. It's doubtful that a steady-state productivity factor is ever achievable because of plantwide interruptions, scheduling fluctuations, and changes in supervision and manpower. Nonetheless, spotchecks can be useful to monitor plant performance. In some plants and companies, direct-labor totals cannot be accurately determined and calculation of the productivity factor *(PF)* is not possible.

Some companies may have a standard cost scheme. Instead of measuring productivity factors, an accounting labor variance, either favorable or unfavorable, is determined. This book is consistent with standard cost plans, and may be used keeping in mind that labor variance, not a productivity factor, is measured periodically.

INSTRUCTIONS FOR THE APPENDIX

The Appendix is useful for converting the unit estimate expressed in minutes into hr/1, hr/10, hr/100, hr/1,000, or hr/10,000 units (*i.e.:* hours per 1, 10, 100, 1,000, 10,000). The estimated unit minute is considered the "precision point" and the conversions are rounded. Estimate the cycle time in minutes, then convert to hr/1, hr/10, hr/100, hr/1,000, or hr/10,000 units. The conversion is handled very simply in the

Appendix. A number of choices such as hr/1, hr/10, hr/100, hr/1,000, or hr/10,000 are available.

The company should adopt a consistent denominator (1, 10, 100, 1,000, or 10,000) and use it for every estimate. This uniform policy prevents careless calculations. The number of decimals for the hour estimate depends upon the denominator. A 1.87 min estimate converted to hr/100 units shows 3.117, while for hr/1000 units it is 31.1667. The increasing number of decimals is intentional. This precision, though exaggerated with respect to the original measurements, is required for time and cost sensitivity. For example, if the unit estimate is .0009 min, after entry on the left margin in the Appendix, we would read .002 hr/100, .0150 hr/1,000, or .15000 hr/10,000 units. If the practice is to select the 1,000 units, the estimator would record .0150 hr/1,000 units.

If the unit estimate is .0019, then we have

	Min per unit	Hr per 1000
	.001	.0167
	.0009	.0150
Total	.0019	.0317

Continuing, assume a unit estimate of 2.01 min. In this unit estimate range, only 2.00 and 2.04 min are shown as entries in the Appendix. The following procedure is used to find the hr/100 (hours per 100 units).

	Min per unit	Hr per 100
	2.00	3.333
	.01	.017
Total	2.01	3.350

Another example of 9.25 min per unit will give for the conversion to hr per 10 as

	Min per unit	Hr per 10
	9.00	1.50
	.25	.04
Total	9.25	1.54

Suppose that an estimate of 36.17 min was determined for an operation. Although it may not be a difficult matter to convert this by means of a calculator, it is just as simple to use tables, such as those given by the Appendix. This would be found as:

Min per unit	Hr per 1	Hr per 10	Hr per 100
30.	.5	5.00	50.000
6.	.1	1.00	10.000
.17	0	.03	.283
36.17	.6	6.03	60.283

Certainly the estimator would not have a need for the three values, but after selection of a policy, there should be a routine for finding the appropriate hour estimate. Notice the increasing number of decimals. In fact, if it is company policy to estimate in units of one (second column from left), then it is unnecessary to evaluate estimates or minor variations expressed in hundredths of a minute, *i.e.,* .17 min.

Pieces per hour (pc per hr) should not be used for calculating estimates. We sometimes refer to pc per hr as a "shop estimate" since it is a crude approximation of output. It is provided in the extreme righthand column of the Appendix and is related to the unit estimate as expressed in minutes. Sometimes, shop people prefer an expression of "pieces per hour" because of their familiarity. However, the "pc per hr" measure for official cost-estimating documents is not as preferred as an hour estimate.

Many of the examples ask for lot estimates. For example, a job is estimated to have 36.17 min of cycle, and 1.75 hr for the setup. What is the lot time for the job? We use the relationship:

$$\text{Lot time} = SU + N\left(\frac{RT}{1}\right)$$

where lot time = total hours for the operation
N = lot quantity
$$RT = \frac{\text{hr}}{1}$$

Continuing the problem with the 36.17 min operation estimate, assume that the operation requires 1.75 hr for setup. What is the lot time for 72 units?

	Hr per 1	Hr per 10	Hr per 100
$\dfrac{RT}{1}$	.6	6.03	60.283
$N \times \dfrac{RT}{1}$	43.20	43.42	43.40
SU	1.75	1.75	1.75
Lot hr	44.95	45.17	45.15

These lot hours are then multiplied by the PHC as given in the book, or the estimator will use the plant machine hours or wage rate for the multiplication.

Productive Hour Costs

II

MACHINE, PROCESS, OR BENCH	ATLANTA	BALTIMORE	BOSTON	BUFFALO	CHICAGO	CLEVELAND
1.1 Power bandsaw cutoff, contour bandsaw, and hacksaw	8.14	9.51	7.90	9.53	8.63	9.76
1.2 Abrasive saw cutoff	8.14	9.51	7.90	9.53	8.63	9.76
1.3 Oxygen cutting	8.50	9.13	9.12	11.10	10.12	10.66
2.1 Plastics molding	8.22	9.13	10.79	10.78	9.99	11.22
2.2 Plastic preform molding	8.07	9.99	10.57	10.56	9.86	11.00
2.3 Thermoplastic injection molding	8.22	10.31	10.90	10.88	10.10	11.36
2.4 Thermosetting plastic molding	8.22	10.31	10.90	10.88	10.10	11.36
2.5 Thermoforming	8.22	10.31	9.79	10.55	9.79	11.00
2.6 Glass cloth layup	8.22	10.02	10.57	10.55	9.79	11.00
2.7 Extrusion	8.22	10.31	9.79	10.55	9.79	11.00
2.8 Blow molding	8.22	10.31	9.79	10.55	9.79	11.00
2.9 Hot and cold chamber die casting	8.76	11.04	11.69	11.67	10.82	12.17
2.10 Isostatic molding press	8.22	10.31	9.79	10.55	9.79	11.00
2.11 Routing and molding	8.22	10.31	9.79	10.55	9.79	11.00
2.12 Banding	8.22	10.31	9.79	10.55	9.79	11.00
3.1 Power shear	8.89	10.07	10.02	11.21	10.35	11.39
3.2 Punch press (first operations)	8.76	10.07	10.12	11.11	10.24	11.28
3.3 Punch press (secondary operations)	8.76	10.07	10.12	11.11	10.24	11.28
3.4 Turret punch press	8.89	10.80	10.12	11.33	10.45	11.54
3.5 Single-station punching	8.76	10.07	9.99	11.11	10.27	11.28
3.6 Power press brake	8.89	10.07	9.88	11.01	10.14	11.20
3.7 Foot brake, kick press, and jump shear	7.07	9.75	9.04	9.53	8.56	9.11

MACHINE, PROCESS, OR BENCH	ATLANTA	BALTIMORE	BOSTON	BUFFALO	CHICAGO	CLEVELAND
3.8 Hand-operated brake, bender, punch press, multiform, coil winder, shear, straightener, and roller	7.07	9.69	9.04	9.53	8.56	9.11
3.9 Nibbling	7.07	9.69	9.04	9.53	8.56	9.11
3.10 Tube bending	8.89	10.07	9.88	11.01	10.14	11.20
3.11 Ironworker	8.89	10.07	9.88	11.01	10.14	11.20
4.1 Marking	7.07	9.69	9.04	9.53	8.56	9.11
4.2 Screen printing	8.29	10.07	9.88	11.01	10.10	11.36
4.3 Laser marking	7.07	9.69	9.04	9.53	8.56	9.11
5.1 Forging	11.19	12.91	10.69	13.38	14.32	14.16
6.1 Engine lathe	11.57	12.79	11.66	12.93	12.73	13.15
6.2 Turret lathe	10.10	12.51	10.88	11.59	12.08	13.62
6.3 Vertical turret lathe	10.10	12.51	10.88	11.59	12.08	13.62
6.4 Numerical controlled turning lathe	9.97	10.46	10.37	12.87	12.38	13.44
6.5 Numerical controlled chucking lathe	9.97	10.46	10.37	12.87	12.38	13.44
6.6 Single spindle automatic screw machine	11.18	13.70	10.69	13.38	14.32	14.16
6.7 Multispindle automatic screw machine	11.18	13.70	10.69	13.38	14.32	14.16
7.1 Milling machine setup	10.51	12.79	12.00	12.50	12.56	14.26
7.2 Knee and column milling	10.51	12.59	12.00	12.50	11.86	14.26
7.3 Bed milling	10.10	12.59	8.45	11.21	10.04	11.93
7.4 Vertical-spindle ram-type milling	10.51	10.82	11.99	12.58	11.86	14.26
7.5 Router milling	9.97	10.82	7.44	9.53	10.64	9.52
7.6 Special milling	10.10	10.82	8.45	9.53	10.04	11.93
7.7 Hand miller	9.97	9.49	8.45	9.53	10.64	9.52
8.1 Machining centers	10.51	12.59	10.88	12.87	11.00	12.99

MACHINE, PROCESS, OR BENCH	ATLANTA	BALTIMORE	BOSTON	BUFFALO	CHICAGO	CLEVELAND
8.2 Rapid travel and automatic tool changer elements	10.51	12.59	10.37	12.87	11.00	12.99
9.1 Drilling machine setup and layout	9.09	11.72	9.55	10.80	12.56	13.64
9.2 Sensitive drill press	9.09	9.49	8.66	10.80	9.50	7.63
9.3 Upright drilling	10.36	10.62	9.55	10.80	11.90	12.44
9.4 Turret drilling	10.36	11.72	10.03	10.80	12.38	15.08
9.5 Cluster drilling	10.36	11.72	10.03	10.80	12.38	15.08
9.6 Radial drilling	10.64	11.72	9.53	11.78	12.44	14.57
10.1 Horizontal milling, drilling, and boring	11.03	13.70	15.01	12.50	12.52	14.26
10.2 Boring and facing	11.03	12.51	11.67	12.50	12.08	12.59
11.1 Turn, bore, form, cutoff, thread, start drill, and break edges	10.10	12.64	10.42	12.93	11.17	12.99
11.2 Drill, counterbore, ream, countersink, and tap	9.76	11.25	9.10	11.78	11.37	11.23
11.3 Face, side, slot, form, straddle, end, saw, and engrave milling	10.23	11.69	9.29	12.52	10.85	11.91
11.4 Tool life and replacement	9.43	11.86	9.82	12.40	11.13	12.05
12.1 Broaching	10.78	12.21	11.57	11.22	12.50	13.15
13.1 Cylindrical grinding	10.78	13.24	12.47	12.38	13.38	13.33
13.2 Centerless grinding	9.43	12.54	11.24	11.22	11.37	11.91
13.3 Honing	8.07	12.40	8.29	9.91	9.64	10.00
13.4 Surface grinding	9.43	13.24	12.47	12.38	13.38	13.33
13.5 Internal grinding	9.43	13.24	12.47	12.38	13.38	13.33
13.6 Free abrasive grinding	8.07	12.40	8.29	9.91	9.64	10.00
13.7 Disk grinding	8.07	12.40	8.29	9.91	9.64	10.00
13.8 Vertical internal grinding	9.43	13.24	12.47	12.38	13.38	13.33

MACHINE, PROCESS, OR BENCH	ATLANTA	BALTIMORE	BOSTON	BUFFALO	CHICAGO	CLEVELAND
14.1 Gear shaper	10.10	13.24	11.57	12.52	12.50	13.29
14.2 Hobbing	10.10	12.60	11.57	12.52	12.50	13.56
15.1 Thread cutting and form rolling	8.76	10.48	11.24	11.22	10.41	11.70
16.1 Shielded metal-arc, flux-cored arc, and submerged welding	8.76	11.42	11.63	12.14	10.53	14.26
16.2 Gas metal-arc welding and gas tungsten-arc welding	8.76	11.42	11.63	12.14	10.53	14.26
16.3 Resistance spot welding	8.42	11.34	8.11	13.01	10.12	10.66
16.4 Torch, dip, and furnace brazing	8.42	9.13	8.11	11.10	10.12	10.66
17.1 Heat treat furnaces	8.61	9.13	8.86	10.77	9.81	10.35
18.1 Drill press deburring	6.39	8.21	7.96	10.15	7.26	9.65
18.2 Abrasive belt deburring	7.00	9.51	9.35	10.24	10.58	13.22
18.3 Pedestal deburring and finishing	6.93	8.68	9.46	10.24	10.80	14.36
18.4 Handheld portable tool deburring	6.39	8.65	7.96	10.15	7.26	9.65
18.5 Hand deburring	6.39	8.65	7.96	10.15	7.26	9.65
18.6 Plastic material deburring	6.93	8.65	7.96	10.15	7.26	9.65
18.7 Loose abrasive deburring	7.00	10.84	7.90	10.15	8.63	9.76
18.8 Abrasive-media flow deburring	7.00	10.84	7.90	10.15	8.63	9.76
19.1 Chemical machining and printed circuit board fabrication	8.11	9.51	11.69	11.73	10.88	12.23
19.2 Electrical discharge machine	10.10	12.60	11.57	12.52	12.50	13.56
19.3 Traveling wire electrical discharge machine	10.10	12.60	11.57	12.52	12.50	13.56
20.1 Mask and unmask bench	7.81	9.51	10.80	10.78	9.99	11.22
20.2 Booth, conveyor and dip painting, and conversion	7.81	8.65	11.75	11.73	10.88	12.23
20.3 Metal chemical cleaning	7.81	8.65	9.46	11.73	10.21	12.23
20.4 Blast cleaning	7.81	10.41	11.01	11.01	10.21	11.47

MACHINE, PROCESS, OR BENCH	ATLANTA	BALTIMORE	BOSTON	BUFFALO	CHICAGO	CLEVELAND
20.5 Metal electroplating and oxide coating	7.68	10.84	11.47	11.45	10.62	11.93
21.1 Bench assembly	7.00	8.65	8.91	10.98	9.67	11.22
21.2 Rivet and assembly machines	7.27	8.65	8.91	10.98	9.67	11.22
21.3 Robot	7.27	8.65	11.24	11.22	10.66	11.70
22.1 Machine, process, and bench inspection	9.22	10.52	10.23	11.54	10.52	11.67
22.2 Inspection table	11.04	12.04	11.40	12.72	12.04	14.29
23.1 Component sequencing	8.76	10.48	11.24	11.22	10.41	11.70
23.2 Component insertion	8.76	10.48	11.24	11.22	10.41	11.70
23.3 Axial-lead component insertion	8.76	10.48	11.24	11.22	10.41	11.70
23.4 Printed circuit board stuffing	7.00	8.65	8.91	10.98	9.67	11.22
23.5 Printed circuit board drilling	10.36	11.72	10.03	10.80	12.38	15.08
23.6 Wave soldering	8.42	9.13	8.11	11.10	10.12	10.66
23.7 Wire harness	7.00	8.65	8.91	10.98	9.67	11.22
23.8 Flat cable connector	7.00	8.65	8.91	10.98	9.67	11.22
23.9 D-subminiature connector	7.00	8.65	8.91	10.98	9.67	11.22
23.10 Single wire termination	7.00	8.65	8.91	10.98	9.67	11.22
23.11 Resistance microspot welding	8.42	11.34	8.11	13.01	10.12	10.66
23.12 Coil winding	9.09	9.49	8.66	10.80	9.50	7.63
24.1 Packaging	7.70	7.98	9.85	7.39	9.69	7.32
24.2 Corrugated-cardboard conveyor	7.70	7.98	9.85	7.39	9.69	7.32
24.3 Case packing conveyor	7.70	7.98	9.85	7.39	9.69	7.32

MACHINE, PROCESS, OR BENCH	DALLAS / FORT WORTH	DENVER	DETROIT	HARTFORD	HOUSTON	LOS ANGELES / LONG BEACH
1.1 Power bandsaw cutoff, contour bandsaw, and hacksaw	7.45	6.48	8.54	9.05	8.01	6.59
1.2 Abrasive saw cutoff	7.45	6.48	8.54	9.05	8.01	6.59
1.3 Oxygen cutting	8.43	9.89	12.37	8.94	13.00	8.45
2.1 Plastics molding	8.52	9.56	12.51	10.89	11.55	9.68
2.2 Plastic preform molding	8.34	9.37	12.25	10.67	11.38	9.44
2.3 Thermoplastic injection molding	8.60	9.66	12.64	11.01	11.74	9.69
2.4 Thermosetting plastic molding	8.60	9.66	12.64	11.01	11.74	9.69
2.5 Thermoforming	8.34	9.37	12.25	10.67	11.34	9.44
2.6 Glass cloth layup	8.34	9.37	12.25	10.67	11.38	9.44
2.7 Extrusion	8.34	9.37	12.25	10.67	11.38	9.44
2.8 Blow molding	8.34	9.37	12.25	10.67	11.38	9.44
2.9 Hot and cold chamber die casting	9.23	10.36	13.55	11.81	12.58	10.50
2.10 Isostatic molding press	8.34	9.37	12.25	10.67	11.38	9.44
2.11 Routing and molding	8.34	9.37	12.25	10.67	11.38	9.44
2.12 Banding machines	8.34	9.37	12.25	10.67	11.38	9.44
3.1 Power shear	9.03	9.99	12.51	9.24	11.90	10.24
3.2 Punch press (first operations)	8.94	9.93	12.37	9.79	11.77	10.15
3.3 Punch press (secondary operations)	8.94	9.93	12.37	9.79	11.77	10.15
3.4 Turret punch press	9.12	10.13	12.51	9.79	12.02	10.35
3.5 Single-station punching	8.94	9.93	12.37	9.79	11.77	10.15
3.6 Power press brake	8.84	9.85	12.03	10.06	11.65	10.03
3.7 Foot brake, kick press, and jump shear	6.95	7.19	8.95	9.05	9.05	7.13

MACHINE, PROCESS, OR BENCH	DALLAS/ FORT WORTH	DENVER	DETROIT	HARTFORD	HOUSTON	LOS ANGELES/ LONG BEACH
3.8 Hand-operated brake, bender, punch press, multiform, coil winder, shear, straightener, and roller	6.95	7.19	8.95	9.05	9.05	7.13
3.9 Nibbling	6.95	7.19	8.95	9.05	9.05	7.13
3.10 Tube bending	8.84	9.85	12.03	10.06	11.65	10.03
3.11 Ironworker	8.84	9.85	12.03	10.06	11.65	10.03
4.1 Marking	6.95	7.19	8.95	9.05	9.05	7.13
4.2 Screen printing	8.60	9.66	12.64	11.01	11.74	9.69
4.3 Laser marking	6.95	7.19	8.95	9.05	11.38	7.13
5.1 Forging	12.60	13.32	12.88	10.67	13.20	13.20
6.1 Engine lathe	11.71	12.75	16.23	11.14	13.31	13.20
6.2 Turret lathe	12.12	12.31	14.68	11.14	13.20	12.42
6.3 Vertical turret lathe	12.12	12.31	14.68	11.14	13.20	12.36
6.4 Numerical controlled turning lathe	11.63	11.41	11.86	9.53	13.78	15.14
6.5 Numerical controlled chucking lathe	11.63	11.41	11.86	9.53	13.78	15.14
6.6 Single spindle automatic screw machine	12.60	14.74	17.57	10.67	13.03	13.56
6.7 Multispindle automatic screw machine	12.60	14.74	17.57	10.67	13.03	13.56
7.1 Milling machine setup	10.67	13.21	15.39	11.79	13.46	10.39
7.2 Knee and column milling	12.20	13.21	15.39	10.54	13.46	12.61
7.3 Bed milling	10.91	10.79	12.32	9.02	12.53	8.77
7.4 Vertical-spindle ram-type milling	12.20	10.79	15.39	10.54	13.46	12.61
7.5 Router milling	10.91	8.41	11.31	9.05	9.51	6.61
7.6 Special milling	10.91	11.72	12.32	9.02	12.53	9.88
7.7 Hand miller	7.45	8.96	11.31	9.05	9.51	6.61
8.1 Machining centers	12.11	11.92	12.04	9.73	13.49	11.54

MACHINE, PROCESS, OR BENCH	DALLAS / FORT WORTH	DENVER	DETROIT	HARTFORD	HOUSTON	LOS ANGELES / LONG BEACH
8.2 Rapid travel and automatic tool changer elements	12.11	9.26	12.04	9.73	13.49	11.54
9.1 Drilling machine setup and layout	10.66	9.26	13.69	11.79	11.52	10.39
9.2 Sensitive drill press	7.63	10.97	13.03	9.67	9.24	9.16
9.3 Upright drilling	10.76	10.89	13.69	9.67	12.10	12.70
9.4 Turret drilling	12.11	10.89	12.00	9.67	12.87	12.70
9.5 Cluster drilling	10.76	10.89	13.03	9.67	12.10	9.16
9.6 Radial drilling	10.97	12.41	14.72	10.57	12.51	11.98
10.1 Horizontal milling, drilling, and boring	12.20	12.82	15.39	10.54	13.46	12.61
10.2 Boring and facing	12.12	12.82	15.39	10.54	13.46	12.61
11.1 Turn, bore, form, cutoff, thread, start drill, and break edges	10.24	11.40	15.46	10.99	11.74	11.47
11.2 Drill, counterbore, ream, countersink, and tap	8.79	9.26	13.69	9.67	11.28	9.60
11.3 Face, side, slot, form, straddle, end, saw, and engrave milling	11.56	12.01	13.00	9.78	11.83	9.32
11.4 Tool life and replacement	10.08	10.89	14.05	10.15	11.62	10.13
12.1 Broaching	11.52	12.43	15.47	10.56	13.05	12.42
13.1 Cylindrical grinding	11.84	13.51	15.74	10.92	13.43	13.24
13.2 Centerless grinding	9.53	10.44	11.91	11.49	13.44	9.88
13.3 Honing	6.43	7.02	8.48	8.52	8.49	6.73
13.4 Surface grinding	11.84	13.51	15.74	10.92	13.43	13.24
13.5 Internal grinding	11.84	13.45	15.74	10.92	13.43	13.24
13.6 Free abrasive grinding	6.43	7.02	8.48	8.52	8.48	6.73
13.7 Disk grinding	6.43	7.02	8.48	8.52	8.48	6.73
13.8 Vertical internal grinding	11.84	13.45	15.74	10.92	13.43	13.24

MACHINE, PROCESS, OR BENCH	DALLAS / FORT WORTH	DENVER	DETROIT	HARTFORD	HOUSTON	LOS ANGELES / LONG BEACH
14.1 Gear shaper	11.64	12.55	15.65	10.67	13.13	12.54
14.2 Hobbing	11.64	12.55	15.65	10.67	13.13	12.54
15.1 Thread cutting and form rolling	8.87	9.41	13.03	11.36	12.10	10.09
16.1 Shielded metal-arc, flux-cored arc, and submerged welding	11.64	11.71	12.47	10.92	13.53	11.86
16.2 Gas metal-arc welding and gas tungsten-arc welding	11.64	11.71	12.47	10.92	13.53	11.86
16.3 Resistance spot welding	8.03	9.89	13.18	8.78	13.00	12.70
16.4 Torch, dip, and furnace brazing	8.43	9.89	12.37	8.94	10.49	8.45
17.1 Heat treat furnaces	8.18	9.58	12.00	8.66	10.18	9.42
18.1 Drill press deburring	6.74	7.45	9.98	9.31	9.05	6.92
18.2 Abrasive belt deburring	7.69	7.81	11.18	9.16	9.25	8.49
18.3 Pedestal deburring and finishing	8.13	7.81	11.53	9.16	9.25	8.49
18.4 Handheld portable tool deburring	6.74	7.45	9.98	9.31	9.05	6.92
18.5 Hand deburring	6.74	7.45	9.98	9.31	9.05	6.92
18.6 Plastic material deburring	6.74	7.45	9.98	9.31	9.05	6.92
18.7 Loose abrasive deburring	7.45	7.81	8.54	9.05	8.01	10.09
18.8 Abrasive-media flow deburring	7.45	7.81	8.54	9.05	8.01	10.09
19.1 Chemical machining and printed circuit board fabrication	9.23	10.36	13.55	11.87	11.62	10.50
19.2 Electrical discharge machine	11.64	12.55	15.65	10.67	13.13	12.54
19.3 Traveling wire electrical discharge machine	11.64	12.55	15.65	10.67	13.13	12.54
20.1 Mask and unmask bench	8.52	9.56	12.51	10.89	11.62	9.68
20.2 Booth, conveyor and dip painting, and conversion	9.23	9.56	13.55	11.81	11.62	9.68
20.3 Metal chemical cleaning	9.04	10.16	13.29	11.58	11.62	9.68
20.4 Blast cleaning	8.69	9.77	12.77	11.58	11.62	9.68

MACHINE, PROCESS, OR BENCH	DALLAS / FORT WORTH	DENVER	DETROIT	HARTFORD	HOUSTON	LOS ANGELES / LONG BEACH
20.5 Metal electroplating and oxide coating	9.04	10.16	13.29	11.58	11.62	10.29
21.1 Bench assembly	8.10	10.74	13.18	9.36	12.23	8.31
21.2 Rivet and assembly machines	8.10	10.74	13.18	9.61	12.23	8.31
21.3 Robot	8.87	10.74	13.03	9.61	12.10	10.09
22.1 Machine, process, and bench inspection	9.41	10.75	13.66	10.43	11.17	9.83
22.2 Inspection table	11.63	11.79	15.14	10.03	11.16	13.33
23.1 Component sequencing	8.87	9.41	13.03	11.36	12.10	10.09
23.2 Component insertion	8.87	9.41	13.03	11.36	12.10	10.09
23.3 Axial-lead component insertion	8.87	9.41	13.03	11.36	12.10	10.09
23.4 Printed circuit board stuffing	8.10	10.74	13.18	9.36	12.23	8.31
23.5 Printed circuit board drilling	12.11	10.89	12.00	9.67	12.87	12.70
23.6 Wave soldering	8.43	9.89	12.37	8.94	10.49	8.45
23.7 Wire harness	8.10	10.74	13.18	9.36	12.23	8.31
23.8 Flat cable connector	8.10	10.74	13.18	9.36	12.23	8.31
23.9 D-subminiature connector	8.10	10.74	13.18	9.36	12.23	8.31
23.10 Single wire termination	8.10	10.74	13.18	9.36	12.23	8.31
23.11 Resistance microspot welding	8.03	9.89	13.18	8.78	13.00	12.70
23.12 Coil winding	7.63	10.97	13.03	9.67	9.24	9.16
24.1 Packaging	6.93	9.54	9.74	9.14	6.71	13.14
24.2 Corrugated-cardboard conveyor	6.93	9.54	9.74	9.14	6.71	13.14
24.3 Case packing conveyor	6.93	9.54	9.74	9.14	6.71	13.14

MACHINE, PROCESS, OR BENCH		MILWAUKEE	MINNEAPOLIS / ST. PAUL	NEWARK	NEW YORK CITY AND NEW JERSEY	PHILADELPHIA AND NEW JERSEY	PITTSBURGH
1.1	Power bandsaw cutoff, contour bandsaw, and hacksaw	11.41	9.52	8.53	6.62	7.64	10.64
1.2	Abrasive saw cutoff	11.41	9.52	8.53	6.62	7.64	10.64
1.3	Oxygen cutting	10.27	8.77	10.03	8.38	10.07	10.19
2.1	Plastics molding	12.85	11.01	11.65	8.06	10.87	11.05
2.2	Plastic preform molding	12.59	10.88	11.48	7.89	10.60	10.82
2.3	Thermoplastic injection molding	12.98	11.23	11.78	8.14	10.95	11.16
2.4	Thermosetting plastic molding	12.98	11.23	11.78	8.14	10.95	11.16
2.5	Thermoforming	12.59	10.88	11.48	7.89	10.60	10.82
2.6	Glass cloth layup	12.59	10.88	11.48	7.89	10.60	10.82
2.7	Extrusion	12.59	10.88	11.48	7.89	10.60	10.82
2.8	Blow molding	12.59	10.88	11.48	7.89	10.60	10.82
2.9	Hot and cold chamber die casting	13.94	12.06	12.63	8.65	11.73	11.97
2.10	Isostatic molding press	12.59	10.88	11.48	7.89	10.60	10.82
2.11	Routing and molding	12.59	10.88	11.48	7.89	10.60	10.82
2.12	Banding machines	12.59	10.88	11.48	7.89	10.60	10.82
3.1	Power shear	13.64	11.33	8.60	7.89	9.01	12.95
3.2	Punch press (first operations)	13.50	11.22	8.53	9.20	8.91	12.82
3.3	Punch press (secondary operations)	13.50	11.22	8.53	9.20	8.91	12.82
3.4	Turret punch press	13.77	11.45	8.69	9.39	9.10	13.08
3.5	Single-station punching	13.50	11.22	8.53	9.20	8.91	12.82
3.6	Power press brake	13.37	11.11	8.43	9.11	8.83	12.69
3.7	Foot brake, kick press, and jump shear	12.39	9.48	7.95	6.42	7.61	9.80

MACHINE, PROCESS, OR BENCH	MILWAUKEE	MINNEAPOLIS / ST. PAUL	NEWARK	NEW YORK CITY AND NEW JERSEY	PHILADELPHIA AND NEW JERSEY	PITTSBURGH
3.8 Hand-operated brake, bender, punch press, multiform, coil winder, shear, straightener, and roller	12.39	9.48	7.95	6.42	7.61	9.80
3.9 Nibbling	12.39	9.48	7.95	6.42	7.61	9.80
3.10 Tube bending	13.37	11.11	8.43	9.11	8.83	12.69
3.11 Ironworker	13.37	11.11	8.43	9.11	8.83	12.69
4.1 Marking	12.39	9.48	7.95	6.42	7.61	9.80
4.2 Screen printing	12.98	11.23	11.95	8.14	10.95	9.80
4.3 Laser marking	12.39	9.48	11.48	6.42	7.61	9.80
5.1 Forging	14.34	13.03	12.68	10.79	12.14	12.35
6.1 Engine lathe	13.47	12.12	12.60	10.41	13.04	11.96
6.2 Turret lathe	13.89	12.67	11.70	10.81	12.68	11.96
6.3 Vertical turret lathe	13.89	12.67	11.70	10.81	12.68	11.96
6.4 Numerical controlled turning lathe	15.03	11.03	11.74	10.71	12.61	12.73
6.5 Numerical controlled chucking lathe	15.03	11.03	11.74	10.71	12.61	12.73
6.6 Single spindle automatic screw machine	14.34	13.03	11.70	9.65	12.44	11.96
6.7 Multispindle automatic screw machine	14.34	13.03	11.70	9.65	12.44	11.96
7.1 Milling machine setup	15.34	10.97	11.24	10.88	11.43	11.96
7.2 Knee and column milling	13.68	11.61	11.24	10.88	12.52	11.96
7.3 Bed milling	13.56	11.58	9.83	8.77	11.51	11.51
7.4 Vertical-spindle ram-type milling	13.68	12.16	11.24	10.88	12.52	11.96
7.5 Router milling	11.41	9.52	8.53	7.42	7.64	11.96
7.6 Special milling	13.56	11.58	11.24	8.77	12.52	11.96
7.7 Hand miller	11.41	9.52	8.53	7.42	7.64	10.64
8.1 Machining centers	14.00	12.16	11.24	10.88	11.43	12.35

MACHINE, PROCESS, OR BENCH	MILWAUKEE	MINNEAPOLIS / ST. PAUL	NEWARK	NEW YORK CITY AND NEW JERSEY	PHILADELPHIA AND NEW JERSEY	PITTSBURGH
8.2 Rapid travel and automatic tool changer elements	14.00	12.16	11.24	10.89	11.43	12.35
9.1 Drilling machine setup and layout	15.34	10.97	8.07	9.81	11.42	11.75
9.2 Sensitive drill press	12.41	9.52	8.32	6.65	7.64	10.64
9.3 Upright drilling	13.03	11.58	8.32	9.81	11.42	11.75
9.4 Turret drilling	14.79	11.17	8.07	6.65	11.43	11.51
9.5 Cluster drilling	12.41	11.02	8.32	9.81	11.94	11.51
9.6 Radial drilling	12.53	12.03	8.32	9.81	11.82	11.75
10.1 Horizontal milling, drilling, and boring	13.68	12.16	11.24	10.88	12.52	12.35
10.2 Boring and facing	13.68	12.16	11.24	10.88	12.52	12.35
11.1 Turn, bore, form, cutoff, thread, start drill, and break edges	13.17	12.40	12.57	9.52	12.67	11.67
11.2 Drill, counterbore, ream, countersink, and tap	12.93	12.03	8.07	8.10	11.90	11.51
11.3 Face, side, slot, form, straddle, end, saw, and engrave milling	13.61	12.16	11.89	9.03	12.37	11.96
11.4 Tool life and replacement	13.28	12.20	10.84	8.89	12.32	11.72
12.1 Broaching	13.73	12.40	12.31	10.28	12.30	11.98
13.1 Cylindrical grinding	14.53	13.05	12.68	10.42	12.12	13.09
13.2 Centerless grinding	12.12	11.58	12.14	8.39	11.21	12.61
13.3 Honing	11.41	9.52	8.53	6.62	7.64	10.64
13.4 Surface grinding	14.53	12.12	12.68	10.42	12.12	13.09
13.5 Internal grinding	14.53	12.12	12.68	10.42	12.12	13.09
13.6 Free abrasive grinding	11.41	9.52	8.53	6.62	7.64	10.64
13.7 Disk grinding	11.41	9.52	8.53	6.62	7.64	10.64
13.8 Vertical internal grinding	14.53	12.12	12.68	10.42	12.12	13.09

MACHINE, PROCESS, OR BENCH	MILWAUKEE	MINNEAPOLIS / ST. PAUL	NEWARK	NEW YORK CITY AND NEW JERSEY	PHILADELPHIA AND NEW JERSEY	PITTSBURGH
14.1 Gear shaper	13.86	12.52	12.42	10.40	12.42	12.10
14.2 Hobbing	13.86	12.52	12.42	10.40	12.42	12.10
15.1 Thread cutting and form rolling	13.39	11.58	12.14	8.39	11.28	11.51
16.1 Shielded metal-arc, flux-cored arc, and submerged welding	14.03	12.21	12.06	9.36	12.88	12.32
16.2 Gas metal-arc welding and gas tungsten-arc welding	14.03	12.21	12.06	9.36	12.88	12.32
16.3 Resistance spot welding	10.27	11.97	11.13	8.38	8.49	10.19
16.4 Torch, dip, and furnace brazing	14.00	11.29	10.03	9.60	10.07	11.36
17.1 Heat treat furnaces	13.58	10.96	9.74	9.32	9.77	11.02
18.1 Drill press deburring	12.00	8.26	8.27	6.64	8.29	9.13
18.2 Abrasive belt deburring	12.50	8.43	10.34	8.14	10.39	9.48
18.3 Pedestal deburring and finishing	12.50	8.43	10.34	8.21	10.50	9.80
18.4 Handheld portable tool deburring	12.00	8.26	8.27	6.64	8.29	9.13
18.5 Hand deburring	12.00	8.26	8.27	6.64	8.29	9.13
18.6 Plastic material deburring	12.00	8.26	8.27	6.64	8.29	9.13
18.7 Loose abrasive deburring	11.41	8.58	8.53	6.62	7.64	10.64
18.8 Abrasive-media flow deburring	11.41	8.58	8.53	6.62	7.64	10.64
19.1 Chemical machining and printed circuit board fabrication	13.94	12.05	12.63	8.01	11.79	11.51
19.2 Electrical discharge machine	13.86	12.52	12.42	10.40	12.42	12.10
19.3 Traveling wire electrical discharge machine	13.86	12.52	12.42	10.40	12.42	12.10
20.1 Mask and unmask bench	12.85	11.11	11.65	8.06	10.82	11.05
20.2 Booth, conveyor and dip painting, and conversion	13.94	12.05	12.69	8.76	11.79	11.05
20.3 Metal chemical cleaning	13.66	11.11	12.38	8.56	11.50	11.27
20.4 Blast cleaning	13.12	11.11	11.90	8.22	11.05	11.27

MACHINE, PROCESS, OR BENCH	MILWAUKEE	MINNEAPOLIS / ST. PAUL	NEWARK	NEW YORK CITY AND NEW JERSEY	PHILADELPHIA AND NEW JERSEY	PITTSBURGH
20.5 Metal electroplating and oxide coating	13.66	12.05	12.38	8.56	11.05	11.27
21.1 Bench assembly	12.28	9.69	7.92	7.76	9.06	10.17
21.2 Rivet and assembly machines	12.28	10.94	7.92	7.76	9.06	10.17
21.3 Robot	13.39	11.58	12.14	8.39	11.28	11.51
22.1 Machine, process, and bench inspection	12.98	11.29	11.12	8.53	10.53	11.49
22.2 Inspection table	13.50	11.45	10.52	10.57	11.77	12.35
23.1 Component sequencing	13.39	11.58	12.14	8.39	11.28	11.51
23.2 Component insertion	13.39	11.58	12.14	8.39	11.28	11.51
23.3 Axial-lead component insertion	13.39	11.58	12.14	8.39	11.28	11.51
23.4 Printed circuit board stuffing	12.28	9.69	7.92	7.76	9.06	10.17
23.5 Printed circuit board drilling	14.79	11.17	8.07	6.65	11.43	11.51
23.6 Wave soldering	14.00	11.29	10.03	9.60	10.07	11.36
23.7 Wire harness	12.28	9.69	7.92	7.76	9.06	10.17
23.8 Flat cable connector	12.28	9.69	7.92	7.76	9.06	10.17
23.9 D-subminiature connector	12.28	9.69	7.92	7.76	9.06	10.17
23.10 Single wire termination	12.28	9.69	7.92	7.76	9.06	10.17
23.11 Resistance microspot welding	10.27	11.97	11.13	8.38	8.49	10.19
23.12 Coil winding	12.41	9.52	8.32	6.65	7.64	10.64
24.1 Packaging	8.29	7.95	6.37	8.04	9.67	10.82
24.2 Corrugated-cardboard conveyor	8.29	7.95	6.37	8.04	9.67	10.82
24.3 Case packing conveyor	8.29	7.95	6.37	8.04	9.67	10.82

MACHINE, PROCESS, OR BENCH	PORTLAND AND WASHINGTON	ST. LOUIS AND ILLINOIS	SAN FRANCISCO / OAKLAND	TULSA	WORCESTER
1.1 Power bandsaw cutoff, contour bandsaw, and hacksaw	12.11	10.63	12.83	8.48	8.57
1.2 Abrasive saw cutoff	12.11	10.63	12.83	8.48	8.57
1.3 Oxygen cutting	12.67	9.23	13.08	10.94	9.82
2.1 Plastics molding	13.12	10.29	14.64	10.35	9.09
2.2 Plastic preforming molding	12.84	10.06	14.34	11.40	6.89
2.3 Thermoplastic injection molding	13.25	10.39	14.80	14.72	9.09
2.4 Thermosetting plastic molding	13.25	10.39	14.80	14.72	9.09
2.5 Thermoforming	12.84	10.06	14.34	9.43	6.89
2.6 Glass cloth layup	12.84	10.06	14.34	9.43	9.09
2.7 Extrusion	12.84	10.06	14.34	9.43	6.89
2.8 Blow molding	12.84	10.06	14.34	9.43	6.89
2.9 Hot and cold chamber die casting	14.20	11.13	15.87	15.69	9.83
2.10 Isostatic molding press	12.84	10.06	14.34	9.43	6.89
2.11 Routing and molding	12.84	10.06	14.34	9.43	6.89
2.12 Banding machines	12.84	10.06	14.34	9.43	6.89
3.1 Power shear	13.33	10.70	13.62	10.13	9.96
3.2 Punch press (first operations)	13.20	10.59	13.62	10.39	10.02
3.3 Punch press (secondary operations)	13.20	10.59	13.62	10.39	10.02
3.4 Turret punch press	13.46	10.79	13.62	10.28	9.96
3.5 Single-station punching	13.20	10.70	13.26	10.17	9.96
3.6 Power press brake	13.06	10.48	13.26	10.17	9.96
3.7 Foot brake, kick press, and jump shear	10.21	8.86	12.90	9.43	8.99

MACHINE, PROCESS, OR BENCH	PORTLAND AND WASHINGTON	ST. LOUIS AND ILLINOIS	SAN FRANCISCO / OAKLAND	TULSA	WORCESTER
3.8 Hand-operated brake, bender, punch press, multiform, coil winder, shear, straightener, and roller	10.21	8.86	12.90	9.43	8.99
3.9 Nibbling	10.21	8.86	12.90	9.43	8.99
3.10 Tube bending	13.06	10.48	13.26	10.17	9.96
3.11 Ironworker	13.06	10.48	13.26	10.17	9.96
4.1 Marking	10.21	8.86	12.90	9.43	8.99
4.2 Screen printing	13.25	8.86	13.62	10.45	9.18
4.3 Laser marking	10.21	8.86	12.90	9.43	8.99
5.1 Forging	14.40	12.10	17.28	12.39	11.38
6.1 Engine lathe	14.66	12.10	17.28	13.03	11.48
6.2 Turret lathe	14.66	12.10	17.28	12.56	11.50
6.3 Vertical turret lathe	14.66	12.10	17.28	12.56	11.50
6.4 Numerical controlled turning lathe	14.74	11.87	17.28	12.40	11.05
6.5 Numerical controlled chucking lathe	14.74	11.87	17.28	12.40	11.05
6.6 Single spindle automatic screw machine	14.40	12.10	17.28	12.39	11.38
6.7 Multispindle automatic screw machine	14.40	12.10	17.28	12.39	11.38
7.1 Milling machine setup	14.74	12.36	17.28	12.57	11.35
7.2 Knee and column milling	14.74	12.36	17.28	12.57	11.35
7.3 Bed milling	13.66	11.39	15.26	10.78	9.06
7.4 Vertical-spindle ram-type milling	14.74	12.36	17.28	12.57	11.35
7.5 Router milling	9.90	9.65	12.43	8.48	8.57
7.6 Special milling	9.90	11.39	12.73	10.78	11.35
7.7 Hand miller	9.90	9.16	12.83	8.48	8.57
8.1 Machining centers	14.24	11.87	17.28	12.40	11.19

MACHINE, PROCESS, OR BENCH	PORTLAND AND WASHINGTON	ST. LOUIS AND ILLINOIS	SAN FRANCISCO/ OAKLAND	TULSA	WORCESTER
8.2 Rapid travel and automatic tool changer elements	14.24	11.87	17.28	12.40	11.19
9.1 Drilling machine setup and layout	14.22	11.35	17.28	11.64	10.10
9.2 Sensitive drill press	13.66	10.71	12.83	9.76	9.67
9.3 Upright drilling	14.22	10.13	17.28	11.41	10.10
9.4 Turret drilling	14.22	10.13	17.28	11.41	9.67
9.5 Cluster spindle	14.22	10.13	17.28	11.41	9.67
9.6 Radial drilling	14.41	10.13	17.28	11.64	11.38
10.1 Horizontal milling, drilling, and boring	14.74	12.36	17.28	12.57	11.35
10.2 Boring and facing	14.74	12.36	17.28	12.57	11.35
11.1 Turn, bore, form, cutoff, thread, start drill, and break edges	14.66	12.10	17.28	12.10	10.88
11.2 Drill, counterbore, ream, countersink, and tap	14.22	12.10	17.28	10.69	9.92
11.3 Face, side, slot, form, straddle, end, saw, and engrave milling	14.74	12.36	17.28	12.57	10.20
11.4 Tool life and replacement	14.54	12.16	17.28	11.80	10.33
12.1 Broaching	14.25	11.74	16.44	12.05	11.10
13.1 Cylindrical grinding	14.84	12.10	17.28	12.16	11.38
13.2 Centerless grinding	13.66	10.71	15.26	10.78	10.14
13.3 Honing	14.84	10.63	12.83	8.48	8.14
13.4 Surface grinding	14.84	10.63	17.28	12.16	11.38
13.5 Internal grinding	14.84	10.71	17.28	12.16	11.38
13.6 Free abrasive grinding	14.84	10.63	12.83	8.48	8.14
13.7 Disk grinding	14.84	10.63	12.83	8.48	8.14
13.8 Vertical internal grinding	14.84	10.71	17.28	12.16	11.38

MACHINE, PROCESS, OR BENCH		PORTLAND AND WASHINGTON	ST. LOUIS AND ILLINOIS	SAN FRANCISCO/ OAKLAND	TULSA	WORCESTER
14.1	Gear shaper	14.40	12.10	17.28	12.18	11.38
14.2	Hobbing	14.40	12.10	16.60	12.18	11.38
15.1	Thread cutting and form rolling	13.66	10.63	14.49	10.78	9.46
16.1	Shielded metal-arc, flux-cored arc, and submerged welding	14.84	11.73	12.62	12.46	10.62
16.2	Gas metal-arc welding and gas tungsten-arc welding	14.84	11.73	12.62	12.46	10.62
16.3	Resistance spot welding	13.77	9.34	13.62	10.94	10.51
16.4	Torch, dip, and furnace brazing	13.09	9.23	12.19	10.61	10.37
17.1	Heat treat furnaces	13.77	9.23	12.62	10.29	10.37
18.1	Drill press deburring	11.74	8.96	12.19	7.73	8.25
18.2	Abrasive belt deburring	12.11	10.67	12.19	8.48	8.64
18.3	Pedestal deburring and finishing	12.25	10.67	12.19	8.48	8.64
18.4	Handheld portable tool deburring	11.74	8.96	12.19	7.73	8.25
18.5	Hand deburring	11.74	8.96	12.19	7.73	8.25
18.6	Plastic material deburring	11.74	8.96	12.19	7.73	8.25
18.7	Loose abrasive deburring	13.66	10.63	12.33	8.48	9.46
18.8	Abrasive-media flow deburring	13.66	10.63	12.33	8.48	9.46
19.1	Chemical machining and printed circuit board fabrication	12.96	10.71	12.76	10.78	8.57
19.2	Electrical discharge machine	14.40	12.10	16.60	12.18	11.38
19.3	Traveling wire electrical discharge machine	14.40	12.10	16.60	12.18	11.38
20.1	Mask and unmask bench	12.96	10.71	12.33	8.48	8.57
20.2	Booth, conveyor and dip painting, and conversion	12.96	10.71	13.05	10.39	9.46
20.3	Metal chemical cleaning	12.96	10.71	13.05	10.39	9.46
20.4	Blast cleaning	12.96	10.63	12.62	9.43	9.46

MACHINE, PROCESS, OR BENCH		PORTLAND AND WASHINGTON	ST. LOUIS AND ILLINOIS	SAN FRANCISCO / OAKLAND	TULSA	WORCESTER
20.5	Metal electroplating and oxide coating	13.03	10.71	12.62	10.39	9.46
21.1	Bench assembly	13.05	9.70	11.75	10.31	9.12
21.2	Rivet and assembly machines	14.16	9.70	12.19	10.31	9.10
21.3	Robot	14.16	10.71	12.62	10.31	9.46
22.1	Machine, process, and bench inspection	14.18	11.14	15.26	10.57	9.82
22.2	Inspection table	15.09	11.57	15.92	12.56	11.61
23.1	Component sequencing	13.66	10.63	14.49	10.78	9.46
23.2	Component insertion	13.66	10.63	14.49	10.78	9.46
23.3	Axial-lead component insertion	13.66	10.63	14.49	10.78	9.46
23.4	Printed circuit board stuffing	13.05	9.70	11.75	10.31	9.12
23.5	Printed circuit board drilling	14.22	10.13	17.28	11.41	9.67
23.6	Wave soldering	13.09	9.23	12.19	10.61	10.37
23.7	Wire harness	13.05	9.70	11.75	10.31	9.12
23.8	Flat cable connector	13.05	9.70	11.75	10.31	9.12
23.9	D-subminiature connector	13.05	9.70	11.75	10.31	9.12
23.10	Single wire termination	13.05	9.70	11.75	10.31	9.12
23.11	Resistance microspot welding	13.77	9.34	13.62	10.94	10.51
23.12	Coiling winding	13.66	10.71	12.83	9.76	9.67
24.1	Packaging	10.02	10.52	7.99	8.32	8.25
24.2	Corrugated-cardboard conveyor	10.02	10.52	7.99	8.32	8.25
24.3	Case packing conveyor	10.02	10.52	7.99	8.32	8.25

Material
Costs

MATERIAL COSTS

Description	Quantity	1985–1986 Cost
FERROUS PRODUCTS		
Bar	*Weight*	*Cost: $ per 100 lb*
Bar, hot-rolled, carbon steel; 1½-in. round OD, 16- or 20-ft lengths; AISI specification 1020, special quality. FOB service center for less than base quantity; FOB mill for base quantity.	120.3 lb 2,000 lb 6,000 lb Base quantity: 10,000 lb	80.90 28.60 26.30 24.90
	Weight	*Cost: $ per 100 lb*
Bar, hot-rolled, carbon steel; ¾-in. square; AISI specification 1020, 20-ft lengths. FOB service center for quantities listed.	38.2 lb 2,000 lb 6,000 lb Base quantity: 10,000 lb	115.50 34.25 30.50 28.00
	Weight	*Cost: $ per 100 lb*
Bar, hot-rolled, carbon steel; AISI specification M1020, merchant quality, 1-in. round, 20-ft random lengths. Standard packaging FOB service center for less than base quantity; FOB mill for base quantity.	53.4 lb 500 lb 2,000 lb 4,000 lb 6,000 lb Base quantity: 10,000 lb	100.66 53.66 34.66 33.83 31.33 29.00
	Weight	*Cost: $ per 100 lb*
Bar, hot-rolled carbon steel, flat 1½ × 5 in. × 16- or 20-ft lengths; ASTM specification A-36. FOB warehouse for less than base quantity; FOB mill for base quantity.	504 lb 2,000 lb 6,000 lb Base quantity: 10,000 lb	60.50 43.00 40.50 38.50
	Weight	*Cost: $ per 100 lb*
Bar, hot-rolled steel, 2 × 2 in. × 16- or 20-ft lengths; AISI specification M1020, merchant quality. FOB warehouse for less than base quantity; FOB mill for base quantity.	272 lb 2,000 lb 6,000 lb Base quantity: 10,000 lb	91.20 46.45 43.37 41.20
	Weight	*Cost: $ per 100 lb*
Bar, cold-finished, carbon steel, ⅝-in. round OD × 10- or 12-ft. lengths; AISI specification C1215, standard quality. FOB service center for less than base quantity; FOB mill for base quantity.	12.5 lb Base quantity: 2,000 lb	123.60 48.60
	Weight	*Cost: $ per 100 lb*
Bar, cold-finished carbon steel; 1-in. OD × 10- or 12-ft lengths, specification 12L14. FOB warehouse for less than base quantity; FOB mill for base quantity.	32.04 lb 2,000 lb 6,000 lb Base quantity: 10,000 lb	126.01 59.61 56.40 56.00

Description	Quantity	1985–1986 Cost
	Weight	*Cost: $ per 100 lb*
Bar, cold-finished. 2-in. round × 12-ft long; AISI specification 1215. FOB service center.	128.2 lb 2,000 lb 6,000 lb Base quantity: 10,000 lb	101.33 61.80 59.33 58.00
	Weight	*Cost: $ per 100 lb*
Bar, cold-finished, carbon steel; ⅝-in. round OD × 10- or 12-ft lengths; AISI specification C1117, standard quality. FOB service center for less than base quantity; FOB mill for base quantity.	12.5 lb 2,000 lb Base quantity: 6,000 lb	172.76 61.63 59.50
	Weight	*Cost: $ per 100 lb*
Bar, hot-rolled, alloy steel; 1½-in. round OD × 20-ft long; AISI specification 4140 oil hardening, annealed, machine straightened. FOB service center for order less than base quantity; FOB mill for base quantity.	120 lb 2,000 lb 6,000 lb Base quantity: 10,000 lb	100.78 67.95 65.06 64.35
	Weight	*Cost: $ per 100 lb*
Bar, cold-finished, carbon; 1½-in OD × 20-ft length; AISI specification 1045, turned, ground and polished. FOB service center.	120.2 lb 2,000 lb 6,000 lb Base quantity: 10,000 lb	110.50 75.35 73.43 73.33
	Weight	*Cost: $ per 100 lb*
Bar, cold-finished, alloy steel; ¾-in. round OD × 10- or 12-ft random lengths; AISI specification 8620, annealed. FOB service center for less than base quantity; FOB mill for base quantity.	18.04 lb 2,000 lb 6,000 lb Base quantity: 10,000 lb	154.25 78.75 74.25 73.75
	Weight	*Cost: $ per 100 lb*
Bar, hot-rolled, annealed, alloy steel; 3-in. round OD × 20-ft random lengths; ASTM specification 4340, commercial quality. FOB warehouse for small orders; FOB mill for base quantity.	481 lb 1,000 lb 5,000 lb Base quantity: 10,000 lb	110.12 92.45 85.49 84.66
	Weight	*Cost: $ per 100 lb*
Bar, cold-drawn, annealed, alloy steel; 4-in round OD × 12-ft stock lengths (approx.); AISI specification 41L40, commercial quality. FOB warehouse for less than mill quantity; FOB mill for base quantity.	513.2 lb 2,000 lb Base quantity: 6,000 lb	103.80 90.40 86.20

Description	Weight	Cost: $ per 100 lb
Bar, alloy, aircraft quality, annealed cold-finished, 3-in. OD × 10- or 12-ft lengths; E 4340, FOB service center for less than base quantity; FOB mill for base quantity.	240 lb 2,000 lb 6,000 lb Base quantity: 10,000 lb	164.04 131.16 129.03 128.40
Bar, hot-rolled, stainless steel; type 304, 2-in. round OD × 10- or 12-ft lengths; forging quality, unannealed, base packaging. FOB service center for less than base quantity; FOB mill for base quantity.	128 lb 2,000 lb 6,000 lb Base quantity: 10,000 lb	321.00 170.00 166.00 162.00
Bar, cold-finished, annealed centerless ground, stainless type 303, 1-in. round OD × 10- to 22-ft mill lengths, boxed. FOB service center for less than base quantity; FOB mill for base quantity.	58.96 lb 2,000 lb 6,000 lb Base quantity: 10,000 lb	378.52 179.50 176.50 173.00
Bar, tool steel, cold-finished; ground 1-in. round OD, 100/144-in. mill lengths, annealed; AISI specification 0 1 grade (C .9%, Cr .5%, W .50%). FOB shipping point.	32 lb 250 lb 1,000 lb Base quantity: 5,000 lb	384.50 292.00 250.00 250.00

Description	Weight	Cost: $ per 1 lb
Bar, tool steel, alloy, oil-hardening die steel; 2-in. round OD, 100/144-in. mill lengths, annealed; AISI 0 1 (C .90%, Mn 1.00%, Cr .50%, W .50%). FOB service center.	288.7 lb 500 lb Base quantity: 1,000 lb	3.18 2.92 2.75
Bar, tool steel, cold finished; ground 1 × 2-in. flats, 100/144-in. mill lengths; AISI specification A2 grade (C 1.00%, Cr 5.00%, MO 1.00%). FOB shipping point.	81.7 lb 250 lb Base quantity: 1,000 lb	4.85 4.22 3.80
Bar, tool steel, cold finished; 1-in. round OD, 100/144-in. mill lengths, annealed. AISI specification M2 grade (C .85%, Cr 4.00%, W 6.00%, Mo 5.00%, V 2.00%). FOB shipping point.	34 lb 250 lb Base quantity: 1,000 lb	6.68 6.40 5.52

Description	Quantity	1985–1986 Cost
Rod Rod, 7/32-in. diameter, 12- to 20-ft lengths, cold-rolled carbon steel; C1018 industrial or standard quality. FOB service center; FOB mill for base quantity.	*Weight* 2.6 lb 500 lb 1,000 lb 2,000 lb 4,000 lb Base quantity: 6,000 lb	*Cost: $ per 100 lb* 147.56 84.50 77.00 73.25 73.00 71.33
Sheet Sheet, hot-rolled, low carbon steel, commercial quality; cut length, .1271-in. minimum and theoretical minimum weight, 48 × 120 in., cut edge, not pickled, base chemistry. FOB service center for less than base quantity; FOB mill for base quantity.	*Weight* 200 lb 2,000 lb 6,000 lb Base quantity: 10,000 lb	*Cost: $ per 100 lb* 81.26 36.13 30.63 29.00
Bands (sheets), hot-rolled, carbon steel; 14 ga or heavier, 24- to 72-in. width, base chemistry, base quantity. Standard tolerances, not edge trimmed, end chopped, temper rolled, or further processed in any manner. FOB service center.	*Weight* 500 lb 2,000 lb 6,000 lb Base quantity: 10,000 lb	*Cost: $ per 100 lb* 48.83 34.58 31.33 31.33
Sheet, cold-rolled, carbon steel; .0344-in. minimum, theoretical minimum weight, 42-in. wide coil (200 lb per in. of width or over), base chemistry, commercial quality, controlled surface texture, surface condition, flatness, limitations and tempers, bare (unwrapped) wire or banded without skids or platforms. FOB service center or mill.	*Weight* Base quantity: 10,000 lb	*Cost: $ per 100 lb* 36.33
Sheet, cold-rolled, carbon steel, commercial quality, oiled; No. 10 (.1345 in.) 36 × 96 in. FOB service center for less than base quantity; FOB mill for base quantity.	*Weight* 135 lb 2,000 lb 6,000 lb Base quantity: 10,000 lb	*Cost: $ per 100 lb* 84.84 42.67 39.50 37.50
Sheet, hot-rolled carbon steel; 7 ga × 36 × 96 in., commercial quality to maximum carbon of 0.15%. FOB warehouse for small quantity orders; FOB mill for base quantity.	*Weight* 500 lb 2,000 lb 6,000 lb Base quantity: 10,000 lb	*Cost: $ per 100 lb* 62.24 42.66 38.73 37.40

Description	Quantity		1985–1986 Cost
		Weight	Cost: $ per 100 lb
Sheet, hot-rolled, low carbon steel; 48 × 120 in., (.0747-in.) 14 ga, pickled and oiled, sheet or coil. FOB service center for less than base quantity. FOB mill for base quantity.		196.9 lb 2,000 lb 6,000 lb Base quantity: 10,000 lb	80.92 44.00 40.25 38.50
		Weight	Cost: $ per 100 lb
Sheet, high strength; 48 × 120 in. ASTM specification A-607 type 1 grade 50, No. 7 (.1793 in.). FOB service center for less than base quantity; FOB mill for base quantity.		300 lb 2,000 lb 6,000 lb Base quantity: 10,000 lb	79.30 43.90 41.30 39.30
		Weight	Cost: $ per 100 lb
Sheet, galvanized, flat, carbon steel; .0262-in. minimum, theoretical minimum weight, 30 × 96 in., commercial coating (standard 1¼ oz), commercial quality, bare (unwrapped), wire or banded. FOB service center for less than base quantity; FOB mill for base quantity.		2,000 lb 6,000 lb Base quantity: 10,000 lb	51.54 47.68 45.80
		Weight	Cost: $ per 100 lb
Sheet, cold-rolled, stainless steel; type 304, 2B finish, 24 ga × 36 × 120 in. FOB service center for less than base quantity; FOB mill for base quantity. Provide protection on skid platforms for larger orders.		24.7 lb 2,000 lb 6,000 lb Base quantity: 10,000 lb	362.70 130.70 126.37 122.70
Plate		Weight	Cost: $ per 100 lb
Plate, carbon steel; 84 × ½ × 240 in; ASTM specification A-36. FOB service center for less than base quantity; FOB mill for base quantity.		2,858 lb 6,000 lb Base quantity: 10,000 lb	42.46 38.58 36.33
		Weight	Cost: $ per 100 lb
Plate, carbon steel, hot-rolled; .40 to .50%, ½ × 60 in. × 20 ft. FOB service center for less than base quantity; FOB mill for base quantity.		4,084 lb 6,000 lb Base quantity: 10,000 lb	49.66 46.33 44.00
		Weight	Cost: $ per 100 lb
Plate, steel, high-strength, low-alloy; ASTM specification A-572, grade 50, ½ × 84 × 240 in. FOB service center for less than base quantity; FOB mill for base quantity.		2,858 lb 6,000 lb Base quantity: 10,000 lb	50.37 47.53 45.33

Description	Quantity	1985–1986 Cost
	Weight	*Cost: $ per 100 lb*
Plate, carbon steel; ASTM specification A-285, pressure vessel quality, grade C, $3/16 \times 84 \times 240$-in. length. FOB service center for less than base quantity; FOB mill for base quantity.	1,072.4 lb 2,000 lb 6,000 lb Base quantity: 10,000 lb	61.43 53.93 50.05 47.80
	Weight	*Cost: $ per 100 lb*
Plate, hot-rolled, stainless steel; type 304, $1/4 \times 72 \times 240$ in., annealed and pickled. FOB service center for order less base quantity; FOB mill for base quantity.	1,339 lb 6,700 lb Base quantity: 10,000 lb	133.50 122.00 119.00
Structural shapes	*Weight*	*Cost: $ per 100 lb*
Structural steel shape, carbon steel; angle $3 \times 3 \times 1/4$ in., 4.90 lb per ft, 40-ft lengths; ASTM specification A-36. FOB mill for base quantity.	196 lb 2,000 lb 6,000 lb Base quantity: 10,000 lb	82.59 28.26 24.93 22.60
	Weight	*Cost: $ per 100 lb*
Structural steel shape, carbon steel; C-channel, C 3×4.1, 4.1 lb per ft, 40-ft lengths; ASTM specification A-36. FOB service center for less than base quantity; FOB mill for base quantity.	164 lb 2,000 lb 6,000 lb Base quantity: 10,000 lb	64.00 28.50 26.00 24.00
	Weight	*Cost: $ per 100 lb*
Structural shapes, carbon steel; $6 \times 4 \times 1/2$-in. angles, 350/400-in. long; ASTM specification A-7. FOB service center for less than base quantity; FOB mill for base quantity.	500 lb 2,000 lb 4,000 lb 6,000 lb Base quantity: 10,000 lb	52.83 31.16 30.33 26.83 24.50
	Weight	*Cost: $ per 100 lb*
Structural steel shape, carbon steel, 8-in. wide flange, 24 lb per ft wide flange section $\times$ 20 ft; ASTM specification A-36. FOB service center for less than base quantity; FOB mill for base quantity.	480 lb 2,000 lb Base quantity: 10,000 lb	66.05 38.05 32.85
Pipe, tube	*Weight*	*Cost: $ per 100 lb*
Tubing, mechanical, carbon steel, electric weld; $1\frac{1}{2}$-in. OD $\times$ 14 ga, 1.256 lb per ft, random mill lengths. FOB service center for less than mill quantity; FOB mill for base quantity.	2,000 lb 6,000 lb Base quantity: 10,000 lb	103.54 95.87 91.75

NONFERROUS PRODUCTS

Description	Weight	Cost: $ per 100 lb
Bar, aluminum; 1 × 2 in. × standard stock lengths of 12 ft; specification 6061-T6511. FOB destination.	28.2 lb	394.67
	500 lb	188.67
	2,000 lb	166.00
	Base quantity: 6,000 lb	163.00

Description	Weight	Cost: $ per 1 lb
Bar, aluminum; 2-in OD × 12 ft (approx.); specification 2024 T4 rounds. FOB destination.	45.8 lb	5.23
	500 lb	2.49
	Base quantity: 2,000 lb	2.22

Description	Weight	Cost: $ per 100 lb
Sheet, aluminum, heat treatable, mill finish; 0.090 × 48 × 144 in.; specification 6061-T6, bare. FOB destination.	61 lb	324.00
	500 lb	183.50
	2,000 lb	157.50
	Base quantity: 6,000 lb	152.50

Description	Weight	Cost: $ per 1 lb
Sheet, flat, aluminum; .125 × 48 × 144 in., mill finish; specification 5052-H32. FOB destination.	84 lb	4.10
	500 lb	1.71
	Base quantity: 2,000 lb	1.51

Description	Weight	Cost: $ per 1 lb
Sheet, flat aluminum; .313 × 48 × 144 in.; specification 2024-T3. FOB destination.	219 lb	3.66
	500 lb	2.84
	2,000 lb	2.62
	Base quantity: 10,000 lb	2.53

Description	Weight	Cost: $ per 100 lb
Sheet, aluminum, non-heat treatable; .125 × 48 × 144 in., mill finish; specification 3003-H14. FOB destination.	84.5 lb	274.30
	500 lb	154.30
	Base quantity: 2,000 lb	136.80

Description	Weight	Cost: $ per 1 lb
Rod, aluminum 2011-T3 alloy; 1-in OD screw machine stock, 12-ft lengths (approx.), (5.5% copper, .5% bismuth). FOB destination.	116 lb	2.42
	500 lb	1.70
	2,000 lb	1.51
	Base quantity: 10,000 lb	1.45

Description	Weight	Cost: $ per 1 lb
Tubing, aluminum hard-drawn; 6063-T832 alloy; 1-in OD × .058-in wall thickness × 12-ft length. FOB destination.	Base quantity: 5,000 lb	3.30

Description	Quantity		1985–1986 Cost
	Weight		*Cost: $ per 1 lb*
Plate, heat treatable aluminum, 1 × 48 × 144 in., aircraft quality; specification 7075-T651, bare. FOB destination.	350 lb		3.42
	500 lb		3.10
	2,000 lb		2.70
	Base quantity: 5,000 lb		2.63
	Weight		*Cost: $ per 100 lb*
Plate, aluminum, heat treatable, mill finish; 0.500 × 48 × 144 in.; specification 6061-T651. FOB destination.	338.9 lb		212.50
	500 lb		202.50
	Base quantity: 2,000 lb		180.00
	Weight		*Cost: $ per 1 lb*
Strip, cartridge brass; 8 in. (wide) × .0160 in. (thick) × coil (26 B & S ga); CDA alloy No. 260 (70% copper, 30% zinc). FOB mill with freight allowed or prepaid.	500 lb		19.82
	Base quantity: 2,000 lb		19.60
	Weight		*Cost: $ per 1 lb*
Rod, yellow brass, free cutting; ⅜- to ½-in OD, random lengths, CDA alloy No. 360 (62% copper, 35% zinc, 3% lead). FOB distributor warehouse for less than base quantity; FOB mill for base quantity.	500 lb		1.37
	Base quantity: 2,000 lb		1.22
	Weight		*Cost: $ per 1 lb*
Sheet, copper; 16-oz thickness ga, 24 × 96 in or copper strip, .058-in thick × 6-in wide × coil. FOB distributor's warehouse for orders less than base quantity; FOB mill for base quantity.	500 lb		2.99
	Base quantity: 2,000 lb		2.83
	Weight		*Cost: $ per 1 lb*
Monel metal, No. 400 alloy, cold-rolled sheet; .078 × 48 × 120 in.; FOB warehouse for less than base quantity; FOB mill for base quantity.	500 lb		6.20
	2,000 lb		5.74
	Base quantity: 5,000 lb		5.70

Operation
Costs

IV

1. SAWING and CUTTING

	Machine	Setup $	Variables	$ per 100 units
1.1	Power bandsaw	1.47	Weight, Cut area	3.84 + .345 (lb) + 1.54 (sq in.)
	Contour bandsaw	1.47	Weight, Cut area	3.84 + .345 (lb) + 3.09 (sq in.)
	Hacksaw	1.47	Weight, Cut area	3.84 + .345 (lb) + 10.8 (sq in.)
1.2	Abrasive saw	1.47	Weight, Cut area	5.33 + 1.44 (lb) + .932 (sq in.)
1.3	Oxygen cutting	5.06	Hand load, Hoist, Roller	15.0 + .759 (in. thk × in. long) 43.3 + .759 (in. thk × in. long) 22.1 + .759 (in. thk × in. long)

AREA in²

2. MOLDING

	Machine	Setup $	Variables	$ per 100 units
2.1	Plastics bench	1.00	Wait, area No wait, area	124 + 1.00 (sq in.) 95.2 + 1.00 (sq in.)
2.2	Preforming	6.90	Number (no.) cavities	.670 − .125 (no. cavities)
2.3	Thermoplastic injection	12.12	Wall thk, No. cavities	(4.01 + 50.5 (in. thk)) ÷ (no. cavities)
2.4	Thermosetting molding	15.15	Wall thk, No. cavities	(33.0 + 55.8 (in. thk)) ÷ (no. cavities)
2.5	Thermoforming	19.58 (no. stations)	Handling, Heating in. thk; Flat in. thk; Mix in. thk; Cavities in. thk	3.26 + 200 (in. thk) 386 (in. thk) 405 (in. thk) 424 (in. thk)
2.6	Glass cloth	2.94	Area, layers	−199 + .842 (sq in.) + 96.0 (no. layer)
2.7	Extrusion	39.16	Volume, cu in. Polyethylene Polystryrene Butyrate Vinyl	 .066 (cu in.) .075 (cu in.) .081 (cu in.) .098 (cu in.)
2.8	Blow molding	97.90	Liquid volume	.813 + .504 (oz)
2.9	Die casting	32.43	Zinc, inserts, No. cavities Aluminum, inserts, No. cavities	(10.0 + 2.70 (insert)) ÷ (no. cavities) (7.89 + 2.70 (insert)) ÷ (no. cavities)
2.10	Isostatic molding	4.90	Length of mold, No. Dia changes	3.94 + .313 (L of mold + 2 × Dia + no. Dia changes)
2.11	Routing and molding	.98	Router L, in.	.294 (in. of routed L)
2.12	Banding	.98	Banded L	.059 (in. of banded L)

3. PRESSWORK

	Machine	Setup $	Variables	$ per 100 units
3.1	Power shear	4.14	Strip W, Blank L	$-1.16 + .207$ (strip W) $+ .078$ (blank L)
3.2	Punch press (first operations)	8.70	Units on strip, Coil strokes per min (spm)	$.593 + 3.00 \div$ units on strip $.427 - .001$ (spm)
3.3	Punch press (secondary operations)	6.65	Blank $L + W$, No. restrokes	$1.05 + .084$ ($L + W$) $+ .818$ (no. restrokes)
3.4	Turret punch press	$2.30 +$ $.63$ (no. station)	Blank $L + W$, No. sizes, No. holes	$3.34 + 1.05$ ($L + W$) $+ .523$ (no. of sizes) $+ .627$ (no. of holes)
3.5	Single-station punching	$1.03 +$ $.51$ (no. $Dia.$)	Blank $L + W$, No. holes	$1.18 + .022$ ($L + W$) $+ .564$ (no. holes)
3.6	Press brake	3.55	Blank $L + W$, Add'l lips	$.831 + .060$ ($L + W$) $+ [.942 + .035$ ($L + W$)] per add'l lip
3.7	Foot brake, kick press, jump shear	3.42 (1st setup) $+ .86$ (add'l action)	Blank $L + W$, Rehandle, Edge or lip, Hole	$1.71 + .036$ ($L + W$) $+ .514$ (no. rehandle) $+ 1.14$ (no. edge or lip) $+ .856$ (no. pierce hole)
3.8	Hand brake, punch press, shear	1.71	Action,	$1.20 + .428$ (action) $+ 1.14$ (rehandle)
	Hand bender, multi-form, roller	1.71	Action,	$1.71 + 2.42$ (action) $+ 1.14$ (rehandle)
	Hand coil winder	1.71	Coil	$1.71 + .710$ (ea. coil) $+ 1.14$ (rehandle)
3.9	Nibbling	1.71	Blank $L + W$, Cut and nibble length	$.214$ ($L + W$) $+ .242$ (cut in.) $+ .485$ (nibble in.)
3.10	Tube bending	9.12	Manual machine	$7.00 + .152$ (L of tube) $+ 1.32$ (no. of degrees bent)
			Hydraulic machine	$9.17 + .044$ (L of tube) $+ .030$ (no. of degrees bent)
3.11	Ironworker	2.54	Shearing operation Punching operation	$.274 + .049$ (part L) $.953 + 1.01$ (no. of punched holes)

4. MARKING MACHINES

Machine	Setup $	Variables	$ per 100 units
4.1 Marking	1.28	Each mark	1.21 + .445 (no. mark)
4.2 Screen printing	Bench: 2.02	Manual	.320 $(L+W+H)$ +.152 (length in.)
	Semiautomatic: 2.53	Semiautomatic	1.01
4.3 Laser marking	1.71	Handling, No. characters:	1.57
		$\frac{1}{8}$ in. high	.539 (no. of characters)
		$\frac{1}{4}$ in. high	1.07 (no. of characters)

5. HOTWORKING MACHINES

Machine		Setup $	Variables	$ per 100 units
5.1 Forging	1500 lb	17.16	$Dia \times L,$	76.2 + 2.00 $(Dia \times L)$
	3000 lb	25.74		83.2 + 2.87 $(Dia \times L)$
	5000 lb	34.32	W	141 + .586 (W) + 1.67 $(Dia \times L)$
	12,000 lb	51.48		150 + 1.02 (W) + 3.05 $(Dia \times L)$

6. TURNING MACHINES

Machine	Setup $	Variables	$ per 100 units
6.1 Engine lathe	5.09 + 1.65 (tool)	No. cuts, Rehandle	7.25 + 4.83 (no. cuts) + 3.82 (rehandle)
6.2 Turret lathe:			
small	14.48 + 2.66 (no. tools)	No. turret stations (tur. sta.), Cross-slide stations (c.s. sta.)	4.42 + 1.29 (no. tur. sta.) + .422 (no. c.s. sta.)
medium			8.05 + 2.44 (tur. sta.) + 3.10 (c.s. sta.)
large			12.1 + 3.38 (tur. sta.) + 3.60 (c.s. sta.)
		Jib load	50.3 (jib load)
6.3 Vertical turret lathe	9.05 + 3.02 (no. tools)	No. tur. sta.;	175 + 10.1 (tur. sta.)
		Indicate and adjusts;	+ 151 (dim. indicate)
		Jib or rehandle	+ 88.0 (jib or rehandle)
6.4 Numerical controlled turning lathe	4.40 + 1.85 (no. tool changes)		47.83 + 20.64 (no. restarts) + .828 (no. tools) + 63.9 (no. rehandles or jig)

Machine	Setup $	Variables	$ per 100 units
6.5 Numerical controlled chucking lathe	6.18 + 1.85 (no. tool changes) + 3.09 (bore jaws)		14.09 + handle (manual = 31.02; jib = 51.66; hoist = 108.40) + rotate (manual = 16.56; jib = 46.47; hoist = 98.39) + 1.03 (no. turret indexes)
6.6 Single spindle automatic screw machine	21.45 + 3.58 (no. tools)	Handle, $Dia \times L$, Tap	.572 (no. station) + 3.86 ($Dia \times L$ other); if steel, + 13.6 ($Dia \times L$ steel) + 8.37 (in. tap)
6.7 Multispindle automatic screw machine	42.90 + 6.44 (no. tools)		(Use Item 6.6 to find spindle requiring maximum cost.)

7. MILLING MACHINES

7.1 Machine setup	Requirements	Setup $
	Plane, shoulder, saw, slab;	13.79
	Slot;	17.56
	Straddle;	22.58
	Secondary operation;	8.78
	+ Make part	2 × Unit Cost

Machine	Variables	$ per 100 units
7.2 Knee and column	lb, Rehandle	16.6 + .101 (lb) + 9.69 (rehandle)
7.3 Bed	lb, Rehandle, Hoist	7.85 + .050 (lb) + 5.85 (rehandle) + 21.7 (hoist)
7.4 Vertical-spindle ram	lb, Rehandle	12.4 + .201 (lb) + 8.83 (rehandle)
7.5 Router	lb, Rehandle	10.6 + .146 (lb) + 6.81 (rehandle)
7.6 Special	lb, Rehandle, Hoist	14.7 + .059 (lb) + 9.50 (rehandle) + 28.9 (hoist)
7.7 Hand miller	lb, Rehandle	7.61 + .266 (lb) + 5.47 (rehandle)

8. MACHINING CENTERS

Machine	Setup $	Variables	$ per 100 units
8.1 Machining center	4.40 + 1.10 (no. clamps) + .55 (no. tool)	No. coordinates, Hoist Rehandle	64.4 + 1.43 (no. coordinate) + 51.4 (no. hoist) + 37.6 (no. rehandle)
8.2 Rapid travel, tool changer elements		in., Tool	.121 (in.) + 3.67 (no. tools)

9. DRILLING MACHINES

9.1 Setup	Machine	Variables	Setup $
	Sensitive, upright, turret	No. spindles	2.13 + .878 (spindle)
	Cluster	No. spindles	.63 + 1.00 (spindle)
	Radial	Constant	12.54
	Layout	No. holes	4.14 + .19 (hole)
		No. lines	+ .29 (line)
		Complicated fixture	9.41

Machine	Variables	$ per 100 units
9.2 Sensitive	lb,	7.04 + .142 (lb)
	Rehandle,	+ .795 (rehandle)
	No. holes,	+ 1.11 (hole)
	No. tools	+ 1.58 (tool)
9.3 Upright	lb,	11.5 + .979 (lb)
	Rehandle,	+ 1.00 (rehandle)
	No. holes,	+ 2.19 (hole)
	No. tools	+ 2.19 (tool)
9.4 Turret	lb,	9.76 + 1.28 (lb)
	Rehandle,	6.56 (rehandle)
	No. holes,	+ 1.24 (hole)
	No. turrets	+ 1.85 (turret)
9.5 Cluster	lb,	11.7 + .148 (lb)
	Rehandle	+ 8.53 (rehandle)
9.6 Radial	lb,	21.7 + .105 (lb)
	Hoist,	+ 22.9 (hoist)
	Rehandle,	+ 14.7 (rehandle)
	No. tools,	+ 4.99 (tool)
	No. holes	+ 3.49 (hole)

10. BORING MACHINES

Machine	Variable	Setup $
10.1 Horizontal milling, drilling, and boring	Auxiliary equipment	7.76 + 8.26 (plate, table, or fixture)

	Variables	$ per 100 units
	Hoist,	44.7 + 139 (hoist)
	Clamps,	+ 57.3 (clamp)
	Tools,	+ 48.4 (tool)
	Line bar,	+ 404 (line bar)
	Cutter change,	+ 37.4 (cutter change)
	Fraction location,	+ 17.1 (fraction location)
	Decimal location,	+ 85.7 (decimal location)
	Travel in.	+ .213 (travel in.)

Machine	Setup $	Variables	$ per 100 units
10.2 Boring and facing	3.02 + 4.23 (head)	Boring stations	12.3 (no. station)

11.1 Turn, bore, form, cutoff, thread, start drill, and break edges

Material	Turning[1] HSS	Turning[1] Carb	Boring[1] HSS	Boring[1] Carb	Form[1] cutoff HSS	Form cutoff Carb	Single-point threading[2]	Threading die[2]
Low-carbon steel, free machining	2.05	.491	3.33	.972 *Rough*				
	3.34	.995	4.61	1.99 *Finish*	6.63	.805	.972	.190
Low-carbon steel	2.73	.615	4.40	1.21				
	4.38	1.15	6.05	2.33	8.70	1.01	.972	.190
Medium-carbon steel	3.63	.749	5.91	1.50				
	5.61	1.74	7.74	3.48	11.2	1.23	1.17	.201
Stainless steel, 300	3.27	1.10	5.33	2.17				
	5.61	1.75	7.74	3.48	11.2	1.78	3.90	.491
Stainless steel, 400	2.17	.927	3.54	1.86				
	4.36	1.99	6.05	3.98	8.70	1.52	3.90	.491
Steel castings, forging	3.42	.681	5.60	1.35				
	5.58	1.46	7.74	2.93	11.2	1.11		
Cast iron, gray	2.25	.491	3.66	.972				
	3.77	.726	5.23	1.44	7.53	.805	1.169	.201
Aluminum	.536	.301	.882	.615				
	.871	.402	1.20	.615	1.74	.502	.649	.167
Copper alloys	1.18	.447	1.93	.882				
	.201	1.07	.280	2.15	.402	.726	.480	.156
Plastics	1.62	.972	2.66	1.96				
	3.25	1.96	4.52	3.90	6.51	1.60	.480	.156

Start drill	Steels:	19.20 (hole)
	Brass, copper:	8.94 (hole)
	Aluminum, plastics:	4.80 (hole)

Break edges	.737 (edge)

[1] Multiply turning, boring, form, by $Dia \times L$ for $ per 100 units. L = length of cut
[2] Multiply threading by $Dia \times L \times$ threads/in. for $ per 100 units. L = length of cut

11.2 Drill, counterbore, ream, countersink, and tap

Sensitive drilling	Soft steel:	13.3 (*Depth* in.) + 25.6 (*Dia* in.) for each hole
	Hard steel:	21.8 (*Depth* in.) + 30.3 (*Dia* in.) for each hole
	Brass:	12.8 (*Depth* in.) + 9.85 (*Dia* in.) for each hole
	Aluminum:	14.6 (*Depth* in.) + 4.17 (*Dia* in.) for each hole
Sensitive reaming		2.52 (*Depth* in.) + 2.87 (*Dia* in.) for each hole
Sensitive countersink		.568 (ea) for each hole

Power drilling, depth in. × *Dia* in.

Diameter	Steel (mild)	Steel (medium), cast iron	Steel (alloy), forgings	Steel, (high tensile)	Aluminum, brass, magnesium, plastic
¼ in.	16.5	20.7	33.0	55.2	6.62
¼ + −¾ in.	8.27	10.3	16.5	27.5	3.33
¾ + −1½ in.	4.13	5.17	8.27	13.83	1.65
1½ + −2½ in.	3.33	4.13	6.62	11.0	1.33
2½ + in.	2.75	3.45	5.52	9.19	1.10

Cluster drilling	Mild steel:	4.36 + 4.55 (depth in.)
	Nonferrous materials:	1.14 + 1.33 (depth in.)

Counterboring, spot facing, and countersinking, depth in. × factor.

Diameter	Steel (mild)	Steel (medium), iron	Steel (hard)
¼ − ¾ in.	5.49	7.21	12.5
¾ + −1½ in.	8.72	11.2	19.6
2 in.	11.0	14.3	24.8

Power reaming, depth in. × factor

Diameter	Steel (mild)	Steel (medium), cast iron	Steel (alloy), forgings, stainless	Steel, (high tensile) titanium	Aluminum, brass, magnesium
⅛ − ½ in.	2.47	3.04	6.45	11.8	1.14
½ − 1 in.	3.51	4.18	8.83	17.25	1.61
1 − 3 in.	4.55	5.32	11.2	22.7	2.08

Tapping, depth in.

Threads / in.	Steel	Stainless steel	Aluminum	Brass	Plastic
56 − 20	3.42	6.26	2.47	2.10	2.28
16 − 4	5.69	8.72	3.98	2.84	2.84

Microdrill	Brass:	2.04 (depth in.)
	Cast iron:	4.14 (depth in.)
	Stainless steel:	5.69 (depth in.)

11.3 Face, side, slot, form, straddle, end, saw and engrave milling: factor × length of cut

Material	Face milling		Side milling		Straddle slot, form		End milling		Sawing
	HSS	Carb	HSS	Carb	HSS	Carb	HSS	Carb	
Low-carbon steel free machining	1.81	.760	2.15	1.12	3.17	1.52	1.63	.455	4.80
Low-carbon steel	4.24	1.96	4.05	2.33	1.21	3.29	2.99	.770	8.98
Medium-carbon steel	6.37	2.900	9.09	3.91	18.2	6.35	8.49	1.77	23.9
Stainless steel, 300	12.8	3.08	9.09	3.91	18.2	6.35	7.48	1.09	23.9
Stainless steel, 400	8.52	2.900	10.9	3.91	21.9	6.35	10.0	1.09	28.8
Steel castings, forging	8.52	3.08	27.3	6.73	36.4	7.25	14.1	1.96	36.0
Aluminum	.250	.184	.357	.184	.912	.357	.357	.184	1.35
Copper alloys	.651	.357	1.97	1.42	3.89	2.00	2.66	.586	2.89
Plastics	.067	.054	1.18	.727	2.44	1.60	.856	.455	3.22
Cast iron	7.33	2.81	15.5	4.92	29.1	9.19	10.7	1.86	29.2

Engraving, each character

Material:	Steel:	3.33
	Brass:	2.96
	Aluminum:	2.73
	Plastic:	1.65

11.4 Tool life and replacement

Operation	Variables	$ per 100 units-min
Turning	Minutes of cutting	
HSS		.311
Carbide		.122
Milling, index throwaway	Each,	
Small tool	Minutes of cutting	.189
HSS		2.24
Carbide		.667
Large tool	Minutes of cutting	
HSS		7.62
Carbide		2.24
Drill	Minutes of cutting	2.41

---

12. BROACHING

Machine	Setup $	Variable	$ per 100 units
12.1 Broaching	7.49	Broach L	11.1 + .228 (in. of broach tool)

---

13. GRINDING and ABRASIVE MACHINING

Machine	Setup $	Variables	$ per 100 units
13.1 Cylindrical	8.69 + 3.34 (tight tolerance)	Traverse stock Removal $\times \dfrac{LD}{W}$;	$15.4 + 158 \left(\text{traverse stock removal} \times \dfrac{LD}{W} \right)$
		Dwell stock removal $\times Dia$;	+ 80.3 (dwell stock removal $\times Dia$)
		Spark $\times \dfrac{LD}{W}$;	+ 2.01 $\left(\text{spark} \dfrac{LD}{W} \right)$;
		Plunge Dia stock removal	5.75 (Dia) + 643 (stock removal)
		Hoist	16.5 (hoist)

D = wheel diameter
W = wheel width
L = length of work to be ground

58

Machine	Setup $	Variables	$ per 100 units
13.2 Centerless	14.77	Infeed	3.18 + 2.61 (in. *Dia* per pass)
		Through feed *L*	1.02 + .227 (in. length per pass)
13.3 Honing	2.89	Circumference in.; .001 in. stock removal per in. *L*	4.82 + (1.25 circumference in.) + 2314 (thousandths stock removal) $\times$ in. of length
		Borozon stones Al. ox. stones	18.1 (cu in.) 31.1 (cu in.)
13.4 Surface	8.02	lb	25.8 + .111 (lb)
		Stock width Traverse depth *L*	+ [.958 (traverse stock width) + 464 (traverse depth *L*)]
		Plunge grind	+ [50.1 (plunge grind depth *L*)]
		Hoist Material effects: Rotary grind: steel (soft), steel (hard), aluminum	139 (hoist) + 1.20 (cu in.) + 1.71 (cu in.) + .557 (cu in.)
13.5 Internal	8.02	.001 stock Removal $\times \dfrac{LD}{W}$	$11.0 + 733 \left(.001 \text{ stock removal} \times \dfrac{LD}{W}\right)$
		Dia in plunge	+ 4.41 (plunge *Dia*)
		Hoist	16.4 (hoist)
13.6 Free abrasive	4.82	Handle, No. sides; No. thousandths; No. pcs in ring	1.13 + 161 (no. sides) $\div$ (no. thousandths $\times$ no. pc in rings)
13.7 Disk grinding	20.04	*L* of grind, Traverse Plunge	3.13 + 160,000 (*L* of grind $\times$ traverse stock removal) $\div$ (*W* of grinding wheel $\times$ rpm); + 6,000 (plunge stock removal) $\div$ rpm
13.8 Vertical internal grinding	20.04	*L* of grind, Traverse stock removal, Plunge stock removal, *W* of grinding wheel, rpm	$41.8 + \dfrac{160{,}000\,(L \times \text{traverse stock removal})}{W \times r} + 6{,}000\,(\text{plunge stock removal})$

14. GEAR CUTTING

Machine	Setup $	Variables	$ per 100 units
14.1 Shaper	12.48	lb *Dia*, stroke *L*; pitch *Dia (PD), L*; Jib	$18.9 + .649$ (lb) $+ 3.48$ (*Dia* $+ .03$) $\times$ stroke *L* $+ 10.9 \times PD \times L$ $+ 83.2$ (jib)
14.2 Hobbing	8.74	*N*, (no. teeth), *L*, hob *Dia* (double approach for helix)	$9.98 + 1.75 \times N$ $\times [L + .07 + 3.12$ (hob *Dia*)]

15. THREAD CUTTING and FORM ROLLING

Machine	Setup $	Variables	$ per 100 units
15.1 Threading, form rolling	6.24 6.24	*L, Dia* Manual load, Automatic load	$2.60 + 1.73$ (*L* $\times$ *Dia*) .520 .281

16. WELDING and JOINING

Machine	Setup $	Variables	$ per 100 units
16.1 Shield metal-arc, flux-cored arc, submerged arc	5.26 (manual) 31.6 (auto)	Each pc Hoist, Reposition, Tack, SMAW manual, FCAW manual, FCAW auto, SAW manual, SAW auto, Clean in.	15.8 (pc) $+ 36.9$ (hoist) $+ 6.69$ (reposition) 2.81 (tack) 7.81 (*L* $\times$ *thk*) 8.78 (*L* $\times$ *thk*) 4.32 (*L* $\times$ *thk*) 4.82 (*L* $\times$ *thk*) 2.67 (*L* $\times$ *thk*) $.210$ (in. *L* clean)
16.2 Gas metal-arc, gas tungsten-arc	4.21	Weld *L*, + no. tacks, Tack, GMAW aluminum, GMAW copper, GMAW steel, GTAW aluminum, GTAW copper	$16.3 + .842$ (weld *L* + no. tacks) $+ 1.58$ (tack) 9.52 (*L* $\times$ *thk*) 7.73 (*L* $\times$ *thk*) 8.54 (*L* $\times$ *thk*) 3.01 (*L* $\times$ *thk*) 4.07 (*L* $\times$ *thk*)
16.3 Resistance spot	4.04	Primary *L* + *W* + *H*, Secondary *L* + *W* + *H*, Spots, Reposition *L* + *W* + *H*	$5.28 + .063$ (primary *L* + *W* + *H*) $+ .302$ (secondary *L* + *W* + *H*) $+ 1.18$ (no. spots) $+ .018$ (reposition *L* + *W* + *H*)
16.4 Torch, dip, furnace brazing	2.02	No. seams, Torch in., Furnace area, Dip area	$9.30 + 2.22$ (no. seams) $+ 4.04$ (torch in.) $+ .506$ (furnace sq in.) $+ .334$ (dip sq in.)

17. FURNACES

Machine	Setup $	Variables	$ per 100 units
17.1 Furnace	.98	Sled load, Fixture load	$1.81 + .314$ (cu in.) $.314 + 1.51$ (W in.)

18. DEBURRING

Machine	Setup $	Variables	$ per 100 units
18.1 Drill press	.36	Box $L + W + H$, No. rehandles, No. holes, $L + W$, Area sq in.	$1.21 + .124$ (box $L + W + H$) $+ 1.83$ (rehandle) $+ .414$ (hole) $+ 1.35$ (wire brush $L + W$) $+ 4.12$ (wheel buff sq in.)
18.2 Abrasive belt	1.06	Conveyor L or moveable table L, in.	$3.88 + .137$ (conveyor table L in.), $+ 1.50$ (moveable table L in.)
18.3 Pedestal	1.08	Box $L + W + H$, No. rehandles, L Area	$.184$ (box $L + W + H$) $+ 1.62$ (rehandle) $+ .540$ (belt grind L, in.) $+ .378$ (wire brush area, sq in.) $+ 3.78$ (buff, polish area, sq in.)
18.4 Handheld portable tool	.73	Box $L + W + H$, No. rehandles, No. holes, Refinish hole, Rotary sanding area, Dual action pass L in., Single action sanding area sq in.	$.487 + .124$ (box $L + W + H$) $+ .109$ (rehandle) $+ .523$ (holes) $+ 1.05$ (refinish hole) $+ 2.79$ (rotary sand in.) $+ .058$ (dual action pass L in.) $+ .240$ (single action sanding area sq in.)
18.5 Hand (manual)	.36	No. rehandle, No. holes, Break edges linear in., No. gear teeth	$1.70 + 1.83$ (rehandle) $+ .792$ (hole) $+ .240$ (break edges linear in.) $+ 1.09$ (teeth)
18.6 Plastic material	.36	Hand degate, Saw degate, Rim flash in., No. holes	$1.58 + 2.07$ (hand degate) $+ .240$ (saw degate) $+ .240$ (flash in.) $+ .727$ (hole) $+ 2.43$ (sand sq in.)
18.7 Loose abrasive	1.73	Box volume, cu in. 0–1 cu in. 1–10 cu in. 10–100 cu in. 100+ cu in.	$.414$ (cu in.) $.345$ (cu in.) $.043$ (cu in.) $.015$ (cu in.)
18.8 Abrasive-media flow deburring	7.23	Fixture parts Weight, lb	$62.9 + 6.02$ (no. pieces in fixture) $+ .713$ (weight of fixture and parts)

19. NON-TRADITIONAL MACHINING

Machine	Setup $	Variables	$ per 100 units
19.1 Chemical machining and printed circuit board fabrication	N/A		
19.2 Electrical discharge	3.75		$44.38 + 13{,}250$ (cu in. soft metal) or $18{,}700$ (cu in. hard metal)
19.3 Traveling wire electrical discharge	18.37	Tool steel graphite Carbide Copper	$134.75(.97)^{-25.4 \text{ in. thk}}$ (in. of travel) $378(.94)^{-25.4 \text{ in. thk}}$ (in. of travel) $71(.94)^{-25.4 \text{ in. thk}}$ (in. of travel)

20. FINISHING

Machine	Setup $	Variables	$ per 100 units
20.1 Mask and unmask	.54	Handle flat $L + W$; Box $L + W + H$; Mask flat $L + W$; Box perimeter $L + W, H$ in. Taping $L \times W$; Plunger spot; Unmask $L + W$	$1.82 + .057$ (handle $L + W$) $+ .185$ (box $L + W + H$) $+ 2.72$ (mask flat $L + W$) $+ [2.72$ (box perimeter $2L + 2W) + 1.09$ (H in.)] $+ .309$ (taping $L \times W$) $+ 2.17$ (plug or spot) $+ .544$ (unmask $L + W$)

Machine	Setup $
20.2 Booth, conveyor, and dip painting and conversion processes	Booth: 2.18 Conveyor: 0 Bench: .54

Variables	$ per 100 units
Handle $L + W + H$	$.218$ (handle $L + W + H$)
Heavy handle	28.2
Pack and unload	$3.91 - .087$ (units on rack)
Basket load, stack out	$4.78 - .033$ (units in basket)
Conveyor	$1.51 \div$ (part spacing in. $\times$ velocity fpm)
Conversion coat	$3.63 + .0076$ (sq in.)
Wrinkle	$5.81 + .041$ (sq in.)
Enamel	$4.18 + .038$ (sq in.)
Epoxy resin	$9.16 + .024$ (sq in.)
Rack, hand dip, unload	$6.75 - .403$ (units on rack)
Rack spraying	$3.05 - .036$ (units on rack)
Fill engraving	9.63 (length of area, in.)
Pack and unpack	4.93

Machine	Variables	$ per 100 units
20.3 Metal chemical cleaning	Degrease 1 unit Degrease multiple units Bright dip Chromate dip	$1.20 + .091$ ($L + W + H$) $.051$ ($L + W + H$) $.392$ ($L + W + H$) $.682$ ($L + W + H$)

Machine	Setup $		
20.4 Blast cleaning	Batch:	2.04	
	Auto:	0	

	Variables	$ per 100 units
	Constant	3.10
	Individual load	.086 (lb)
	Bulk load	$11.7 \text{ (no. units)}^{-.786}$
	Rack, unrack	$5.06 \text{ (no. units)}^{-.438}$
	Tumble blast	.256 (lb)

Machine	Setup $	
20.5 Metal electroplating and oxide	String up/take down:	.53
	Still plating:	1.06
	Barrel:	2.12

	Variables	$ per 100 units
	String up/take down	$2.78 + .722 \ (H \text{ in.})$
	Hang through hole, unhang	1.76
	Bright alloy	$3.36 + .659 \ (L + W + H)$
	Cadmium	$-4.92 + 1.03 \ (L + W + H)$
	Copper	$-.244 + 1.08 \ (L + W + H)$
	Gold	$-5.77 + 1.17 \ (L + W + H)$
	Nickel-rhodium	$-5.64 + 1.17 \ (L + W + H)$
	Silver tin	$-5.41 + 1.30 \ (L + W + H)$
	Anodize	$-4.38 + 1.03 \ (L + W + H)$
	Blacken	$-3.37 + .659 \ (L + W + H)$
	Chemical polish	$-4.06 + .818 \ (L + W + H)$
	Passivate	$-3.16 + .605 \ (L + W + H)$

21. ASSEMBLY

Machine	Setup $	Variables	$ per 100 units
21.1 Bench assembly	N/A		
21.2 Riveting and assembly	1.93	Each minor part;	$2.58 + 1.74$ (minor part)
		Each cycle	$+ .957$ (cycle)
21.3 Robot	0.00	Tool zone,	$3.38 + .533$ (zone)
		Each point	$+ .181$ (point)

22. INSPECTION

Machine	Setup $	Variables	$ per 100 units
22.1 Direct labor	0.00	Inspected for:	
		fraction	.053
		.005	.615
		.001	3.72
		.0005	9.34
		feature	.018
22.2 Inspection labor	Bench: .60		
	Machine: 3.01		
		Micrometer	3.97
		Plug, scale	2.05
		Radius, visual	.806
		Thickness	3.62
		Vernier	1.61
		Plug, ring, thread	5.22
		External ring	1.20
		Comparator	15.5

23. ELECTRONIC FABRICATION

	Machine	Setup $	Variables	$ per 100 units
23.1	Electrical component sequencer	.52		.19 (no. of components sequenced per board)
23.2	Component insertion	5.21		4.17 + .281 (components per board inserted)
23.3	Axial-lead component insertion	4.89		5.41 + .099 (no. of components loaded)
23.4	Printed circuit board stuffing	.00		493 + 16.2 (no. of elements) + 1.93 (total no. of pins of elements) + 11.8 (no. of cleanings) + 67.2 (no. of connectors) + 87.03 (no. of additional inspections)
23.5	Printed circuit board drilling	2.48		(2.22 + .842 × no. of holes drilled per side) ÷ (no. of working spindles)
23.6	Wave soldering	4.15	Two operators	22.04 − 1.27 (conveyor ft per min) + 1.01 (fraction of boards inspected)
			One operator	24.59 − 1.27 (conveyor ft per min) + 1.01 (fraction of boards inspected) − .032 (no. of successive boards)
23.7	Wire harness	.48		.106 (no. of wires × L of main trunk and branches)
23.8	Flat cable connector assembly	.97	Manual operation	.467 for one connector or .934 for two
			Semi-automatic	.050 for one connector or .10 for two
23.9	D-Subminiature connector assembly	N/A		
23.10	Single-wire termination	1.74		.803 + .030 (in. of L)
23.11	Resistance micro-spot welding	1.01		2.53 + 1.00 (no. of parts) + .439 (no. of welds)
23.12	Coil winding	.95	Toroid type	.228 (no. of turns per unit)
			Bobbin type	34.87 + .033 (no. of turns per unit)

24. PACKAGING

	Machine	Setup $	$ per 100 units
24.1	Packaging	N/A	
24.2	Corrugated-cardboard packaging conveyor	4.50	17.69 + 7.87 (no. of cardboard parts) + 1.29 (no. of cushioning pads) + .035 (in. of strapping by automatic machine) or .25 (in. of strapping by manual methods)
24.3	Case packing conveyor	.00	16.96 ÷ (cases per min × boxes per case)

Element
Estimating
Data

V

GIVEN A TABLE AND a TIME VARIABLE

1. IF TIME DRIVER (VARIABLE) IS LESS THEN THE
   MINIMUM VALUE OF THAT TABLE, USE THE
   THRESHOLD TIME.

2. IF THE VARIABLE FALLS BETWEEN 2 VALUES
   ALWAYS GO TO THE HIGHER VALUE.
   (NEVER INTERPOLATE!!!)

3. IF THE VARIABLE EXCEEDS THE UPPER
   VALUE OF THE TABLE USE THE ADDITIONAL
   VALUE IF GIVEN OTHERWISE ABE VALUES

1.1 Power Bandsaw Cutoff, Contour Band Sawing and Hacksaw Machines

DESCRIPTION

An important first operation in any shop is the sawing of materials and bar stock for subsequent machining operations. Although other machine tools can do cutting-off operations, special machines are necessary for production and miscellaneous work. This section discusses straight and contour sawing in metal.

A power bandsaw cutoff machine has a long continuous band with many cutting edges which result in a low tooth load, and it is intended for repetitive cutoff work. The work can be solid, tubing, nested material, angles, structurals, and special geometry. Machines vary but head and stockfeed can be manually or hydraulically servo-controlled. Flatness of ± 0.002 in./in. of cut and stock repeatability of ± 0.005 in. are claimed. Sawguides and coolant systems apply cutting fluids directly to the point of cut. Band tension is either adjustable or preset. Bandsaw blades with bimetal construction and proper selection of band velocities affect performance. A power cutoff bandsaw is shown in Figure 1.1A.

Machines similar to Figure 1.1A handle up to 12 × 16-in. rectangular or 12-in. round stock. Indexing up to 24 in. under servo-control aids repeatability of length. Band drive of 85 to 450 fpm (feet per minute) is possible and feed control maintains a constant cutting rate regardless of workpiece cross-section. Vises are quick positioning with hydraulic clamping force.

The vertical band machine (contour machine), although sometimes used for cutoff, has greater ap-

plication in shaping by sawing off unwanted material, both externally and internally. The band is vertical; the work is carried on a horizontal table and is fed into the band. Machines are available in a wide range of sizes, and throat depth varies from 16 to 60 in. Irregular contours such as slots, miter, and notch are possible. Machining time is usually slower because the machine may be cutting to a layout line. A vertical universal bandsaw is shown in Figure 1.1B. These machines allow the upright column to move parallel with the long dimension of the table or bed. Additionally, the upright column can tilt to a maximum of 45° for miter cutting without turning or moving the work.

FIGURE 1.1A Horizontal sawing operation using power cutoff bandsaw. *(DoAll Company)*

The reciprocating power hacksaw, which may vary in design from a light-duty, crank-driven saw to a large heavy-duty machine hydraulically driven, has long been a favorite because of its simplicity. Machines are manual, semi-, or fully automatic. Methods of saw feeding vary from gravity to positive or uniform pressure feeds. Quick return strokes are common. Cutting speeds are nominally fixed and depend on the material being cut, usually ranging from 80 to 160 spm (strokes per minute).

Band blades include hardback carbon steel, intermediate-alloy steel, and high-speed steel with welding of a high-speed cutting edge possible. The backing material provides flex life and weldability. Blade width can vary from $\frac{1}{16}$ to 2 in., either raker or wave set.

ESTIMATING DATA DISCUSSION

The bandsaw cutoff, contour band, and hacksaw machines are usually ready to use and little time is required for setup. Adjustments may be required for stock stops, band speed, nesting fixtures, vise, feed adjustment, tilt or miter, and dolly discharge. Raw stock, quantity required, its size, convenience, and geometry are the biggest factors. Cranes, power or chain hoists, jib or monorail, fork truck, etc., may bring the material nearby. Material handling cranes can affect the setup estimate.

A major factor is the number of machines an operator will handle. In Element 1 of Table 1.1, load part has provisions for manual, hoist, or chain crane. Cranes are required for the heavier loads. Handling could be done during prior sawing, and thus would not be allowed. If positioning is hydraulically controlled, time is required. Automatic provi-

sions for discharge, such as tipoff, or manual gathering of parts from a chute depends on the machine.

In Elements 10 and 11, Sawing, distinctions are made for three machines. Power bandsawing, similar to Figure 1.1A, uses the first table, and sawing time is given in min/sq in. Contour or universal bandsawing uses a slower rate and sometimes the saw follows a scribe line. The data are for a 1 in. × .035 in. × 144 in. blade. Optimum cutting rates are obtained by sawing solid materials because many teeth are uniformly loaded, but in pipe, tubing, and structural sections, about one-fifth of the total cross-sectional area is metal. A limited number of teeth (minimum of 3) are engaged while sawing sections, the loading per tooth increases and a reduction in cutting rate must be made. The adjustment factor increases the cutting time, and the data, given for 5-in. diameter solids, is necessary. The contour bandsawing time is for straight cuts using a 1 × .035 in. blade with contour sawing attachment. For contours, multiply time by adjustment factor according to blade width. Note the following table of adjustments for power bandsaw and contour operations:

Wall thk	Factor cutting time
up to $\frac{3}{16}$	2.5
$\frac{3}{16}-\frac{3}{8}$	2.0
$\frac{3}{8}-\frac{5}{8}$	1.7
$\frac{5}{8}-1$	1.4
over 1	1.4

Width	Factor cutting time
1	1.2
$\frac{3}{4}$	1.3
$\frac{1}{2}$	2.0
$\frac{3}{8}$	2.9
$\frac{1}{4}$	4.0

Blade life, Element 9, depends on the machine blade length and is given as area in sq in. of sawing. The time to change the blade is divided by the number of pieces. Weld time is separate from installing blade.

Power hacksawing data are given for stock size and can be used directly. The sawing data must be increased by 50% for medium machines and 100% for light gravity machines. If irregular shapes are cut, the times must be multiplied by the factors such as brass, 1.13; steel, 1.2; and die steel, 1.5.

When estimating operation costs in Section IV, multiply the factors by weight and cut area and add to the constant. The sum is base cost per 100 units. If the operator tends two or more machines, divide the total costs by the number.

EXAMPLES

A. Estimate the time to cutoff SAE 1035 8-in. solid OD bar stock 5.75 in. long. Raw stock is purchased in 10-ft lengths, and the traveler calls for 26 pc. Tolerances as customarily found with power bandsaw cutoff machines are adequate. A 1-in. band is used and a kerf of 0.035 in. requires 12.53 ft of length, or two 10-ft bars. One operator full time is assumed.

Table	Description	Time
1.1-S	Setup	.17 hr
1.1-1	Handle 10-ft. bar with double hitch sling. Two bars required $(2 \times 3.38)/26$	.26 min
1.1-32	Automatic stock feed	.06
1.1-3	Open and load vise	.01
1.1-4	Raise and lower head (2 times)	.08
1.1-6	Start and stop blade	.04
1.1-10	Sawing, 1 pc., $.06 \times 50.27$ sq in. bandsaw cutoff	3.02
1.1-9	144-in. blade life, 26×50.27 sq in. $= 1307$ sq in. of work material, about $\frac{1}{4}$ of blade life, or $\frac{1}{4} \times 1.20 \times \frac{1}{26}$	.01
1.1-7	Unload part, 86.7 lb, tipoff	.15
	Unit estimate	3.63 min
	Total estimate for lot	1.74 hr

B. A die block, $\frac{1}{2}$ in. thick, has an internal cut of straight perimeter of 18 in. and 4 corner radii of 1 in. each. A hole is predrilled to allow passage of the blade. A contour bandsaw is used, and quantity of one is required. The bandsaw width is 3/8 in.

Table	Description	Time
1.1-S	Setup	.17 hr
1.1-1	Handle, 6 in. $\times$ 6 in. block, 5.2 lb	.08 min
1.1-9	Insert and weld blade, 2 assumed	6.36
1.1-10	Saw 18 in. straight $.38 \times 18 \times \frac{1}{2} \times 4$	13.68
1.1-10	Saw four $\frac{1}{2}$-in. radii, or a total circumference distance of 3.14, time $= .38 \times 3.14 \times \frac{1}{2} \times 4$	2.39
1.1-6	Start and stops	.08
1.1-7	Unload	.08
1.1-8	Air-clean table, wipe excess oil	.62
	Unit estimate	23.29 min
	Total estimate	.56 hr

C. Four $3 \times 3 \times \frac{1}{4}$-in. cold rolled steel angles are to be nested and sawed simultaneously by a large power hacksaw. The shop order requires 1600 parts. Stock size is 8 ft and the length of each part is 12 in. Each angle has a cross-sectional area of 1.44 sq in. and weighs 4.9 lb/ft.

Table	Description	Time
1.1-S	Setup	.17 hr
1.1-1	Each 8-ft angle weights 39.2 lb, and manual nesting time is .40 for the first 35 lb, and .010 for each add'l lb, or .44 min divided by 8 or	.06 min

1.1-2	Position against stop	.04
1.1-3	Open and close vise, .14/4	.03
1.1-4	Raise and lower blade, .08/4	.02
1.1-6	Start and stop blade	.01
1.1-11	Saw using an irregular shape factor, $1.44 \times .54 \times 1.15$	.89
1.1-9	Blade life for 16-in. hacksaw $1200/1.44 = 833$ parts before blade change, assume 2 blades, or 1.2/800, roughly	.01
1.1-8	Air-clean part	.13
1.1-7	Unload part, gather	.07
	Unit estimate	1.26 min
	Total estimate for lot	33.77 hr

D. Estimate the operation cost of Example A above using Item 1.1 of Section IV. Find the $/100 units ($ per 100 units) and lot cost for 26 pc.

Item	Description	Cost
1.1	Setup cost	$ 1.47
1.1	Constant for cycle work	$ 3.84
1.1	$.345 \times 86.7$ for handling	29.91
1.1	1.54×50.27 for sawing	77.42
	$/100 units	$111.17
	Lot cost for 26 pc	$ 30.33

TABLE 1.1 POWER BANDSAW CUTOFF, CONTOUR BAND SAWING AND HACKSAW MACHINES

Setup   **.17 hr**

Operation elements in estimating minutes

1. Load part or stock on table or rack

Weight	3	8	12	25	35	Add'l
Manual-one	.04	.08	.12	.16	.43	.011
Manual-nest	.04	.07	.10	.13	.40	.010

Ft		5	25	– move distance
Sling, hoist, move		3.38	3.75	

Ft		5	15
Jib crane, chain		.64	.70

2. Position against stop

Weight	3	8	12	25	35	Add'l
Manual-one	.05	.06	.07	.11	.13	.003
Manual-nest	.03	.04	.05	.09	.11	.003

Part length, in.		3	6	12	24
Automatic stock feed		.03	.06	.12	.23

Align to mark	.15

3. Open and close vise

Vise handle 4 turns	.14
Quick release	.06
Automatic	.01

4. Raise <u>or</u> lower blade or head

   Set to work   .04

5. Position table or miter for cut   .06

6. Start <u>and</u> stop blade for sawing   .04

7. Unload part

Weight	3	8	12	25	35	Add'l
Manual-stock	.04	.08	.12	.16	.43	.011
Manual gather	.03	.07				

Ft	10	15
Jib crane	1.00	1.08

Dolly   .21
Tipoff   .15

8. Air-clean part, vise, or table   .13
   Cloth-clean table or vise   .17
   Wipe part with hand   .05
   Wipe excess oil   .49

9. Saw blade installation and life

Blade length	16	60	144	180
Life, area, sq in.	1200	2250	5400	6750
Time to change blade			1.20	
Weld blade together			1.98	

10. Power bandsaw cutoff

Material	In. thk	Cutting rate min/sq in.
1008–1013	less than 1	.10
150–175 Bhn	1–3	.07
	3–6	.06
	6+	.07
1015–1035	less than 1	.09
160–175 Bhn	1–3	.07
	3–6	.06
	6+	<u>.06</u>
1040–1092	less than 1	.16
160–205 Bhn	1–3	.14
	3–6	.10
	6+	.11
1115–1132	less than 1	.09
140–165 Bhn	1–3	.07
	3–6	.06
	6+	.06

Material	In. thk	Cutting rate min/sq. in.
3115–3130	less than ½	.23
180–220 Bhn	½–1	.23
	1–3	.16
	3–6	.16
	6+	.19
Die steels	less than ½	.38
217–241 Bhn	½–1	.38
	1–3	.33
HSS tool	3–6	.33
Steels	6+	.46
Ni Mo Steel	less than ½	.20
4608–4621	½–1	.23
190–210 Bhn	1–3	.21
	3–6	.21
	6+	.26

11. Power hacksawing, min

Stock Size	Brass		1015–1035 1115–1132		1320 3130		4608 Die steels	
	Rd.	Sq.	Rd.	Sq.	Rd.	Sq.	Rd.	Sq.
½	.20	.20	.24	.24	.55	.55	.60	.60
1	.36	.40	.40	.48	.82	1.07	1.01	1.30
2	.84	1.16	1.19	1.66	1.67	2.31	4.21	5.38
3	2.30	3.01	3.35	4.41	4.61	6.06	9.56	12.18
4	4.33	5.60	6.37	8.26	8.74	11.31	17.04	21.70
5	6.95	8.93	10.26	13.21	14.04	18.06	26.65	33.94
6	10.14	13.00	15.01	19.26	20.51	26.31	38.39	48.90
per sq in.	.36		.54		.73		1.36	

1.2 Abrasive Saw Cutoff Machines

DESCRIPTION

The abrasive saw cutoff machine can be hand-operated or power-driven for downstroke cutting. Figure 1.2, a picture of a manual machine, allows for either wet or dry cutting. The machine is designed for cutting barstock or conventional or nonconventional geometry to length. The cutting tool is an abrasive wheel and wheel speeds and horsepower are important to productivity. Wheel speeds up to 16,000 fpm are possible with certain wheel materials. Abrasive wheels can be reinforced, regular, or have special bonds. Options exist for manual or air-operated vises.

Machines, both smaller and larger than Figure 1.2, can be purchased with equivalent performance. The wheels may use a bond of shellac, resinoid, or plastic. Shellac-bonded wheels are soft for cutting hard materials, the resinoid-bonded wheels are for dry cutting and high-speed production, and the rubber-bonded wheels are best for wet cutting. Materials cut include metals, plastics, etc.

ESTIMATING DATA DISCUSSION

The abrasive saw is usually ready to use and little time is required for setup. Adjustments are required for the stock stops of various lengths. Changing a wheel takes 3 min, and this is usually prorated into the run time by the number of parts. For short runs, the change wheel can be a part of the setup for convenience in estimating.

Stock racks are usually next to the machine or the material is trucked nearby. Loading of bar, plate, angles, tube stock, or special materials is similar to that of the hacksaw. The average floor to floor time for handling is given by Element 1 and is based upon weight in lb.

Element 7, if it is a special length or geometry, must be divided by the number of parts. The length is divided by the drawing dimension plus stock for later facing, if required for tolerances greater than commercial tolerances, and the kerf thickness, .020 to 3/8 in.

The abrasive sawing time is influenced by part geometry, physical properties of the material, finish of part (burr-free, heat checking, tolerance), and wheel condition. The time to cut is usually incidental to overall floor-to-floor time and depends on material, machine horsepower, and wet or dry cut. Speeds and feeds, as usually understood in other machining operations, are not as significant with abrasive sawing. The downfeed is considered important. Cost of additional feed time required due to wheel wear is usually negligible. A grinding ratio of volume of metal cut to volume of wheel consumed

FIGURE 1.2 Manually operated abrasive cutoff machine with 20-in. cutoff wheel. *(A.P. de Sanno & Sons, Inc.)*

varies with downfeed.

Abrasive sawing, as given in Table 1.2, is a composite of several machines and materials. For gang sawing of two or more parts, find total area and divide by number of parts in vise. Gang loading can increase handling time above values listed.

To find the operational $/100 units, as given by Section IV, multiply the factors by the weight and cut area and add to the constant. The constant is always included, and the weight and cut factors are cost additions for handling and sawing. The $/100 units and lot cost are found in Typical Estimate B.

EXAMPLES

A. Find the estimated time for 125 pc of $1\frac{1}{2}$ in. OD CRS bar in 6-in. lengths. The stock is 12-ft long and the abrasive disk is $\frac{3}{32}$ in. thk. Commercial tolerances.

Table	Description	Time
1.2-S	Setup	.17 hr
1.2-1	Load and unload piece, (76-lb bar, 3.2-lb pc)	.14 min
1.2-7	Cutoff part	.16
1.2-6	Wheel wear (20 min of wheel life from .16 × 125 and 20/30 ×	
	3 min divided by 125)	.02
	No checking allowances	00
	Unit estimate	.32 min
	Total estimated time for lot	.84 hr

B. Find the cost for 40 pc of $2\frac{1}{2}$ in. × 7-in. long square CRS material. Use Item 1.2 of Section IV. (Density equals .28)

Item	Description	Cost
1.2	Setup total	$ 1.47
1.2	Constant for cycle work	$ 5.33
1.2	Weight, 1.44 × (2.5)² × 7 × .28 for handling	17.64
1.2	Area, 0.932 × (2.5)²	5.83
	$/100 units	$28.80
	Lot cost	$12.99

TABLE 1.2 ABRASIVE SAW CUTOFF MACHINES

Setup   **.17 hr**

Operation elements in estimating minutes

1. Load stock on side table, position stock against stop, advance and retract disk, part aside (use part weight)

Weight	.1	2.0	4.4	8.1	13.1	18.0	24.2	31.6	40.2
Min	.10	.12	.14	.17	.21	.25	.30	.36	.43

Weight	51.4	63.7	78.5	97.0	119.3
Min	.52	.62	.74	.89	1.07

Load bar, angle, pipe on side table

Light, up to 25 lb	.25
Medium, 26–100 lb	.50
Heavy, over 100 lb	1.50

2. Vise, tighten and loosen on stock, position stock against stop, advance grinder disk to work, retract disk, and part aside   .20

3. Start and stop blade   .04

4. Position and clear coolant line   .04

5. Air clean
   - Part   .06
   - Part and vise   .08

6. Change wheel   3.00
   Life of abrasive disks
   - hard steel   30.00
   - soft steel   15.00

7. CRS material abrasive sawing

Saw dimension	½	1	1½	2	3
Round	.04	.09	.16	.24	.41
Square	.04	.11	.19	.28	.49
Hexagon	.04	.10	.17	.26	.44

Hard steel and tungsten material

Saw dimension	½	1	1½	2	3
Round	.16	.26	.36	.45	.61
Square	.17	.29	.39	.49	.67
Hexagon	.16	.27	.37	.46	.63

Rectangular steel bar (CRS Material)

W	Thk	Min	W	Thk	Min
1	¼	.04	2	¼	.07
	½	.07		½	.11
	¾	.09		¾	.15
1½	¼	.06		1	.18
	½	.09		1½	.23
	¾	.12	3	½	.15
	1	.15		1	.23
				1½	.31
				2	.37

Steel Pipe and structural angles

	1	2	3	4	5	6
Nominal pipe size	.22	.30	.39	.45	.50	.56
Equal side angle by average thk	.21	.28	.42	.48		

1.3 Oxygen Cutting Processes

DESCRIPTION

Oxygen cutting is the burning of iron or steel where the temperature of the metal is raised to the point where it oxidizes in an atmosphere of oxygen. It is always necessary to add some fuel to sustain the reaction. This process is sometimes called flame cutting, a term that is misleading since the flame does not do the cutting. Fuel gases of several varieties may be used. Gouging, grooving, piercing, bevel cutting, and scarfing are processes that use the oxyfuel cutting principles.

Many machine varieties are available. The simplest is the small "tractor type," which has a small motor-driven carriage that follows a track with a speed control. The torch can be positioned in several ways. Shape-cutting machines range from manually controlled machines to a magnetized roller that follows a templet. A photocell tracer can be used to follow a line or edge of a silhouette. X–Y servo motors can be adopted and patterns can be recorded on punched tape for numerical control.

Figure 1.3 is a heavy-duty shape-cutting machine that can use oxyfuel gas or plasma arc. Automatic shape-cutting of rectangles, circles, etc., is possible using optical tracing or NC.

ESTIMATING DATA DISCUSSION

Three values are given for setup as these figures depend upon whether torch cutting is manual, or whether there is machine cutting, with or without a templet. The manufacture of the templet is estimated by using Table 11.1, as given for drill-press and sheet metal work, when templet production is classified as direct-labor.

The run-time data cover general oxygen fuel-cutting operations performed with stationary, mobile, or manual flame-cutting machines. The required time to complete a flame-cutting operation varies with material type, condition and thickness, length of cut, tip and fuel, and operating pressures.

In the pickup element, the material is from the table for less than 12 lb, and from the floor if more than 12 lb. Large bars, pieces, or sheets are located on a skid and moved with an electric hoist using hooks. Torch ignition and shutoff may be for each torch, or a flame-tube may allow for one ignition/shutoff. The position tracking or tracer roller are for templet or guided-roller cuts. Torch position adjustment, if not automatically controlled, may be combined with a preheat of material. Also, material preheat has been separated.

Cutting can be straight-line beveling, circle cutting, hand-guided shape cutting, tracer-templet, or optical-templet controlled. Though the time is affected by several variables, a consolidated time, or min/in., is related to the material thickness for machine or manual cutting. Hole-piercing standards are one per occasion. The place part aside depends

FIGURE 1.3 Heavy-duty shape cutting oxyfuel machine. *(Union Carbide Corporation)*

upon size of the part, size of equipment, and general shop practice. If cutting is usually poor, it may be necessary to chip or knock scrap from the kerf or edge of the finished part or the raw material. Tong, glove, mark piece, and measure elements may be optionally done during the automatic cut time.

If more than one part is cut simultaneously, the elements must be divided by the number of active torches. Stack cutting is also possible.

Three entry variables are provided for oxygen cutting in Section IV. The factor is multiplied by the product of material thickness and cut-length and added to the handling constant. The result is base cost per 100 units.

EXAMPLES

A. Using a shape-cutting machine where tracing is done by a magnetized rotor which rolls along the edge of a steel templet, estimate the following job. The part is an $11 \times 15\frac{1}{2}$-in. rectangle with an irregular $10\frac{1}{4}$-in. radius off the piece, a 15° angle edge cut, and a $2\frac{17}{32}$-in. partial circle. Total cut perimeter is $52\frac{3}{8}$-in. Material is $\frac{5}{8}$-in. thick and AISI 4130, and is supplied in 48×144 in.-plates. A total of 15 parts is required. Two warmups per part are required. Each oxyfuel cut supplies on part and a templet is available.

Table	Description	Time	
1.3-S	Setup	.7	hr
1.3-1	Pickup sheet from stack, hoist, 1.04/15	.07	min
1.3-1	Roll to position near stops each time	.64	
1.3-3	Position tracer	.15	
1.3-2	Ignite and shut off torch	.05	
1.3-7	Position material, 2 warmups	1.40	
1.3-8	Cut $52\frac{3}{8}$ in. of $\frac{5}{8}$-in. stock, $52.375 \times .08$	4.9	
1.3-4	Reposition stock for next piece	.15	
1.3-5	Part aside, hoist	.86	
1.3-5	Return reduce sheet to pile, hoist, $\frac{.86}{15}$	.06	
1.3-5	Clean center and preheat holes, $\frac{.36}{15}$	.02	
	Unit estimate	7.59	min
	Lot estimate	2.598	hr

B. Estimate the base cost for Example A, except apply roller handling using Item 1.3 of Section IV.

Item	Description	Cost
1.3	Setup constant	$ 5.06
1.3	Constant for roller handling	$22.10
1.3	Cutting area, .759 $\times$ ⅝ $\times$ 52.375	24.65
	$/100 units	$46.95
	Lot cost for 15 parts	$12.10

TABLE 1.3   OXYGEN CUTTING PROCESSES

Setup

Hand cutting	.3 hr
Machine cutting	.5 hr
Add'l for templet	.2 hr

Operation elements in estimating minutes

1. Pick up

Weight	12	12–60
Size	2 $\times$ 2 ft	3 $\times$ 6 ft
Time	.08	.18

Hoist	1.04
Roller	.64

2. Ignite and shutoff torch — .05/ea

3. Position tracking roller or tracer, engage, disengage — .15

4. Reposition stock on frame to cut next piece — .15
   Add for C-clamp if used to hold stock — .13

5. Clean center hole of tip with wire, prorate — .19
   Clean preheat holes, prorate — .17

6. Put on and remove glove
   One — .08
   Two — .16

7. Position material or torch, warmup material — .70
   Warmup material only thk: ½ in., .14; 1 in., .15; 2 in., .18; 3 in., .21

8. Cut or pierce
   Cut thickness, min/in.

Thk machine	Thk manual	Min	Thk machine	Thk manual	Min
.1		.06	3.3	2.4	.16
.3		.07	3.8	2.9	.17
.5	.2	.07	4.4	3.3	.19
.7	.4	.08	5.1	3.8	.21
1.0	.6	.09	5.8	4.4	.23
1.3	.9	.10	6.5	5.0	.25
1.6	1.1	.11	7.4		.28
2.0	1.4	.12	8.3		.30
2.4	1.7	.13	Add'l		.030
2.8	2.1	.14		Add'l	.037

Pierce hole, each

Thk	Min	Thk	Min
$1/16$	.19	$1/2$	.45
$1/8$	.23	$5/8$	.53
$1/4$	.31	$3/4$	.60
$3/8$	.38	1	.75

9. Mark piece with pencil, scribe, or chalk   .05
   Measure material with scale   .21
   Add'l dimension   .05

10. Part aside
    Toss aside   .09
    Place on stack   .12
    Hoist   .86
    If tong grip required, add   .03

11. Knock any scrap loose from part with hammer   .12
    Aside scrap
    Pierce to tote box or barrel   .12/ea
    Through frame to floor   .09/ea

2.1 Plastics Molding Bench

DESCRIPTION

Plastic compounds differ greatly and lend themselves to a variety of processing methods. This section is concerned with bench processing where the operator is closely involved. These estimating data are in contrast to semiautomatic or fully automatic methods of plastic processing.

A variety of equipment ranging from hand-operated to automatic presses is available. The simplest type is the hand-operated press. Separate molds, which are loaded and unloaded outside the press, are used and the principal function of the press is to supply pressure. Some presses, also manually controlled, have the molds permanently mounted on the platens.

ESTIMATING DATA DISCUSSION

These data consider a variety of elements, and the properties of the plastic material affect the selection of the elements.

The setup time includes the minimum kinds of elements, since all tooling, materials, etc. are located within the bench area.

The operation may or may not include a designed mold with inserts. For instance, a case-encapsulation would use a container. Thus, the container has a bearing on selection. Mold preparation is considered by Elements 1, 3, 4, 5, and 9. The application of the material may vary depending on whether the material form is granular, powder, liquid, or preform. Inserts, both loose and tight tolerance, are considered. Deburring of flash, opening of holes, etc., or secondary processing operations are found in Table 21.6. Some elements involve waiting for air to escape, cooling, or press-holddown, and their inclusion in the estimate depends on whether other work is provided for this potentially available time.

Operation estimates, as provided in Section IV, for plastics bench include the entry variable that accounts for the operator waiting for the mold to cool or for air escape (yes or no?), and also accounts for surface area. Once the cost factor is multiplied by the surface area of the part being molded and is added to the constant, the result is base cost per 100 units.

EXAMPLES

A. A part, having a surface area of 63 sq in., is to be cast with a loose-fitting insert using a hand-operated molding press where platen temperature can range from 200–400°F. The mold is limited to a daylight opening of 18 × 18 × 10 in. Estimate the unit time if the operator waits for preheating and air escape.

Table	Description	Time
2.1-S	Setup	.1 hr
2.1-1	Clean mold	2.47 min
2.1-2	Obtain insert	.11
2.1-2	Place insert relative to mold	.06
2.1-3	Mold release	3.30
2.1-4	Assemble mold	.95
2.1-4	Move mold to machine	.75
2.1-5	Preheat	1.16
2.1-9	Free pour premixed materials	.44
2.1-9	Wait for escaping air, cooling	3.30
2.1-10	Clean off excess	.17
2.1-14	Remove part from mold and aside	.18
	Unit estimate	12.89 min

B. Find the $/100 units for the above Example A. Assume that the operator waits and is idle during preheating and the escape of air. Use Item 2.1 of Section IV to find the base cost.

Item	Description	Cost
2.1	Constant cost for "waiting" assumption	$124.00
2.1	Surface area = 63 sq in., 1.00 × 63	63.00
	$/100 units	$187.00
	Unit cost	$ 1.87

TABLE 2.1   PLASTICS MOLDING BENCH

Setup   .10 hr

Operation elements in estimating minutes

1. Clean mold

Surface area	0–25	26–50	51–75	Add'l
Min	1.29	2.15	2.47	.02

2. Handle   .11
   Turn over piece   .03
   Place part or insert relative to 2nd part: loose tol   .06
                                   tight tol   .09

3. Mold release and wipe clean

Surface area	0–25	26–50	51–75	Add'l
Min	1.00	2.50	3.30	.05

4. Assemble mold, small   .58
                      medium   .95
   Move mold to machine, unload   .75

5. Preheat mold, small   .85
                    medium   1.16

6. Weigh components and mix
   Foaming, casting, potting, bonding   2.39
   Encapsulation (without mold)   .28

7. Sand surface, per sq in.   .07

8. Assemble, load, disassemble syringe or gun   .55

9. Force plastic into container by syringe or gun
   Small surface area   .07
   Large surface area   .28
   Remove cover, pour, remove excess, close mold   1.82
   Free pour into container   .44

Apply adhesive by knife or brush, per sq in. .07
Apply adhesive by dipping .09
Apply adhesive to groove by syringe gun, per linear in. .09
Rise of foam in mold, wait for escaping air

Surface area	0–25	26–50	51–75	Add'l
Min	1.00	2.15	3.30	.05

10. Clean off excess from part .17

11. Assemble and disassemble screw and nut .28

12. Cure filled mold 1.16
Cure tray of parts .28

13. Disassemble mold 1.89

14. Remove part from mold and aside, small .18
Complicated or large .44

2.2 Plastic Preform Molding Machines

DESCRIPTION

Plastic materials differ greatly and can be processed by a variety of methods. Each material is best adapted to one of the methods, although many can be fabricated by several. The material used in most processes is in powder, granular, or liquid form. For some materials there is a preliminary operation of preforming. This is an operation that involves conforming several differently mixed or mulled materials into small pellets of proper size and shape. The preforms have the same density, mass, and speedup as subsequent molding operations by rapid-mold loading, although on some machines the making of preforms is integral to the production of the finished parts, and therefore, these estimating data would not be used. Preforms are used for compression and transfer molding processes. Preforming is usually required to save time and labor in preparing charges of molding materials for multiple cavity molds.

ESTIMATING DATA DISCUSSION

The preform machines are usually setup in a go-mode and a limited amount of work is required for setup. The number of cavities is sometimes fixed with a machine.

The operation estimate is one number only, and it depends on the machine strokes and the number of cavities. If the preform machine is rotary, and there is only one die, then the number of cavities is one. The estimate is for one machine. If more than one machine is tended by the operator, then estimated minutes are divided by that number. A manual machine is assumed to operate at half the speed of an automatic machine. To find the production estimate for machine speeds not given use the following formula:

$$\text{min/preform} = \frac{1}{\text{spm} \times \text{no. of cavities in die}}$$

It is necessary to know the number of preforms to produce one part, including runners and gates. The gram mass of the part is divided by the gram mass of the preform.

The operational estimating data, as found in Section IV, are used to calculate the $/100 units for a benchmark location and time. The cost equation subtracts from a constant a quantity which is found by multiplying by the no. of cavities in a die for each stroke. The minimum is one, while larger dies may have two, three, or even more cavities per stroke. Obviously there cannot be a negative cost. When that happens, detail estimating is required. Multiple cavity dies, as this points out, are more economical.

EXAMPLES

A. Find the preforms estimate for a quantity of 80,000 finished parts produced by compresssion-type molds. One operator controls two automatic machines. The machines operate at 25 spm, and the cavity number and size are 3 and ¾ in. OD × 2 in. The gram mass for each preform is 12 and the part is 40 g. Thus, the number of parts is approximately 4 preforms per shot.

Table	Description	Time
2.2-S	Setup	.2 hr.
2.2-1	Operate machine, .013 ÷ 2 machines = .0065	
	.0065 × 4 preforms	.026 min
	Unit estimate	.044 min
	Lot estimate	59.0 hr

B. Find the base cost per 1000 parts to produce preforms. The preform machine works at 50 spm, and there are two cavities, and one operator tends three machines. Four preforms are requested per finished part.

Item	Description	Cost
2.2	Constant	$ .670
2.2	Two cavities, 2 × .125	−.250
	Total	$ .42
	Prorated over 3 machines	(100 preforms) $ .14
	Four preforms per unit	(100 units) .560
	$/1000 units	(1000 units) $5.600

TABLE 2.2 PREFORM MOLDING MACHINES

Setup

Rotary	.2 hr
Multiple cavity	1.0 hr

Operation elements in estimating minutes

1. Time per preform for one machine

No. cavities	Machine spm				Manual	
	25	40	50	80	25	40
1	.040	.025	.020	.013	.047	.029
2	.020	.013	.010	.006	.023	.015
3	.013	.008	.007	.004	.015	.009
4	.010	.006	.005	.003		
5	.008	.005	.004	.003		

2.3 Thermoplastic Injection Molding Machines

DESCRIPTION

An injection molding machine plasticizes and injects thermoplastic materials into a mold that is held between clamped platens. Clamping is usually one of two types—mechanical (toggle) or hydraulic. The molding of thermoplastic materials is a time-pressure-temperature dependent process.

Automatic injection molding is often done by machines which perform each operation in se-

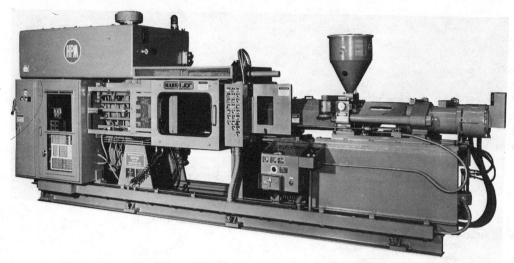

FIGURE 2.3 Injection molding machine, 200-ton clamping force. (HPM Division, Koehring)

quence with the elements controlled by electromechanical devices. In semiautomatic molding, the press operator removes molded pieces from the press following the cycle, and after closing the gate, starts the next cycle. In fully automatic molding, the operations are clock controlled, and a machine tender checks the pieces from time to time. Hoppers are filled automatically with preconditioned compound.

Presses are available with horizontal or vertical movement. Vertical-movement presses are desirable for insert or loose coring types of molds. Capacities of injection presses are rated in oz of material molded per cycle or in cu in. of material displacement.

Some machines having fast cycle times for injection, cooling, open eject, and close are intended for thin wall disposable parts. For instance, Figure 2.3 involves hydraulic clamping action, infinite stroke adjustment, continuous screw recovery, nozzle shutoff, and prepressurized melt chamber.

ESTIMATING DATA DISCUSSION

The data are average for small part weights and include semiautomatic and automatic machine char-

acteristics. The estimate is selected from the described elements. The molding cycle time may be composed of several of the elements, and it is divided by the number of cavities in the mold. Work elements are possible during the transfer and hold time. If the total time for these work elements is less than the automatic portions of the cycle time, then the basic cycle time need not be increased. If the work time is greater than the automatic machine elements, either increase dwell time or decrease work elements during hold time. Timers and automatic cycle equipment are simple to measure in the shop and can supplement these data. Furthermore, the properties of the plastics affect the estimate.

The cycle time of any product in injection molding depends upon product variables such as material, size of part, wall thickness, part geometry and dimension tolerances, and various equipment variables. The materials we consider are polyethylene, polypropylene, polyestryrene (which are called polymaterials), and nylon.

Costs can be estimated directly using Item 2.3 of Section IV. The rule of thumb adds a constant to a factor which is multiplied by thickness. The resulting sum is divided by the number of cavities.

EXAMPLES

A. Estimate the molding time for a polyethylene piece described as flat with a wall thickness of 0.1 in. The mold has 3 cavities. The lot will require 5000 units. Determine if the operator can perform minor finishing work on the part during the machine cycle. A semiautomatic machine is available.

Table	Description	Time	
2.3-S	Setup	1.0	hr
2.3-1	Close mold	.017	min
2.3-2	Injection	.043	
2.3-3	Hold low pressure	0	
2.3-4	Screw return	.05	

Table	Description	Time	
2.3-5	Holding/cure	.05	
2.3-6	Open mold	.033	
	Subtotal automatic elements	.19	min
	Work elements		
2.3-8	Open guard gate, remove parts, close gate	0.8	
	Cycle estimate, total	.27	min
	Unit estimate	.09	min
	Work elements during automatic cycle		
2.3-16	Degate, .07 + 2 × .03	.13	min
2.3-18	Stack dispose, .04 + 2 × .10	.06	
	Subtotal manual elements	.19	min

As manual elements during the automatic cycle are equal, no additional time is necessary for the cycle time of .27 min.

	Unit estimate	.09	min
	hr/1000 units	1.5000	
	Lot estimate	8.5	hr

B. Estimate the time for 10,000 polypropylene pieces molded with a maximum wall thickness of ⅛ in. The part has a cylinder-like shape and will be molded one-at-a-time. Ejection by the machine is automatic.

Table	Description	Time	
2.3-S	Setup	3.0	hr
2.3-1	Close mold	.017	min
2.3-2	Injection	.083	
2.3-3	Boost	.050	
2.3-4	Screw return	.17	
2.3-5	Holding	.33	
2.3-6	Open mold	.05	
2.3-7	Eject	.05	
	Subtotal automatic elements	.75	min
	Work elements		
2.3-18	Stack dispose	.05	min
2.3-19	Cardboard separation	.003	
2.3-13	Visual inspect	.05	
	Subtotal manual elements	.103	min

As manual elements are less than automatic, additional time is unnecessary for the cycle time.

	Unit estimate	.75	min
	hr/1000 units	12.5000	
	Lot estimate	128	hr
	Prorated setup and unit estimate	.768	min

C. A polyethylene tray having a wall of 0.095 in., 6 cavities in a mold, and a quantity of 100,000 units is to be estimated. Assume a manually-controlled machine.

Table	Description	Time	
2.3-S	Setup, box-like part	2.0	hr
2.3-8	Open gate, remove parts, close gate	.08	min
2.3-1	Mold close	.017	
2.3-2	Injection	.057	
2.3-3	Hold low pressure/boost	.025	
2.3-4	Screw return	.11	
2.3-5	Hold and cure	.12	
2.3-6	Mold open	.042	
	Subtotal	.457	min
	Cycle estimate	.457	min
	Work elements during machine cycle		
2.3-16	Degate, first part	.07	min

Table	Description	Time
2.3-16	Add'l parts, 5 × .03	.15
2.3-18	Stack dispose, first part	.04
2.3-18	Add'l parts, 5 × .01	.05
2.3-19	Cardboard	.001
	Work elements during automatic time	.311 min

As the work elements estimated during the machine cycle are less, no additional time needs to be added to the cycle time of .457 min.

Unit estimate		.075 min
hr/10,000 units		12.5
Lot estimate	127	hr

D. A thin wall cup, 0.035 in., is made in a 6 cluster die. The material temperature is low to allow faster cooling. Determine a unit estimate since indefinite production requirements eliminate the need for setup. The material is polyethylene. The finished part does not require degating or any further processing. One operator tends 4 machines.

Table	Description	Time
2.3-1	Mold close	.017 min
2.3-2	Injection	.050
2.3-3	Pressure and boost	.050
2.3-4	Screw return	.17
2.3-5	Cure polyethylene	.083
2.3-6	Mold open	.050
2.3-7	Eject	.050
	Cycle time	.47 min
	Time per unit, .47/6 (for cluster die)	.078 min
	Direct-labor unit estimate (for 4 machines)	.020 min
	hr/10,000 units	3.33333

E. Re-estimate the direct-labor unit cost for Estimate C. The die has 6 cavities in the mold.

Item	Description	Cost
2.3	Setup subtotal	$ 12.12
2.3	Cycle constant, divided by 6 cavities, 4.01/6	.67
2.3	Cycle variable, 50.5 × .095/6	.80
	$/100 units	$ 1.47
	$10,000 units	146.96
	Lot cost for 100,000 units	$1,481.70

F. Find the $/100,000 unit cost for estimate D.

Item	Description	Cost
2.3	Constant, 4.01/6	$ .67
2.3	Cylindrical thin part, 50.5 × .035/6	.29
	$/100 units	$ .96
	$/10,000 units	$ 96.29

TABLE 2.3 THERMOPLASTIC INJECTION MOLDING MACHINES

Setup

Flat-like	1 hr
Box-like	2 hr
Cylinder-like	3 hr

	Automatic Machine Elements Maximum Wall Thickness								
	1/16			.1			1/8		
	Flat	Box	Cyl.	Flat	Box	Cyl	Flat	Box	Cyl.
1. Mold Close	.017	.017	.017	.017	.017	.017	.017	.017	.017
2. Injection									
Poly materials	.033	.042	.050	.043	.057	.070	.050	.067	.083
Nylon	.017	.025	.033	.017	.030	.043	.017	.033	.050
3. Hold low pressure/boost									
Poly materials		.025	.050		.025	.050		.025	.050
4. Screw return									
Poly materials	.050	.11	.17	.050	.11	.17	.050	.11	.17
Nylon	.033	.12	.20	.033	.12	.20	.033	.12	.20
5. Holding/cure									
Polyethylene	.017	.050	.083	.047	.12	.18	.067	.16	.25
Polypropylene	.050	.11	.17	.090	.18	.27	.12	.23	.33
Polystyrene	.017	.042	.067	.037	.072	.11	.05	.092	.13
Nylon	.017	.042	.067	.027	.025	.11	.033	.083	.13
6. Mold open	.033	.042	.050	.033	.042	.050	.033	.042	.050
7. Eject		.025	.050		.025	.050		.025	.050

	Manual Elements	
	First part	Add'l
8. Open gate, remove parts, close gate	.08	
9. Lubricate mold (per in., 15 cycles)	.01	
10. Load powder into hopper (prorated)		
1 or 2 cavities	.005	
3 or more cavities	.02	
11. Cardboard interlayer for dispose	.003	
12. Pierce holes in part (air fixture)	.04	
13. Visual inspect parts	.05	.03
14. Twist off part from runner	.04	
15. Clip off part from runner	.06	.03
16. Guillotine degate	.07	.03
17. Saw off gate	.11	
18. Stack dispose	.05	.01
19. Cardboard separation	.001	.003

2.4 Thermosetting Plastic Molding Machines

DESCRIPTION

Thermosetting materials undergo a chemical change on heating and cure to an infusible shape. The two general methods considered for this estimate are compression and transfer molding. In compression molding, the plastic is placed in a heated mold. An upper die moves downward and compresses the material into a shape. Continued heat and pressure pro- duce the chemical reaction to harden the material. In transfer molding, the thermosetting material is loaded into a reservoir, and once a semifluid, the mass is forced through screws into mold cavities.

Figure 2.4 is an automatic compression press with an integral preformer.

FIGURE 2.4 Automatic compression press with preformer. (*Penwalt Corporation*)

ESTIMATING DATA DISCUSSION

Besides the usual chores for setup, the time includes the setup and teardown and heat and cooling of electrically heated molds perhaps to 400°F.

Element 1 deals with operator control of opening and closing of the press. In Element 2, the entry variable is the major transverse section thickness for curing. This element is sensitive to the particular material chosen. If a cooling fixture is used, Element 4 is added. Air cleaning of the mold depends upon the number of cavities. Inserts can be individually hand loaded, or gang-fixture loaded, or loaded singly with a loader. If the molding machine does not produce its own preforms, then Element 7 can be a candidate to include in the estimate.

Element 9 is for hand molding only where compression transfer machines are used. Some elements, such as Elements 10 through 12, could be done simultaneously to cure time and is not included if their time is less than the mold time. If the work elements during cure time are greater, increase the cycle time, or reduce the embedded work time during the cure.

If a faster estimate process is required, Item 2.4 of Section IV can be used. A constant cost is always included. A simple factor increases for wall thickness.

EXAMPLES

A. A part is to be compression-molded using premixed powders. The material, a phenolic resin, will have a maximum wall thickness of ⅜ in., and a 2-cavity die is anticipated with typical runners and sprue. As tolerances are considered close, a cooling fixture will be designed for postcuring to prevent distortion. Each part has 2 inserts and lot size is 250 units.

Table	Description	Time
2.4-S	Setup	1.5 hr
2.4-1	Open and close press, per shot	.38 min
2.4-2	Cure, per shot	1.92
2.4-3	Unload parts, per shot	.05
2.4-4	Load part onto cooling fixture	
	1st	.24
	2nd	.04
2.4-5	Air clean mold, per shot	.15
2.4-6	Load inserts, 4 × .05	.20
2.4-7	Load powder in cavity, per shot	.20
2.4-9	Hand compression molding	.91
	Molding cycle estimate	4.09 min
	Unit estimate	2.05 min

Work elements during Element 2

Table	Description	Time
2.4-10	Load powder in cup and preheat	.10 min
2.4-11	Degate part and visual inspect	.03
2.4-11	Deburr flash and gate	.16
2.4-4	Unload parts from cooling fixture	.24
	Unit estimate	.53 min

Since total cycle time of work elements during cure time is less, the molding cycle estimate is unadjusted.

Lot estimate   10.04 hr

B. Transfer molding for a furane resin part is to be estimated. A metal insert, 2 preforms, and a 4-mold cavity die are planned. Wall thickness will be $3/16$ in. maximum. Tolerances require a cooling fixture. A quantity of 3200 is planned.

Table	Description	Time
2.4-S	Setup	1.5 hr
2.4-1	Open and close press	.38 min
2.4-2	Cure per shot	1.46
2.4-3	Unload part, per shot	.09
2.4-4	Load parts on cooling fixture	.32
2.4-5	Air clean molds	.15
2.4-6	Load 4 inserts	.20
2.4-7	Load 2 preforms, 4 cavities	—
	Molding cavity estimate	2.60 min
	Unit etimate	.65 min

Work elements during Element 2

2.4-10	Preheat performs	.09 min
2.4-10	Preposition preforms	.08
2.4-11	Degate part	.12
2.4-11	Deburr flashing	.28
		.57 min

Since work elements are less than cure time, no additional time is added to molding estimate.

Lot estimate   36.17 hr

C. Re-estimate Example B above, except find base cost for a lot quantity of 3200 units. Use Item 2.4 of Section IV.

Item	Description	Cost
2.4	Setup	$ 15.15
2.4	Constant cost	$ 33.00
2.4	Wall thickness, $3/16 \times 55.8$	10.46
	Subtotal	$ 43.46
	Divide by 4 cavities, (100 units)	10.87
	Lot cost	$347.70

TABLE 2.4 THERMOSETTING PLASTIC MOLDING MACHINES

Setup   **1.5 hr**

Operation elements in estimating minutes

1. Open press, close press   .38

2. Cure preheated material

Wall thickness	Transfer	Compression	Wall Thickness	Transfer	Compression
.06	1.15	1.46	.56	2.46	3.54
.12	1.30	1.71	.62	2.54	3.80
.18	1.46	1.98	.68	2.69	4.06
.25	1.61	2.23	.75	2.85	4.32
.31	1.77	2.50	.81	3.00	4.58
.37	1.92	2.75	.87	3.16	4.84
.43	2.08	3.02	.93	3.35	5.16
.50	2.23	3.28	1.00	3.47	5.36
			Add'l	.30	.55

3. Unload parts
   Transfer mold, per shot .... .09
   Compression mold, 1 to 3 parts .... .05
   Add'l .... .03

4. Load or unload part on cooling fixture
   1st part .... .20
   Add'l .... .04

5. Air clean mold
   1–4 cavities .... .15
   Add'l cavity .... .02
   Air clean knockout pins and occasional raise press ... .05

6. Load inserts
   By hand, per insert .... .05
   Gang loader, per loader .... .20
   Single loader, per loader .... .05

7. Load preforms, per preform .... .05
   Load powder in cavity
   Small .... .07
   Large .... .20

8. Index mold .... .09

	Handmolding Elements	
	Small	Large
9. Remove bottom plate	.09	.17
Remove force	.09	.22
Kick out parts and dispose plate	.11	.17
Replace bottom plate	.07	.13
Replace force and slide mold into press	.11	.22

Note: Work elements during cure time

10. Preheat preforms in oven, 1–5 preforms .... .07
    Add'l .... .02

    Load powder in cup and preheat, per cup .... .10

    Reposition preforms convenient .... .02

11. Degate part and visual inspect, per part .... .03

    Deburr flash or gate
    1st part .... .10
    Add'l .... .06

12. Stack inserts .... .02

    Load inserts into loader, per insert .... .05

2.5 Thermoforming Machines

DESCRIPTION

The thermoforming process consists of heating a thermoplastic sheet to its softening temperature and forcing the hot and flexible material against the contours of a mold by means of tools, plug, solid molds, etc., or pneumatic differential air pressure. When held to the mold and allowed to cool, the plastic retains the shape and detail of the mold. This technique is applicable only to thermoplastic materials and not to thermosets, due to the heating and cooling action. In thermoforming, the raw materials do not have sharp melting temperatures and softening is gradual. This is a factor of importance in the forming of the thermoplastic sheet.

Many different techniques and production equipment exist for production thermoforming machines. Methods include straight vacuum, drape, match mold, slip ring, plug assist, and others. Any thermoforming machine must provide a method for heating the sheet, clamping, a device to raise and lower the mold into the plastic sheet or vice versa, vacuum, air pressure, and controls. Machines may be classified according to single-station, in which the sheet is fed and the machine can perform only one operation at a time. A multiple-station can perform two or more operations simultaneously. Figure 2.5 illustrates the process of thermoforming.

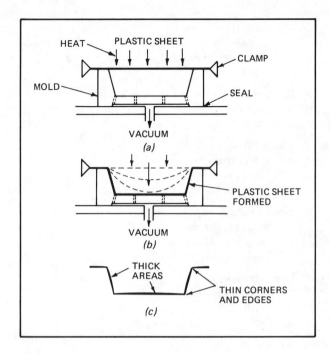

FIGURE 2.5 Thermoforming process.

ESTIMATING DATA DISCUSSION

Setup is provided for one-, two- or three-station machines. A one-stage machine performs loading, heating, forming, and cooling successively. A two-station or double-ended thermoformer shares a common oven. Considering the estimating of direct labor, cycle time is identical to a one-station machine. A three-station machine does have a different cycle for direct labor. The cycle time is the longest elemental time of loading, heating or forming, and cooling. Usually, when wall thickness is less than ½ in., the longest time is for forming and cooling, while for walls thicker than ½ in., the heating takes the longest time.

In a typical operation, the sheet is clamped in a frame, the frame is moved between or under heaters, and to a forming station. Load and unload elements are divided into small and large. A small sheet is less than 12 × 12 in. In Element 2, the forming and cooling station is dependent upon the nature of the mold. "Flat" implies flat-like. "Cavities" are suggestive of a mold requiring deep draw-down. "Medium" is a mold that has flat areas and minor draw-down requirements of a mold.

EXAMPLES

A. Estimate the time to thermoform a tote box where raw material thickness is .2 in., and is 80% polyethylene and 20% filler. A quantity of 1000 units is to be produced in a single-station machine. Also, compare this to a three-station machine. Find lot time for a large sheet. The mold has ridged cavities to strengthen the box.

Table	Description	Time	
2.5-S	One-station setup	2	hr
2.5-1	Load and unload	.25	min
2.5-2	Heat	1.75	
2.5-2	Form and cool (cavities)	3.66	
	Unit estimate	5.66	min
	hr/100	9.433	
	Lot estimate	96.33	hr

Three-station machine

Table	Description	Time	
2.5-5	Three-station setup	6	hr
2.5-2	Forming and cooling	3.66	min
	Unit estimate	3.66	min
	hr/100	6.1	
	Lot estimate	67	hr

B. A simple box-like part uses polyethylene as the principal material. Thickness of raw material is .3 in. A three-station thermoforming machine is to be used. Find the lot time for 440 units which are flat-like.

Table	Description	Time	
2.5-S	Three-station setup	6	hr
2.5-1	Loading and unload	0	min
2.5-2	Form and cool .3 in.	6.00	
	Unit estimate	6.00	min
	Lot estimate	50	hr

C. Re-estimate A above using Item 2.5 of Section IV.

Item	Description	Cost
2.5	One-station setup, subtotal	$ 19.50
2.5	Load and unload, handling	$ 3.26
2.5	Heat, $200 × .2	40.00
2.5	Form and cool for cavities, 424 × .2	84.80
	Cycle subtotal, $/100 units	$ 128.00
	Lot cost, 1000 parts, 128.06 × 10 + 19.58	$1300.18
2.5	Setup, three-station, subtotal, 19.58 × 3	$ 58.74
2.5	Forming and cooling (cavities), 424 × .2	84.80
	$/100 cost for cycle	$ 84.80
	Lot cost, 84.80 × 10 + 58.74	$ 906.75

TABLE 2.5   THERMOFORMING MACHINES

Setup

1 Station	2 hr
2 Stations	4 hr
3 Stations	6 hr

Operation elements in estimating minutes

1. Load and unload station

Small sheet	.15
Large sheet	.25

2. Heating, forming and cooling

Material	In. Thickness	Heating Station	Forming and Cooling Station		
			Flat	Medium	Cavities
Butyrate	.065	.47	1.00	1.05	1.10
	.100	.95	2.00	2.10	2.20
Polyethylene	.100	1.05	2.00	2.10	2.20
	.135	1.12	2.14	2.25	2.35
	.140	1.31	2.50	2.63	2.75
	.160	1.57	3.00	3.15	3.30
	.175	1.57	3.00	3.15	3.30
	.200	1.75	3.33	3.50	3.66
	.220	1.97	3.75	3.94	4.13
	.260	2.63	5.00	5.25	5.50
	.300	3.15	6.00	6.30	6.60
	.375	5.25	10.00	10.50	11.00

2.6 Glass-Cloth Layup Table

DESCRIPTION

This operation consists of laying successive thicknesses of glass-fiber cloth and resin in place. Care is taken to prevent air entrapment. A paint brush used with a dabbing stroke forces a room-temperature catalyzed resin into the cloth. The resins change from a liquid state to a rigid, predetermined, fixed shape. The methods involved in these data are for hand layup, usually with a mold.

Besides the glass fiber cloth and resin, the equipment usually consists of oven, knife, portable tables, wax, and scissors. Parts requiring wire mesh or other inserts are not considered in these data.

of cut cloth, prepare mold, vacuum layup, cure, remove from mold, clean mold, and identify part. Time for curing of the layup is not included. Part configuration is flat or nearly flat.

Element 1 deals with the dry layup preimpregnated cloth, while Element 2 is a wet layup. Entry variables are area of the layup, sq in., and layers of cloth. If values other than those shown are desired, factors for additional layers of cloth and for 500 sq in. of area are available. The data are essentially for flat work with a minimum of compound surfaces.

For operation estimating, multiply the cost factors by area in sq in. and no. of layers. Add to the negative constant to find the base \$/100 units. Disregard the value if the sum is negative and use elemental methods for estimating.

ESTIMATING DATA DISCUSSION

A setup distinction is made between dry- and wet-hand layups. The operation elements usually consist

EXAMPLES

A. Estimate the time to layup 1750 sq in. of flat glass-fiber for a small quantity of 10. Dry layup will be used for 9 layers of cloth. Estimate lot time.

Table	Description	Time
2.6-S	Dry layup	.25 hr
2.6-1	Basic 1300 sq in. and 8 layers	103. min
2.6-1	Adjustment for area, $\frac{4}{5} \times (34.8 + 42.2)/2$	30.8
2.6-1	Adjustment for layer, $(9.3 + 14.2)/2$	11.8
	Unit estimate	145.6 min
	Lot estimate	24.52 hr

B. Repeat Estimate A above, but use Item 2.6 of Section IV to find the lot cost for a quantity of 15.

Item	Description		Cost
2.6	Setup		\$ 2.94
2.6	Constant cost, negative	(100 units)	−\$199.00
2.6	Area factor, .842 × 1750		1473.50
2.6	Layer factor, 96.0 × 9		864.00
		(100 units)	\$ 2138.50
	Lot cost		\$ 323.72

TABLE 2.6 GLASS-CLOTH LAYUP TABLE

Setup

Dry layup	.25 hr
Wet layup	.35 hr

92

Operation elements in estimating minutes

1. Dry layup

Area	Layers of cloth							Add'l
	2	3	4	5	7	8	10	
20	18.0	18.8	20.3	21.0	22.4	23.2	24.6	.7
100	19.5	21.0	23.0	24.2	26.6	27.8	30.2	1.2
300	23.8	26.6	30.1	32.6	37.7	40.2	45.2	2.5
700	32.2	37.9	44.2	49.4	59.6	64.8	75.1	5.2
1300	45.5	55.4	66.1	75.4	94.0	103	122	9.3
2000	61.3	76.1	92.2	106	134	149	177	14.2
2400	70.9	88.9	108	125	160	177	211	17.2
Add'l 500 sq in.	11.9	15.8	19.8	23.6	31.0	34.8	42.2	

2. Wet layup

Area	Layers of cloth							Add'l
	2	3	4	5	7	8	10	
20	18.5	19.9	21.7	22.8	24.9	26.0	28.1	1.1
100	20.3	24.1	24.7	26.3	29.6	31.2	34.5	1.6
300	24.9	28.3	32.4	36.6	41.7	44.8	50.9	3.1
700	33.9	40.3	47.5	53.5	65.5	71.4	83.3	6.0
1300	47.9	58.9	70.8	81.2	102	113	133	10.4
2000	64.4	80.9	98.6	114	146	162	193	15.7
2400	74.6	94.4	116	135	173	192	230	19.0
Add'l 500 sq in.	12.5	16.7	20.9	25.0	29.0	33.1	37.1	45.1

2.7 Extrusion Molding Machines

DESCRIPTION

Extrusion converts raw thermoplastics in powdered or granular form into a continuous melt stream which is then formed into a variety of shapes. The process forces hot melt through a die which has an opening similar to the desired cross section. It differs from other molding processes in that it is a continuous process and forms an almost endless product that may be cut, sawed, chopped, rolled, or otherwise altered to a desired length. Commercial extrusion provides ram extrusion, rotating screw, and a single extruder screw operation. Wire covering, sheet and flat film, blown or tubular film, coating, and tube and pipe extrusion are popular profiles.

The screw geometry and material processed are factors affecting speed of production. For the profile pipe and sheet, as estimated here, an average screw design and polystyrene are assumed.

Figure 2.7 is a sketch of sheet extrusion.

ESTIMATING DATA DISCUSSION

Setup of 4 hr is assumed necessary for extruded operations. Materials are polyethylene, polystyrene, butyrate, and vinyl. Two products are considered, i.e., sheets and pipe. The entry variables for Element 1 are thickness, length, and width in in. The values are expressed in min/unit.

Element 2 deals with tube estimating. Extra

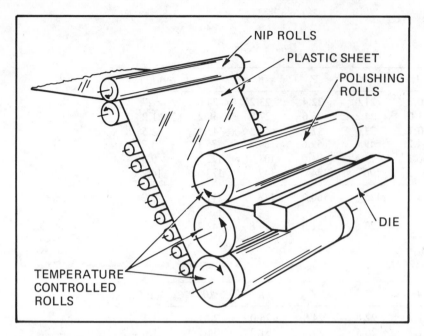

FIGURE 2.7 Sheet extrusion.

variables are wall thickness (w.t.), material, and outside diameter (OD).

Costs can be estimated directly for extrusion. If sheet is to be extruded, find the volume and multiply by the factor. The resulting number is $/100 units. Item 2.7 is adopted for sheets.

EXAMPLES

A. Estimate the time to extrude 2000 sheets of polystyrene of ¼-in. wall thickness, 24-in. width, and 24-in. length. Find lot time.

Table	Description		Time
2.7-S	Setup	4	hr
2.7-1	Sheet production, ¼ × 24 × 24	.66	min
	Unit estimate	.66	min
	Lot estimate	26.00	hr

B. Find the total time to produce 1500 ft of polyethylene tube with a wall thickness of ⅜ in. and dia of 2.5 in.

Table	Description		Time
2.7-S	Setup	4	hr
2.7-2	Feet time, .16 × 1500 ft	240	min
	Estimate for 1500 ft	240	min
	Lot estimate	8.00	hr

C. Estimate the cost of A above using Item 2.7.

Item	Description	Cost
2.7	Setup subtotal	$ 39.16
2.7	Cycle, .075 × ¼ × 24 × 24	$ 10.80
	$/100 units	$ 10.80
	Lot cost	$255.16

94

TABLE 2.7 EXTRUSION MOLDING MACHINES

Setup   **4 hr**

Operation elements in estimating minutes

1. Extrude sheets

Material		Polyethylene			Polystyrene			Butyrate			Vinyl		
Thick.	W / L	12	24	36	12	24	36	12	24	36	12	24	36
1/8	12	.07	.14	.21	.08	.16	.25	.09	.18	.28	.11	.21	.32
	24		.29	.43		.33	.49		.37	.55		.43	.64
	36			.65			.74			.83			.96
	48	.29	.57	.86	.33	.66	.99	.37	.74	1.11	.43	.85	1.28
1/4	12	.14	.29	.43	.16	.33	.49	.18	.37	.55	.21	.43	.64
	24		.57	.86		.66	.99		.74	1.11		.85	1.28
	36			1.29			1.48			1.66			1.92
	48	.57	1.15	1.72	.66	1.32	1.98	.74	1.48	2.21	.85	1.71	2.57
3/8	12	.21	.43	.65	.25	.49	.74	.28	.55	.83	.32	.64	.96
	24		.86	1.29		.99	1.48		1.11	1.66		1.28	1.92
	36			1.93			2.22			2.49			2.89
	48	.86	1.72	2.58	.99	1.98	2.96	1.11	2.21	3.32	1.28	2.57	3.85
1/2	12	.29	.57	.86	.33	.66	.99	.37	.74	1.11	.43	.85	1.28
	24		1.15	1.72		1.32	1.98		1.48	2.21		1.71	2.57
	36			2.58			2.96			3.32			3.85
	48	1.15	2.29	3.44	1.32	2.63	3.95	1.48	2.95	4.43	1.71	3.42	5.13

2. Extrude tube
Min/ft of tube

Material		Polyethylene					Polystyrene				
w.t.	OD	1.0	1.5	2.0	2.5	3.0	1.0	1.5	2.0	2.5	3.0
1/8		.022	.034	.047	.059	.072	.025	.039	.054	.068	.083
1/4		.037	.063	.088	.113	.138	.043	.072	.101	.129	.158
3/8		.047	.085	.122	.160	.197	.054	.097	.140	.183	.226
1/2			.100	.150	.200	.250		.115	.173	.230	.287

w.t.	Butyrate					Vinyl				
1/8	.028	.044	.060	.076	092	.033	.051	.070	.089	.107
1/4	.048	.081	.113	.145	.177	.056	.093	.131	.168	.205
3/8	.060	.109	.157	.205	.253	.070	.126	.182	.238	.294
1/2		.129	.193	.258	.322		.149	.224	.299	.374

2.8 Blow Molding Machines

DESCRIPTION

Blow molding is used in manufacturing hollow plastic products. Although differences in processes exist, all have the requirement of a parison, which is a tube-like plastic shape, in common. The parison is inserted into a close mold and air is forced into the parison to expand it onto the surfaces of the mold where it sets up into the finished product.

The parison can be made by extrusion or injection molding. It may be made and immediately used, or it may be premade and later reheated and transferred to the blow mold. However, the basic process remains the same; (1) melt the material; (2) form the molten resin into a parison; (3) seal the end of the parison, except for an area in which blowing air can enter; (4) inflate the parison inside the mold; (5) cool; (6) eject; and (7) trim flash, if necessary. The sequence is automated and machines include controlling instruments which monitor the time for each step, pressure, temperature, and material consumption. Figure 2.8 is a sketch of a three-station injection blow molding process, but other process arrangements are also available.

ESTIMATING DATA DISCUSSION

In blow molding the parison can be produced by extrusion or injection. The process, for estimating purposes, is divided into estimating of parison, production, and blow molding. To find parison production, use Table 2.3 or Table 2.7. For blow molding, the material is high density polyethylene. A minimum wall thickness of 0.010 in. is held. The bottle volume expressed in oz is the variable. Blow molding is a process oriented mainly to high-volume production. In many cases, the equipment is made for production of special bottles, such as the 64-oz beverage bottle.

Blow molding can be estimated directly in $/100 units. Item 2.8 of Section IV is used for this calculation. The cost driver is volume expressed in oz.

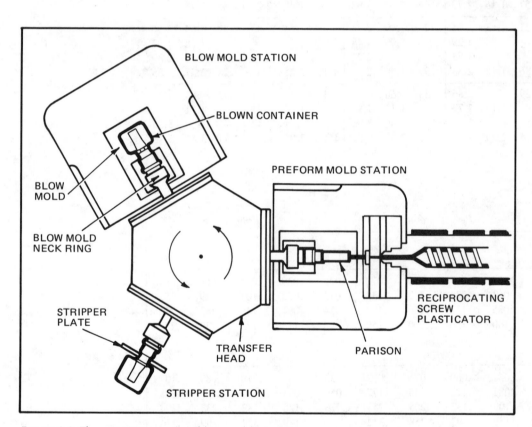

FIGURE 2.8 Three-station injection blow molding process.

EXAMPLES

A. Estimate the unit time to produce a round 64-oz juice bottle with a 38-mm neck. The minimum wall thickness is .010 in. Material is high-density polyethylene. Assume that the injection process is prior to blow molding of the parison. Find the estimate for 10,000 units, and a lot time for 100,000 containers. Assume consecutive production of the parison and bottle.

Table	Description	Time	
2.3-S	Setup injection of parison	3	hr
2.3-1	Mold close, injection	.017	min
2.3-2	Injection	.042	
2.3-3	Hold low pressure injection	.025	
2.3-4	Screw return injection	.11	
2.3-5	Holding	.05	
2.3-6	Mold open	.042	
	Subtotal injection	.284	min
2.8-S	Setup for blow molding	10	hr
2.8-3	Blow molding, subtotal	.248	min
	Unit estimate	.532	min
	hr/10,000 units	88.66666	
	Lot estimate	899.66	hr

B. Estimate the above problem for blow molding only. Use Item 2.8 of Section IV.

Item	Description	Cost	
2.8	Setup subtotal	$	97.90
2.8	Constant for cycle		.81
23.8	.504 × 64 oz		32.26
	$/100 units	$	33.07
	$/10,000 units	$	3306.60
	Lot cost for 100,000 containers	$33,163.90	

TABLE 2.8   BLOW MOLDING

Setup   **10 hr**

Operation elements in estimating minutes

1. Injection molding of parison   See Table 2.3

2. Extrusion molding of parison   See Table 2.7

3. Blow molding

Bottle size, oz	Min
16	.100
20	.112
24	.124
28	.137
32	.149
48	.199
64	.248

2.9 Hot- and Cold-Chamber Die-Casting Machines

DESCRIPTION

Die casting is a process in which molten metal is forced by pressure into a metal mold known as a die. Because the metal solidifies under a pressure from 80 to 40,000 psi, the casting conforms to the die cavity in both shape and surface finish. Die casting is a widely used permanent-mold process and two methods of this process are hot and cold chamber.

FIGURE 2.9A Front side of a cold-chamber die casting machine, 250 die lock end force 2.7–5.5 lb aluminum shot weight. *(HPM Division, Koehring)*

The distinction between these two methods is determined by the location of the melting pot. In the hot-chamber method, the melting pot is intergral with the machine and the injection cylinder is immersed in the molten metal. The injection cylinder is actuated by air or hydraulic pressure that forces metal into dies to complete the casting. Machines using the cold-chamber process have a separate melting furnace and metal is introduced into the injection cylinder by manual ladling or through mechanical means. Hydraulic pressure forces the metal into the die. Usual metal pressure ranges from 1500 to 3000 psi for hot-chamber and 2500 to 10,000 psi for cold-chamber machines.

Lot-melting alloys of zinc, tin, and lead are the most widely used materials cast in hot-chamber machines. Die casting of aluminum, magnesium, and brass requires higher pressures, thus melting temperatures are heated in auxiliary furnaces and ladled into the plunger cavity nearby the dies.

Figure 2.9A is a 250-ton cold-chamber machine used to produce small, high-production parts. Shot weights for this size machine range from 2 to 4 lb. Typically, the dies are multicavity, ranging from 6 to 10 cavities per die. Typical wall thicknesses are from .060 to .090 in., and the overall cast surface area is approximately 100 to 125 sq in. for cold chamber. For the hot-chamber method, typical wall

FIGURE 2.9B Front side of a 400-ton die casting machine with integral shot end. *(HPM division, Koehring)*

thicknesses are .045 to .090 in. with multiple cavity tooling. The number of cavities ranges from 8 to as high as 24 in zinc alloy.

Figure 2.9B is a 400-ton machine and it is about twice as big as the 250-ton machine. Larger parts are cast on these machines with a typical number of cavities ranging from 2 to 6. With cold-chamber machines the typical wall thickness ranges from .080 to .160 in., while for hot-chamber machines the thickness is .060 to .130 in. Shot weights are 4 to 8 lb, and 6 to 14 lb for the cold- and hot-chamber machines.

Typical parts for the 250-ton cold-chamber machine are small faucet handles, electrical conduit fittings, small gears, hose couplings, etc., and typical shots/hr range from 150 to 250/hr. Hot-chamber machines can manufacture a variety of parts, such as door handles, hardware, clock parts, etc., where good finish and mechanical properties are necessary. Shots/hr would range from 250 to 500.

ESTIMATING DATA DISCUSSION

Setup data include the entry variable of die surface area. It does not include initial tool tryout. The data, as shown by Table 2.9, are for hot- and cold-chamber die-casting machines. Shot and dwell time is average. Automatic, semiautomatic, and manual machines are considered. The times are for a die having one or several units, and the total cycle time must be divided by the number of cavities. Certain elements, air clean die for instance, are given as 1 in 3 average, 0.05 min, the per unit time. The total elemental time is 0.15 min, and if other prorata occurrences are believed more appropriate, the value of 0.15 is divided by the frequency per shot. If for Element 8, load insert, the first insert time is higher, it is possible to have work elements during shot and dwell time, Element 4. If the total time for work elements done during transfer plus hold, as found in Element 9, can be less than or equal to Element 4, the time is done without increasing cost. The unit estimate equals the cycle min divided by the no. of cavities in the casting die.

Entry variables for operation estimating are zinc or aluminum, inserts, and no. of cavities. Multiply the factor by the number of inserts, if any, add to the constant, and divide the total by the no. of cavities in the die. The result is base $/100 units.

EXAMPLES

A. Estimate a 5-lb aluminum cold-chamber die-cast part, where the die has 4 cavities. A 400-ton manual machine and lot of 20,000 units is planned. The die has a large surface area, about 30 sq in. is anticipated.

Table	Description	Time
2.9-S	Setup	4.50 hr
2.9-5	Open and close guard door	.10 min
2.9-1	Open and close die	.08
2.9-3	Ladle 5 lb	.10
2.9-4	Shot and dwell	.17
2.9-6	Unload cluster	.09
2.9-7	Clean and lubricate die	.17
	Die cavity estimate	.71 min
	Unit estimate	.18 min
	Lot estimate	64.50 hr

B. A zinc part has 2 inserts, and 1 part is made per shot. Find the $/unit using Item 2.9 of Section IV.

Item	Description	Cost
2.9	Constant cost	$10.00
2.9	Install inserts, 2.70 × 2	5.40
	Total (100 units)	$15.40
	Unit estimate	$ .15

TABLE 2.9 HOT- AND COLD-CHAMBER DIE-CASTING MACHINES

Setup

Die surface area:	10 sq in.	1.5 hr
	20 sq in.	3.0 hr
	35 sq in.	5–6 hr

Operation elements in estimating minutes

1. Open and close die

ton	250	400	600	800	1000
min	.04	.08	.12	.14	.16

2. Trip to close, ladle metal, and fire shot .... .16

3. Ladle metal

lb	2	5
min	.06	.10

4. Shot and dwell
   - Zinc .... .14
   - Aluminum .... .17

5. Open and close guard door
   - Manual .... .10
   - Automatic .... —

6. Eject for part drop

ton	250	400
min	.04	.06

   Machine sense for part drop .... .02

   Remove part or cluster
   - Zinc .... .05
   - Aluminum .... .09

7. Clean or lubricate
   Air clean die, per unit
   - Zinc (1 in 3 ave.) .... .05
   - Aluminum (1 in 1 ave.) .... .18

   Lubricate die
   - Zinc (1 in 5 ave.) .... .04
   - Aluminum (1 in 2 ave.) .... .17

   Clean and lube die (automatic) .... .05

   Lubricate shot plunger (1 in 10 ave.) .... .01

   Skim off slag and clean shot plunger .... .005

8. Load insert in die
   - 1st .... .14
   - Add'l .... .07

   Load insert in die using holder .... .30

9. Simultaneous work elements during shot and dwell time

Break part from runner, Toss		.13
	Stack 1st	.17
	Add'l	.04
Degate cluster with press		.16
Get and place inserts in holder		
1st		.14
Add'l		.07
Return ladle to melting furnace		.08

Note: Visual inspection occasionally done. Also total time for work elements done during shot and dwell time can be equal to or be less than Element 4. If greater than, either increase dwell time or decrease work elements.

2.10 Isostatic Molding Machines

DESCRIPTION

Isostatic molding has a die inside a rubber mold that is subjected to a circumferential and head pressure. A pressure cycle is started with the filling of dry powder into the mold before the pressure is applied. Molded parts range up to a maximum of 4 in. in height and 3 in. in diameter as covered by these data. Pressures up to 9000 psi are used to mold the ceramic body about the die. Once the desired pressure is reached, the mold remains subjected to this pressure for a brief period of time. After pressing is complete, the molded part exits the pressing unit on a carrousel carrying the next mold to be pressed.

ESTIMATING DATA DISCUSSION

Setup time includes obtaining the production order form, selecting the necessary die and mold, installing the dies on the machine, setting the molding pressure, and acquiring the appropriate ceramic body.

Element 1, position mold and remove die, consists of positioning the mold over the die. Following the completion of pressing, it also includes removing the molded part and setting it aside. The time is considered constant.

Element 2 is clean die, wipe and blow with air hose. Time is a variable. The independent variable is girth + number of internal diameter (NDC) changes,

$L + W + H + NDC$. Girth is the smallest-sized box which will enclose any shape. In the case of a cylinder, girth is the sum of height plus two diameters. Girth is an easy calculation, and isostatic molded parts are correlated to girth. The number of diameter changes, NDC, is a number which affects the molded part removal and die cleaning time. Element 3 is for positioning the mold over the die plus wait time for press completion. Time includes pressing and rotation of the pressing unit over the carrousel. The time variable is solely dependent on girth. The estimator, in order to expedite application, should use higher table values rather than interpolating. For example, if $L + 2(Dia) + NDC = 7.72$, use 0.17.

Isostatic molding considers ceramic powders, and several types were part of the observations. The data are expressed for a single operator only. No adjustments should be made for two or more operators. No time is allowed for simultaneous molding and filling since these times are embedded in Elements 2 and 3. An occasional spray is used on the die to reduce powder adhesion. Time is included in Element 1.

Base costs for isostatic molding can be estimated directly by using Item 2.10. The entry variables for production run cost per 100 units are length of mold, two diameters, and number of diameter changes. A diameter change causes difficulty in removal. For this reason, the number of diameter changes are critical. Always use the constant cost in the calculation.

EXAMPLES

A. A blasting cap, made from AD-85-I ceramic body, is to be molded. The part has a girth of 4.9 in. and has two internal diameter changes. Determine the unit and lot estimates for 8037 parts.

Table	Description	Time
2.10-S	Setup	.5 hr
2.10-1	Position mold, remove die	.13 min
2.10-2	Clean die, $L + 2(Dia) + NDC = 6.9$	.15
2.10-3	Replace mold over die, $L + 2(Dia) + 4.9$	.09
	Unit estimate	0.37 min
	Lot estimate	50.06 hr

B. A hemispherical blasting cap is to be molded from 85-S ceramic body. The cap has one internal diameter change. The outside diameter and height dimensions are 2.2 and 1.1 respectively. If the molding pressure is 3000 psi and 9680 caps are to be produced, determine the unit estimate, hr/100 units, and lot estimate.

Table	Description	Time
2.10-S	Obtain production request and ready machine	.5 hr
2.10-1	Set mold and finished parts aside	.13 min
2.10-2	Wipe and blow die	.11
2.10-3	Reposition mold and wait	.09
2.10-4	Fill and press	.00
	Unit estimate	0.33 min
	hr/100 units	.550
	Lot estimate	53.74 hr

C. Using the aggregated time estimating relationships, estimate a part that has two diameter changes, $Dia = 2$ in., with a mold length of 3.5 in.

Item	Description	Cost
2.10	Setup	$4.90
2.10	Cycle constant	$3.90
2.10	Length of mold = 3.5, $3.5 \times .313$	1.10
2.10	Molding, $2 \times 2 \times .313$	1.25
2.10	Diameter changes, $2 \times .313$	.63
	Unit estimate	$6.96

TABLE 2.10   ISOSTATIC MOLDING MACHINES

Setup   **0.5 hr**

Operation elements in estimating minutes

1. Handle and remove parts and mold   0.13
2. Clean die, wipe and blow

$L + 2(Dia) + NDC$	Min	$L + 2(Dia) + NDC$	Min	$L + 2(Dia) + NDC$	Min
0.5	0.03	5.5	0.12	10.5	0.22
1.0	0.04	6.0	0.13	11.0	0.23
1.5	0.05	6.5	0.14	11.5	0.24
2.0	0.06	7.0	0.15	12.0	0.25
2.5	0.07	7.5	0.16	12.5	0.26
3.0	0.08	8.0	0.17	13.0	0.27
3.5	0.09	8.5	0.18	13.5	0.28
4.0	0.10	9.0	0.19	14.0	0.29
4.5	0.10	9.5	0.20	14.5	0.30
5.0	0.11	10.0	0.21	15.0	0.31

3. Reposition rubber mold and molding

L + 2(Dia)	Min	L + 2(Dia)	Min	L + 2(Dia)	Min
.5	.11	4.5	.09	8.5	.08
1.0	.11	5.0	.09	9.0	.08
1.5	.10	5.5	.09	9.5	.07
2.0	.10	6.0	.09	10.0	.07
2.5	.10	6.5	.09	10.5	.07
3.0	.10	7.0	.08	11.0	.07
3.5	.10	7.5	.08	11.5	.07
4.0	.09	8.0	.08	12.0	.07

2.11 Routing and Molding Machines

DESCRIPTION

The routing and molding machine is used in wood-working and consists of a material removal process, which is similar to milling. The machine is used for cutting long even grooves, routes, or molds in sheet wood such as particle board. The rotary bit is driven by an electric motor.

The machine has a large table for holding cumbersome pieces, and has clamps to keep the part steady for long straight cuts. The router guide is constructed of two vertical runners on which the assembly slides. The assembly is counter-weighted by a weight and pulley system for easier operation. The machine is essentially manual.

Two operations are estimated. First there is the horizontal route. The part slides along the rack giving a straight horizontal cut. The other operation is the vertical route, which consists of placing the board in the desired position, employing air clamps, and completing a vertical route for various lengths. Different combinations of the vertical and horizontal routes are possible.

ESTIMATING DATA DISCUSSION

In setup, the worker uses a pattern piece to make the initial settings, runs a practice piece, and checks the piece for accuracy. A bit change occurs once for each lot of parts. Load and unload times are constant.

In the vertical route, after the board is loaded, it is moved until it is visually aligned with marks on the rack. The worker then depresses a footpedal actuating two air clamps to the work in place. For multiple routes there is another time for realigning the board for the next route. This time is simply multiplied by the number of vertical routes. Once the board is in place, the worker grasps the router assembly and pulls upward until it hits the stops and then returns the assembly to the bottom. This time estimate is given as a rate per length of cut.

All estimating is done for two workers, one loader, and one processor. The data includes both operators.

EXAMPLES

A. Estimate the time to produce 64 pieces of particle board (11 × 24 in.) with one horizontal route along the long edge. Give the unit estimate, lot estimate, and hr/100 units.

Table	Description	Time
2.11-S	Setup	.10 hr
2.11-1	Load board	.06 min
2.11-2	Horizontal route alignment	.06
2.11-3	Horizontal route, 24 × .03	.14
2.11-1	Unload part	.06
	Unit estimate	.32 min
	Lot time	.44 hr
	hr/100 units	.534

B. An order just came in for 25 cabinets. Each cabinet has two sides 11 × 32 in. which need a route along each short side. Find the unit and lot estimate.

Table	Description	Time
2.11-S	Setup vertical	.10 hr
2.11-1	Load board	.06 min
2.11-2	2 vertical routes lineup	.32
2.11-3	2 vertical routes rate, 22 × .004	.18
2.11-1	Unload board	.06
	Unit estimate	.62 min
	Lot estimate	.36 hr

C. The estimator wants to determine base costs for a routing operation. These base costs are for direct labor. For this example, use the factor given by Item 2.11 of Section IV and multiply by the distance routed. The result includes handling, positioning, and routing and is termed $/100 units. This value is multiplied by 2 for a lot of 200 units. Adding the setup cost given by Item 2.11 results in the lot cost.

Item	Description	Cost
2.11	Setup subtotal	$ .90
2.11	Route 88 in., 88 × .294	$25.87
	$/100 units	$25.87
	Lot cost	$52.72

TABLE 2.11   ROUTING AND MOLDING MACHINES

Setup	.10 hr

Operation elements in estimating minutes

1. Routing and molding		
	Vertical routing	.008 min/in
	Horizontal routing	.006 min/in
2. Aligning		
	Vertical route	.16 ea.
	Horizontal route	.06
3. Handling		
	Load manually	.06
	Unload manually	.06

2.12 Banding Machines

DESCRIPTION

The purpose of a bander is to attach a thin and pliable plastic strip of material to an unfinished part edge. An example is the banding of unfinished panel edges (mostly wooden), which are necessary for appearance. The strip of material can vary in thickness from about .02 in. to 1 in. Height restrictions are from $\frac{1}{4}$ to 2 in. while part length is from 4 to 150 in.

The bander has a variable feed rate. The machine has a reservoir of glue or adhesive. It is capable of trimming excess material from all sides of the panel, which eliminates costly hand trimming of parts. Two operators are necessary to operate the machine. Their work is to load and unload the machine.

ESTIMATING DATA DISCUSSION

The estimating data cover the operation of a variable speed banding machine. The data describe the operation times for a banding machine considering startup, setup, and an operation-time table.

Startup refers to the time spent melting the glue. This operation needs to be done once per day and may not be included in a specific estimate.

The basic setup moves the lot of parts to the bander and restocks the banding material.

The operation elements for the bander have been condensed into one table. Loading, banding, and unloading can occur at the same time. One axis is the number of inches to be banded per unit of output. The other axis is the speed of the bander. The table includes the time for two operators.

EXAMPLES

A. A panel is to be banded for 95 in. The speed of banding is 47 ft/min. Startup time will be ignored because of the large number of parts run that day. Determine the unit and setup estimates.

Table	Description	Time
2.12-S	Setup	.05 hr
2.12-1	Band	.21 min
	Unit estimate	.21 min

B. A quantity of 54 panels is to be banded for 69 in. Machine banding velocity is 43 ft/min. Since this is the only parts run of the day, startup is included. Determine the unit and lot estimate.

Table	Description	Time
2.12-S	Heat glue to melting temperature	.75 hr
2.12-S	Basic setup	.05
	Startup and setup total	.80 hr
2.12-1	Band 69 in. @ 43 ft/min	.20 min
	Unit estimate	.20 min
	Lot estimate	.98 hr

C. The lot is 33 units. Panels are to be banded 44 in. on two edges at a speed of 40 ft/min. Startup time is to be ignored. Determine the lot estimate.

Table	Description	Time
2.12-S	Setup	.05 hr
2.12-1	Band one side	.19 min
2.12-1	Band second side	.19
	Unit estimate	.38 min
	hr/100 units	.635
	Lot estimate	.26 hr
	pc/hr	157

D. Use Item 2.12 given in Section IV to estimate the cost for 730 panels. Each panel will have 83 in. banded. Find the $/100 units and lot cost.

Item	Description	Cost
2.12	Setup subtotal	$ .98
2.12	83 × .059	$4.90
	$/100 units	$4.90
	Lot cost	$5.05

TABLE 2.12   BANDING MACHINES

Setup

Basic		.05 hr
Startup, heat glue to melting temperature		.75 hr

Operation elements in estimating minutes

1. Band, per occurrence

In. Banded	Speed, ft/min				
	39	41	43	45	47
30	.16	.15	.14	.13	.13
43	.18	.17	.16	.15	.14
58	.20	.19	.18	.17	.16
75	.22	.21	.20	.19	.18
96	.26	.24	.23	.22	.21
115	.29	.27	.26	.25	.23
121	.30	.28	.27	.25	.24

3.1 Power Shear Machines

DESCRIPTION

The power shear machine is used for shearing sheets of steel, aluminum, brass, etc. It can be powered mechanically or hydraulically. Hold-down plungers are spaced across the bed to prevent movement of the sheet during the guillotine squaring-shear cutting action. In operation, the sheet is advanced on the bed so that the line of cut is under the shear.

When the foot treadle or pedal is depressed, the hold-down plungers clamp on the material and the blade cuts progressively across the sheet.

Power-squaring shear machines may have features of thickness adjustment in thousandths, adjustable pressure hold-fingers, side gage, and front-operated back gages. Horsepower (hp) ranges between 5–25 hp. Figure 3.1 has a 60 spm cutting speed, back gage range of 36 in., and front gage

FIGURE 3.1 Power squaring shears with a capacity of $^3/_{16}$ in. x 4 ft to $^3/_{16}$ in. x 14 ft in mild steel. (*Lodge & Shipley Company*)

range of 55 in. Now, consider estimating data for the variety power shear machines.

ESTIMATING DATA DISCUSSION

Several elements have width and length entry variables, and usually the estimator will jump to the next higher number rather than interpolate. The data are independent of thickness and weight, as this factor is averaged into the data. The data are for one operator. If with heavier gages the estimator concludes two operators are necessary, double the estimate.

Element 2 includes the get, move, and release of the raw material on the shear bed. The shear machine time, Element 4, may be selected from foot-pedal or push-against mechanical electronic probes to actuate the guillotine squaring shear. Following the reverse element, the trim element may be used. The trim element includes one shear machine time. The strips or blanks may be processed by an automatic back stacker, they may be loose behind the machine, or they may be on the front edge, etc., after the final shear. Elements 7, 8, and 9 are for various conditions for removing the strips or blanks.

The edges, if they are to be rolled or deburred, are passed through a *timesaver,* and Element 11 includes pickup of the blanks, feed the blanks through the roll-edging machine, align, and stack. A surfacing operation is also provided in Table 21.2. Some companies include Element 11 as part of the assigned work to the shear operator.

For operation estimating, as given by Item 3.1 of Section IV, the values are for shearing blanks from sheets. If the shearing concludes with strips, multiply the time by one-third and use that value. For blanks, the width is the part-width and conforms to the strip narrow dimension. After strips have been made, blanks are sheared, and the dimension represents length running along the strip. Multiply the factors by the strip width and blank length and add to the negative constant. Disregard any final negative value that might arise from a small part, for example, and use elemental estimating data.

EXAMPLES

A. Determine the time to shear 37 × 80-in. strips and 4¼ × 37-in. blanks from 48 and 144-in. 14-gage, hot-rolled, pickeled, and oiled steel sheets. The requirements are for 200 blanks, and each sheet will provide eighteen 4¼ × 37-in. blanks. Make strips from sheet.

Table	Description	Time	
3.1-S	Setup	.4	hr
3.1-2	Get sheet, .75/18	.042	min
3.1-3	Trim one edge, .14/18	.008	
3.1-5	Reverse 48 × 80 in., .15/18	.008	
3.1-3	Trim, .09/18	.005	
3.1-7	Remove 37 × 80 from machine, .14/18	.008	
3.1-9	Remove scrap, 2 pcs, 2 × .04/18	.004	
	Unit estimate	.075	min

B. Make 4¼ × 37-in. blanks from 37 × 80-in. 14-gage steel sheets.

Table	Description	Time	
3.1-S	Setup	.4	hr
3.1-2	Get strip 37 × 80, .34/18	.019	min
3.1-3	Trim one edge, .07/18	.004	
3.1-4	Push shear, 4¼ in. 17 times	.01	
3.1-7	Remove last piece from machine, .07/18	.004	
3.1-11	Roll edges using timesaver	.12	
	Unit estimate	.157	min
	Lot estimate	1.573	hr

C. A part, 3.25 × 6.15 in. is power sheared from a 48 × 120-in. sheet. Using Item 3.1 of Section IV, find the unit cost. Strip width is 3.25 in. and blank length is 6.15 in. Find the $/100 units.

Item	Description	Cost
3.1	Constant cost, negative	−$1.16
3.1	Strip width factor, .207 × 3.25	.67
3.1	Blank length factor, .078 × 6.15	.48
	Total (Do not use.)	negative value

Therefore estimate cost using Table 3.1, and multiply by PHC or average shear labor wage.

D. Estimate the unit cost for Example B above.

Item	Description	Cost
3.1	Constant cost, negative	−$1.16
3.1	Strip width factor, .207 × 4.25	.88
3.1	Blank length factor, .078 × 37	2.89
	$/100 units	$2.61
	Unit cost	$ .026

TABLE 3.1 POWER SHEAR MACHINES

Setup   **.40 hr**

Operation elements in estimating minutes

1. Start and stop   .03

2. Get one sheet or strip and load on machine

	Length							
Width	60	72	84	96	108	120	136	144
6			.05	.13	.21	.29	.40	.47
12			.09	.17	.25	.34	.45	.50
20		.06	.14	.23	.31	.39	.51	.56
24		.09	.17	.25	.34	.42	.53	.58
30	.05	.13	.21	.29	.38	.46	.57	.63
36	.09	.17	.25	.34	.42	.50	.61	.67
48	.17	.25	.34	.42	.50	.58	.69	.75

Hoist transport   1.79

3. Trim and square (includes a shear) one sheet or strip

	Length							
Width	60	72	84	96	108	120	136	144
24	.02	.04	.05	.06	.07	.09	.10	.11
36	.04	.05	.06	.07	.09	.10	.12	.12
48	.05	.06	.07	.09	.10	.11	.13	.14

4. Shear:

1 ft on and off: .02

Push length	5	7	10	13	16	20	in
Shear min	.01	.02	.04	.05	.07	.08	

Push length	25	30	35	40	45	50
Shear min	.12	.14	.16	.18	.22	.24

5. Reverse—turn sheet, strip, or blank, around or over, or rotate side

Width	Length						
	30	60	72	96	108	120	144
12		.04	.06	.09	.11	.13	.16
24	.01	.06	.07	.11	.13	.15	.18
36	.03	.07	.09	.13	.15	.16	.20
48	.05	.09	.11	.15	.16	.18	.22

Hoist reversal   1.27

6. Relocate—after reversal, use trim element

7. Remove blank or scrap from machine and place on pile or table, blank size

Width	Length				
	20	30	36	40	48
10		.04	.05	.07	.09
15		.05	.07	.08	.10
20	.04	.07	.08	.09	.12
30	.07	.09	.11	.12	.14

Hoist aside of sheet, strip, blank, or scrap   1.42

8. Remove piece and drop—50% of 7, blank size

9. Remove—pick up from back of machine, blank size
   to   6 × 18:   .01
   to   18 × 24:   .02
   Above   24:   .04

10. Move material
    Walk to rear of shear and return   .36
    Move truck from rear to front   .35
    Hand truck skid of stock or parts away and return   .88

11. Roll edges on abrasive belt machine

Length	Min	Length	Min
4.0	.03	24.2	.08
7.5	.04	32.7	.10
11.9	.05	43.4	.12
17.3	.06	56.8	.15

3.2 Punch Press Machines (First Operations)

DESCRIPTION

First operations for punch press machines are construed to involve strip or coil stock materials. There are many operations including blanking, perforating, cutting, etc. Part design, type of die, and press selection must be known or visualized by the esti-mator in estimating this high-speed production process. This operation may occur on a variety of presses. The advantage of an inclined press over a straight-side press, or vice versa, is dictated by governing conditions within the plant. These estimating data focus on the manual or automatic elements, rather than a specific press. A straight-side eccen-

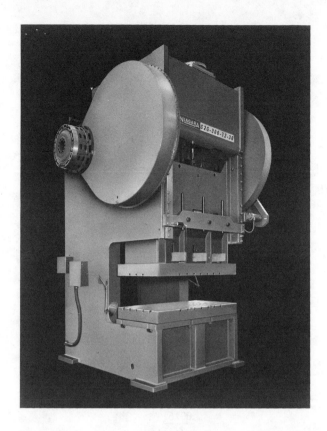

FIGURE 3.2 A 300-ton double crank gap frame press. (*Niagara Machine and Tool Works*)

tric-geared press is shown in Figure 3.2. These presses have large die areas and long stroke with engagement high upon the stroke for drawing. Figure 3.2 has a front-back bolster dimension of 42 in. and a left-right dimension of 72 in.

ESTIMATING DATA DISCUSSION

The setup is 0.8 hr. This includes setup and teardown to a clean bolster plate. Exceptions for additional setup hours are provided.

The elemental times are affected by part design, die, and presses. These factors are either identified for separate selection, or are averaged in the data. The estimating data are for single gang dies. Divide the final estimate by the number of gangs when using a multiple gang die. When one operator tends two or more presses, divide number of estimated man-minutes by the number of machines assigned to the operator. In a progressive die, for instance, each stroke of the press produces one part.

Raw material is either strips or coils. The strips have been previously sheared to width, and lengths can vary up to the length of the sheet stock. Coils are thinner material and length varies with the application. Strip stock calls for operator handling, while coil stock requires operator tending.

Elements 1 and 4, loading and oiling strip(s), can be for one unit or for a bundle, and the unit time depends on the number of pieces per strip and the

strips handled. In Element 6, strip advance depends on the type of stop, pins of various kinds, or a sight-stop. If the part advance, which depends on the layout of the part on the strip, exceeds 6 in., additional increments of time can be calculated and included.

Machine time selection for strips depends on several factors. Some or all of the part advance may occur during the ram upstroke. In continuous run, the operator trips the pedal and the press continues to stroke until the material is run or the operator stops the press. This method of operation may be used on strip stock, providing the advance time does not exceed two-thirds of the continuous machine time, and it is believed that the motion pattern is acceptable. If the advance is slower than a continuous press stroke cycle, then intermittent stroking, using either a foot pedal or hand buttons to trip the press, is necessary. In intermittent run, there is a clutch lag time included for engagement. Conditions for intermittent run depend on the opportunity to advance the strip during ram upstroke.

Machine time for automatic coil operation may be the only operational time included in the estimate. Several average conditions are given where the minutes exceed the expected direct output from spm. Also, some spm averages, based upon press tonnage, are given. For a specific job, the speed of a press depends upon the length of stroke, nature of operation (blanking vs. drawing), physical properties of the material, and the method and speed of loading and unloading the work.

Operational cost can be found by using Item 3.2 of Section IV. The setup constant is $7.44. Two selections are possible, "strips" or "coils". The number 2.67 is divided by the number of units on the strip and added to .528 to give cycle cost expressed as $/100 units. For coil work, we deduct .0009 × spm and subtract from the constant. If this quantity is negative, we are required to use element data.

EXAMPLES

A 6-ft strip has a width of 1.36 in. and a weight of 1.72 lb. The number of pc/ft is about 6, thus the advance is 2 in. The die is visualized to have an open-end stop, and a press machine having an 83 crank rpm is planned for the process. Estimate the job with different assumptions.

A. Assume intermittent machine operation and advance during the nonmachine cycle.

Table	Description	Time
3.2-1	Load 10 strips, .20 ÷ (36 × 10)	.0006 min
3.2-2	Pick up strip, move to die, .035 ÷ 36	.001
3.2-3	Assemble strip to die, .019 ÷ 36	.0005
3.2-4	Oil 5 strips, .25 ÷ 36 × 5	.0014
3.2-5	Trip press, each piece	.006
3.2-6	Advance strip	.007
3.2-7	Medium-speed press machine time	.022
3.2-8	Dispose of scrap, .092 ÷ 36	.0026
	Unit estimate	.0411 min

B. Consider the same problem with intermittent run, but die and part conditions allow some of the machine cycle for advance of stock.

Table	Description	Time
Repeat	Repeat Elements 1–6 from above Example A	.0165 min
3.2-7	Machine time	.0170
3.2-8	Dispose of scrap, .092 ÷ 36	.0026
	Unit estimate	.0361 min

C. Estimate the same job for continuous running.

Table	Description	Time
Repeat	Repeat Elements 1–4 from above Example A	.0031 min
3.2-5	Trip press, .006 ÷ 36	.0002
3.2-6	Advance strip, within machine time	0
3.2-7	Continuous run	.017
3.2-8	Dispose of scrap, .092 ÷ 36	.0026
	Unit estimate	0.0229 min

D. Estimate the $/100 units of Example A above using Item 3.2 of Section IV.

Item	Description	Cost
3.2	Constant cost	$ .593
3.2	Divide strip cost by 36 units on strip, 3.00 ÷ 36	.083
	$/100 units	$ .676

E. Estimate the $/1000 units of Example C above using Item 3.2 of Section IV.

Item	Description	Cost
3.2	Constant cost	$ .427
3.2	Let continuous run imply 83 spm, .001 × 83	−.083
	$/100 units	$ .344
	$/1000 units	$3.44

TABLE 3.2 PUNCH PRESS MACHINES
(FIRST OPERATIONS)

Basic Setup	.80 hr
Add for features of ejection, knockout, rubber cushion, subplate	.05 ea
Oven, rewind reel, straightener	.25 ea

Operation elements in estimating minutes

1. Load strip(s) from skid to feed board	.20
Load coil on reel by truck, crane, hoist	4–25
2. Pick up strip and move to die	.035
3. Insert strip in die	.019
Add'l weight over 2 lb	.006/lb
Add'l for no pins or mechanical stops	.004
Add'l for width over 6 in., each 6 in.	.016
4. Oil strip(s)	.25
5. Trip press, each piece or first piece only	
Foot pedal	.006
Hand buttons	.015
6. Advance strip	
To push or pull stops	.007
Over pin stop	.017
Over mechanical stop	.028
Add'l per in. of advance over 6	.001

7. Strip stock, punch

Speed	Crank rpm	Continuous, min	Intermittent run, min	Intermittent run and partial advance, min
Low	30	.020	.026	.019
	50	.021	.025	.018
Medium	80	.017	.022	.017
	110	.016	.020	.015
Higher	150	.013	.018	.013
	250	.007	.011	.006
	500	.003	.004	.003

8. Roll feel, punch

spm	min	spm	min	spm	min
100	.014	200	.008	600	.0017
125	.012	225	.006	700	.0014
150	.011	250	.004	800	.0013
175	.009	500	.002	1000	.001

9. Press tonnage, punch

Press capacity, tonnage	min
22	.017
48	.020
75	.018
150	.092
Higher	.11+

Double if fiber, thin rubber, or paper

10. Remove strip skeleton from die, dispose   .092

3.3 Punch Press Machines (Secondary Operations)

DESCRIPTION

Press work estimates can be developed on the source of power (manual, mechanical, hydraulic, pneumatic); ram (single or double acting); design of frame (bench, inclinable, gap, arch, straight-side, horn, pillar); according to method of applying power (crank, cam, eccentric, screw); purpose of press (squaring shears, brake, punching, drawing, extruding, forming, coining); or types of dies. But in this section, two basic types of secondary punch-press operations are considered. The first is the operation which utilizes conventional dies. The second type uses standard punches and dies. Either operation may be single or multiple stroke. In a single-stroke operation, the operator picks up a part, loads the part, trips the press, and removes and places the part aside. In multiple-stroke operations, the operator picks up a part, loads the part, trips the press, relocates the part, trips the press, and continues the relocation and tripping until the operation is completed.

Any die, other than a first-operation die, is considered a second-operation die. It may be the fifth, second, etc., for the specific part, but in die terminology it is considered a second-operation die. Many operations that can be classified as second operations on sheet metal include coining, countersinking, drawing, dinking, embossing, extruding, flattening, forming, necking, notching, piercing, pinching, redrawing, shaving, shearing, sizing, slotting, staking, stamping, swaging, trimming, etc.

One type of press that is useful for both first and secondary operations is shown in Figure 3.3. The mechanical advantage of the box section gives stiff support to the crankshaft at the point of load appli-

cation. In addition to operator-station palm buttons, plug-in foot switches are available. This press can be inclined to allow rear ejection of parts. Punching holes in thick steel plates or blanking steel with shear or drawing operations usually requires a slow-punch movement to reduce shock and to increase

FIGURE 3.3 A 90-ton open-back inclinable press with front-to-back crank shaft. *(Niagara Machine and Tool Works)*

die life. Figure 3.3, a 90-ton OBI press, is available in 72, 60, 46, or 36 spm speeds.

ESTIMATING DATA DISCUSSION

Element 1 is an inclusive element involving the following: stock from skid, box, etc. to bolster plate; load-in die or on punch and die; stroke of press where hands touch buttons; ram down and up; release of buttons; remove part, stack in box, on skid, etc.; and occasional clean out of slugs. A machine stroke constant of .048 standard min is used. The reposition element starts at release of buttons following ram ascent, reach to piece in die or on die and punch buttons, reposition, turn around or over in die, punch buttons, and ram descends. The estimates are one-man, and if two operators are required, the values are doubled. All ferrous and nonferrous materials are included in stock sizes. Distinctions for presses are averaged. While the time to perform the operation varies with type of operation and part, only the blank size has been used as the time driver for location points on part, size, and weight methods of ejection, speed of machine.

The operation estimates given by Item 3.3 of Section IV are driven by the blank size or length plus width, and the number of restrokes. A restroke may occur after the initial hit.

EXAMPLES

A. A part has been blanked to dimension $8 \times 22\frac{1}{2}$ in. and one secondary operation of piercing holes using a pierce die is planned. A lot quantity of 2820 is required.

Table	Description	Time
3.3-S	Setup	.65 hr
3.3-1	Blank $L + W = 32\frac{1}{2}$ and using next higher table value	.23 min
	Unit estimate	.23 min
	Total lot estimate	11.46 hr

B. A $\frac{1}{4}$-in. plate is to be notched and pierced in a secondary operation. A lot quantity of 2820 units is planned for a flat blank size of 26×32 in.

Table	Description	Time
3.3-S	Setup	.65 hr
3.3-1	Blank size of 58 in., but using next higher table entry	.36 min
3.3-3	Addition for heavy plate	.08
	Unit estimate	.44 min
	Total lot estimate	21.33 hr

C. Estimate the cost of Example A above using Item 3.3 of Section IV. Blank $L + W = 30\frac{1}{2}$ in.

Item	Description	Cost
3.3	Setup	$ 6.65
3.3	Constant cost	$ 1.05
3.3	Blank $L + W$ factor, .084 $\times$ 30.5	2.562
	$/100	$ 3.61
	Lot cost	$108.51

TABLE 3.3   PUNCH PRESS MACHINES
(SECONDARY OPERATIONS)

Setup   **.65 hr**

Operation elements in estimating minutes

1. Pierce, blank, form, emboss, 1 stroke   *length + width*

L + W	Min	L + W	Min	L + W	Min
2.0	.071	24.0	.18	79.4	.45
2.7	.075	25.8	.19	84.0	.48
3.5	.078	27.7	.20	88.9	.50
4.3	.082	29.7	.21	93.9	.53
5.1	.086	31.8	.22	99.2	.55
6.0	.091	34.0	.23	104.8	.58
6.9	.095	36.3	.24	110.7	.61
7.9	.100	38.8	.25	116.8	.64
8.9	.105	41.3	.27	123.3	.67
9.9	.110	44.0	.28	130.1	.70
11.0	.116	46.8	.29	137.2	.74
12.2	.122	49.8	.31	Add'l	.005
13.4	.128	52.9	.32		
14.7	.134	56.1	.34		
16.1	.141	59.6	.36		
17.5	.143	63.2	.37		
19.0	.155	66.9	.39		
20.6	.163	70.9	.41		
22.2	.171	75.1	.43		

Note: Estimate is for one operator. Double if size requires two operators.

2. Reposition part and restroke, each time

L + W	Min
0–10	.06
11–20	.09
21–30	.14
31–60	.16

3. Miscellaneous

Deduct for air eject if small part	.033
Deduct for toss if medium part	.021
Add for parts that tangle	.018
Two-station die complete 1 part per stroke, add	.021
One-station die complete 1 part each 2 strokes, add	.036
Pry part out of nest, add	.06
For 7-ga or ¼-in. plate:	
2.0–17.5	.05
19.0–52.9	.06
56.6–	.08

3.4 Turret Punch Press Machines

DESCRIPTION

Turret punch presses are especially adapted for the production of flat sheet metal parts having varied hole patterns of many sizes. For some presses, a templet locates the holes, and the hole size is selected from a cylindrical turret containing punches. Other turret punch presses are NC, CNC, or DNC. Tools are located in the turret for instant use.

Figure 3.4 is an example of a 30-ton CNC machine having a 50-in. throat. It handles sheets up to 48 × 72 in., and there are 32 turret stations. Position and hit speed on this machine is 175 hits/min with 1-in. centers. Slower speeds are necessary for longer distances. Now, consider estimating data for the general class of turret punch press machines.

ESTIMATING DATA DISCUSSION

Setup is related to the number of tool stations. If standard tools are garrisoned permanently in the turret, it may be unnecessary to include this as a tool item for setup. But the number of different punch and die configurations is used as a time driver.

Usual elements of setup are also included. Neither templet or tape programming is included, but tape preparation may require 15 to 30 min per tape.

The load and unload time is related to blank size or length plus width *(L + W)*. Fingers which clamp the blank may be used. A reposition of the blank is included for operational selection.

Depending on the selection of the turret by the NC tape, Element 2 includes turret rotation and piercing the first hole or hit. Element 3 is used for piercing holes remaining after the first hole. For instance, if ten .250-in. holes were pierced, Element 2 covers the first hole and Element 3 provides for the remaining nine holes. The distance between holes and rotational time between successive punch and die sets are averaged. A hole or opening may not be the result of one hit. Thus, Element 4 is time per hit. Openings, splitting, nibbling, notching, shearing, and punching action may call for hits rather than holes. A faster and slower time are two distinctions that are recognized. The hit time for the faster machine is 0.008 min for typical parts and

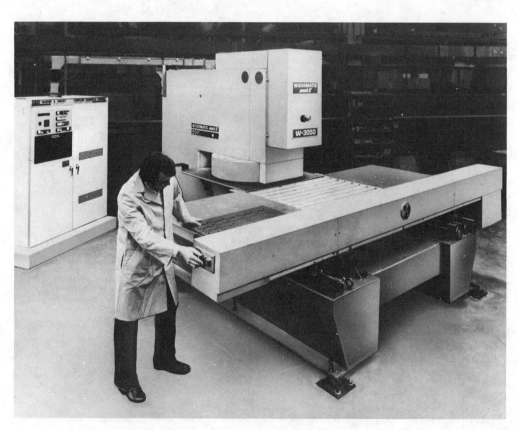

FIGURE 3.4 Turret punch press, 30 ton with 50-in. throat and 32 tool stations. (*Wiedemann Division, Warner & Swasey Company*)

0.033 min for slower machines. These values are incorporated into a table allowing for selection.

The operational estimating data in Item 3.4 of Section IV uses entry variables of blank length plus width, number of hole sizes, and number of holes. The sum of four quantities gives a base $/100 units. Setup has the entry variable of tools used for making the part.

EXAMPLES

A. A sheet metal part, 12.255 × 10.065 in. 7 ga aluminum has 7 different sizes of holes, 2 similar corner-angle notches, and 1 slot for a total of 49 openings. The slot is odd-shaped, and requires 2 hits of a specially shaped punch. Each notch requires 2 hits. Total number of hits is 52 and the number of tool stations is 10. Lot quantity is 63. Using a high-speed machine, find the unit, lot, and the shop estimates.

Table	Description	Time
3.4-S	Setup for 10 stations	.83 hr
3.4-1	Load and unload blank, $L + W = 22.320$ in.	.34 min
3.4-2	First hit of each size, 10	.65
3.4-4	Remaining hits $= 52 - 10 = 42$	.40
	Unit estimate	1.39 min
	Lot estimate	2.29 hr
	Shop estimate	43 pc/hr

B. Estimate the unit cost of Example A above. Use Item 3.4 of Section IV to find the lot cost for 63 units.

Item	Description	Cost
3.4	Setup, $2.30 + 0.63 \times 10$	$ 8.60
3.4	Constant cost	$ 3.34
3.4	Blank factor, $1.05 \times (12.2 + 10.1)$	23.42
3.4	Size factor, $.523 \times 10$	5.23
3.4	Number of holes, $.627 \times 55$	34.49
	$/100 units	$66.48
	Lot cost	$50.48

TABLE 3.4   TURRET PUNCH PRESS MACHINES

Setup

No. of stations	1	2	3	4	5	6	7	8	9	10
Hr	.28	.34	.40	.46	.52	.58	.65	.71	.77	.83

No. of stations	11	12	13	14	15	16	17	18	19	20	Add'l
Hr	.89	.95	1.01	1.07	1.14	1.20	1.26	1.32	1.38	1.44	.061

Operation elements in estimating minutes

1. Handle

L + W	Min	L + W	Min	L + W	Min
8.0	.22	36.6	.42	93	.76
15.5	.27	51.2	.53	121	.87
24.9	.34	69.5	.66	Add'l	.007

Reposition part end for end, small   .76

118

2. Rotate turret and punch first hole or hit of each size

No.	Min	No.	Min	No.	Min
1	.07	8	.52	15	.98
2	.13	9	.59	16	1.05
3	.20	10	.65	17	1.11
4	.26	11	.72	18	1.18
5	.33	12	.78	19	1.24
6	.39	13	.85	20	1.31
7	.46	14	.91	Add'l	.065

3. Punch remaining holes

Hole	Min	Hole	Min	Hole	Min
1	.04	18	.65	50	1.80
2	.07	19	.68	55	1.98
3	.11	20	.72	60	2.16
4	.14	22	.79	65	2.34
5	.18	24	.86	70	2.52
6	.22	26	.93	75	2.70
7	.25	28	1.01	80	2.87
8	.29	30	1.08	85	3.05
9	.32	32	1.15	90	3.23
10	.36	34	1.22	95	3.41
11	.40	36	1.29	100	3.59
12	.43	38	1.37	105	3.77
13	.47	40	1.44	110	3.95
14	.50	42	1.51	115	4.13
15	.54	44	1.58	120	4.31
16	.57	46	1.65	125	4.49
17	.61	48	1.72	Add'l	.036

4. Punch remaining hits

Low-Speed Machine				High-Speed Machine			
Hits	Min	Hits	Min	Hits	Min	Hits	Min
1	.03	20	.66	1	.008	20	.16
2	.07	30	.99	2	.02	30	.24
3	.10	40	1.32	3	.02	40	.32
4	.13	50	1.65	4	.03	50	.40
5	.17	60	1.98	5	.04	60	.48
6	.20	70	2.31	6	.05	70	.56
7	.23	80	2.64	7	.06	80	.64
8	.26	90	2.97	8	.06	90	.71
9	.30	100	3.30	9	.07	100	.79
10	.33	Add'l	.033	10	.08	Add'l	.008

3.5 Single-Station Punching Machines

DESCRIPTION

Punching machines have power-driven punch and their location may be by numerical control, stops, or a punched-hole templet. These machines are designed for hole-punching from prototype to medium-run quantities. Tooling changeover is minimal, as the punch holder swings out and a replaceable punch can be inserted. Die removal is simple as well. Finger-gripping of parts is common. If a machine is templet controlled, the operator locates a stylus point in each pilot hole, and concurrently the workpiece is positioned under the punch. The ram is automatically tripped, punching the hole. Templet pilot holes can be color-keyed to specific punch sizes, permitting the operator to punch all holes of the same size or shape before changing the punch and die. Front and back gage setting for hole locations are also available.

Figure 3.5 is an example of a hole-punching machine having a throat depth of 30 in., maximum hole diameter of $3\frac{1}{2}$ in. in 12 ga, sheet size of 30 × 60 in., and a maximum of 165 hits/min.

ESTIMATING DATA DISCUSSION

For each size hole the setup is 0.15 hr and includes items of work customarily associated with machine setup and teardown to a neutral machine table. Oftentimes, in successive hole diameters, the only work is a hole diameter change. The subsequent setup is reduced. Run time includes only Element 1, as it involves a pickup blank or strip, punch, and piece aside to stack. For certain materials, such as stainless steel or materials over $\frac{3}{16}$ in. thick, or diameters over ¾ in., oil time may be allowed, as found in Element 2.

The operational setup costs for single-station punching, as given in Item 3.5 of Section IV, depend upon the number of diameters. If eight different sizes are required, the cost per hole is multiplied by 8 and added to the constant to find the setup cost. Setup cost is applied on a per occurrence basis. The unit time depends upon the blank length plus width and number of holes. The factors are multiplied by blank length plus width and holes and added to the constant.

EXAMPLES

A. A sheet metal blank, 13 ga hot-rolled, pickeled and oiled stock, has a $L + W$ dimension of 27.15 in., and 13 holes are punched. Estimate the lot time for 75 parts and hr/100 units.

FIGURE 3.5 Hole punching machine with a 30-in. throat and a 30 x 60 in. maximum sheet size. (*Strippit Houdaille*)

Table	Description	Time
3.5-S	Setup for 1 hole	.15 hr
3.5-1	Pierce 13 holes in blank of $L + W = 27.15$, $.39 + 3 \times .03$	.48 min
	Unit estimate	.48 min
	Lot estimate	.75 hr
	hr/100 units	0.800

B. Using the description given in Example A above, find the $/100 units and lot estimate.

Item	Description	Cost
3.5	Setup, $1.03 + .51(1)$ for 1 hole	$1.54
3.5	Constant	$1.18
3.5	Blank, $.022 \times 27.15$	.60
3.5	Holes, $.627 \times 13$ .561	~~8.15~~ 7.33
	$/100 units	~~$9.93~~ 9.11
	Lot cost	~~$8.99~~ 8.37

TABLE 3.5   SINGLE-STATION PUNCHING MACHINES

Setup

1st hole diameter	.15 hr
Subsequent hole diameter	.05 hr

Operation elements in estimating minutes

1. Pick up blank, punch, blank aside

					Holes						
$L + W$	1	2	3	4	5	6	7	8	9	10	Add'l
3	.13	.17	.20	.23	.25	.29					.03
3.5	.12	.15	.19	.22	.25	.28	.31				.03
4	.11	.14	.18	.21	.24	.28	.31	.34			.03
6	.10	.13	.17	.20	.23	.26	.30	.33	.36	.40	.03
15	.09	.12	.15	.19	.22	.25	.29	.32	.35	.39	.03
25	.10	.13	.17	.20	.23	.26	.30	.33	.36	.40	.03
30	.11	.14	.18	.20	.22	.25	.29	.32	.35	.39	.03
32	.12	.15	.19	.21	.23	.26	.30	.33	.36	.40	.03
34	.13	.17	.20	.22	.24	.28	.31	.34	.37	.41	.03
36	.14	.18	.21	.24	.28	.31	.34	.37	.41	.44	.03
40	.15	.19	.22	.25	.29	.32	.35	.39	.42	.45	.04
44	.17	.21	.24	.29	.33	.37	.42	.46	.51	.55	.04

Add'l $L + W$ .015   Add'l hole   .05

2. Oil time

Holes	1	2	3	4	5	6	7	8	9	10	Add'l
Min	.03	.04	.06	.07	.08	.09	.10	.11	.12	.13	.01

3. Reposition 180°, flip, or turn

$L + W$	25	35	44
Min	.03	.04	.05

3.6 Power Press Brake Machines

DESCRIPTION

Press brakes are used to brake, form, seam, trim, and punch light-gauge sheet metal. Pressure capacity of a press brake is established by the material, length of work, thickness of the metal, and radius of the bend. Minimum inside radius of a bend is usually limited to material thickness. Press brakes have short strokes and are generally equipped with an eccentric type of drive mechanism.

Conventional power press brakes may be either hydraulic or mechanical. Hydraulic presses are more popular for larger tonnages. Figure 3.6 is a small hydraulic press brake equipped with numerically controlled programmable back gage and depth stop, which enables an operator to punch in a program of a sequence of different dimensions at various positions on a sheet and the press automatically adjusts to the settings.

ESTIMATING DATA DISCUSSION

Setup hours depend on brake length and number of stops. The length of a 30-in. brake separates the time per length. Setup standards are for conventional machines.

The operation elements are compiled with time as the central column. The data are constructed to require lip length (lip in.) of the folded metal, then dropping down to the sum of the blank width and length $(L + W)$. At this intersection move horizontally to the middle and read min. The first braking elements are composed of the work needed to move the material to and from the machine. Any additional brakes include work to reposition the material and expose a new lip. In a corresponding way, for each additional brake, start by using the next higher lip length, then descend vertically to the next higher blank $L + W$. At this point, move horizontally to the center for time.

Operation estimating, as provided in Item 3.6 of Section IV, requires blank size, or $L + W$ whether additional lips are formed or not. The first parenthesis provides cost for the first lip, and the second parenthesis gives additional cost for each lip that is formed.

FIGURE 3.6 A 100-ton capacity hydraulic press brake with NC programmable backgage and depth stop. (Niagara Machine & Tool Works)

122

EXAMPLES

A. A sheet metal part having a flat blank size of 16 × 24 in. has two folds of 4 in. along the 16-in. dimension and 6 in. along the 24-in. dimension. Standard commercial tolerances are required. A lot of 756 is planned.

Table	Description	Time
3.6-S	Setup	.30 hr
3.6-1	4-in. lip and 16 + 24 = 40 in.	.21 min
3.6-1	Reposition and brake 6 in., use the 8-in. lip and 46.3 blank size	.16
	Unit estimate	.37 min
	Total lot estimate	4.96 hr

B. Using Example A above, find the $/unit. The information for cost estimating is to be taken from Item 3.6 of Section IV.

Item	Description	Cost
3.6	Setup subtotal	$ 3.55
3.6	Constant for first lip	$ .831
3.6	Blank size factor, .060 × 40	2.40
3.6	Constant for second lip	.942
3.6	Second lip factor, .035 × 40	1.40
	$/100 units subtotal	$ 5.573
	Lot cost for 756 units	$45.68
	Unit cost	$ 0.060

TABLE 3.6 POWER PRESS BRAKE MACHINES

Setup

	Stops	
Brake length	1	2
Under 30 in.	.25 hr	.30 hr
30 in.	.30 hr	.35 hr

Operation elements in estimating minutes

1. Brake

First brake, L + W						Add'l brake, L + W				
Lip in.						Lip in.				
1	2	4	8	16	Min	16	8	4	2	1
2.0					.05					
3.6	3.5				.06					2.9
5.3	5.2				.07				5.5	5.7
9.2	9.1	9.0			.08		10.3	11.5	12.1	12.3
11.5	11.4	11.2	10.9		.09		14.1	15.3	15.9	16.1
14.0	13.9	13.7	13.4		.10		18.3	19.4	20.0	20.3
16.7	16.6	16.5	16.2		.11	20.5	22.9	24.0	24.6	24.9
19.7	19.7	19.5	19.2	18.5	.12	25.5	27.9	29.1	29.7	30.0
23.1	23.0	22.8	22.5	21.9	.13	31.1	33.5	34.7	35.3	35.6
26.7	26.6	26.5	26.1	25.5	.14	37.2	39.6	40.8	41.4	41.7
30.7	30.6	30.5	30.2	29.5	.16	44.0	46.3	47.5	48.1	48.4
35.1	35.1	34.9	34.6	33.9	.17	51.4	53.8	54.9	55.5	55.8
40.0	39.9	39.8	39.4	38.8	.19	59.5	61.9	63.1	63.7	64.0
45.4	45.3	45.1	44.8	44.2	.21	68.5	70.9	72.0	72.6	72.9
51.2	51.2	51.0	50.7	50.0	.23	78.4	80.7	81.9	82.5	82.8
57.7	57.6	57.5	57.2	56.5	.25	89.2	91.6	92.8	93.3	93.6

| First brake, L + W (Cont'd.) | | | | | | Add'l brake, L + W (Cont'd.) | | | | |
| Lip in. | | | | | | Lip in. | | | | |
1	2	4	8	16	Min	16	8	4	2	1
64.8	64.8	64.6	64.3	63.6	.28	101.1	103.5	104.7	105.3	105.6
72.7	72.6	72.4	72.1	71.5	.30	114.3	116.6	117.8	118.4	118.7
81.3	81.2	81.0	80.7	80.1	.34	128.7	131.1	132.3	132.8	133.1
90.8	90.7	90.5	90.2	89.6	.37	144.6	146.9	148.1	148.7	149.0
101.2	101.1	100.9	100.6	100.0	.41	162.0	164.4	165.6	166.2	166.5
112.6	112.6	112.4	112.1	111.4	.45					
125.3	125.5	125.0	124.7	124.1	.49					
139.1	139.0	138.9	138.6	137.9	.54					
154.4	154.3	154.1	153.8	153.2	.59					
171.2	171.1	170.9	170.6	170.0	.65					

Additional lip in., add .00028
Additional $L + W$, add .0035

Additional lip in., add .0062
Additional $L + W$, add .0021

Note: When $L + W = 100$ in. or $L = 7$ in.
for 7 ga, time is for 2 workers.

2. If parts must be stacked, add   .03
   For locating part on pins, add   .08

3. Miscellaneous
   For 7 ga and ¼-in. plate, add for first brake   .09
   Each add'l brake   .11

3.7 Jump Shear, Kick Press, and Foot Brake Machines

DESCRIPTION

These machines are light duty and require leg and body motions to effect the shear, pierce, or brake operation. Motorized power is not involved. The stock cannot be oversized to the machine, i.e., stock too thick or long or hard temper to be sheared, pierced, or braked. Machine limitations with respect to the material must be known. These estimating data are between bench and powered sheet-metal machines. A jump shear as shown by Figure 3.7 has a 36 in. maximum shearing width of 16 ga mild steel. Now consider estimating data for the general class of jump shear, kick press, and foot brake machines.

ESTIMATING DATA DISCUSSION

The elemental data are the "get and place" type with entry variables as width and length of the sheet, strip, or blank. Times are for single operator, except for sizes in excess of 24 × 48 in. For a sheet 48 × 96 in. to be handled, two operators are suggested

FIGURE 3.7 Foot-operated shear with 36-in. wide capacity in 16 ga mild steel. (*Di-Acro Division, Houdaille Industries, Incorporated*)

and Element 1 time is doubled or $2 \times .18 = .36$ min. Elements 2.4, and 5 also use Element 1.

Operational costs can be estimated using information of Item 3.7 in Section IV. These kind of estimates are faster even though for individual operations they are not as accurate as the elemental approach. The estimator can make the choice: to use the elemental or time approach, or find the base cost as provided in Section IV. The first setup as given in Section IV is higher than subsequent setups. Runtime, as expressed by dollars per 100 units, has the entry variable of blank size, $L + W$, for initial handling. If any rehandling is required for different lips for braking, edges for shearing, or holes for piercing, a rehandle cost per occurrence is provided on a per occurrence basis.

EXAMPLES

A. Shear a 6×48-in. strip from sheet stock 24×48 in. in size. Determine unit estimate and pc/hr for blanks 6×6 in.

Table	Description	Time
3.7-1	Pick up sheet, 2 operators, 18/24	.008 min
3.7-2	Locate and lock, 2 operators, 1 time $1 \times .18/24$	.008
3.7-3	Shear, 2 operators, 2 times, $\times .12/18$	.013
3.7-4	Reposition and lock, 2 operators, 2 times	.016
3.7-5	Remove pc, 6×48, 2 operators, 3 times, $3 \times .12/18$	.020
	Unit estimate	.065 min
	pc/hr	839 units

B. Shear a 6×6-in. blank from a strip 6×48 in. Determine unit estimate and pc/hr.

Table	Description	Time
3.7-1	Pick up strip, .09/8	.011 min
3.7-2	Locate and lock, .09/8	.011
3.7-3	Shear 7 times, .42/7	.06
3.7-4	Relocate and lock	.09
3.7-5	Unlock and remove, 1 pc, .06/6	.01
3.7-6	Pick up 7 pc	.04
	Unit estimate	.222 min
	pc/hr	270 units

C. Pierce 2 holes in the blank 6 x 6 in.

Table	Description	Time
3.7-1	Pick up piece	.04 min
3.7-3	Pierce hole	.05
3.7-4	Reposition against stop	.04
3.7-3	Pierce second hole	.05
3.7-1	Remove piece	.04
	Unit estimate	.22 min
	pc/hr	272 units

D. Find the unit cost for Example B above using Item 3.7 of Section IV. A shear action is required.

Item	Description	Cost
3.7	Constant	$1.71
3.7	Handle factor, $.036 \times 12$	.432
3.7	Shear, one jump	1.14
	$/100 units	$3.282
	Unit cost estimate	$ .033

E. Estimate the unit cost to pierce two holes in a blank, 6 × 6 in.

Item	Description	Cost
3.7	Constant	$1.71
3.7	Handle factor, .036 × 12	.432
3.7	Pierce 2 holes, .856 × 2	1.712
	$/100 units	$3.854
	Unit cost	$ .039

TABLE 3.7 JUMP SHEAR, KICK PRESS, AND FOOT BRAKE MACHINES

Setup

1st	.4 hr
Each add'l	.1 hr

Operation elements in estimating minutes

1. Pick up part to machine bed

	Length										
Width	3	6	9	12	18	24	36	48	60	72	96
3	.03	.04	.04	.04	.05	.06	.07	.08	.09	.10	.13
6	.03	.04	.05	.05	.06	.07	.08	.09	.10	.12	.14
12			.05	.06	.07	.08	.09	.12	.12	.12	.13
18					.07	.08	.09	.12	.12	.12	.13
24						.09	.10	.09	.09	.12	.15
36							.12	.09	.12	.14	.15
48								.12	.15	.18	.20

2. Locate and lock (use Element 1)

3. Shear or brake or pierce

Length	12	24	36	48
Time	.06	.07	.08	.09

Pierce hole   .05

4. Reposition and lock (use Element 1)
   Unlock and reverse piece (use Element 1)

5. Remove pc (use Element 1)

6. Unlock and remove to table or cart

	Length								
Width	9	12	18	24	36	48	60	72	96
3	.06	.06	.07	.08	.09	.10	.12	.13	.15
6	.06	.07	.08	.09	.10	.12	.13	.14	.16
12	.07	.08	.09	.10	.12	.14	.16	.14	.15
18			.09	.10	.12	.14	.16	.14	.15
24				.12	.13	.12	.12	.14	.17
36					.14	.12	.14	.16	.17
48						.14	.16	.19	.21

3.8 Hand-Operated Brake, Bender, Punch Press, Multiform, Coil Winder, Shear, Straightener, and Roller Machines

DESCRIPTION

This equipment is hand-operated and is classified as bench equipment, although some may be free standing. Like foot-operated equipment, the forces necessary to process thin gage sheet or foil stock are restricted to what an operator is physically able to perform. The equipment is varied. Figure 3.8A shows a hand-operated bender with a capacity of $\frac{1}{16}$ to 1 in. round steel bar. Round, square, hexagonal, channel, flat, and tubing can be handled by this machine. Figure 3.8B is a box finger brake and is rated to 16 gage mild steel. Figure 3.8C is a single-station punch with 4-in. capacity in 16 gage mild steel. Figure 3.8D is a 12-station turret punch press.

general terms and are similar to get-place tables developed from time studies. Parts are small and light and are hand held. Small production quantities, where predesigned tooling is the exception rather than the rule, are the jobs that would use these estimating data.

Operational costs, as found in Item 3.8 of Section IV, are estimated by recognizing that the brake, shear, punch, and bender work is termed "actions", and if two holes are pierced, then two actions are used. The actions are added to the handling time. If a reposition or a different lay or lip are required, a rehandle cost is added to the sum.

ESTIMATING DATA DISCUSSION

Inasmuch as the various pieces of equipment are small, manually operated, sheet-metal bench tools, additional tooling is normally general purpose and immediately available. The setup is 0.2 hr per item of equipment.

Elements for this equipment are described in

FIGURE 3.8B Box finger brake. *(Di-Acro Houdaille)*

FIGURE 3.8A Hand-operated bender. *(Di-Acro Houdaille)*

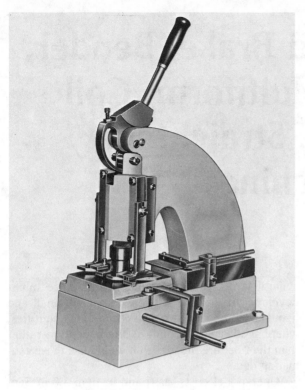

FIGURE 3.8C Single-station punch, hand operated. (*Di-Acro Houdaille*)

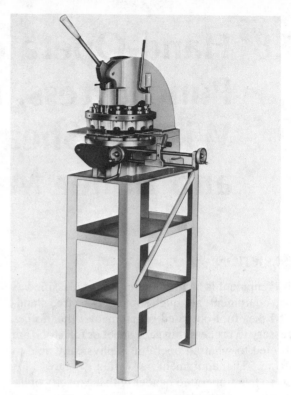

FIGURE 3.8D A 12-station turret punch press. (*Di-Acro Houdaille*)

EXAMPLES

A. Estimate the time to shear a 1.105 × 0.872-in. blank from 0.005-in. thick material, where sheet size is 18 × 24-in. stock. The shear is followed by a multiform operation. Compute the estimate as setup and hr/100 units.

Table	Description	Time	
3.8-S	Shear setup	0.2	hr
3.8-1	Pick up, move, position against stop	0.06	min
3.8-3	Shear twice	.04	
3.8-4	Reposition for 1 shear	.08	
3.8-5	Piece aside	.02	
	Unit estimate for shear blank	0.20	min
3.8-S	Multiform setup	0.2	hr
3.8-1	Pick up, transport, position, clamp	0.07	min
3.8-3	Multiform	.07	
3.8-5	Piece aside	.02	
	Unit estimate for multiform	.16	min
	Total setup	0.4	hr
	hr/100 units	.600	

B. A wire spring has 13 turns, ½ in. OD mandrel and 2 half-circle ends. Find the unit time to make this spring.

Table	Description	Time	
3.8-S	Wire-form and multiform setup	0.4	hr
3.8-2	Advance wire against stop	.03	min
3.8-2	Position mandrel, lock wire, back off, and remove	.51	
3.8-3	Wind wire turns, 10 × .03	.30	
3.8-3	Cut wire	.05	
3.8-3	Form one end with multiform	.07	
3.8-4	Reposition for multiform of end	.15	
3.8-5	Piece aside	.02	
	Unit estimate	1.13	min

C. Combine both operations in Example A above and find the unit cost using Item 3.8 of Section IV.

Item	Description	Cost
3.8	Shear constant	$1.20
3.8	Two shear actions, .428 × 2	.856
3.8	Reposition for shear	1.14
3.8	Form constant	1.71
3.8	One form action	2.42
	$/100 units	$7.326

TABLE 3.8 HAND-OPERATED BRAKE, BENDER, PUNCH PRESS, MULTIFORM, COIL WINDER, SHEAR, STRAIGHTENER, AND ROLLER MACHINES

Setup	**.2 hr**

Operation elements in estimating minutes

1. Pick up, transport, position, clamp	
For brake, multiform, sheet roller	.07
For bender, punch-press forming	.18
Pick up transport, position against stop	
For notch, shear, pierce	.06
Pick up, transport	.02
2. Advance strip or wire against stop	.03
Position mandrel, lock wire, back off, remove wire	.51
3. Process	
Brake, release	.05
Form or bend, release	.19
Punch press form	.05
Multiform	.07
Notch, shear, or pierce	.02
Air shear	.01
Cut wire	.05
Wind wire turns	.03/turn
Hand straighten	.25
Roll sheet flat or curving	.15
Position between blocks and hammer blocks	.11
4. Reposition, clamp for each add'l lay	.08
Reposition, reform, and release	
Form or bend	.35
Punch press	.09
Brake	.08
Multiform	.15
Notch, shear, or pierce	.08
5. Piece aside	.02
Piece aside, reach for new part	.06

3.9 Nibbling Machines

DESCRIPTION

The nibbling process is used to cut odd shapes in ferrous, nonferrous and nonmetallic materials. Depending on the machine, cuts up to approximately ½-in. thick can be made in mild steel. The nibbling machine has a punch that moves with a

FIGURE 3.9 Nibbler punching machine *(Trumpf America, Incorporated)*

rapidly oscillating stroke in a die. A cut is made by moving the material against the pilot of the punch and inching the material along following each punch stroke. Templets or scribe lines are used as guides. Some nibbling machines can fold, bead, louvre, flange, and slot. Sizes of machines are rated by throat depth and the maximum thickness of mild steel that can be cut. An example of a nibbler is given in Figure 3.9.

ESTIMATING DATA DISCUSSION

There are two operation elements: handle part and cut or nibble. The entry variable for handling part is length plus width $(L + W)$ of the sheet metal blank. For process time, Element 2, the entry variable is cut or nibble length. Cutting is assumed to be in a straight line while nibbling is curving. The processing times are for soft thin metals.

Operational base costs, as found in Item 3.9 of Section IV, are related to blank size, $L + W$, and cut and nibble length. The first factor is multiplied by the blank overall maximum $L + W$ to give handling cost. Cut is straight work and nibble is curved work. The lengths for cut and nibble are determined from the the drawing and the lengths multiply the factors.

EXAMPLES

A. Find the unit min to nibble a 17-in. curve and cut a 15-in. straight line on a 5052 H2 aluminum blank which is 20 × 10 in. in size.

Table	Description		Time
3.9-1	Blank size = $L + W = 30$		.42 min
3.9-1	Reposition, 1 required		.29
3.9-2	Nibble 17-in. contour		.60
3.9-2	Cut 10-in. L		.17
	Unit estimate		1.48 min

130

B. Estimate the unit cost for Example A above.

Item	Description	Cost
3.9	Blank handling, .214 × 30	$ 6.42
3.9	Cut 15 × .242	3.63
3.9	Nibble 17 × .485	8.25
	$/100 units	$18.30

TABLE 3.9   NIBBLING MACHINES

Setup   **.2 hr**

Operation elements in estimating minutes

1. Handle part

L + W	Min	L + W	Min
12.0	.16	31.2	.42
13.2	.18	34.3	.47
14.5	.20	37.8	.51
16.0	.22	41.6	.56
17.6	.24	45.7	.62
19.4	.26	50.3	.68
21.3	.29	55.3	.75
23.4	.32	60.9	.82
25.8	.35	67.0	.91
28.4	.38	Add'l	.0007

Reposition   .29

2. Cut or nibble

Cut L	Nibble L	Min	Cut L	Nibble L	Min
2.0	0.9	.03	18.4	9.1	.31
2.5	1.1	.04	20.2	10.1	.34
3.1	1.5	.05	22.3	11.1	.37
3.9	1.8	.07	24.5	12.2	.41
4.9	2.3	.08	26.9	13.4	.45
6.1	2.9	.10	29.6	14.8	.50
7.1	3.5	.12	32.6	16.3	.55
7.8	3.8	.13	35.8	17.9	.60
8.6	4.2	.14	39.4	19.7	.66
9.4	4.6	.16	43.4	21.7	.73
10.4	5.1	.17	47.7	23.9	.80
11.4	5.6	.19	52.5	26.3	.88
12.6	6.2	.21	57.7	28.9	.97
13.8	6.8	.23	63.5	31.8	1.07
15.2	7.5	.26	Add'l		.017
16.7	8.3	.28		Add'l	.033

3.10 Tube Bending Machines

DESCRIPTION

The manufacturing process being estimated is tube bending. Machines used to bend tubes may be hydraulic or manual. The machines are able to bend any kind of metal tube, but are machine limited to the range of diameter. Cold forming is the principle used as temperature is not involved. A mandrel and die fixture for a certain diameter are necessary to match each tube diameter size. For example, a tube with a 2-in. diameter requires a mandrel that fits snuggly inside the tube. A die fixture is needed to fit tightly to the outside of the tube.

These machines can bend tubes of various lengths. Figure 3.10 shows the function of a typical tube bending machine. It is a requirement that there be enough tubing left in the fixture (about 4 in.) so that the tube can still be securely held. There is also a limit as to how close the tangent points can be to each other for the bending process.

The quality of the bent tubing as described in these data is important. It is necessary to avoid wrinkles or bumps on the outside of the tube.

ESTIMATING DATA DISCUSSION

Besides the usual chores for setup, the time includes interchanging the dies from the preceding cycle to dies that are compatible for a tube in the present cycle. If the diameter of the preceding tube is the same, then the setup is zero. If quality requirements demand, a plaster cast of an acceptable tube can be constructed. A time is provided for this work.

The elemental times are most influenced by the degree of bend and the length of each tube. For a manual tube bending machine, Elements 1, 4, 5, and 7 are basically constant since they are not influenced greatly by any time drivers. For Elements 2 and 3, load tube on mandrel and line up tangent points, the time depends on the length of the tube, which is given in inches. Element 6, bend, is influenced by the degree of bend required by the tube. The amount of bend is in degrees. If the specifications of the tube are important, a plaster cast or fixture is provided to check the degree of bend, points of tangency, and length of tube. Here, Element 8, inspect with plaster cast, is considered to be constant.

For the hydraulic tube bender, Element 3, line up tangent points, is not a variable element since stops are provided on the bender, which line up the tangent points automatically. Element 6 is the only variable time element in the cycle and is a function of the amount of bend which is in degrees.

Another method used to estimate setup and cycle times is the operation cost estimating relationship given by Item 3.10 of Section IV. Rule-of-thumb equations are given. The setup cost is constant, but the $/100 ($ per 100) units depends upon the length of the tube (in inches) and the amount of bend (in degrees). The setup is the same for either manual or hydraulic machines. The $/100 units equation differs between the two machines.

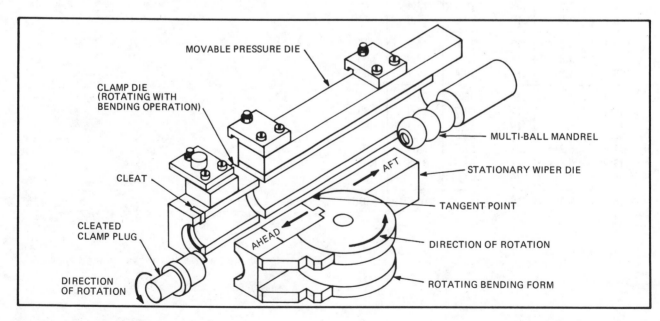

FIGURE 3.10 A tube bending machine.

132

EXAMPLES

A. Estimate the time to bend a .75 in. OD tube to 85°. The tube is 7.2-in. long. There is an interchange of dies and inspection. Work is on the hydraulic tube bender. Find the unit estimate, hr/100 units, and total setup.

Table	Description	Time
3.10-S	Clean up, get tube etc.	.33 hr
3.10-S	Interchange dies	.56
3.10-S	Inspect	.10
3.10-1	Oil inside of tube	.15 min
3.10-2	Put tube on mandrel	.049
3.10-3	Line up tangent points	.11
3.10-4	Set/remove clamp die	.13
3.10-5	Set/remove movable pressure die	.12
3.10-6	Bend	.20
3.10-7	Remove tube from machine	.06
	Unit estimate	.82 min
	Hr/100 units	1.367
	Total setup	.99 hr

B. Estimate the time to bend a tube 14.4-in. long with a 20°-bend. There is no interchange of dies nor any inspection. This job is done on the manual tube bender.

Table	Description	Time
3.10-S	Clean up, get tubes, etc.	.33 hr
3.10-1	Oil inside of tube	.15 min
3.10-2	Put tube on mandrel	.072
3.10-3	Line up tangent points	.14
3.10-4	Set/remove clamp die	.13
3.10-5	Set/remove movable pressure die	.11
3.10-6	Bend	.18
3.10-7	Remove tube from machine	.04
	Unit estimate	.823 min

C. Estimate the time to bend a tube 15.6-in. long with a 40.1°-bend. There is no interchange of dies, but there is an inspection of the finished tube. The bend is done with the hydraulic tube bender. Find the unit estimate, hr/100 units, and lot time for 15 units.

Table	Description	Time
3.10-S	Clean up, get tubes, etc.	.33 hr
3.10-S	Inspection	.10
3.10-1	Oil inside of tube	.15 min
3.10-2	Put tube on mandrel	.072
3.10-3	Line up tangent points	.11
3.10-4	Set/remove clamp die	.13
3.10-5	Set/remove movable pressure die	.12
3.10-6	Bend	.094
3.10-7	Remove tube from machine	.058
3.10-8	Inspect with plaster cast	.02
	Unit estimate	.75 min
	Hr/100 units	1.250
	Lot setup	.62 hr

D. Estimate the time to bend a tube 1-ft long with a 16.5°-bend. There is no interchange of dies, but there is an inspection of the finished tube. The bend is done with the manual tube bender. Find the lot time for 1850 units.

Table	Description	Time
3.10-S	Clean up, get tubes, etc.	.33 hr
3.10-S	Inspection	.10
3.10-1	Oil inside of tube	.15 min
3.10-2	Put tube on mandrel	.064
3.10-3	Line up tangent points	.13
3.10-4	Set/remove clamp die	.13
3.10-5	Set/remove movable pressure die	.11
3.10-6	Bend	.15
3.10-7	Remove tube from machine	.04
	Unit estimate	.77 min
	Hr/100 units	1.283
	Lot estimate	24.17 hr

E. Re-estimate Example A using the cost estimating relationships given by Item 3.10 of Section IV. For this example, find the $/100 units, total setup cost, and lot cost for 80 units.

Item	Description	Cost
3.10	Setup	$ 9.12
3.10	Constant for cycle	9.17
3.10	Length of tube = 7.2 in.; 7.2 × .044	.32
3.10	Bend = 85°; .030 × 85	2.55
	$/100 units	$12.04
	Total setup cost	9.12
	Lot cost for 80 units	$21.67

F. Use Example B as described above and re-estimate using a base-cost approach. The location of these direct-labor costs are given by Item 3.10 of Section IV. Find the $/100 units, setup cost, and lot cost for 80 units.

Item	Description	Cost
3.10	Setup	$ 9.12
3.10	Constant for cycle	7.00
3.10	Length of tube = 14.4 in.; 14.4 × .152	2.19
3.10	Bend = 20°; 20 × .132	2.64
	$/100 units	$11.83
	Total setup cost	9.12
	Lot cost for 80 units	$18.58

TABLE 3.10   TUBE BENDING MACHINES

Setup

Clean up, get tubes, basic	.33 hr
Interchange dies, if necessary	.56 hr
Make plaster cast for inspection	.10 hr

Operation elements in estimating minutes

1. Oil inside of tube   .15

2. Load tube on mandrel

In. L	1.2	2.6	4.0	5.5	8.2	9.2	11.1	13.4	15.8
Min	.033	.037	.040	.044	.049	.053	.059	.064	.072

3. Line up tangent points

Manual machine

In. L	7.2	8.7	10.2	12.0	13.9	16.0
Min	.090	.099	.11	.12	.13	.14

Hydraulic machine .11

4. Set/remove clamp die 13

5. Set/remove movable pressure die, manual .11

                                      hydraulic .12

6. Bend

Manual machine

Degree of bend	18	20	22	24	27	30	33
Min	.15	.16	.18	.20	.22	.24	.26

Degree of bend	36	40	44	50	54	60
Min	.29	.32	.35	.39	.43	.47

Hydraulic machine

Degree of bend	32	36	40	43	48	53
Min	.071	.078	.086	.094	.11	.13

Degree of bend	63	69	76	84	92
Min	.14	.15	.17	.18	.20

7. Remove tube from machine; manual, .04

                                        hydraulic .06

8. Inspect tube with plaster cast .02

3.11 Ironworker Machines

DESCRIPTION

The ironworker is a general purpose machine and may be operated by either one or two operators independently. Each may perform a variety of work which includes, shearing, punching, or other similar processes (blanking, notching, piercing, etc.).

The shearing operation involves pushing the strip, barstock, etc., through the machine until it impacts a triggering mechanism, where the bar or sheet is cut and the finished part drops into a waiting bin. Once the stock has been completely sheared, the remaining end piece is removed, and a new piece is prepared for shearing. This process continues until the lot requirement is completed.

Similarly, the punching process involves a handling and positioning time, after which the part is punched. In addition, if several punches are required for a part, a rehandling and repunching time enter the estimating process. After the punch or punches have been performed, the finished part is then tossed into a waiting bin, and the cycle is repeated.

ESTIMATING DATA DISCUSSION

A distinction is provided for shearing and punching. Usually, shearing starts with stock to be separated. Punching deals with individual blanks.

Many of the operation elements require information on the number of pieces that are to be sectioned from raw material. The shear length is the length required for a sheared part.

The estimator selects the elements, keeping in mind that the units for setup are in hours while the cycle elements are in minutes. Notice also that it is important to select the cycle time that is related to one unit of output, since much of the ironworker operations deal with multiples. For example, oil piece is done every 50 pieces or so. The element time to oil is greater than that shown by Element 7, but it has been divided by 50 units. So, this is a requirement every 50 units or so.

The estimator may prefer to deal directly with dollars for setup and $/100 units for operations. The ironworker may be estimated for these base costs using Item 3.11 of Section IV.

EXAMPLES

A. A lot of 1900 parts is to be made 7-in. long from 58 strips of metal. Thirty-three parts/strips may be sheared. Find the unit estimate.

Table	Description	Time
3.11-1	Slide strip onto rollers	.001 min
3.11-2	Push and shear strip	.02
3.11-3	Remove end piece	.003
3.11-9	Inspect part	.01
3.11-4	Settle parts	.005
	Unit estimate	.039 min

B. A lot of 500 parts 35.5-in. long is to be sheared from 84 strips with 6 parts/strip. Find the unit, hr/100 units, and lot estimate.

Table	Description	Time
3.11-S	Shearing setup	.30 hr
3.11-1	Slide strip onto rollers	.005 min
3.11-9	Position and inspect	.01
3.11-2	Push and shear strip	.06
3.11-3	Remove end piece	.01
3.11-4	Settle parts	.005
	Unit estimate	.09 min
	Hr/100 units	.150
	Lot estimate	1.05 hr

C. A quantity of 2000 parts is to be punched once per part. Part length equals 35.5 in. Find the unit estimate.

Table	Description	Time
3.11-5	Pick up stock	.05 min
3.11-7	Lubrication time	.03
3.11-6	Positioning	.05
3.11-7	Punch	.02
3.11-9	Inspection	.01
3.11-8	Drop finished part	.02
3.11-4	Settle parts	.005
	Unit estimate	.185 min

D. Five hundred 28-in. long parts are to be punched twice. Find the unit, hr/100 units, and shop estimate.

Table	Description	Time
3.11-S	Punching setup	.15 hr
3.11-5	Pick up stock	.05 min
3.11-7	Lubrication	.03
3.11-6	Positioning	.02
3.11-7	Punch	.02
3.11-6	Repositioning	.03
3.11-7	Punch	.02
3.11-9	Inspection (measurement)	.01
3.11-8	Drop finished part in bin	.02
3.11-4	Settle parts	.005
	Unit estimate	.205 min
	Hr/100 units	.342
	Shop estimate	292 pc/hr

136

E. Reconsider Example A given above. Now find the base cost for shearing 100 units.

Item	Description	Cost
3.11	Constant	$.274
3.11	Shearing, $7 \times .049$	.343
	$/100 units	$.617

F. The estimator wants to find the lot cost, including the setup cost and the run cost, for 500 parts which are punched twice. Notice Example D above.

Item	Description	Cost
3.11	Setup cost subtotal	$ 2.54
3.11	Constant for punching	.953
3.11	Two punches, 2×1.01	2.02
	$/100 units	$ 2.973
	Lot cost	$17.41

TABLE 3.11 IRONWORKER MACHINES

Setup

Shearing operation	.30 hr
Punching operation	.15 hr

Operation elements in estimating minutes

1. Slide bar or strip onto rollers for shear   .05/bar

No. of pieces from bar	1	5	10	20	50
Prorated min	.05	.01	.005	.003	.001

2. Push and shear; part drops into bin

Push L, in.	10	20	30	40
Prorated min	.02	.03	.04	.06

3. Remove end piece, shear

No. of pieces from bar	1	3	10	30	60
Prorated min	.03	.01	.003	.001	.0005

4. Settle sheared parts in bin   .20

Push L, in.	10	20	30	40
Prorated min	.005	.007	.01	.005

Settle punched parts in bin   .005

5. Pick up single part for punching, blanking, notching, etc.   .05

6. Position single part for operation   .02
Reposition for extra strike   .03

7. Punch, notch, etc.   .02
Lubricate strip or part, prorated over 50 punches   .03

8. Drop finished part in bin   .02

9. Inspect or count part   .01

4.1 Marking Machines

DESCRIPTION

Permanent impressions can be made by forcing a high-speed steel-lettered die into a metal surface. These cold impressions are used for marking, numbering, graduating, embossing, knurling, and tag or nameplate making. But these estimating data refer to metal marking. Machines for metal marking are hydraulic, mechanical, or pneumatic powered. Impact, rolling, or cold forming are some of the cold-working principles employed. Even though metal is the primary object of these data, plastics, leather, etc. can be similarly marked. Figure 4.1 is an example of a high-production metal-marker machine. Production of this machine is 2500 tubes per hr.

ESTIMATING DATA DISCUSSION

Entry variables for Elements 1, 2, or 3 are part size: small, medium, or large. Small parts are handled easily, no dimension exceeds 3 in., and weight does not exceed $1/5$ lb. Medium parts have no dimension or weight that exceed 9 in. and 3 lb respectively, while large parts are limited to 20 in. and 8 lb.

For manual operation, Element 1 is always required. If semi- or fully automatic, knowledge of loading is required. The target for the part in Element 2 is either universal or fitted nest.

The marking or machine time is given by Element 5. For machines that have a lever which is rolled and manipulated by the operator, Element 5 will be used.

A ram action that is vertical and uses pressure to force the marking die into the surface adopts Element 6. A round surface is covered by Element 7.

Operational costs are provided in Item 4.1 of Section IV. The variable is based upon the number of markings.

FIGURE 4.1 High-production metal marker. (*George T. Schmidt, Incorporated*)

EXAMPLES

A. A medium-size part is loaded in a fitted nest and a pressure-stamping machine is used. Find the lot time for 1800 parts.

Table	Description	Time	
4.1-S	Setup	.15	hr
4.1-1	Get and aside part	.050	min
4.1-2	Load in fitted nest	.044	
4.1-6	Pressure stamp	.038	
	Unit estimate	.132	min
	Lot estimate	4.11	hr

B. Estimate the cost for Example A above using Item 4.1 of Section IV.

Item	Description	Cost
4.1	Setup	$ 1.28
4.1	Constant	$ 1.21
4.1	Stamp	.45
	$/100 units	$ 1.66
	Lot cost	$31.16

TABLE 4.1   MARKING MACHINES

Setup   **.15 hr**

Operation elements in estimating minutes

		Part Size	
	Small	Medium	Large
1. Get and aside part	.035	.050	.11
2. Load and unload part in:			
universal nest	.022	.028	.035
fitted nest	.038	.044	.050
3. Place part against stop	.030	.042	.048
4. Clamp with C			
Install and remove			.22
Tighten or loosen			.05
Quick-acting vise			.04
5. Manual rotation of handle to stamp			
Length of stamp < .7 in.			.006
Length of stamp ≥ .7 in.			.011
6. Pressure stamp			.038
7. Machine roll stamp			
Length of stamp, 0–3 in.			.036
Length of stamp, > 3 in.			.066

4.2 Screen Printing Bench and Machines

DESCRIPTION

The apparatus for manual screen printing consists of a base equipped with gages or jigs for registry of the part to be screened. The base is hinged with a frame which can be raised and lowered. The frame is often counterweighted. A silk screen or other material is held taut within the frame. After a piece has been located, the frame is lowered and paint, previously applied on the screen, is wiped across using a rubber squeegee. This forces a paint film through the mesh that is not blanked off by the stencil onto the surface of the work beneath. The frame is raised; the piece is removed, and it is replaced by a second. The operation is then repeated.

In semiautomatic screen printing, the manual work of screen manipulation has been removed, leaving loading and unloading for the operator. Figure 4.2 is an example of a semiautomatic machine. A variable speed drive with 400 to 1140 impressions/hr can be maintained. For this model, materials ranging from printed circuits to fabrics to metals ¾ in. in thickness can be accommodated. The printer can be adapted to conveyorized or turntable operation. Integrated automatic and convey-orized-oven units are also available. Infrared heating elements are used to dry the ink.

ESTIMATING DATA DISCUSSION

A fixed screen is one mounted on the silk-screen bench while a free screen is portable and placed on the part by hand. The setup and the cycle operation separates the estimating data on this basis.

The first operation is the initial screening, as the subsequent operation requires less work. Entry variables are first or following operation, fixed or free screen, part box size ($= L + W + H$) and the length of the squeegee pass for the silk screen area. The time is found at the intersection of these entry variables, and is total for handling and silk screening. Following the first screen for an operation, additional screening for that operation would use the additional screen at the bottom of the table. Element 1 is for manual screen printing.

Screen printing can alternately be estimated in terms of setup \$ and \$/100 units using Item 4.2 of Section IV. Two entry facts that are information from the design are girth and length of silk screen. The girth is computed as $L + W + H$.

EXAMPLES

A. A part, $L + W + H = 15.7$ in., has one bench-mounted screening operation followed by a portable screen on a different area. The screen lengths are 12 in. and 5 in. Determine lot time for 118 units.

FIGURE 4.2 Screen printing press. *(Lawson Printing & Drying Machine Company)*

Table	Description	Time
4.2-S	Fixed screen and 1 free screen, .2 + .10 + .05	.35 hr
4.2-1	First operation, $L + W + H = 15.7$, fixed screen at screen length of 12 in.	.43 min
	First operation, free screen at 5 in.	.49
	Unit estimate	.92 min
	Lot time	2.16 hr

B. The part previously silk screened in Example A above is to have additional screening. Operational facts are 1 fixed screen of 7 in. and 2 free screens of 4 and 9 in. Estimate pc/hr.

Table	Description	Time
4.2-S	Fixed screen and 2 additional portable screens	.54
4.2-1	Second operation, fixed screen at L of 7 in., $L + W + H = 15.7$	.22 min
4.2-1	Free screen, second operation, $L = 4$ in.	.30
	Unit estimate	.52 min
	Shop estimate	115 pc/hr

C. Find the base cost for the part described in Example A above. Use information from Item 4.2 of Section IV.

Item	Description	Cost
4.2	Bench setup, first screen	$ 2.02
4.2	Second screen, same setup, 50%	1.01
4.2	Setup subtotal	$ 3.03
4.2	First screen, $.320 \times 15.7 + 12 \times .152$	$ 6.85
4.2	Second screen, $.320 \times 15.7 + 5 \times .152$	5.78
	$/100 units subtotal	$12.63
	Lot cost	$17.94

TABLE 4.2   SCREEN PRINTING BENCH AND MACHINES

Setup

Screen machine	.25 hr
Fixed screen bench	.2 hr
Free screen	.10 + .05 hr/screen

Operation elements in estimating minutes

1. Manual screen printing

Part		$L + W + H$		Length of Screened Area							
First Operation		Following Operations									
Fixed	Free	Fixed	Free	3	5	6	7	9	12	14	18
		11		.16	.18	.18	.19	.21	.23	.26	.29
3		13		.17	.18	.19	.20	.22	.25	.27	.30
6		15		.18	.19	.20	.21	.23	.26	.28	.31
9		16		.19	.20	.21	.22	.25	.27	.29	.32
10		19	9	.20	.21	.22	.23	.26	.28	.30	.33
11	6	22	14	.22	.23	.25	.26	.28	.30	.32	.36
11		24	18	.25	.26	.27	.28	.30	.32	.35	.38
12		26	21	.27	.28	.29	.30	.32	.35	.37	.40
13	11	29	26	.32	.33	.35	.36	.38	.40	.42	.46

Part		L + W + H		Length of Screened Area							
First Operation		Following Operations									
Fixed	Free	Fixed	Free	3	5	6	7	9	12	14	18
15	13	32	31	.36	.37	.38	.39	.41	.43	.46	.49
17	14	33	32	.40	.41	.42	.43	.46	.48	.50	.53
19	15	35	34	.43	.45	.46	.44	.49	.51	.53	.57
20	18	36	36	.48	.49	.50	.51	.53	.56	.58	.61
21	21	37	37	.52	.53	.54	.56	.58	.60	.62	.66
23	22	39	39	.58	.59	.60	.61	.63	.60	.68	.71
25	25	40	40	.63	.64	.66	.67	.69	.71	.77	.77
26	27			.70	.71	.72	.77	.76	.78	.80	.84
29	32			.72	.78	.78	.80	.82	.85	.87	.90
33	35			.85	.86	.86	.88	.90	.92	.95	.98
36	38			.93	.95	.96	.97	.98	1.01	1.04	1.07
39				1.04	1.05	1.06	1.07	1.09	1.10	1.13	1.15
40	41			1.15	1.16	1.17	1.18	1.20	1.23	1.25	1.28
43	43			1.26	1.27	1.28	1.29	1.31	1.34	1.36	1.39
Add'l				.15	.16	.17	.18	.20	.22	.24	.27

Hook and unhook part   .27
Rubber stamp   .10

2. Semiautomatic screen printing
Rotary turntable
5 × 5-in. area, metal part   .06

Conveyor handling and printing

Impressions/hr	200	500	1000	1500
Min/unit	.30	.12	.06	.04

4.3 Laser Marking Machines

DESCRIPTION

Laser marking is a means of noncontact pressure marking useful for a variety of nontransparent materials such as synthetics and rubber, metal, and diamond. After the continuous-wave laser radiation exits a laser head, and becomes an enlarged beam, mirrors controlled by galvanometers focus the beam on the workpiece. At the point of focus, the laser vaporizes the material of the workpiece, and as it is scanned in the X and Y directions it traces out a trench to engrave whatever character, symbol, or pattern is established by the computer program.

On some machines, software is provided on tape and is loaded into random-access read/write memory using a tape reader that is part of the system. Once loaded, the program may be modified from the control panel. Figure 4.3 shows a machine capable of 4 mil dia focused spot size. Engraving fields up to 3½ × 3½ in. are available.

ESTIMATING DATA DISCUSSION

Setup times allow for average programming, and if the program is saved on any storage medium, the amount is reduced to 0.1 hr.

Part handling is associated with part size. Very small implies parts are difficult to control. Although they can be easily handled in handfuls, tweezers are sometimes used. Small parts are easy to manage with the fingers. No dimension exceeds 3 in. and weight does not exceed ¼ lb. Medium-sized parts

FIGURE 4.3 Laser marking machine. (JEC Lasers, Inc.)

are easily handled by one hand; maximum dimension is 9 in.

A door has to be opened to allow entry of the part. Following the marking, the door has to be open for removal. A time of 0.04 min allows for both actions.

Laser marking depends upon character height. Distinctions for flourishes, strokes, and various character differences are averaged. Material is considered hard. Count the number of different height characters to find a time.

If the estimator wishes to find direct-labor cost, Section IV approaches can give base costs. The cycle constant provides for a small production part, and the variable is the number of characters. Multiply the character cost by the number and add it to the constant to determine base cost for 100 units.

EXAMPLES

A. A fragile transistor has "2N" and "4856" laser marked on top of the metal cover unit. The unit is very small and is loaded into a nest. The characters are ⅛-in. high. Find the lot time for a new order where the quantity is 75 units.

Table	Description	Time	
4.3-S	Setup program and initialize	.3	hr
4.3-2	Open and close door	.04	min
4.3-2	Start and stop	.02	
4.3-1	Get and aside part, stack	.042	
4.3-1	Place into nest	.033	
4.3-3	Laser mark 6 characters, ⅛ in. high	.30	
	Unit estimate	.435	min
	Lot estimate	.90	hr

B. A machine tool dial is laser marked. It has 360 marks on the circumference. Every major 5° has ⅜-in. long marks for a total of 36. Each minor mark is $3/_{16}$-in. long and there are 324 marks. The dial is loaded on an indexable mandrel. There are ninety-nine $3/_{16}$-in. numerals. Find the unit estimate to make one part. Assume door is opened for each mark, and the part is indexed to position the dial.

144

Table	Description	Time	
4.3-S	Setup	.3	hr
4.3-2	Open and close door (360 + 99) .04	18.36	min
4.3-2	Start and stop, controllable, once	.02	
4.3-1	Medium part load on indexable mandrel	.045	
4.3-3	Major lines, 36 at ⅜-in. height 2.83 + (36 − 25) .113	1.24	
4.3-3	Minor lines, 324 at $\frac{3}{16}$-in. height 1.40 + (324 − 25) .056	18.14	
4.3-3	Numbers, 99 at $\frac{3}{16}$-in. height 1.40 + (99 − 25) .056	5.54	
4.3-1	Reposition (360 + 98) .01	4.58	
	Unit estimate	47.93	min
	Lot estimate	1.10	hr

C. Find the operational cost of a part that is laser marked. Ten characters are about ⅛-in. high while another 14 are ¼-in. high. A lot of 25 units is required.

Item	Description	Cost
4.3	Setup subtotal	$ 1.71
4.3	Cycle constant	$ 1.57
4.3	⅛-in. high characters, 10 × .539	5.39
4.3	¼-in. high characters, 14 × 1.07	14.98
	$/ 100 units	$21.94
	Lot cost	$ 7.20

TABLE 4.3   LASER MARKING MACHINES

Setup

Program and initialize	.3 hr
Preprogrammed	.1 hr

Operation elements in estimating minutes

1. Handling

Get and aside part

Part size	Toss aside	Stack aside
Very small	.027	.042
Small	.021	.039
Medium	.030	.045

Turn over part

Part size	Min
Very small	.009
Small	.012
Medium	.015

Place and position part into nest or against pins

Part size	Nest	2 Pins
Very small	.033	.045
Small	.030	.039
Medium	.036	.051

Reposition part	.01

2. Machine operation

Open and close door	.04
Start and stop	.02

3. Laser mark, min

Character height (in.)	No. of characters							
	1	2	3	4	5	6	7	8
$1/8$	.04	.08	.11	.15	.19	.23	.27	.30
$3/16$	.06	.11	.17	.22	.28	.34	.39	.45
$1/4$	.08	.15	.23	.30	.38	.45	.53	.60
$5/16$	.09	.19	.28	.38	.47	.56	.66	.75
$3/8$	.11	.23	.34	.45	.57	.68	.79	.90
$1/2$	.15	.30	.45	.60	.75	.90	1.05	1.20

Character height (in.)	No. of characters							
	9	10	12	14	17	20	25	Add'l
$1/8$	.34	.38	.46	.53	.65	.76	.95	.038
$3/16$	.50	.56	.67	.78	.95	1.12	1.40	.056
$1/4$	.68	.75	.90	1.05	1.28	1.50	1.88	.075
$5/16$	.85	.94	1.13	1.32	1.60	1.88	2.35	.094
$3/8$	1.02	1.13	1.36	1.58	1.92	2.26	2.83	.113
$1/2$	1.35	1.50	1.80	2.10	2.55	3.00	3.75	.150

5.1 Forging Machines

DESCRIPTION

These estimating data are intended for hammer- or drop-forging machines. Hammer forging consists of hammering heated metal between flat dies in a steam- or air-powered hammer. Drop forging differs from hammer forging in that closed-impression, rather than open-face, dies are used. The forging is produced by impact or pressure which compels hot and pliable metal to conform to the shape of the die cavity. Repeated blows on the metal gradually change the form, and the number of steps in the process varies according to the size and shape of the part, forging qualities of the metal, tolerances, machine, and crew size. For parts of large or complicated shapes, a preliminary shaping operation using more than one set of dies is possible.

Two principal types of drop-forging hammers are the steam or air hammer, and the gravity drop or board hammer. In the former, the ram, hammer, and upper die half are lifted by steam or air pressure and the force of the blow and the number of blows per min can be controlled by throttling the steam or air. Figure 5.1 is a 5000-lb. drop hammer. Now we consider the general class of forging machines and their estimating data.

ESTIMATING DATA DISCUSSION

Setup data are linked to machine rating and while the number of forges, die complexity, and mass are significant factors, these in turn are related to forge size. The setup times are independent of the crew size. For a total time, multiply setup by crew size.

There are three time drivers used for estimating the operational time or weight of the raw billet, diameter multiplied by billet length, and forge machine rating. Crew sizes vary with forge machine rating. For the 1500-, 3000-, 5000-, and 12,000-lb.

FIGURE 5.1 A 5000-lb drop hammer. (*Chambersburg Engineering Company*)

machine rating, typical crew sizes are 2, 3, and 4 men. A maximum crew is the hammerman, helper, furnace, and trim press operator. All elemental times are for the hammerman only, and for a total elemental time, the hammerman's time is multiplied by crew size since the hammerman is the controlling factor. Material forgeability is averaged in these data. Furthermore, the number of blows for rolling, fullering, blocking, etc., is not always accurately known, and these data are averaged, although rough and finishing forging is related to the number of blows.

In Element 1, the hammerman places the tongs on the billet, which has been placed on the die block by the furnace attendant. Also in Element 1, the hammerman places his tongs on the billet and positions the billet in either the roll and breakdown impression or in the forge impression. Billet weight is the initial weight including tong hold and extra stock for fullering.

In roll and breakdown, the entry variable is diameter by billet length. For instance, a 2-in. billet of 20-in. length would be entered as 40. The hammerman rolls and breaks down the billet to prepare the billet for the forge impression. The helper blows the scale from the dies and oils the dies. Element 3 has the hammerman position the billet in the bend impression, finish forge impression, or, on the flat part of the die and bend, straighten or flatten the billet. It may include placing the billet on the flat part of the die to pop scale.

In reposition billet, the hammerman removes the billet from one impression and positions the billet in another impression. A forge billet either follows a roll and breakdown or does not. In these elements, the hammerman forges the billet while the helper blows the scale from the die and oils the dies as necessary.

In the element "Move billet to trimmer, trim and cutoff flash," the hammerman moves the billet to the trimmer and positions the billet on the trimmer, while the operator trims the billet and cuts off the flash. After the billet has been trimmed and the flash removed, the hammerman slides the billet into the tote box while the helper walks to the furnace and places a cold bar in the furnace.

For example, in Element 7, the hammerman removes the billet from the die block and places the billet on the table while the operator returns to the hammer. A tong and hook are used by the hammerman helper and trim press operator to remove the billet from the die block using an overhead moveable hook and tongs. In Element 7, the hammerman picks up the tongs, either from the table or the pail of water near the table, and returns to the hammer.

The hammerman walks to the table and picks up previous billet and returns to the hammer. The operator forges a tong hold and places the billet on the table, and the operator returns to the hammer. In "change tongs," the hammerman holds the billet out and the helper picks up tongs, fastens tongs to extended end, and the operator removes the tongs he is holding and asides tongs, taking the tongs the helper is holding. Helper returns to blow and oil while the operator turns and places billet on die.

The restrike element requires the hammerman to pick up trimmed billet, place billet on die, and strike billet using ram. Operator moves billets to table.

In "trim and restrike," the hammerman takes the billet to the trimmer, trims, returns to the hammer, and restrikes billet, then places billet on table.

Section IV cost data for forging are for four machines or 1500-, 3000-, 5000-, and 12,000-lb. forges, and for crew sizes of 2, 3, and 4 respectively. If crews are other than these, ratios can be used to make adjustments. If two or more units are trimmed from each forging, the values are divided by the number in each forging. Entry values are weight and the product of $Dia \times L$ (diameter multiplied by length), both expressed in inches. The $Dia \times L$ measure is for the raw billet.

EXAMPLES

A. A connecting rod requires heavy stock on one end and lighter stock on the other. Singly, these require fullering and rolling while in multiple-die impression dies, grain flow permitting, these can be nested to eliminate blows. Consider a 1500-lb. forging machine making two pieces per platter and a gross weight of 1.42 lb per forging for all multiples. With two parts end to end, we estimate 2 blows for fullering, 2 blows for rollering, 5 blows for blocking, and 3 blows for finishing. The bar Dia and L is approximately 1-in. OD by 1.125-ft long for 3.6 lb. Estimate the unit time for a hammerman and helper.

Table	Description	Time
5.1-1	Tongs on billet and position	.08 min
5.1-2	Roll and breakdown, 1×1.125 ft = 12 ⅛ in.	.31
5.1-3	Reposition and pop scale	.06

148

Table	Description	Time
5.1-4	Reposition and rough forge	.21
5.1-4	Reposition, finish forge, 3 blows, $5 \times .12$	.60
5.1-5	Move billet to trimmer and trim, 2 times	.26
5.1-5	Operator returns to hammer from trimmer	.10
	Multiple estimate for hammerman	1.62 min
	Multiple estimate for hammerman and helper	3.24 min
	Unit estimate	1.62 min

B. A flange forging, C–1020 material, $1\frac{1}{2}$ in. round, cut $7\frac{9}{16}$ in. will give 4 cuts per bar. Nine hammer blows (3 in roller, 2 in blocker, 3 in the finisher, and 1 cutoff) is required to forge the part. This would result in 36 hammer blows per bar. A 3000-lb. forging press and a two-man crew is anticipated. Find the crew hr/100 units. This estimate will be calculated for 4 pc per bar.

Table	Description	Time
5.1-6	Operator picks up billet, forges tong hold	.28 min
5.1-1	Position billet, 4 lb	.08
5.1-2	Roll and breakdown, $Dia \times$ billet $L = 11.3$ in.	.25
5.1-4	Forge billet, $.39 \times 4$	1.56
5.1-6	Trim	.24
	Estimate for bar	2.41 min
	Unit estimate for hammerman	.60 min
	hr/100 for crew	8.03

C. A $6\frac{1}{2}$-in. OD bar, 11-in. long, AISI 8822 material, is used for a heavy-duty gear shaft. Two hubs are forged from the material, match tolerances are commercial, and a long run is planned, but quantities are within one die set life. Crew size for a 12,000-lb. rated forge machine is 4 operators. Find lot time for 375 units. Each bar weighs 103 lb.

Table	Description	Time
5.1-S	Setup	3.0 hr
5.1-7	Load billet with tong and hook	.18 min
5.1-7	Operator picks up tongs and returns to billet	.09
5.1-7	Forges tong hold	.74
5.1-2	Roll and breakdown, $Dia \times$ billet $L = 71.5$	.63
5.1-4	Forge billet, 2 hubs, 2×1.45	2.90
5.1-6	Operator places part in tote box and returns	.11
	Unit estimate for hammerman	4.65 min
	Crew estimate	18.60 min
	Lot estimate	128.25 hr

D. Re-estimate Example A above using Item 5.1 of Section IV. Use the 1500-lb. machine values.

Item	Description	Cost
5.1	Constant	$ 76.20
5.1	$Dia \times L = 12.125$	
5.1	12.125×2.00	24.25
	$/200 units	$100.45
	$/100 units	$ 50.29

E. Find the cost for 100 units for Example C above. Use the 12,000-lb. forge cost data in Item 5.1 of Section IV.

Item	Description	Cost
5.1	Constant	$150.00
5.1	Weight factor 1.02 × 103	105.06
5.1	$L \times Dia$ factor 3.05 × 6.5 × 11	218.08
	$/100 units	$473.14

TABLE 5.1   FORGING MACHINES

Setup

1500-lb hammer	1 hr
3000-lb hammer	1.5 hr
5000-lb hammer	2 hr
12,000-lb hammer	3 hr

Operation elements in estimating minutes

1. Handling and position

Tongs on billet .10

Tongs on billet and position 1500 lb, 3000 lb hammer .10

Billet weight	5000 lb 12,000 lb. hammer
4	.08
11	.10
22	.13
33	.16
39	.18

Position billet on die to make 2 parts, 3000 lb hammer .10

Helper moves billet to die block 1500-lb hammer .10

Position billet

Weight	Min
6	.08
31	.10
58	.13
97	.16

2. Roll and breakdown
   $Dia \times$ billet L

Hammer lb				
1500	3000*	5000	12,000	Min
1	1			.06
5	5	1		.13
11	8	8		.19
17	12	15	3	.25
21	14	23	18	.31
27	18	30	35	.38
37	25	46	71	.50
	33		98	.63
	39			.75
	46			.88

*2 impression die

3. Reposition

Reposition, bend, flatten, pop scale, or straighten 1500-lb hammer   .06
5000- and 12,000-lb hammer   .13

Reposition billet, 5000- and 12,000-lb hammer

Weight	Min
5	.06
35	.08
65	.10
95	.12
124	.14

3000-lb hammer
Reposition billet, flop billet 180° on die   .09
Pop scale or flatten billet   .09
Place billet on edge roll and draw as required   .15
Reposition and flatten billet or pop scale   .11

4. Reposition and forge

Reposition and rough forge (follows bend or flatten 1 blow) 1500-lb hammer

Dia × billet L	Min
4	.11
6	.14
9	.16
12	.19
15	.21

Reposition, finish forge, turn billet over, strike 1 blow, 1500-lb hammer   .12

Reposition and forge, follow roll and breakdown, 1500-lb hammer

Dia × billet L	Min
3	.13
5	.19
8	.28
10	.34

Rough forge, 3000-lb hammer

Dia × billet L	Min
3	.10
5	.15
7	.23
12	.34
17	.51
26	.75

Forge billet, follow roll and breakdown, 3000-lb hammer

Dia × billet L	Dia < 3	Dia ≥ 3
5	.15	.35
10	.31	.55
15	.46	.75
20	.64	.95
25	.80	1.20

Reposition and forge, no breakdown, 3000-lb hammer

Dia × billet L	Min
4	.45
10	.56
16	.70
23	.88

Reposition and finish forge

Dia × billet L	1500-lb hammer	3000-lb hammer
3	.11	.23
5	.16	.29
7	.20	.38
10	.26	.46
13		.60
17		.74
22		.91

Forge billet, 5000- and 12,000-lb hammer, no breakdown and 1 impression

Dia × L	2 ≤ Dia < 5	2 ≤ Dia < 5, L ≥ 10	5 ≤ Dia ≤ 6	6 < Dia ≤ 7
5	.49			
9	.54			
16	.60		.70	1.01
18	.63		.88	1.03
24	.69	.23	1.09	1.06
34		.29	1.44	1.14
44		.35	1.79	1.21
58		.44		1.33
76		.55		1.46
98		.69		1.63
126		.86		

Forge billet, follow roll and breakdown, 5000-lb hammer

Dia × billet L	Min
2	.25
7	.31
15	.39
24	.49
32	.61
46	.76

Forge billet, 12,000-lb hammer

Dia × billet L	1 impression after breakdown
6	.13
8	.16
11	.20
13	.25
16	.30
21	.39
26	.48
35	.60
44	.75
55	.93
66	1.16
84	1.45

5. Elements for 1500-lb hammer

Move billet to trimmer and cut off piece	.10
Move billet to trimmer and trim	.13
Move billet to trimmer, trim, and cut off flash	.18
Operator returns to hammer from trimmer	.10
Operator returns to hammer, holds tong and throws billet on floor, helper places cold bar in furnace	.13
Helper places billet in furnace	.11
Operator places billet in tote box and returns to hammer	.11
Helper strikes knockout pin	.09
Restrike	.13

6. Elements for 3000-lb hammer

Helper removes billet from die block, operator picks up tongs and returns to hammer	.08
Operator places billet on table, returns to hammer	.08
Operator returns to hammer and positions with tongs	.09
Operator and helper move billet to trimmer, trim and punch out center, and replace pin	.30
Operator turns billet 180°, takes billet to trimmer, positions, trims and cuts off flash	.21
Operator moves billet to trimmer, trims and returns to hammer, helper positions billet and straightens billet on second press, returns to hammer	.24
Operator picks up trimmed part, positions part in die, restrikes	.15
Operator takes billet to trimmer, trims and returns to hammer, places part in die, restrikes to reforge or straighten, removes part to box	.23
Operator places part in tote box and returns to hammer	.11
Operator picks up billet, forges tong hold, places billet on table, and returns to hammer	.28
Changes tongs and places tongs on billet	.11
Cool dies	.10
Helper strikes knockout pin	.13

7. Elements for 5000-lb and 12,000-lb hammer

Operator moves billet to table

Weight	9	29	39	70
Min	.08	.12	.13	.15

Operator moves billet to table and returns to hammer

Weight	10	30	60	88
Min	.10	.13	.16	.20

Helper and trim press operator remove billet from die block with tong and hook

Weight	10	56	120
Min	.11	.14	.18

Operator picks up billet, forges tong hold, places billet on table, and returns to hammer

Weight	9	28	47	67
Min	.38	.48	.59	.74

Operator returns to hammer from table	.09
Changes tongs and places tongs on billet	.13
Restrike	.26
Trim and restrike	.31

6.1 Engine Lathes

DESCRIPTION

The engine lathe is an all-purpose turning machine tool. It cuts cylindrical forms with a single-point cutter moving parallel to the axis of rotation of the work. These estimating data are principally for the manufacturing classification of engine lathes, where numerical control is not a primary feature. If tracer machines or numerical control are involved, we choose to interpret these machines as requiring special treatment, and other estimating data scattered throughout the turning section can be adopted. A typical medium-size engine lathe is shown in Figure 6.1. Now, consider estimating data for the general class of engine lathes produced by many manufacturers.

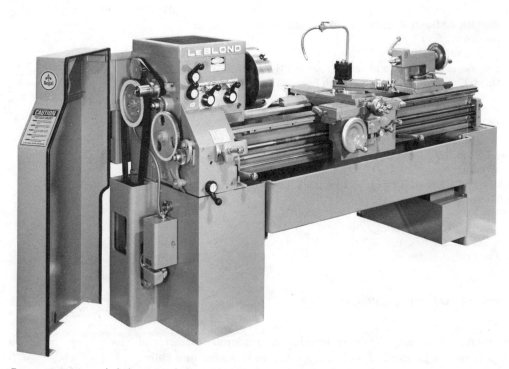

FIGURE 6.1 Manual shift engine lathe with 15½-in. swing over bed and carriage wings. (Le Blond)

ESTIMATING DATA DISCUSSION

Setup is composed of four elements. The basic time includes typical chores and has the entry variables of holding device and no. of tools. If a tool is to be used for multiple cuts of two or more dimensions, time is provided for additional dimensions. Make-piece can be included in setup, if that is company policy. Time for cut adjustment is provided for a critical tolerance.

The cycle time is arranged into five major groups. Element 1 deals with handling. This handling also includes disposal. If the part is heavy, large, or awkward, two hands may be required, which is covered by the term *large*. One-handed handling is either undesignated, or it is *small*. A variety of elements are described in Element 4; while the listing is extensive, the estimator may have to decompose the element into 2/3 and 1/3 ratios for elements that may not appear because of

the wide adaptability of engine lathes. The first part of the element is the two-thirds contribution of the time.

The time for turning and allied machining, turning tool replacement, and part inspection are found in other tables.

Section IV estimating, which deals with base cost per 100 units for the engine lathe, provides cost for setup, handling, and machine manipulation related to the number of separate cuts such as rough turn, finish turn, thread, break edges, and cut off. These are five cuts, and the factor is multiplied by 5. For turning, threading, boring, cut off, break edges, etc. and other chip-cost, see Item 11 in Section IV. Their explanation is given under elemental estimates. If rehandling, such as reverse piece, is required, a cost is provided. Setup depends upon the number of separate tools.

EXAMPLES

A. An irregular-shaped valve consisting of SAE 4130 steel casting has several machine elements. The part requires two hands for loading because of its irregularity. The schedule of the cuts is given by the description below. Find the unit estimate for the cycle.

	Description	Time
6.1-1	Load and unload in 4 jaw chuck	.30 min
6.1-4	Position cross-slide tool, set for depth advance tool to work, engage feed, .09 + .09	.18
11.1-2	Make face cut, 2.81-in. OD, 1.81-in. ID, length of cut = .5 in., rough pass with carbide, .12 × .5	.06
6.1-4	Retract and advance cross slide	.09
11.1-2	Finish cut, 2.81-in. OD, 1.81-in. ID, length of cut = .5 in., finish pass with carbide, .28 × .5	.14
6.1-4	Change tool, set for proper dimension	.40
6.1-4	Advance tool to work, engage feed, and retract, .09 + .03	.12
11.1-3	Trial cut, 1.570-in. ID, clean up surface by rough bore, use medium carbon steel, .52 × .25	.13
22.1	Mike dimension	.16
11.1-3	Finish bore 1.570-in. ID, use medium carbon steel, .72 × .25	.18
6.1-4	Retract tool for rough and finish and dial tool, .09 + .09 + .06	.24
6.1-4	Position to bore 1.81-in. ID	.16
6.1-4	Hand dial tool to mark	.06
11.3-3	Rough bore 1.81-in. OD, 1.65 in. long, HSS tool point, use medium carbon steel, .60 × 1.65	.99
4.3-3	Finish bore, .83 × 1.65	1.37
6.1-4	Retract tool for rough and finish boring, .09 + .09	.18
6.1-5	Turn coolant on and off, 6 times, 6 × .03	.18
6.1-4	Turn spindle on and off, 7 × .06	.42
6.1-5	Air-clean part	.10
11.1-7	Break edges	.16
11.4-1	Tool life, 3.07 min of mixed cutting materials	.07
	Unit estimate	5.69 min

B. A bell-body has an internal thread, 2.75-in. in length, and a nominal diameter of .875 in. The part which is brass can be handled with one hand, and is loaded in a collet. A lot has 65 units. Find the lot time.

	Description	Time
6.1-S	Collet, 2 tool	.46 hr
6.1-1	Load collet	.13 min
6.1-4	Start and stop spindle	.06
6.1-4	Advance tail stock, lock, unlock, return	.18
	Drill for hole to be threaded, 2.75 + .39 = 3.14 in. for lead and drill distances	
11.2-4	Use power drilling, brass, .75-in. ID, .10 × 3.14	.31
6.1-4	Advance and retract carriage	.11
11.1-5	Threading, 7 threads per in., .18 × 2.75	.50
6.1-4	Reposition tool, set depth, engage feed for 3 passes, .16 × 3	.48
6.1-4	Clear tool	.09
6.1-5	Blow threads clean	.05
11.1-7	Break 1 edge internal	.06
	Unit estimate	1.97 min
	Lot estimate	2.59 hr

C. Estimate the cost of a lot of 250 pc for Example A above. There are 6 cuts and 4 edges to break with a file. The part material is medium-carbon steel. Use Items 6.1, 11.1, 11.4, 22.1.

Item	Description	Cost
6.1	Setup constant	$ 5.09
6.1	Tool factor, 1.65 × 3	4.95
	Setup subtotal	$ 10.04
6.1	Cycle constant	$ 7.63
6.1	Six cuts, 6 × 4.83	28.98
11.1	Face cut, carbide, .5 × 1.74	.87
11.1	Face cut, finish, carbide, .5 × .749	.37
11.1	Rough bore, HSS, .25 × 1.57 × 5.91	2.32
11.1	Finish bore, HSS, .25 × 1.57 × 7.74	3.04
11.1	Rough bore, HSS, 1.65 × 1.81 × 5.91	17.65
11.1	Finish bore, HSS, 1.65 × 1.81 × 7.74	23.12
11.1	Break 4 edges, 4 × .737	2.95
11.4	Tool life for 3 min, 3 × .311	.93
22.1	Mike dimension, .005-in. tolerance	.62
	$/100 units subtotal	$ 88.48
	Cycle unit cost	$ .88
	Lot cost	$231.24
	Unit cost	$ .92

TABLE 6.1 ENGINE LATHES

Setup in estimating hours

1. Basic time

Holding device	No. of tools		
	1	2	3
Collet	.34	.46	.57
Chuck	.48	.57	.69
Fixture	.52	.63	.75

2. Multiple cuts, no. of cuts per tool
ONLY IF MORE THEN ONE   .06/occurrence

3. Make piece (optional): 2 × hr/unit

4. Adjust cut

Tolerance	Over .01	.0031 .010	.0011 .0030	.0001 .0010
hr	.03	.08	.12	.15

Operation elements in estimating minutes

✳ 1. Pick up part, move and place, pick up and lay aside
    Load and unload collet or air chuck,
        Small   .13
        Large   .20
    Load and unload T-wrench chuck,
        Small   .18
        Large   .30
    Load fixture, clamp and unclamp, unload,
        Small   .20
        Large   .40
    Load, unload arbor without arbor nut   .39
    Load, unload arbor with arbor nut   .60
    For each add'l pc on arbor add   .11
    Load and unload collet with tweezers   .20
    Load and unload collet with split bushings   .15
    Load and unload plate fixture   .51
    Load and unload expanding arbor   .10
    Place between and remove from centers,
        Small   .12
        Large   .68
    Center to work and lock tail stock   .08
    Jib load part
    Chuck jaws   5.30
    Fixture   4.29

✳ 2. Clamp and unclamp
    Put on and remove dog,
        Small   .12
        Large   .20
    Press pc on and off mandrel   .21
    Hammer pc to seat or loosen   .05

✳ 3. Part manipulation
    Unload, turn end for end, reload T-wrench chuck,
        Small   .20
        Large   .35
    Unload, turn end for end in collet,
        Small   .05
        Large   .10

✳ 4. Engine lathe machine operation
    Start and stop spindle   .06
    Reverse spindle   .04
    Raise and lower splash shield   .07
    Dial tool post to mark   .06
    Engage and disengage feed (cross-slide or carriage)   .03
    Change feed direction   .03
    Advance and retract cross-slide or tool   .09
    Advance and retract cross-slide to dial reading   .16
    Lock and unlock carriage   .07
    Advance and retract carriage   .11
    Advance carriage to dial indicator, lock, unlock, retract carriage   .10
    Advance and retract tailstock   .15
    Advance tailstock, lock, unlock, and return tailstock   .18
    Dwell   .05
    Advance and retract compound   .13
    Advance compound to dial reading and return   .17
    Cut in or out half nut lever   .04
    Change tool in tool post, set for proper position   .40

✳ 5. Machining
    Turn, bore, form, cutoff, thread, start drill   See Table 11.1
    Drill, ream, counterbore   See Table 11.2

✳ 6. Part inspection   See Table 22.21

6.2 Turret Lathes

DESCRIPTION

A principal characteristic of turret lathes is the consecutive arrangement of tools. With a hexagon or octagon turret and a cross-slide turret, many possibilities exist for prearranging the selection of tools. Controls for these machines are restricted to manual or electric, and numerical control turret lathe machines are found elsewhere. Two figures are shown which illustrate a ram and saddle type machine. In Figure 6.2A, a 4½-in. capacity ram type is shown. Usually, ram-type turret lathes are faster than saddle types. Figure 6.2B shows a saddle type which has the advantage of heavier cuts. Power rapid traverse is available for hex and square turrets. Preselection of speeds and feeds are options provided by various manufacturers. Now, we consider the estimating for the general class of turret lathe machines.

ESTIMATING DATA DISCUSSION

In determining the setup value, the basic time given by Element 1 has the no. of tools as the entry variable. A duplex tool using one turret, or a combination-turning box tool would count as two tools. Setup Element 2 accounts for different types of holding equipment, or special machine-mounted tools, or gages have times selected from Element 3. Should there be critical tolerances, Element 5 is applied.

The three types of turret lathes are identified as small, medium, and large. Even though the variety that really exists exceeds this classification, we have limited the variations. The machine distinctions are refined with elements suitable for a particular machine tool. The types are classified with respect to maximum collet diameter as small (1 in. or less), medium (more than 1 in. to 3 in.), and large (more than 3 in. to 6 in.). Turret lathes come in many sizes from 1/2-in. to 10-in. diameters. Nor do we categorize between ram or saddle machines, but some elements deal with these distinctions. Because of the varied machining operations performed on the turret lathe, tables can also serve for identical operations performed on other and more specialized machines.

Turret lathes will permit the functioning of several tools simultaneously. It is possible to have a hexagonal-turret tool perform a drilling element at the same time a cross-slide tool turns or faces. The longer of these simultaneous operations is selected. It may be possible to gage or break edges during machine cuts.

Element 1 deals with many variations of handling. Principally, the holder may be a collet, chuck, or fixture. Various opportunities for clamping are suggested.

Element 3 deals with machine operations. Major distinctions are made for the turret, cross-slide, and carriage. Element 4 is a consolidation of the various

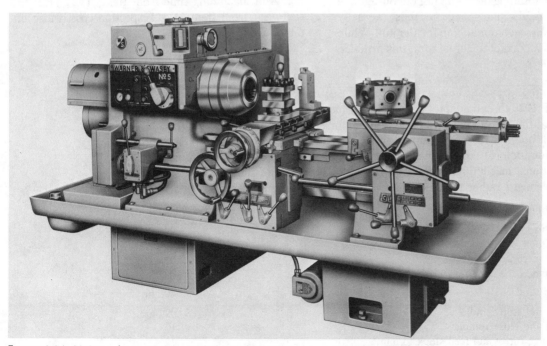

FIGURE 6.2A Universal ram-type turret lathe with a 4½-in. capacity. *(Warner and Swasey)*

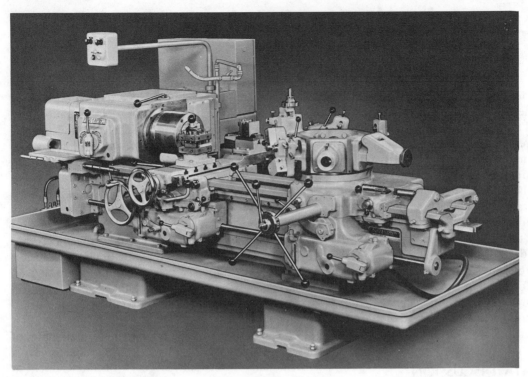

FIGURE 6.2B Saddle type universal turret lathes. (*Jones & Lamson*)

elements and can simplify element selection. This element is for routine parts. The consolidated sets usually include start and stop, advance turret and feed stock, retract, index, advance, and engage feed. Additional position oil line and splash guards are included. If elements other than these are anticipated, they may be added; conversely, elements can be deducted to facilitate ease of usage.

Elements 5, 6, and 7 are found using other tables. These machining tables do not encourage the adjustment of feeds and speeds to those actually available on the selected machine for the job. While the estimator can correct to actual rpm, this practice is time consuming and may not improve accuracy. See the discussion on this technique given by the machining tables.

While Table 6.2 deals with hours for setup and minutes for cycle time, another approach is possible. Item 6.2 of Section IV provides current base-cost for turret lathe operations. Item 6.2 is simpler, as assumptions have been made to facilitate ease. Data in Item 6.2 provide only machine manipulation and loading. Add machining time from Items 11.1, 11.2, and tool wear from Item 11.4. Inspection cost is also obtained from Item 22.1.

EXAMPLES

A. An SAE 1020 thread adapter is completely machined on a large-size turret lathe. The schedule of the turrets is as follows: (1) combination stock stop and start drill, (2) drill, (3) boring bar, (4) reamer mounted in floating holder, (5) recessing tool using a quick-acting slide tool, (6) tap mounted in square turret position 1. The stock diameter is 3 in., and additional machining data are stated below. Find the lot time for a quantity of 315. Develop elements rather than use the consolidated handling elements.

Table	Description	Time	
6.2-S	Seven tools for setup	3.0	hr
6.2-S	Bar stock	.2	
6.2-S	Make piece 2 $\times$ .11	.22	
6.2-S	Tolerance checking for .001 in. tolerance	.08	
	Setup total	3.40	hr
6.2-3	Start and stop spindle	.09	min
6.2-1	Open and close spindle	.10	
6.2-3	Advance turret and feed stock to 6 in.	.29	
6.2-3	Index duplex holder for start drill	.07	

Table	Description	Time
6.2-3	Advance turret and engage feed	.05
11.1-6	Start drill for $1\frac{1}{4}$-in. tap drill dia	.85
6.2-3	Return turret, index, advance, and engage feed, for 5 turrets, $5 \times .16$	.80
11.2-4	Drill $1\frac{7}{64}$-in. hole, 4 in. long, $.23 \times 4.25$	.98
11.1-3	Bore 2.5-in. long × 1.65-in. OD, HSS, rough, $.31 \times 2.5$	.78
11.2-5	Ream 1.65-in. OD, $.27 \times 2.5$	.68
11.1-3	Machine recess $1\frac{3}{4}$-in. ID, $\frac{1}{4}$-in. long, use finish bore time, $.43 \times .25$	.11
6.2-3	Quick-acting tool holder up and down	.03
11.2-3	Tap $1\frac{1}{4}$–7 NC, 1.25 in. long, 32×1.25	.40
6.2-3	Reverse spindle	.15
11.1-7	Break edges	.08
11.1-4	Cut off 3-in. OD, length of cut = .68 in. and $.26 \times .68$ using carbide	.18
	Unit estimate	5.91 min
	hr/unit	.098
	Lot time	34.5 hr

B. A cast iron air-starting cam is partially machined on the turret lathe. Drilling, facing, and boring are the machining elements. The part weighs 3 lb and is irregular. Holding is by chuck. Turret positions are (1) center drill, (2) drill, (4) boring, and square turret position (1) faces. Use an elemental approach to find unit and setup time. A medium-size turret lathe will be used with a two-jaw chuck.

Table	Description	Time
6.2-S	3 hex and 1 square turret tools	2.0 hr
6.2-S	Chuck	.1
6.2-S	Make-piece, (not allowed)	
6.2-S	Tolerances, .001	.08
		2.18 hr
6.2-1	Get, load in chuck with T-wrench	.37 min
6.2-3	Start and stop	.09
6.2-3	Advance turret, engage feed	.05
11.1-6	Center drill for $1\frac{13}{32}$-in. hole	.25
6.2-3	Return, index and advance	.07
11.2-3	Drill $1\frac{13}{32}$-in. hole, $2\frac{3}{8}$-in. long, $.33 \times 2.37$	.78
6.2-3	Return and skip index for turret	.07
6.2-3	Change speed	.04
6.2-3	Face end using square turret, advance and engage, carbide tool	.07
11.2-2	Face end $2\frac{1}{4}$-in. length of cut, $2\frac{3}{4}$-in. OD, $.07 \times 2.25$	.16
6.2-3	Advance turret, engage feed, hex no. 4	.05
6.2-3	Bore 1.501-in. hole, $2\frac{1}{4}$-in. long, carbide tooling, $.06 \times 2.25$	.14
6.2-3	Return turret to hex position 1, estimate	.05
11.2	File burrs during boring	0
22.1	Gage part during drill hole time	0
	Unit estimate	2.19 min

C. Re-estimate Example A above using a base-cost method. Part material is low-carbon steel. The machine is a large turret lathe. Find first the unit cycle cost because of addition of "make-piece" time to setup. Use Items 6.2, 11.1, and 11.2.

Item	Description	Cost
6.2	Setup constant	$14.48
6.2	Tool factor, 7×2.66	18.62
6.2	Make-piece, 2 × unit estimate, 2×1.82	3.64
	Setup subtotal	$36.74
6.2	Constant for large turret lathe	$12.10
6.2	Six turret tools, 6×3.38	20.28
6.2	One cross-slide tool, 1×3.60	3.60

Item	Description	Cost
11.1	Start drill	$ 19.20
11.2	Drill $1\frac{7}{16}$-in., 4 in. deep, $1\frac{7}{16} \times 4 \times 4.13$	23.75
11.1	Bore, HSS tool, $2.5 \times 1.65 \times 4.40$	18.15
11.2	Ream 1.65 in., 2.5×4.55	11.38
11.1	Finish bore recess, $2.5 \times 1.65 \times 4.40$	18.15
11.2	Tap $1\frac{1}{4}$-in.–7 NC, $1.25 \times 7 \times 5.69$	49.79
11.1	Break edges, $2 \times .737$	1.47
11.1	Cut off 3-in. OD, carbide, $3 \times 1.5 \times 1.10$	4.55
	Cycle $/100 subtotal	$182.42
	Unit cost for setup	$ 1.82
	Lot cost for 315 units	$611.36
	Unit cost with setup prorated	$ 1.94

TABLE 6.2 TURRET LATHES

Setup in estimating hours

1. *No. of tools*	1	2	3	4	5	6	7	8	Add'l
Hr	1.09	1.27	1.45	1.63	1.82	2.00	2.17	2.35	.15

2. Holding tool
Collet	.2
Chuck	.1
Bar stock	.2
Face plate, fixture	.4

3. Miscellaneous
Dial indicator	.2
Cross-slide indicator stop	.2
Install carriage bed stop	.2
Large manual chuck	.4
Bore soft jaws	.3
Tap chasers	.3
Box tool rollers	.1

4. Make-piece (optional): $2 \times$ hr/1 unit

5. Adjust cut:

Tolerance	Over .01	.0031 .010	.0011 .0030
Hr	.03	.08	.12

Operation elements in estimating minutes

1. Handling

	Small	Medium	Large
		Type of turret lathe	
Get, load, close collet, open collet, and unload part	.13	.19	.25
Get, load in air chuck, clamp, unclamp, and unload		.21	.36
Get, load in chuck with T-wrench, clamp, unclamp, and unload		.37	.50
Get, load in fixture, clamp, unclamp, and unload		.99	1.15
Catch cutoff part and unload	.03	.03	
Open and close collet, feed stock by hand	.12	.14	
Unclamp, unload, turn end-for-end, load, and clamp in collet	.07	.12	.21
Unclamp, unload, turn end-for-end, load, and clamp in chuck		.12	.25
Unclamp, unload, turn end-for-end, load, and clamp in with T-wrench in chuck		.75	.85
Open and close collet			.10
Relieve stress (before a finish bore, etc.)			1.00
Jib load in chuck, unload, 0–24 in.			2.15
Jib load in chuck or fixture, 24+ in.			3.15

2. Cleaning and lubricating

	Type of turret lathe		
	Small	Medium	Large
Position and clear coolant line	.04	.04	.04
Air-clean collet	.05	.05	.16
Air-clean part	.06	.06	.13
Air-clean fixture or chuck		.07	.18
Place and remove oil guard		.08	.10

3. Turret lathe machine operation

	Type of turret lathe		
	Small	Medium	Large
Start and stop spindle	.05	.05	.09
Speed, change range or high–low	.02	.04	.05
Reverse spindle and change back	.03		.15
Shift gears			.20
Advance turret and feed stock			
to 3 in.	.03	.11	
to 6 in.	.04	.15	
to 9 in.	.04	.18	
by hand		.12	
Turret. Advance and return	.03	.04	
Advance turret and engage feed	.05	.05	.05
Engage and disengage feed	.03		.08
Return	.07		
Return, index, and advance	.03	.07	.15
Return, index, advance, and engage feed	.06	.08	.16
Return and skip index	.04	.07	.07
Index, stop roll	.02		
Lock and unlock carriage or cross-slide	.07		.09
Return and index		.04	
Engage feed		.02	.03
Disengage feed		.01	
Index and back index			.07
Unlock and advance			.08
Unlock saddle, retract, index, advance, engage feed			.22
Advance and lock			.10
Change feed			.03
Cross-slide. Advance			.09
Advance and engage feed		.07	.10
Advance to dial stop and lock			.20
Lock and unlock		.05	.06
Return			.07
Unlock and return			.10
Disengage feed and return			.08
Index square turret, 1 station		.04	.07
Advance and return	.03	.13	
Index cross-roll stop			.04
Advance, engage feed, and return		.14	.17
Advance cross-slide to stop, lock, unlock, and return		.26	
Change feed direction, engage		.05	
Carriage. Engage feed			.03
Lock and unlock			.07
Advance			.04
Advance and engage feed		.11	.11
Advance to dial indicator and lock			.11
Return			.04
Unlock and return		.06	.07
Return, index stop roll			.10

	Type of turret lathe		
	Small	Medium	Large
Return, index stop roll, and advance		.14	.16
Return, index, advance to indicator stop, and lock			.20
Reset self-opening die or tap	.03	.04	.04
Index duplex holder		.07	.07
Move slide holder up and down		.08	.13
Move quick-acting holder up and down		.05	.08
Engage lead screw	.06		
Dwell	.03	.03	.03

4. Consolidated handling elements

Bar stock elements, small and medium turret lathes, min

No. turrets	1	2	3	4	5	6	1	2	3	4	5	6
No. cross-slides	1	1	1	1	1	1	2	2	2	2	2	2
Small	.27	.33	.39	.45	.51	.57	.30	.36	.42	.48	.54	.60
Medium	.41	.49	.57	.65	.73	.81	.54	.62	.70	.78	.86	.94

Collet elements, small and medium turret lathes, min

No. turrets	1	2	3	4	5	6	1	2	3	4	5	6
No. cross-slides	0	0	0	0	0	0	1	1	1	1	1	1
Small	.28	.34	.40	.46	.52	.58	.31	.37	.43	.49	.55	.61
Medium	.44	.52	.60	.68	.76	.84	.58	.72	.86	1.00	1.14	1.28

No. turrets	1	2	3	4	5	6
No. cross-slides	2	2	2	2	2	2
Small	.34	.40	.46	.52	.58	.64
Medium	.72	.86	1.00	1.14	1.28	1.42

Chuck elements, medium turret lathes, min

No. turrets	1	2	3	4	5	6	1	2	3	4	5	6
No. cross-slides	0	0	0	0	0	0	1	1	1	1	1	1
Medium	.46	.54	.62	.70	.78	.86	.60	.74	.88	1.02	1.16	1.30

No. turrets	1	2	3	4	5	6
No. cross-slides	2	2	2	2	2	2
Medium	.74	.88	1.02	1.16	1.30	1.44

Bar stock elements, large turret lathes, min

	No. turrets					
Cross-slides	1	2	3	4	5	6
1	.55	.71	.87	1.03	1.19	1.35
2	.72	.88	1.04	1.20	1.36	1.52
3	.89	1.05	1.21	1.37	1.53	1.69
4	1.06	1.22	1.38	1.54	1.70	1.86
5	1.23	1.39	1.55	1.71	1.87	2.03

Collet elements, large turret lathes, min

	No. turrets					
Cross-slides	1	2	3	4	5	6
1	.81	.97	1.13	1.29	1.45	1.61
2	.98	1.14	1.30	1.46	1.62	1.78
3	1.15	1.31	1.47	1.63	1.79	1.95
4	1.32	1.48	1.64	1.80	1.96	2.12
5	1.49	1.65	1.81	1.97	2.13	2.29

Chuck castings, large turret lathes, min

| Cross-slides | No. turrets | | | | | |
	1	2	3	4	5	6
1	1.06	1.22	1.38	1.54	1.70	1.86
2	1.23	1.39	1.55	1.71	1.87	2.03
3	1.40	1.56	1.72	1.88	2.04	2.20
4	1.57	1.73	1.89	2.05	2.21	2.37
5	1.74	1.90	2.06	2.22	2.38	2.54

5. Machining

    Turn, bore, form, cut off, thread, start drill, and break edges   See Table 11.1

    Drill, counter bore, ream, counter sink, or tap   See Table 11.2

6. Turning tool replacement   See Table 11.4

7. Part inspection   See Table 22.1

6.3 Vertical Turret Lathes

DESCRIPTION

A vertical turret lathe resembles a vertical boring mill, but has the additional characteristics of a turret for tool mounting. The VTL includes a rotating horizontal table with the turret mounted to ram on the cross-rail. There may be side heads provided with square turrets. This machine facilitates the mounting, holding, and the machining of large-diameter heavy parts. Only chucking or fixture work is done on a VTL. The main and auxiliary turrets function in the same manner as the hexagon and square turrets on a horizontal lathe. The side head has a rapid traverse and feed independent of the turret, which provides for simultaneous machining adjacent to elements performed by the turret. The machine can be provided with numerical control, manual or automatic operation. Control permits automatic operation of each head, including rate and direction of feed, change in spindle feed, indexing of turret, starting, and stopping. Simultaneous cutting by the overhead turret or the side head is possible. Tool changer with ram is another option. Figure 6.3 is a 36 in. VTL configured with a five-station turret.

ESTIMATING DATA DISCUSSION

The setup basic time is a required constant. It includes punch in/out, instructions and study, install and remove tape, clean chips, adjust rail height, assemble dial indicator for indicating fixture, and reverse.

In Element 2, various holding devices are considered. A jib and sling hoist to an eyebolt on the 3-jaw chuck or fixture, position on machine table, indicator (fixture only), secure to table, clean, and reverse work elements. Round and standard jaws are secured by positioning T-nuts in the slot of the machine table, positioned, secured, and removed. Standard jaws require two cap screws. Locator pins have the T-nut positioned in a machine table slot, secured, turned selected height pin into locator pin base, and reverse. Spring loaded jacks have T-nut positioned in machine table slot, position, secure with one cap screw, and adjust jack to piece, and reverse. The work is similar for an adjustable jack.

Element 3 deals with tool installation. Tool installation involves cleaning turret face, securing tool block or bar to machine turret, positioning tool holder in tool block or bar, and reverse.

Should the manuscript instructions require inspection, work involves obtaining mike or other gage, checking piece, and aside to storage.

Consider the description of several cycle-time elements. Handling includes these general items of work: remove chips from fixture using air hose, brush, or rag; get sling(s), eyebolts, attach, position, and aside hoist; place chip guards in position on machine; and reverse. Clamping, Element 2, involves turning and positioning of clamp, obtaining wrench and tightening and reverse.

In Element 3, the program stop involves removing chips, obtaining tools, and inspection.

FIGURE 6.3 Vertical turret lathe with side turret and NC control. *(Bullard)*

If the part has received heavy cutting, and is unable to be moved or inspected, the cooling involves flooding by coolant, and approximations are provided in Element 3.

Operational costs for the VTL may also be estimated using Item 6.3 of Section IV. These data are for dollars setup per occurrence and dollars per 100 units. The variable for setup is the no. of tools. Entry variables for run time are tool stations, indicate a dimension and adjust tooling to match dial indicator or other information, and additional time for jib handling or a turnover. Machining costs are derived from Section IV, Item 11.

EXAMPLES

A. A heavy high-temperature alloy part is to be turned on the vertical turret lathe. One main bore, one step bore, two faces, and outside turning are performed on the forging. An NC vertical turret lathe is planned. Find the lot time for 74 parts. The machining schedule is given by the list of elements. Cutting velocity from Table 11.1 is 40 fpm. Use cutting approach with formulas rather than tables.

Table	Description	Time
6.3-S1	Basic time	.35 hr
6.3-S2	Round jaws	.14
6.3-S3	Six tools, 6 × .12	.72
		1.21 hr
6.3-1	Jib load to chuck and unload	7.18 min
6.3-2	Clamp	1.38
6.3-3	Start program and back two turrets	.38
11.1-2	Face 26.5-in. OD rough with carbide	

$$\text{min/in.} = \frac{26.5\,\pi}{12 \times .021 \times 40} = 8.26 \text{ and}$$

length of cut = 2.1 in.   17.35

166

11.1-3	Bore step 18.1-in. ID rough with carbide	
	$\text{min/in.} = \dfrac{18.1\,\pi}{12 \times .021 \times 40} = 5.64$ and	
	length of cut = 1.3 in.	7.33
11.1-2	Finish face 26.5-in. OD with carbide	
	$\text{min/in.} = \dfrac{26.5\,\pi}{12 \times .015 \times 60} = 7.71$ and	
	length of cut = 2.1 in.	16.19
6.3-1	Jib turnover and clamp, 5.28 + 1.38	6.66
11.1-2	Face 26.5-in. OD at 8.26 min/in. for length = 4.1, while simultaneous turning 26.5-in. OD for length of 7.1 in. using side tool. Accept longer time of two cuts or 4.1 × 8.26	33.87
11.1-3	Counter bore 17.3-in. hole rough with carbide for a length of 1.2 in.	
	$\text{min/in.} = \dfrac{17.3\,\pi}{12 \times .021 \times 40} = 5.39$	6.47
11.1-3	Finish counterbore, carbide for 1.2 in.	
	$\text{min/in.} = \dfrac{17.3\,\pi}{12 \times .015 \times 60} = 5.03$	6.04
6.3-3	Cool off piece	3.00
6.3-3	Turret manipulation to return during cooling	.00
22.1-3	Inspection for 6 dimensions, 6 × .16	.96
11.4-1	Tool life and replacement for 87 min, 87/40 × 36	.79
	Unit estimate	107.60 min
	Lot hr	133.92

B. Estimate the setup, cycle, and lot cost for Example A above using Items 6.3, 11.1, and 11.4 of Section IV. The lot quantity is 74 units. Use cost values rather than a specific sfm of 40. Material is closest to a steel casting.

Item	Description	Cost
6.3	Setup constant	$ 9.05
6.3	Six tools, 6 × 3.02	18.12
	Setup subtotal	$ 27.17
6.3	VTL cycle constant	$175.00
6.3	Jib load	88.00
6.3	Six stations, 6 × 10.1	60.60
11.1	Face 26.5-in. OD rough with carbide, 2.1 × 26.5 × .681	37.90
11.1	Bore 18.1-in. ID rough with carbide, 1.3 × 18.1 × 1.35	31.77
11.1	Finish face 26.5-in. OD, 2.1 × 26.5 × 1.46	81.25
11.1	Bore 17.3-in. hole, 1.2 × 17.3 × 1.35	28.03
11.1	Finish counterbore, 1.2 × 17.3 × 2.93	60.83
	Cool piece, 3 min, 3/60 × 12.07 (12.07 = PHC) × 100	60.35
11.4	Tool life, 80 min × .122	9.76
	$/100 units subtotal	$633.49
	Cycle cost	$ 6.33
	Unit cost with a share of setup cost	$ 8.93
	Lot cost	$660.66

TABLE 6.3   VERTICAL TURRET LATHES

Setup elements in estimating hours

1. Basic time	.35
2. Install and take down Fixture	.48

Chuck	.32
Invert jaws (chuck only)	.07
Round jaws	
2 jaws	.07
4 jaws	.14
Standard jaws	
2 jaws	.23
4 jaws	.46
Locator pins (3)	.25
Spring loaded jacks (4)	.34
Adjustable jack, ea	.07
Piece clamp, ea	.07

3. Tool

Tool block or flanged bar, ea	.12
Bar holder, ea	.14

4. Inspection, per requirement | .02 |

Operation elements in estimating minutes

1. Handling

Manual load and unload

Weight	25	50
To table clamps	3.93	6.28
To fixture	1.55	2.21
To chuck	1.95	2.60

Jib load, unload

To fixture	6.03
To chuck	7.18

Overhead crane load and unload

To fixture	10.77
To chuck	11.43

Turnover

Jib or chuck or fixture	5.28
Overhead crane or chuck or fixture	9.44

2. Clamp, unclamp

Fixture, per clamp	.65
Chuck or standard jaws	1.38

3. Machine operation

Start, stop	.15
Engage feed	.16
Align piece per program instructions	
Adjustable jacks with surface gage	3.23
Indicate chuck, fixture, and time with rough surface	6.82
Indicate chuck, fixture, and true with finish surface	12.30
Program stop for inspection dimension per tool	1.03
Turret advance, retract, index, or clear	

No.	1	2	3	4	5
Time	.19	.38	.57	.76	.95

Ram or side slide, advance, retract, index, ea	.30
Flood piece for cooling	
Light	1.00
Massive	3.00

4. Machining

Turn, bore, form, thread, start drill, and break edges	See Table 11.1
Drill, counterbore, ream, or tap	See Table 11.2

5. Tool wear and replacement | See Table 11.4 |

6. Inspection | See Table 22.1 |

168

6.4 Numerically Controlled Turning Lathes

DESCRIPTION

The machines described in this section are turning lathes with numerical control (NC). They are designed for heavy-duty production. Slant and horizontal bed type are varieties within this description. Vertical turret lathes and chucking type horizontal machines are considered elsewhere. There is a variety of configurations for the multiple-slide turrets or tool changer as arranged in various positions on the machine. These turrets are able to hold a total of four to twelve or more tools.

NC lathes, in general, have advantages over automatic turret lathes in that starting, stopping, feeds, speeds, tool indexing or changing, and the tool path are controlled automatically by tape.

Figure 6.4A is a machine that behaves as a turning model if it is supplied with a tailstock. With an 18-in. swing over the bed, and a 3-in-hole through spindle, the number of ID/OD tools depends upon the needs. In this model, tools can be arranged in various ID/OD combinations. Figure 6.4B is a combination lathe and has a versatility for turning and chucking.

ESTIMATING DATA DISCUSSION

The basic setup time is always provided. It includes general machine cleanup, sweep chips, position chip guard, and operator self-cleaning. It also includes remove tape from reader, wind up on two spools, and return to tape container. General cleanup, manuscript caring, and job instructions also are provided for. The NC manuscript or process sheet is verified for the tools, and the first tool is gathered along with the first mike, dogs, and other general or special purpose tooling. The foregoing is included in the basic time. The basic time covers only the first tool. Another element considers any additional tools or mike.

The setup element for adjust tool offset is initiated after the cycle is started, and a trial of approximately 1/4 in., mike diameter, and adjust offset are included. At the completion of the job, the operator returns all offsets to zero for the finishing tool.

A time consideration is provided to mike each decimal tolerance which is used once per each decimal tolerance on the shaft. Placing and removing a steady rest with a jib and sling is provided. On some models,

FIGURE 6.4A A numerically controlled turning lathe. (*Waterbury Farrel, Division of Textron, Inc.*)

FIGURE 6.4B A numerically controlled combination lathe. (*Waterbury Farrel, Division of Textron, Inc.*)

the steady rest is on a swing mechanism, and the time to set up the steady rest is the same. The opportunity to load and unload a tailstock depends upon the specific machine. On some machines the tailstock is hinged and may swing down.

Place and remove part includes obtain jib and sling, sling part, hook up, and move to lathe. It also includes wipe centers on both part and lathe, position between centers, advance and lock tailstock, unhook and remove sling, aside jib and sling. Obtain jib and sling, sling part, hook up, unlock and clear tail, move to box or pallet, remove, and aside sling and jib also are included.

The place and remove part with jib element includes obtain jib and sling, sling part, hook up, and move to lathe. Wipe centers on both part and lathe, position between centers, advance and lock tailstock, unhook and remove sling, aside jib, and sling also are included, as are obtain jib and sling, sling part, hookup, unlock and clear tail, move to box or pallet, and remove and aside sling and jib.

Place and remove part with the overhead crane includes notify hooker for first part only, wipe centers on both part and lathe, position between centers, advance and lock tail, remove, and aside sling. After the machining is concluded, it includes notify hooker, obtain steel tape and chalk, locate and mark balance line, aside tape and chalk, sling part while crane is in transit, unlock and clear tail, and guide from between centers.

The element turn part 180° with jib includes obtain jib and sling, sling part, hook up, unlock and clear tail, turn part 180°, wipe centers on both part and lathe, position between centers, advance and lock tail, unhook, remove sling, and aside sling and jib.

The turn part 180° with overhead crane includes notify hooker, obtain steel tape and chalk, locate and mark balance line, aside tape and chalk, obtain sling, sling part while crane is in transit, turn part 180°, wipe centers of both part and lathe, position between centers, advance and lock tail, unhook, and remove and aside sling and jib.

The elements secure and release and dog with one bolt include obtain dog from spindle center and position on part, secure by hand, obtain wrench from tool tray on top of headstock and secure tight, aside wrench, obtain wrench from tool tray and loosen bolt, wrench and hand, aside wrench, remove, and aside dog to spindle center.

If the surface is to be protected, the element guard when dogged on finished surface involves obtain guard from tool tray on top of lathe and place under bolt, and remove and aside guard to tool tray.

Position, open, close, and adjust steady rest includes position to turned spot, slide on machine ways, obtain box wrench from tool tray and secure steady rest to ways with one bolt, close steady rest and secure with wrench, position two bottom rollers to part and secure with wrench, and loosen clamping bolt on side.

Position top roller to part and secure with wrench, secure clamping bolt, aside wrench to tool tray and obtain chip shield and place also are included. Also included are: remove chip shield and aside to chip pan, obtain wrench from tool tray, unclamp and retract rollers, release nut and reposition bolt, open steady rest, release rest from ways and slide toward headstock, and aside wrench to tool tray.

This cycle start time allows for a total stop when programmed or necessary.

The stop and start spindle and start feed element accommodates programmed or planned feed stops.

A set speed manually will cover walk to control panel, turn tape control knob and turn toggle to desired position, push start button to return to normal operation, and turn tape control knob to auto.

Set tool from shaft end with length gage, shaft not faced, means that the direct-labor operator will obtain gage from bench and place on turret for a controlled length. This distance is from the tool to the end of the shaft. Turn the incremental adjustment knob. If length of shafts are not consistent, set the length each time shaft is turned or placed in the machine.

Set tool from shaft end with length gage (shaft faced) considers obtain gage from bench and place on turret for measurement of decimal length. This is the distance from the tool to the end of the shaft.

Incremental adjustment follows. Set length each time shaft is turned or placed in machine, as length of shafts is not consistent.

Set tool with gage block from finished shoulder implies that the operator obtain gage from bench, position to shaft, position tool to gauge by turning the incremental adjustment knob, and pushing the left or right job button. Aside gage to bench eventually.

Adjust tool, incremental, includes a trial cut and the tool is adjusted for the rough and finish cuts first end, finish cut second end. Afterwards, mike an adjustment may have to be made.

Operation base costs may be estimated using the information from Item 6.4 of Section IV. Setup costs depend on the number of tools that are likely to be changed for this job. Some tools are considered a part of the routine configuration. Entry variables for the cost per 100 units are the number of restarts, tools, and whether or not a part reposition or job is required. A restart includes cycle start and stop, gage dimension, and adjust tool if necessary. Tools mean the number of tools required for the job. If a reposition or jig handling is required, cost for that work can be added. Item 6.4 does not include machining cost (see Item 11), rapid traverse (see Item 8.2), operator inspection (see Item 22), or tool wear (see Item 11.4).

EXAMPLES

A. An 8-in. SAE 4140 shaft is turned for several diameters and lengths. The schedule of *Dia* and *L* is listed below. An NC heavy-turning lathe is used. Determine setup, unit time, and lot time for 10 units. An NC tape is unavailable at the time of the estimate.

Table	Description	Time
6.4-S1	Basic time	.39 hr
6.4-S2	Check tool magazine for 4 tools	.08
6.4-S4	Check 4 dimensions	.08
		.55 hr
6.4-1	Place and remove part with crane between centers	4.39 min
6.4-1	Dog, 1 bolt	.63
6.4-2	Set tool with gage	.57
6.4-2	Cycle start	.08
11.1-2	Rough machine, 7.85-in. OD × 69.60-in. long, carbide, 1 pass, .32 × 69.60	22.27
6.4-2	Stop and start spindle, start feed	.11
6.4-2	Mike and adjust tool	.57
11.1-2	Turn rough 7.25-in. OD × 54.15-in. long, carbide, .32 × 54.15	17.33
6.4-1	Turn part with crane	2.54
6.4-1	Dog, 1 bolt	.63
6.4-2	Set tool with gage	.57
6.4-1	Cycle start	.08
11.1-2	Rough machine 6.95-in. OD × 39.90-in. long, carbide, .28 × 39.90	11.17
11.1-2	Rough machine 6.45-in. OD × 18.25-in. long, .28 × 18.25	5.11
6.4-2	Start and stop spindle, start feed	.11
6.4-2	Mike and adjust tool	.57
11.1-2	Finish machine, .65 × 18.25	11.86
6.4-1	Turn part 180°, overhead crane	2.54

6.4-1	Dog, 1 bolt	.63
6.4-2	Set tool with gage	.57
6.4-2	Cycle start	.08
11.1-2	Finish cut 7.85-in. OD $\times$ 15.45-in. long, .75 $\times$ 15.45	11.59
6.4-2	Start and stop spindle, start feed	.11
6.4-2	Mike and adjust tool	.57
11.1-2	Finish machine 6.95-in. OD $\times$ 21.65-in. long, .65 $\times$ 21.65	14.07
6.4-4	Indexing of tools, 8 times	.27
8.2	Rapid traverse, 237 in., 200 in./min	1.50
11.4-1	Tool wear for 93.21 min, 93.21/40 $\times$ .22	.51
	Unit estimate	111.02 min
	Lot time	19.05 hr

B. Find base cost for Example A above using Items 6.4, 8.2, 11.1, 11.4 and 22.1. The material for this example, however, is medium-carbon steel.

Item	Description	Cost
6.4	Constant setup	$ 4.94
6.4	Tool changer, 4 $\times$ 1.85	7.40
	Setup subtotal	$ 12.34
6.4	Cycle constant	$ 47.83
6.4	Jib load	63.90
11.1	Rough turn, 7.85 $\times$ 69.6 $\times$ .749	409.22
22.1	Mike tools, 3 times, 3 $\times$ .615	1.85
11.1	Rough turn, 7.25 $\times$ 54.15 $\times$ .749	294.05
6.4	Crane turn around	63.90
11.1	Rough turn, 6.95 $\times$ 39.90 $\times$ .749	207.70
11.1	Rough turn, 6.95 $\times$ 18.25 $\times$ .749	95.00
11.1	Finish turn, 6.45 $\times$ 18.25 $\times$ 1.74	204.82
6.4	Crane turn around	63.90
11.1	Finish turn, 6.95 $\times$ 21.65 $\times$ 1.74	261.81
6.4	Tools, 8 $\times$ .828	6.62
11.4	Tool wear for about 90 min, 90 $\times$ .122	10.98
	$/100 units	$1731.58
	Lot cost	$ 185.50

TABLE 6.4   NUMERICALLY CONTROLLED TURNING LATHES

Setup in estimating hours

1. Basic time	.39

2. Tools

Check tool magazine for required tools	.02/tool
Additional tool	.03
Additional micrometer	.005
Mike per decimal tolerance	.01
Dog, additional	.01
Adjust tool offset, per finishing tool	.04
Place and remove	
Steady rest	.05
Driving center	.06
Fixture	
to spindle	.05
to face plate	.22

3. Delete program block   .05

4. Tolerance   .02
   Check per decimal tolerance

5. Miscellaneous elements
   Change insert   .03
   Grind tool bit   .07
   Check tool or gage   .02
   Clean surface plate   .03
   Hone tool   .02

Operation elements in estimating minutes

1. Handling
   Place and remove part between centers using jib   3.23
   Place and remove part with overhead crane   4.39
   Turn part 180° with jib   1.49
   Turn part 180° with overhead crane   2.54
   Secure and release dog with one bolt   .63
   Secure and release dog with two bolts   1.07
   Change dog   .29
   Position, open, close, and adjust steady rest   1.70
   Protect surface, if finished, when dogged, add'l   .14

2. NC lathe machine operation
   Cycle start   .08
   Stop and start spindle, start feed   .11
   Set speed manually   .16
   Shift gears   .25
   Adjust tools
        Set tool from shaft end with length gate
             Shaft end not faced   .72
             Shaft end faced   .29
        Set tool with gage block from finished shoulder   .57
             Adjust tool, incremental   .16

3. Blow chips, rake   .25

4. Index, change tool, advance, retract cross slide turret

Tools	1	2	3	4	5	6	7	8	Add'l
Min	.03	.07	.10	.13	.16	.19	.22	.25	.03

5. Machining
   Turn, trim, break edges   See Table 11.1
   Rapid traverse   See Table 8.2

6. Turning tool replacement   See Table 11.4

7. Part inspection
   Mike   .33
   Vernier caliper   .78
   Groove gage   .77
   Plug gage   .44
   Thread gage   .66
   For other gaging   See Table 22.1

6.5 Numerically Controlled Chucking Lathes

DESCRIPTION

The machines described here are chucking lathes with numerical control. Figure 6.5 shows a typical NC chucking lathe. They are designed for heavy duty production. Internal contouring and external machining are the usual features. Turrets may be slant-bed mounted and have short tool projections. Coolant is provided externally or through boring bars and drills. Basic chuck sizes are from 12 to 36 in., and maximum swings are associated with these sizes. Turrets may be hexagonal or octagonal. Other machine tool designs are also possible. For some machines, the chuck can be removed and bar work is possible. Specific estimating data for universal NC turning lathes are not given, except that the estimator may examine both Sections 6.4 and 6.5 for selection of information. Adaptation of the data from both sections is useful for universal NC turning lathes.

These chucking lathes may have one or more turrets with a capacity of holding from 4 to 12 or more tools. NC chuckers have the advantage of reduced setup data over standard machines because much of the data are supplied to the machine by the NC tape. Repeat orders or smaller lots benefit from a machine having these controls. Machine cutting time can be reduced with multiple cuts, as two or more surfaces may be machined with only one action of the end working hexagon turret, or in combination of a cross-slide and a turret. Two or more axis machines can offer simultaneous coutouring. Chip disposal may be by an end chute. Older models may require stopping the machine and raking.

ESTIMATING DATA DISCUSSION

The basic setup is always provided. It includes tape, manuscript and print handling, and punch in/out. It allows for setting offsets to zero, changing, indexing, or resetting of jaws and their blowing, and adjust coolant lines.

The checking of the tool magazine includes checking of required tools in load position and indicator lights, and provides for new cutting edge, index, or replace insert.

Changing tools involves checking tool catalog, obtaining bar or insert or insert holder, remove holder from magazine, place in holding fixture, remove bar by releasing screws, and place and secure next bar.

Spacer work obtains spacers, T-slot bolts, wipe chuck, place and secure, and aside. The discussion provided in 6.4, Numerically Controlled Turning Lathes, is also appropriate for chucking lathes, although estimating data are different.

The handling elements include a place and remove part with jib where the part exceeds 50 lb. The operator obtains the jib with hook, hooks part from box or pallet, transports to chuck, blows chuck, and wipes part as required. Position part in chuck, secure jaws, adjust coolant, followed by aside jib with hook, close sliding guard, and start cycle. Open sliding guard, and blow chips as required. Obtain jib with hook, hook part, align driver to chuck, release jaws, transport to box or pallet and release.

Place the element and remove part by the hand includes obtain part from box or pallet, transport to chuck, blow chuck, wipe part as required. Position part in chuck, secure jaws, adjust coolant, close sliding guard, start cycle. After a machining element, open sliding guard, and blow chips as required. Align driver to chuck, release jaws, and transport to box or pallet.

The element handling turn part 180° with jib involves open sliding guard and blow chips as required. Obtain jib with hook, hook part, align driver to chuck, release jaws. Transport part to bench, rehook part from opposite end, transport part to chuck. Blow chuck,

FIGURE 6.5 A numerically controlled chucking lathe. (*Waterbury Farrel, Division of Textron, Inc.*)

wipe part as required. Position part in chuck, secure jaws, adjust coolant. Aside jib with hook and finally close sliding guard and start cycle.

If the operator turns the part 180° by hand for a part that is less than 50 lb., the operator will open sliding guard, blow chips as required. Align driver to chuck, release jaws, turn part 180°. Blow chuck, wipe part as required, position part in chuck, secure jaws, adjust coolant, close sliding guard, and finally start cycle.

Seat part element requires obtain shim or feeler gage from pocket or bench, check from part to locator pins, obtain lead hammer, seat part, check with shim or feeler, and finally aside gage and hammer.

Push bar may be required. If it is, the operator will switch to manual control, clear push bar to remove part as required. Place plate on push bar, advance to hold part, resecure jaws, clear, aside plate, and finally return turret to zero.

In checking with a plug gage, the operator will obtain plug gage from bench, assemble to bore, check, remove and aside to bench. A thread gage requires obtain thread gage from bench, turn on, check, turn off and aside to bench.

The estimator can find base cost directly by using Item 6.5 of Section IV. This method is faster and relatively accurate. The major setup items include a basic cost which is always used, and costs for tool changes and boring of soft chuch jaws. Cycle time can be estimated as $/100 units, which is base cost for the run time once the setup is qualified. The cycle cost is for operation of the numerically controlled chucking lathe only. It includes a constant cost which allows for starting and stopping and one tool adjustment. The constant cost is always allowed. The handling may be manually, jig, or hoist. A rotate part is also available. The estimator will make a selection of the kind of handling depending upon weight and the equipment that is available. Once the machine manipulation is completed, the estimator will refer to Items 8.2 for rapid travel; 11.1 for turning, boring, and various machining elements; 11.2 for drilling; 11.4 for tool life; and 22.1 for direct labor inspection.

EXAMPLES

A. An oil-field valve bonnet is machined from a large steel forging. The round forging, $21\frac{1}{4}$-in. OD × 20-in. long has a forged bore of 8 in. and a total weight of 1700 lbs. A series of machined bores and turning are scheduled and is shown below. Both ends are faced and have step bores. Simultaneously machining is used. Some diameters exceed Table 11.1 values, so use the formula min/in. $= \dfrac{\pi Dia}{12fV}$ (see Estimating Data Discussion for Sec. 11.1). Find unit estimate, hr/10 units, and lot time for 9 units. A large NC chucker will be used.

Table	Description		Time	
6.5-S	Basic time		.29	hr
6.5-S	Check tools, 7		.14	
6.5-S	Change two holders		.28	
6.5-S	Adjust tool offsets with gage block for one dimension		.10	
			.81	hr
6.5-1	Place and remove part with hoist		5.16	min
6.5-1	Seat part		.54	
6.5-2	Cycle start		.08	
11.1-2	Rough face left end, $21\frac{1}{4}$-OD × 6.63-in. long cut, carbide, 1 pass, $V = 360$ *fpm*, $f = .020$ *ipr*, and min/in. $= \dfrac{\pi \times 21.25}{12 \times .020 \times 360} = 0.77$			
	Length of cut $= 6.63 + .125 = 6.76$ in., where .125 in. is safety stock. $6.76 \times .77$		5.20	
11.1-2	Finish face $21\frac{1}{4}$-in. OD × 6.63-in. long, carbide, $V = 475$ *fpm*, $f = .007$ *ips*, and min/in. $= \dfrac{\pi \times 21.25}{12 \times .008 \times 475} = 1.67$			
	Length of cut $= 6.76$ in., 6.76×1.67		11.31	
11.1-3	Rough bore 8-in. ID × 19.5-in. long to 8.4-in. OD .63 × 19.5		12.29	
11.1-2	Rough turn $21\frac{1}{4}$-in. OD to $20\frac{3}{4}$-in. OD partial length of 10-in. carbide. min/in. $= \dfrac{\pi \times 21.25}{12 \times .020 \times 360} = .77$			
11.1-2	Time $= .77 \times 10$		7.70	
11.1-2	Finish turn $20\frac{3}{4}$-in. OD, 1.67×10		16.70	

6.5-1	Reverse bonnet with hoist into chuck	2.10
6.5-1	Seat part	.54
6.5-2	Cycle start	.08
11.1-2	Rough face right end, same as above	5.20
11.1-2	Finish face right end, same as above	11.31
11.1-2	Rough turn 21¼-in. OD to 19⅛-in. OD dimension. Two passes at approximate .5 in. depth of cut	
	Stock removal each. Length = 10.1 in.	
	First pass at 0.77 in./min., 10.1 × .77	7.78
	Second pass, 0.77 in./min., 10.1 × .77	7.78
11.1-2	Finish turn 18.93 in. OD, 9⅛ inches long	

$$\text{min/in.} = \frac{\pi \times 18.93}{12 \times .020 \times 360}$$

$$= .69$$

	9⅛ × .69	6.28
11.1-3	Finish bore 8.5-in. ID × 19.0 in. length. Carbide.	
	Previously bored from other side to 8.4 in. ID. Table value at 9-in. Dia, 19.0 × .98	18.62
11.1-3	Counterbore original 8.5-in. ID to 8.618-in. ID. Length = 9.125 in.	
	Finish pass. Carbide. 9.125 in. × .98	8.94
11.1-2	Finish turn 18.48-in. OD simultaneously to counterbore 8.618-in. ID.	

$$\text{Length of 18.48-in. OD is 9.125 in. min/in.} = \frac{\pi \times 18.48}{12 \times .020 \times 360}$$

$$= .67$$

	9.125 × .67	(6.11)
	This finish turn time is less than boring time, so it is not added to total	
6.5-3	Deburr, allow 2 times	
6.5-3	Blow chips, twice	.52
6.5-4	Index, 13 times	.50
8.2-1	Rapid traverse, approximately 125 in. at 200 in./min	.63
11.4-1	Carbide tool replacement, use stainless steel as an approximate material, machining time = 125 min of carbide, .36 min from table for 40 min., so for 125 min	1.13
	Unit estimate	130.82 min
	Hr/10 units	21.81
	Total lot estimate	20.45 hr

B. A cast brass nozzle will have a few final machining elements performed on a chucker. Assume material as a copper alloy for turning purposes. The machining schedule is given below. The normal lot release is 410 per month. Determine the unit estimate, hr/100 units, lot time, and the calendar total time for 12 equal lot orders.

Table	Description	Time
6.5-S	Basic time	.29 hr
6.5-S	Check tools, 5	.10
6.5-S	Change tools, 5	.25
		.64 hr
6.5-1	Load and unload by hand	1.32 min
6.5-2	Cycle start	.08
11.1-2	Face 2½-in. OD to nominal dimension, 1⁵⁄₁₆-in. length of cut, HSS	
	Finish pass, .14 × 1⁵⁄₁₆	.18
11.2-3	Drill ⅞-in. Dia, 7½-in. long, .09 × 7.5	.68
11.2-6	Tap 1-in. coarse thread, 8 threads 3-in. long, .316 × 3	.48
11.1-4	Contour end shape, depth = .5 in., L = 3 in. Dia = 4 in., .40 × 3	1.12
11.1-4	Contour ¼-in. O-ring groove of 4¼-in. OD. Length of cut = ¼ in.	
	H55. 1.06 × .25	.27
11.1-7	Break edges, 1 inside and 4 outside edges	.16
6.5-4	Index 5 times	.17
	Unit estimate	4.46 min
	Hr/100 units	7.433

Lot time   31.117 hr

Annual hours   373.4   hr

C. Re-estimate Example B above using base costs given by Items 6.5, 11.1, 11.2, and 11.4 of Section IV.

Item	Description	Cost
6.5	Setup	$ 6.18
6.5	Setup and check tools	9.25
	Subtotal	$15.43
6.5	Cycle constant	$14.09
6.5	Manual load and unload	31.02
6.5	Index 5 times	5.15
11.1	Face, 2½-in. OD, 1⁵⁄₁₆-in. length, 2.5 × 1.31 × 1.18, HSS	3.86
11.2	Drill ⅞ in., .875 × 7.5 × 1.65	10.83
11.2	Tap 1-in. coarse threads, 8 threads 3-in. long, 3 × 2.84	8.52
11.4	Contour and form, *Dia* = 4 in., *L* = 3 in., 4 × 3 × .402	4.82
11.1	Contour ¼-in. oil ring groove, 4½-in. DC, *L* = ¼ in., 4.5 × .25 × .402	.45
11.1	Break edges, 5 times × .737	3.69
6.5	Index turret 5 times, 5 × 1.03	5.15
	$/100 units	$87.58
	Lot cost	$25.94

TABLE 6.5   NUMERICALLY CONTROLLED CHUCKING LATHES

Setup in estimating hours

1. Basic time	.29
2. Check tool magazine for required tools	.02/tool
3. Change tool	
Bar by hand	.05
Bar by hoist	.07
Holder	.14
Bushings/sleeve on boring bar	.04
4. Place and remove locator pins	.17
5. Place, secure, remove chuck spacers	.09
6. Adjust tool offset after gage block and checking length	.10
Set end stops	.12
7. Bore soft jaws	.17
8. Check per decimal tolerance	.02

Operation elements in estimating minutes

1. Handling	
Place and remove part, manual, 50 lb	1.32
Place and remove part, jib, .50 lb	2.44
Turn or rotate part, manual hoist, 500 lb	5.16
Turn or rotate part, jib	.74
Seat part	2.10
Push bar	.54
Index part	1.06
By hand	.73
By hoist	1.26
Index fixture by jib	3.50
2. NC lathe machine operation	
Cycle start	.08
Program stop, check length, adjust tool offset	1.98
Start and stop chuck, start feed	.11
Set feed manually	.16

Adjust tools	.16
Set tools with gagebock	.57
Adjust tool, incremental	.16

3. Blow chips, rake   .25
   Stamp   .09
   Deburr   .26

4. Index, change tool, advance, retract

Tools	1	2	3	4	5	6	7	8
Min	.03	.07	.10	.13	.17	.20	.23	.27

Tools	9	10	11	12	13	14	15	16
Min	.30	.33	.37	.40	.43	.47	.50	.53

Tools	17	18	19	20	Add'l
Min	.57	.60	.63	.67	.04

5. Machining

Turn, bore, form, thread, start drill, break edges	See Table 11.1
Drill, counterbore, tap	See Table 11.2
Turning tool replacement	See Table 11.4
Rapid traverse	See Table 8.2

6. Part inspection

Mike per dimension	.33
Vernier caliper	.78
Plug gage	.44
Thread gage	.66
For other gaging	See Table 22.1

6.6 Single-Spindle Automatic Screw Machines

DESCRIPTION

The automatic screw machine (ASM) does work similar to the turret lathe. Automatic screw machines can be single or multiple spindle. A multiple spindle may contain 4, 5, or 6 spindles. Automatic screw machines provide controlling movements for the turret and cross-slides to have tools feed into the work at desired feeds, withdrawn, and indexed to the next position. The machine produces parts with little attention from the operator. Many automatic screw machines not only feed in an entire bar of stock, but also are provided with a magazine to have bars fed through the machine automatically.

A 1 1/4-in. collet size automatic screw machine is shown in Figure 6.6. A choice of 2-speed or 4-speed drive units is an option. Now, consider the general class of single-spindle automatic screw machines.

ESTIMATING DATA DISCUSSION

The setup has a constant time for single-spindle machines. Additionally, time is provided for each tool for standard tolerances. If exceptional tolerances are required, the affected tool is increased by 0.15 hr.

The first four elements are for nonmachining work. These elements may occur during machining time, and when that happens no time is allowed. For instance, turret positioning, indexing, and retracting may be done during a cross-slide element and the maximum time of the two simultaneous choices is added to the estimate.

Estimates for ASM machining time, by custom, are made in revolutions. The first step finds the cutting speed (peripheral speed of the work passing the tool) for the material to be cut. Element 5 provides a sample of materials that are popular for

FIGURE 6.6 A 1½-in. automatic screw machine. *(Brown & Sharpe)*

screw machine work. Typically, we have selected low-carbon steel, resulfurized (e.g., 1212); medium carbon-steel, resulfurized (e.g., 1145); low-carbon lead steel (12L14); medium- and high-carbon leaded steel (41L30); free-machining stainless steels, annealed (430F); and an average of aluminum and brass bar stock. Entry variables for Element 5 are tool type, cut conditions, and material. The sfm and feed are noted for a selected tool and material.

Screw machines are sometimes estimated using cams which are pre-engineered for a certain part. This method is accurate, but often times a cam design may be unavailable and our method is prior to any cam design.

The next step is to plan a sequence of machining elements and assign them to various turret positions or cross-slides. The spindle speed in rpm can be calculated using the formula:

$$rpm = \frac{12}{\pi}\left(\frac{sfm}{Dia}\right) = 3.82\left(\frac{sfm}{Dia}\right)$$

where *Dia* is the largest or initial diameter of the feature being machined or tool diameter.

However, the calculated spindle speed may not be practical for all machining elements. Each element should be questioned before using an estimated spindle speed. If the turning cutting diameter is based on stock diameter, the corresponding spindle speed may be too high for tapping or

threading, unless special speed reducers are used, or the machine has a step-down velocity option.

More than likely, the calculated rpm will not match available gear-ratio rpm's, and the estimator can adjust to the nearest actual rpm and estimating can proceed. Conversely, if it is uncertain which one of several machines will produce the parts, knowledge of the specific rpm will be unknown, and if the improved accuracy resulting from rpm adjustment is minor, the estimator may want to overlook rpm recalculation, as we do in our problems. Finally, some materials, notably free-maching brass or aluminum, may exceed the available rpm of the machine, and thus the maximum rpm is a logical candidate.

Temporary rpm's are calculated for each machining element, but a practical rpm is chosen that can be effective with all the machining elements (tapping and knurling exempted). The rpm's are found in the following table. If the cutting length is not included, rpm's for various lengths can be added together for a constant feed. For example, at .0005 feed, 1000 + 1500 = 2500 would be the rpm for 1½ in.

Number of revolutions for length of cut and feed

Feed/in.	Length					
	¹/₃₂	¹/₁₆	¹/₈	¹/₄	¹/₂	1
.0005	63	125	250	500	1000	1500
.0010	31	63	125	250	500	750
.0015	21	42	83	167	333	500
.0020	16	31	63	125	250	375
.0025	13	25	50	100	200	300
.003	10	21	42	83	167	250
.004	8	16	31	63	125	188
.005	6	13	25	50	100	150
.006	5	10	21	42	83	125
.007	4	9	18	36	71	107
.008	4	8	16	31	63	94
.009	3	7	14	28	56	83
.010		6	13	25	50	75
.012		5	10	21	42	63
.015			8	17	33	50
.020			6	13	25	38

One operator may tend 2, 3, 4, or more single-spindle machines depending upon lot quantities.

Operation costs can be estimated using Item 6.6 of Section IV. These data provide setup cost per occurrence and $/100 units. Setup costs are different for single- or multiple-spindle work and the entry variable depends on the tooled turret and cross-slide stations. Costs for run time are affected by handling, material, and length of cutting. For single-spindle work, the number of nonsimultaneous turret actions are developed, and this number multiplies the factor. For machining, distinctions are made for steel and other materials (or brass, aluminum, and similar free-machining materials). The length is added for all independent cuts, including drill point approach, etc. Length is multiplied by stock diameter, and this product multiplies the cost factor. A tap, thread, or knurl cost per in. is averaged for several materials. The costs are divided by the number of machines per operator.

EXAMPLES

A. CDA 360 brass is used for a bushing 1.245 in. in length for a 1.125-in. OD. The total part length is 1.390 in., including .015-in. facing and 1.25-in. cutoff. A single spindle machine with a 6-hole turret is used. The machining schedule is given below. Two form elements using the cross-slide are not added since they overlap with turret elements. Run part at 500 sfm or 1534 rpm.

Table	Description	Time	
6.6-S	Setup	3.0	hr
6.6-S	Tools, 8 × .25	2.0	
6.6-1	Feed stock twice	.012	min
6.6-2	Index turret	.006	
6.6-5	Center drill ⅛-in. OD, drill point = .063 + approach (= .030) = .093 in. The drill feeds at 31 revolutions (rev)	31	rev
6.6-2	Index turret	.006	
6.6-5	Step drill through cutoff width, and length of cut = 1.390 in., .625-in. OD, 1.390 ÷ .015	93	rev
6.6-2	Index turret	.006	
6.6-2	Position recess. The element chamfers the inside edge and is pushed to cut by a cross-slide. The position for recess is estimated to be two indexes	.012	
6.6-5	Recess .015 in. deep at .002	8	rev
6.6-2	Index turret	.006	
6.6-5	Ream, flat bottom, and face. A ⅝-in. counterbore will be reamed, flat-bottomed, and the end faced using a combination tool. Total tool travel = .340 in. and .340 ÷ .002	170	rev
	A dwell is used for flat bottom	5	rev
6.6-5	Ream .436/.437-in. hole, and travel = .936-in. depth, approach = .014 in., and into cutoff = .010 in. for total of .960-in. Rev = .960 ÷ .010	96	rev
6.6-5	Cutoff uses a ¾-in. formed *Dia.* Travel from OD to ID = .157 in. for .157 ÷ .003	52	rev
	Front slide forms the 1-in. *Dia*		
6.6-5	The tool will travel .068-in. + .012-in, approach = .080-in., and .080 ÷ .003 = 26 rev, but is done during step drill operation, and is simultaneous (simo) and not allowed.		
6.6-5	Form using rear slide travels a total of .210-in. and at .003 ipr rev = 70, but this is done simo to drilling and reaming operations		
6.6-2	Clear	.018	
	Subtotal min	.090	
	Subtotal rev	455	
	Min = 455 ÷ 1534	.297	
	Unit estimate	.387	min
	hr/1000 units	6.444	
	pc/hr	155	

B. A threaded part is made from 5/8-in. hex mild steel. A turning velocity of 917 is determined from 150 sfm. Find pc/hr as if one operator was tending one machine.

Table	Description	Time	
6.6-1	Advance material to bar stop	.006	min
6.6-2	Retract, index, and advance turret	.024	
6.6-5	Point and chamfer, .16-in. of cut and approach, .16 ÷ .003	53	rev
6.6-5	Retract, index, and advance turret	.024	
6.6-5	Turn thread *Dia*, 1¼-in. length of cut and approach, 1.25 ÷ .004	312	rev
6.6-2	Retract, index, and advance turret	.024	
6.6-5	Thread ⁵⁄₁₆–18 on and off, ¾-in. long, .75 × 18 = 13.5 + 3 for lead, rpm = 245, min = 16.5 ÷ 245 × 2	.13	
6.6-2	Clear turret and index	.036	

6.6-3	Advance side tool (.036) simo during turning	
6.6-5	Form chamfer, $\frac{1}{8}$-in. of cut $\frac{1}{8} \div .003 = 42$ rev which is done simo during turning	
6.6-3	Advance side tool (.012) done simo	
6.6-5	Cut off part, $\frac{3}{16}$-in. length of cut, .002 feed	94 rev
	Subtotal min	.24
	Subtotal rev	459
	Min = 459 ÷ 917	.50
	Unit estimate	.74 min
	hr/1000 units	12.33
	pc/hr	81

C. Re-estimate Example A above using a base-cost approach.

Item	Description	Cost
6.6	Single-spindle setup constant	$ 21.45
6.6	Eight tools, 8 × 3.58	28.64
	Setup subtotal	$ 50.09
6.6	Six working stations (excludes 2 simo stations), 6 × .572	$ 3.43
	Total machine length = .093 + 1.39 + .015 + .34 + .96 + .157 = 2.955-in. of metal length. The rpm is based upon original OD, 1.125-in. OD × 2.955 × 3.86	13.01
	$/100 units subtotal	$ 16.44
	Lot cost for 2500 units	$460.98

TABLE 6.6   SINGLE-SPINDLE AUTOMATIC SCREW MACHINES

Setup

Single-spindle, basic	3.00 hr
Install and adjust tool, ea	.25 hr
Add'l or fine tolerance, per tool affected	.15 hr

Operation elements in estimating minutes

1. Material advance to stock stop .006

    Load bar in collet .30

2. Turret operation

Index	.006
Back turret tool from work, index, advance new tool	.024
Back turret tool from work, index to start position, advance cross-slide	.036
Clear turret from work	.018

3. Cross slide operation

Advance cross-slide tool to work	.012
Start or stop machine	.02

4. Simultaneous elements

Remove parts from pan	0
Count	0
Inspection	0
Clean chips	0

5. Cutting speeds and feeds for HSS tools for ASM

Tool	Width (W), dia, or depth (D)	Feeds	Free-machining resulfurized			Annealed stainless steels	Low-carbon leaded steels	Aluminum, Brass	
			Low	Medium	High			Feed	sfm
Counterboring		.004	150	120	105	120	160	.002	175
Turning Single point, box		.007	225	190	170	150	235		Max rpm or 500
Center drill	$1/8$ OD	.003	125	115	100	115	135	.003	200
Cutoff tool Angular, Circular, Straight	.062 W .125 W	.002 .0025	140 140	115 115	110 110	120 120	150 150	.003 .003	340 340
Button die			40	30	20	20	40		35
Chaser die			45	35	25	25	45		45
Drill Twist	.02 OD .04 $1/16$ $3/32$ $1/8$ $3/16$ $1/4$ $5/16$ $3/8$ $1/2$ $5/8$	.0005 .001 .001 .002 .003 .004 .005 .007 .008 .010 .012	125 125 125 125 125 125 125 125 125 125 125	115 115 115 115 115 115 115 115 115 115 115	100 100 100 100 100 100 100 100 100 100 100	115 115 115 115 115 115 115 115 115 115 115	135 135 135 135 135 135 135 135 135 135 135	.0005 .001 .001 .002 .003 .004 .007 .008 .010 .012 .015	200 200 200 200 200 200 200 200 200 200 200
Form tool Circular	.125 W .250 W	.0025 .003	140 140	115 115	110 110	120 120	150 150	.003 .004	340 340
Knurl, turret side		.015 .002	150 150	110 110	110 110	110 110	160 160	.020 .004	165 165
Pointing, facing		.003	225	190	170	150	235	.004	200
Reamer	≤ $1/8$ > $1/8$	.005 .008	140 140	115 115	95 95	120 120	150 150	.007 .010	240 240
Tap		.002	60	50	35	40	65		80
Recessing		.002	150	120	105	120	160	.002	175

6. Tool wear and replacement

See Table 11.4

6.7 Multispindle Automatic Screw Machines

DESCRIPTION

The automatic screw machine (ASM) provides rapid production of screw machine parts. The process is similar to that of the turret lathe. The automatic screw machines that are discussed here are multispindle machines. Multispindle ASM contains five or more spindles. (See Figure 6.7.) The machine automatically provides movement by the turret and cross-slides to have various tools fed into the waiting stock at certain feeds, withdrawn, and indexed to the next position. The process is very similar to that of a gatling gun

FIGURE 6.7   A five-spindle automatic screw machine. (*Davenport Machine Tool Division, Dover Corporation*)

which rotates each time it fires a bullet. These machines are self-sufficient and require little direct attention from the operator, other than the loading of the new stock and periodic inspection of parts. These machines feed in the raw bar stock automatically and can take up to a 12 or 20-ft length of bar with a maximum diameter of about 1 in. to several inches. Machine capacities vary.

One operator may tend three or more machines. In the case of multiple machine operation the estimator "de-joints" the direct-labor time by dividing the cycle estimate, which is the time for floor-to-floor for one unit from one machine, by the number of machines tended by the operator. Now consider estimating data for the general class of multispindle automatic screw machines.

ESTIMATING DATA DISCUSSION

Setup effort is broken down into a basic time plus additional time for installation and adjustment of tools. If the estimator believes that tolerance considerations for the specific multiple ASM requires additional time, time is provided for each tool.

Before proceeding with discussion of the elements, it is useful to point out practical steps for estimating jobs that are done on these kinds of machines.

From the part print, note the grade, size and shape of the material, tolerances, micro-finish, and concentricity requirements. Process the part from the end of cutoff piece. Plan the sequence of elements starting with internal tool slide followed by the external tool slide; then cross slide elements position by position.

Determine the tool travel required for the tool slide, cross slides, auxiliary slides, recessing cross travel, and the number of threads to be cut. Sometimes tool travel is composed of safety stock, approach, part length, and over travel. From Element 6, determine cutting velocity and spindle rpm. Check surface speeds on outside diameter, drills, and taps. Also select drilling and drill speeder ratios.

From Element 6, determine recommended feed advance per revolution for the tool slide and each cross slide. Determine the approximate number of revolutions required to finish a piece by dividing the tool travel for each position by the maximum recommended feed advance for the tool in that position. The position requiring the most revolutions is the time of the job.

The first five elements in the element listing are for non-machining time. These elements sometimes occur during machining time, and if this happens no time is allowed.

Estimates for the machining time for the automatic screw machine are customarily made in revolutions. This book continues that tradition which is unique among machining estimating. Element 6 provides cutting speeds and feeds for low-carbon lead steel (12L14) and for brass. Table 6.6 may be examined for additional data. Entry variables for Element 6 are tool type, cut conditions, and material. The SFM and feed are shown for different tools and materials.

The machining elements are sequenced and assigned to various spindles. The spindle speed in rpm is calculated using

$$\text{rpm} = \frac{12}{\pi}\frac{(sfm)}{(Dia)} = 3.82\frac{(sfm)}{(Dia)}$$

where *Dia* is the largest or initial diameter of the bar stock being machined or the tool diameter.

Usually, the calculated rpm will not match the gear-ratio rpm's. The corresponding spindle speed for cutting may be too high for drilling, tapping, or threading so the estimator may need to adjust the rpm to the nearest actual rpm and then he or she can proceed with the estimating.

Temporary rpm's are calculated for each machining element, but a practical rpm is chosen that can be effective with all of the machining elements, except tapping and knurling. The calculated rpm's are shown in the discussion for single spindle ASM. For multispindle work, the longest machine element establishes the unit time. Other spindle rpm's being less are not the limiting production requirement. For the automatic screw machine, the independent variable is the number of revolutions that each machining element needs to perform its function.

Operation costs can be estimated directly using Items 6.6 and 6.7 of Section IV. These data provide setup cost per occurrence, and cycle costs are expressed in $/100 units. Setup costs depend on the tooled turret and cross-slide stations. In multiple-spindle work, the longest-time station establishes unit cost. For machining, distinctions are made for steel and other materials (brass, aluminum, and similar free-machining materials). The length of cut should consider safety stock (which is usually very small or $\frac{1}{64}$ in.) approach, print length, and overtravel. The estimator will also want to refer to Item 6.5 for additional instructions.

EXAMPLES

A. 12L14 steel is used to make a part .422 in. in length for a .445-in. OD. A five-spindle machine is used. Stock size of $\frac{1}{2}$ in. is required. The rpm is 2500. Find the estimate. Assume one operator per machine.

Table	Description	Time
6.7-S	Setup, 9 tools	10.05 hr
6.7-1	Load bar stock .15 × 5 bars/320 units per bar	.00 min
6.7-1	Tap bar into position .10 × 5/320	.00
6.7-1	One index time	.05
6.7-6	Position 1: Spot drill .125 *Dia* for .125-in. depth rev = $\frac{1}{8}$ ÷ .0012 = 100 rev. Knurl, narrow ground 1 roll knurl. rev = 33.	
6.7-6	Position 2: Drill $\frac{3}{16}$-in. *Dia* halfway with main tool. Rough form .445-in. *Dia* with cross slide. Drill distance = .245 in. ÷ .0024 = 100 rev Rough form .420 ÷ .0025 = 168 rev	
6.7-6	Position 3: Drill past cutoff $\frac{3}{16}$-in. *Dia*. Finish form .445-in. *Dia* with cross slide. Drill distance = .25 in. ÷ .0024 = 100 rev Finish form .445 OD. .420 ÷ .0024 = 175 rev	
6.7-6	Position 4: Ream drill $\frac{13}{64}$ in. thru. $\frac{13}{63}$ ÷ .0045 = 45 rev	
6.7-6	Position 5: Pickoff and burr .005 = 100 rev Cutoff .445-in. OD. .445 ÷ .0025 = 178 rev	178 rev
	Longest machining element position 5	178 rev
	Machine time	.07 min
	Unit estimate	.12 min
	Pc/hr	500

B. A part is made from $\frac{1}{4}$-in. brass on a five-position machine. The part is .45-in. long and .235 in. in diameter. A turning velocity of 1528 rpm is determined from 100 sfm. Find the unit estimate and pieces per hour. Assume one operator per three machines. Find the hr/1000 units where one operator tends three ASM's and the lot time for 10,000 parts.

Table	Description	Time	
6.7-S	Setup, 7 tools	9.15	hr
6.7-1	Index	.05	min
6.7-1	Position stock	.00	
6.7-6	Position 1: Spot drill .125 *Dia* $\frac{1}{8}$ ÷ .0010 = 125 rev. Rough form .235-in. *Dia* with cross slide L.O.C. = .40 in. rev = .40 ÷ .0025 = 160 rev		
6.7-6	Position 2: Knurl, narrow ground 1 roll knurl rev = 33. Drill thru $\frac{1}{8}$ *Dia*. Drill dist. = .45 in. ÷ .0025 = 200 rev, maximum	200 rev	
6.7-6	Position 3: Ream drill $\frac{9}{64}$ in. thru $\frac{9}{64}$ ÷ .0045 = 32 rev		
6.7-6	Position 4: Finish form .235-in. *Dia* with cross slide L.O.C. = .40 ÷ .0024 = 167 rev		
6.7-6	Position 5: Cutoff .235-in OD. .235 ÷ .0020 = 118 rev		
	Longest machining element position 2	200 rev	
	Machine time	.13	min
	Unit estimate	.18	min
	Pc/hr	333	
	Net unit estimate	.06	min
	Hr/1000 units	1.0000	hr
	Lot time	19.15	hr

C. A .375-in. part is made from 12L14 steel on a five-position machine. The part is .275 in. in diameter. The turning velocity is 2500 rpm. Find the unit estimate. One operator tends four machines. Find the net unit estimate. Find the lot hours to charge for direct-labor cost for 50,000 parts.

Table	Description	Time	
6.7-S	Setup, 7 tools	9.15	hr
6.7-2	Index	.05	min
6.7-6	Position 1: Rough form .275 *Dia* with cross slide L.O.C. = .25 in. rev = .25 ÷ .0025 = 100 rpm		
	Drill halfway drill distance = .1875 in. ÷ .0025 = 100 rpm		
6.7-6	Position 2: Finish form .275 *Dia* with cross slide L.O.C. = .25 in. rev = .25 ÷ .0024 = 104 rpm		
	Ream ⅛ in. halfway ⅛ ÷ .0045 = 28 rev		
6.7-6	Position 3: Knurl, narrow ground, 1 roll knurl rev. = 33		
6.7-6	Position 4: Finish form .255-in. OD. L.O.C. = .05 in. .05 ÷ .0024 = 21 rev		
6.7-6	Position 5: Cutoff .275-in. OD. .275 ÷ .0025 = 110 rev, maximum	110	rev
	Longest machining element position 5	110	rev
	Machine time	.04	min
	Unit estimate	.09	min
	Pc/hr	667	
	Net unit estimate	.023	min
	Lot estimate for order of 50,000	47.48	hr

D. A multi-spindle screw machine part is made from 12L14 steel. The part is .40 in. in diameter and .375 in. in length. The rpm is 2000. Find the unit estimate as a floor-to-floor estimate.

Table	Description	Time	
6.7-S	Setup, 8 tools	9.60	hr
6.7-2	Index	.05	min
6.7-6	Position 1: Spot drill .125 in. with .125 *Dia* rev = .125 ÷ .0012 = 100 rev		
	Rough form .40-in. *Dia* with cross slide L.O.C. = .35 .35 ÷ .0025 = 140 rev		
6.7-6	Position 2: Drill thru ⅛-in. *Dia* L.O.C. = .375. .0025 = 200 rev		
	Finish form .40 *Dia* with cross slide .35 ÷ .0024 = 146 rev		
	Maximum position.	200	rev
6.7-6	Position 3: Ream drill ⅛ thru. ⅛ ÷ .0045 = 28		
	Finish form .38-in. *Dia* with cross slide .05 ÷ .0025 = 20 rev		
6.7-6	Position 4: Pickoff and burr .005 = 100 rev		
6.7-6	Position 5: Cutoff .40 in. OD. .40 ÷ .0025 = 160 rpm		
	Machine time	.10	min
	Unit estimate, floor-to-floor time	.15	min

E. Brass is used as a material for a screw machine part. The part diameter is .45-in. OD and is .375 in. in length. Turning velocity is 1500 rpm. Find the lot time to produce 1000, 5000, 10,000 units. Assume one operator per machine.

Table	Description	Time	
6.7-S	Setup, 7 tools	9.15	hr
6.7-2	Index	.05	min
6.7-6	Position 1: Spot drill .125 *Dia* ⅛ in. ⅛ ÷ .0010 = 125 rev. Rough form .45-in. OD with cross slide L.O.C. = .35 in. .35 ÷ .0025 = 140 rev		
6.7-6	Position 2: Drill halfway L.O.C. = 1875 in. .0025 = 75 rev. Finish form .45-in. *Dia* L.O.C. = .35 in. .35 ÷ .0024 = 146 rev		
6.7-6	Position 3: Finish form .43-in. OD L.O.C. = .10 in. .10 ÷ .0015 = 67 rev		
6.7-6	Position 4: Ream drill ⁹⁄₆₄ in. halfway ⁹⁄₆₄ ÷ .0045 = 32 rev		

6.7-6   Position 5: Cutoff .45 in. OD .45 ÷ .0025 = 180 rev, maximum   180 rev

Machine time	.12 min
Unit estimate	.17 min
Pc/hr	353
Lot time for 1000 units	11.983
Lot time for 5000 units	23.32
Lot time for 10,000 units	37.48

F. Re-estimate Example A above using a base-coat approach. The data for these calculations are found under Items 6.6 and 6.7 of Section IV. These operational costs find the direct-labor cost as if the operator were tending only one machine.

Item	Description	Cost
6.7	Setup, constant	$ 42.90
6.7	Tools, 9 × 6.44	57.96
	Setup subtotal	$100.92
6.7	Index cost	$ 1.19
6.6	Position 1: .125-in. *Dia* drill, .125-in. depth. .125 × .125 × 13.6 = $.21	
6.6	Position 2: $\frac{3}{16}$-in. *Dia* drill, .245-in. long. $\frac{3}{16}$ × .245 × 13.6 = $.62	
6.6	Position 3: $\frac{3}{16}$-in. drill, .25-in. long $\frac{3}{16}$ × .25 × 13.6 = $.64	
6.6	Position 4: Ream drill $\frac{13}{16}$ in., .422-in. long $\frac{13}{64}$ × .422 × 13.6 = $1.17	
6.6	Position 5: Cutoff, length of cut = .211 in. long, *Dia* = .445 in. OD. .445 × .211 × 13.6 = $1.28	
	Select position which has greatest cost	1.28
	$/100 units	$ 2.47
	Setup cost	$100.92

G. Find the direct-labor cost for Example B above. Assume one operator for three machines. Find the cost for 10,000 parts.

Item	Description	Cost
6.7	Setup, constant	$ 42.90
6.7	Tools, 7 × 6.44	45.08
	Setup subtotal	$ 87.98
6.7	Index cost	$ 1.19
6.6	Position 1: .125-in. drill, $\frac{1}{8}$-in. L.O.C. .125 × $\frac{1}{8}$ × 3.86 = $.06 Form .235-in. *Dia*, L.O.C. = .40 in. .235 × .40 × 3.86 = $.36 Note that this is a simo. operation and $.36 is greater.	
6.6	Position 2: $\frac{1}{8}$-in. *Dia* drill, L.O.C. = .45 in. $\frac{1}{8}$ in. × .45 × 3.86 = $.22	
6.6	Position 3: Ream drill $\frac{9}{64}$ in., .45-in. L.O.C. $\frac{9}{64}$ × .45 × 3.86 = $.24	
6.6	Position 4: Form .235-in. *Dia*, L.O.C. = .40 in. .235 × .40 × 3.86 = $.36	
6.6	Position 5: Cutoff .235-in. OD L.O.C. = 117 .235 × .117 × 3.86 = $.11	
	Select maximum position cost	.36
	Cycle $/100 units	$ 1.55
	Direct labor $/100 units	.52
	Cost for 10,000 units	$139.65

TABLE 6.7 MULTISPINDLE AUTOMATIC SCREW MACHINES

Setup

Multiple spindle, basic	6.00 hr
Install and adjust tool, ea	.45 hr
Add'l or fine tolerance, ea	.15 hr
Six–eight cams, entirely changed	10–12 hr
Changing gearing only	4–6 hr
Changing gearing partially for family of parts	2–3 hr

Operation elements in estimating minutes

1. Pick up bar, load in spindle	.15
Tap bar into position	.10
2. Index	.05
3. Position oil guards, turn on oil	.00
4. Operation	
Start or stop machine	.00
5. Simultaneous elements	
Inspection	.00
Remove parts	.00
Clean chips	.00

6. Cutting speeds and feeds

Tool	Width (W), Dia, or Depth (D)	Feeds	Low-carbon leaded sfm steel	Brass Feed	Brass sfm
Spot drill	$\frac{1}{8}$	.0012	135	.0010	200
Drill	$\frac{3}{16}$	.0024	135	.0022	200
	$\frac{3}{16}$	.0025	135	.0024	200
Form tool	.125W	.0025	235	.0025	340
	.125W	.0025	235	.0024	340
Reamer	$\frac{13}{64}$	.0045	150	.0045	240
Cutoff tool, straight	.125W	.0025	150	.0025	340
Pickoff and burr		.0050	135	.0050	200
Knurl		.0075	150	.0075	240

See Table 6.6, Element 5, for additional data.

MILLING MACHINES

7.1 Milling Machines Setup

ESTIMATING DATA DISCUSSION

These data are for setup of milling machine operations. The units are estimating hours. There are three elements: 1) basic time; 2) make part time; and 3) tolerance checking. Entry variables are the holding device and the type of milling cut and cutter for Element 1. Several entry choices are available. While not all setups are covered, the estimator can adapt the list as necessary to other setup requirements.

Element 2 deals with the making of a part. The inclusion of this element in the setup is optional with the estimator. Certainly, the making of one or several parts is necessary for the completion of a setup. The time to make one or several parts is also included in the unit estimate or hours per lot. There is the chance of "double estimating." The time required to complete the setup may be longer than the entire production run. Also, if the first part is scrapped and additional material is provided for this eventuality, the "make time" is a reason-

able inclusion. If the element will be included, the estimator determines the operation estimate first. Then it is converted to hours per unit (hr/unit). This value is multiplied by 2 for the usual case of requiring one part to complete a setup. If the hours per unit is relatively large, its importance to the setup is tangible. Multipliers other than the suggested 2, such as 1, 3, or 4, may be chosen by the estimator as conditions warrant.

Element 3 is concerned with exceptional tolerance requirements of a setup. This would exclude "cut and try," but include "measure" for critical dimensions. Commercial milling practices are included in basic time, Element 1.

Examples showing the use of these data are given with the type of milling machine.

Milling setup can be evaluated using a base cost approach if it is desired to use dollars directly. Item 7.1 of Section IV is read to provide setup cost. Examples using this item are found in other milling Typical Estimates.

TABLE 7.1   MILLING MACHINES SETUP

Setup in estimating hours

1. Basic time

Type of milling cut and cutter / Holding device	Cutter used in prior operation	Plane surface (End, shell, face)	Shoulder cut (End or shell)	Slot profile (End or shell)	Saw slab, form (Plain)	Slot (Peripheral)	Straddle mill (2 cutters)	Three-cutter gang
Holding device in prior operation. (Dial table only.)	.15	.55	.60	.90	.55	1.00	1.35	1.60

Type of milling cut and cutter / Holding device	Cutter used in prior operation	Plane surface (End, shell, face)	Shoulder cut (End or shell)	Slot profile (End or shell)	Saw slab, form (Plain)	Slot (Peripheral)	Straddle mill (2 cutters)	Three-cutter gang
Holding device in prior operation is re-setup.	.30	.70	.75	1.00	.70	1.15	1.45	1.75
Small part. (Placed manually.)	.50	.90	1.00	1.25	.90	1.40	1.70	2.00
Large part. (Hoist required.)	.60	1.00	1.05	1.30	1.00	1.45	1.75	2.05
Vise.	.70	1.15	1.15	1.45	1.15	1.65	1.90	2.20
Table setup. (Part length ≤ 12 in.)	.90	1.30	1.35	1.40	1.20	1.60	1.90	2.15
Table setup. (Part length > 12 in.)	1.05	1.45	1.50	1.55	1.45	1.70	2.00	2.30
Collet or chuck. (No index.)	.50	.90	1.00	1.25	.90	1.40	1.70	2.00
Collet or chuck. (With index.)	.85	1.25	1.30	1.55	1.25	1.70	2.00	2.30
Index device in prior operation. (Part relocated.)	.35	.75	.85	1.10	.75	1.25	1.55	1.85
Index. (Device with tail stock.)	1.05	1.50	1.55	1.80	1.50	1.95	2.25	2.55
Angle plate.	.80	1.20	1.25	1.55	1.20	1.65	2.00	2.25

2. Make piece (optional): $2 \times$ hr/1 unit

3. Tolerance checking:

Tolerance	hr
$^{1}/_{64}$ –.011	.03
.01 –.0051	.05
.005–.0031	.08
.003–.0011	.10
.001–	.13

7.2 Knee and Column Milling Machines

DESCRIPTION

Knee and column machines are utility milling machines. The name is derived from the column-shaped main frame and the knee-shaped projection from the column, which supports the saddle and work-holding table. The machines have general adjustments of their moving members. Three styles are included: plain (horizontal arbor), universal, and vertical.

The plain milling machine is usually used in jobbing shops and tool rooms. It may be adapted to quantity production with attachments and fixtures. The main elements of this machine are the column, spindle, overarm, knee, saddle, and table. Figure 7.2 is an example of the plain machine. It has a 60 × 13.7-in. table with 16 speeds that range from 25–1500 rpm and 16 feeds ranging from 1/2 to 60 ipm. Controls are located in front and back.

The vertical knee and column machine has the spindle vertical, or placed parallel to the column face, and at right angles to the top surface of the table. The vertical knee and column machine is adapted to operations with end and face mills, profiling interior and exterior surfaces, milling dies and metal molds, and for locating and boring holes in jigs and fixtures.

The universal milling machine resembles the plain type. The chief difference is that the table is supported and carried by the housing, which is swiveled in a horizontal plane. The universal milling machine can mill helices in addition to those operations of the plain machine. Now consider the following estimating data for the general class of knee and column milling machines.

ESTIMATING DATA DISCUSSION

Data provided in Table 7.2 include operating elements only. Element 1 deals with the basic part handling. Entry variables are weight and holding devices. As part weight increases, its distance and holding container is expected to vary, consistent with quantity, of course. There are four major categories of holding devices. Element 1 allows for the operator's movement time to and from the machine and part and grasping and releasing time. However, the tabular values in Element 1 do not include clamping.

The listed elements in 1 include the necessary

movements to accomplish the action. For instance, "seat with mallet" includes reaching and grasping the mallet, and letting go of the mallet in its nearby resting spot after seating. Similarly, "wipe off parallels" involves the use of a rag; its inclusion in the element is implied. The "load and unload part in collet, angle plate, cup arbor, chuck and dividing head" does include the necessary clamping action. These last loading and unloading times are a compilation of the more complete work, thus allowing the estimator a choice of how the element is applied.

If the handling work is done during a machine cut, a portion of the element can be deducted. For example, from 1/3 to 1/2 can be deducted if loading is partially compensated by the machine cut. If the weight is less than 1 lb and a knee and column machine is used, the values should be considered a necessary threshold value. While the estimator can interpolate tabular values for greater precision, the better practice is to apply the higher value in estimating.

The clamp and unclamp elements are provided in Element 2. With knowledge of what is expected, the estimator selects the appropriate matching work. The time values are for both clamp and unclamp. If

FIGURE 7.2 Plain general purpose milling machine. (Cincinnati Milacron)

loosening or tightening will occur during the machine-controlled rapid retract time, the values are reduced 25%. The necessary wrenches are assumed to be on the machine table or not more than an arm's reach from the operator.

In Element 3, the convention for rotate or turn part in vise, does not include the opening or closing. It does, however, include fixture and part manipulation. For the listed elements in 3, the work is inclusive.

Element 4 lists those elements suitable to knee and column milling operation. Some are single purpose, start or stop spindle, while others are consolidated, and use the word ''and'' to include the inclusive property. The ''start'' element, for example, is used in several elements in various ways. Depending upon the need, a particular one is selected. Whenever the spindle, saddle, knee, or table is moved, an average distance is figured. Thus, the rapid traverse or rapid retract rate of the machine is assumed. An alternate approach is to use individual elements and determine the distance for rapid traverse and retract, then use the specific machine traverse rate for that distance. This approach, while accurate, is more time consuming. (The following examples show how it is done.) In some plain milling operations only one elemental value may be needed, while complicated vertical milling operations may require a combination of elements to give machine operation. Some operating elements may be done during machine operation and would not be entirely required. The automatic or manual machine operations depend upon the specific machine being estimated, but all elements are provided.

Element 5 deals with cleaning, lubricating, and wiping. Type of tool, air hose, brush, oil hose, rag, or hand and area are the entry variables.

Handling base costs can also be figured using Item 7.2 of Section IV. Entry variables are weight and rehandling, if necessary. The rehandle includes clamp, unclamp, and machine operation in addition to part manipulation. A rehandle is only included if there is a reposition, turn over, or end-for-end followed by a different machining cut. This item does not include machining, tool replacement, inspection, or setup.

EXAMPLES

A. A rocker shaft bracket is constructed of aluminum. Four parts are cast together and an operation is necessary to separate each. While sawing the parts, the two outside ends can be milled. Thus, three saws and two side mills can be gauged on an arbor. For milling the two ends the job requires two standard high-speed steel side mills, 8-in. diameter, 3/4-in. wide. To mill apart the four pieces of the valve rocker shaft requires three 8-in. diameter, 5/16-in. wide staggered teeth standard HSS cutter. All cutters are set for right-gang cut. A horizontal arbor knee and column milling machine is available. The hand-clamping fixture must be provided with four clamping points to prevent the four brackets from shifting the fixture as they are milled apart. Two quick-acting clamps control each final part. Depth and length of cut are 1 1/4 in. each. The part weighs 13.2 lb. Find the unit and lot estimate for 680 units.

Table	Description	Time	
7.1-1	Setup 5-gang cutter, 2.35 + 2 × .30	2.95	hr
7.1-2	Make part, 2 × hr/1 = 2 × .008	.02	hr
7.1-3	Tolerance, not required		
7.2-1	Load and unload part	.24	min
7.2-1	Seat with mallet	.11	
7.2-2	Clamp and unclamp with quick-acting clamps, 2 × 4 × .04	.32	
7.2-4	Start and stop spindle	.06	
7.2-4	Trip lever, rapid traverse ready to cut, retract for clearance and stop	.30	
	Length of cut = cutter approach, safety stock + over travel = 3.46 + .14 + 0 = 3.60 in.		
11.3-3	Mill 3.60 in. Check to find longest time for sawing or side milling. 3.60 × .07	.25	
7.2-5	Position mist	.05	
	Unload 3 pieces at 3.3 lb each or 3 × .13	.39	
7.2-5	Brush away chips	.14	
7.2-5	Wipe locators with rag	.15	
11.4-7	Cutter replacement, not allowed		
22.1	Part inspection, not allowed		
	Total time for 4 units	2.01	min

		.50	min
Unit estimate		.50	min
hr/100 units		.838	
Lot estimate		8.67	hr

B. An 18-in. long SAE 1020 steel bar requires a shell mill operation, 2 × 2 in. along one edge. A vertical knee and column machine will be used. Simple table clamping is required. Each part weighs 93 lb. A similar previous operation is used. A 4-in. HSS shell mill will be considered. Find unit and lot time for 40 parts.

Table	Description	Time	
7.1-1	Holding device in prior operation is resetup	.70	hr
7.1-2	Make part time, 2 × .12	.24	hr
7.1-3	Tolerance, not allowed		
7.3	Load and unload, hoist	1.44	min
7.2-2	Allen screws, 4 × .21	.84	
7.2-4	Start and stop spindle, table	.06	
	Approach, safety allowance + over travel = .27 + .11 = .38 in.		
	Total distance milled = 18.38		
11.3-1	Mill 18.38 in. distance, 18.38 × .24	4.41	
8.2	Rapid travel 6 in., retract 24 in., at 300 in./min	.08	
7.2-5	Start coolant	.05	
7.2-5	Blow off table	.15	
11.4-2	Tool life and replacement	.30	
	Unit estimate	7.33	min
	Lot estimate	5.83	hr

C. Estimate Example B above using a base cost approach. The information for this cost estimate is found using items 7.1, 7.2, 11.3 and 11.4. The material is low-carbon steel and the tool is HSS. The lot number is 50 units. Estimate the cycle effort prior to setup because unit cost is required for setup value.

Item	Description	Cost
7.1	Setup constant for second operation	$ 8.78
	Make part, 2 × unit cost = 2 × 1.23	2.46
	Setup subtotal	$ 11.24
7.2	Cycle constant	$ 16.60
7.2	Weight factor, 93 × .101	9.39
7.2	Use rehandle for hoist	9.69
11.3	Machine cost, 18.38 × 4.24	77.93
11.4	Tool life; assume 4 min of machining, 4 × 2.24	8.96
	$/100 unit subtotal	$122.57
	Unit cost (required for setup)	$ 1.23
	Lot estimate	$ 72.53
	Average of lot, cost/unit	$ 1.45

TABLE 7.2   KNEE AND COLUMN MILLING MACHINES

Setup   See Table 7.1

Operation elements in estimating minutes

1. Pick up part, move and place; pick up and lay aside

	Weight						
Holding Device	1.0	2.5	5	10	15	25	35
Open vise; parallels; simple fixture without pins or stops	.08	.10	.13	.16	.19	.20	.22
Simple fixture with locating pins or blocks; between centers; V-block with stops	.08	.11	.14	.18	.21	.23	.25

	Weight						
Holding Device	*1.0*	*2.5*	*5*	*10*	*15*	*25*	*35*
Complex fixture with pins or blocks to fit piece; chuck or comples clamps	.09	.12	.16	.20	.24	.26	.27
Blind fixture with stops or pins; index plate with alignment; or align to mark or dial on fixture	.10	.13	.17	.22	.27	.29	.32

Seat with mallet	.11
Wipe off parallels	.26
Unwrap and wrap pc for protection	.14
Straighten several loose pcs in fixture or vise	.02/ea
Check squareness and tap with mallet to align	.51
Place gage on surface and remove	.19
Level piece	.18
Assemble split bushing or insert for hold; disassemble	.16
Pry part out	.06
Use feeler or shim for locating	.18
Load and unload in collet	.24
Load and unload part to angle plate	1.01
Load and unload part in cup arbor	.48
Load and unload part in dividing head and tail stock	.39

2. Clamp and unclamp

Vise, 1/4 turn	.05
Vise, 2 turns	.12
Small quick clamp	.04
Medium quick clamp	.05
Large quick clamp	.06
Small cam clamp, 90°–180° throw	.02
Medium cam clamp, 90°–180° throw	.03
Large cam clamp	.04
Hand (star) wheel, 2 turns	.09
Thumb wheel or screw, 2 turns	.07
Position U-clamp/ea	.08
Allen screw (2 finger turns, 2 wrench turns)/ea	.18
Hex nut/ea	.21
Air cylinder: 1 in., .06; 3 in.,	.07
C-washer, on and off	.10

3. Part or part and fixture or attachment manipulation

	Weight			
Rotate, flip	*10*	*20*	*30*	*45*
90°	.05	.07	.09	.11
180°	.06	.09	.11	.14

Trunnion fixture

Rotate	*90°*	*180°*	*270°*
Min	.11	.13	.16

	Weight				
Turn part in vise	*5*	*10*	*20*	*30*	*45*
Min	.06	.07	.09	.13	.15

Pin and unpin	.09
Turn part end-for-end in dividing head and tail stock	.25
Turn table, lock and unlock	.14
Turn table, turn per 3°	.01
Index cup arbor to 90°	.16
In collet end-for-end	.09
Between centers, end-for-end	.34

4. Knee and column milling machine operation

Start or stop spindle	.03
Start and stop spindle	.06
Reverse spindle	.04
Spindle clamp, lock and unlock	.05
Table clamp, lock and unlock	.07
Cross slide, lock and unlock	.14
Knee, lock and unlock	.25
Start, advance work to cutter feed	.12
Trip lever, rapid traverse ready to cut, after cut retract for clearance and stop	.30
Advance table transversly to stop and lock	.17
Unlock table, return transversly	.10
Raise, lower spindle, clamp, unlock	.21
Change feed to speed	
Single lever	.04
Double lever	.07
Engage clutch	.03
Adjust table dial to mark (horizontal)	.50
Adjust table dial to mark (vertical)	.32
Adjust cross feed dial to mark (vertical)	.29
Adjust spindle dial to mark (vertical)	.29
Adjust cutter or table to micrometer depth of cut	.20
Back work from cutter and stop machine	
Lever hand feed	.05
Screw hand feed	.10
Boring tool adjust	.38
Tool change for horizontal machine	4.90
Tool change for vertical machine	2.80

5. Cleaning, lubricating or wiping

Clean with air hose	
Small area 6 × 6-in. or under	.07
72 × 12-in. area	.12
12 × 12 to 12 × 24-in. area	.15
12 × 24 to 18 × 48-in. area	.18
Small fixture	.11
Large fixture	.20
Partial T-slots add'l	.15
Blow lube and chips from machined recess	.13
Brush chips	
Small area and fixture	.12
Medium area, fixture to 12 × 12 in.	.14
Large area, fixture to 12 × 24 in.	.20
Complex area and fixture	.26
Empty chips from inside of container	.11
Lubricate tool or piece	
Oil tool or piece with brush	.07
Adjust coolant or mist hose	.05
Place or remove splash guard	.08
Wash part	.06

Clean area, holding device
    Wipe locators with fingers   .04
    Wipe 6 × 6-in. area by hand   .05
    Wipe V-block or centers or attachment with rag   .15
    Wipe vise with rag   .12

6. Machining

    Face, side, slot, form, straddle, end, or saw milling   See Table 11.3
    Drill, counter bore, ream or tap   See Table 11.2

7. Milling cutter replacement   See Table 11.4

8. Part inspection   See Table 22.1

9. Rapid traverse   See Table 8.2

7.3 Bed Milling Machines

DESCRIPTION

Bed milling machines are manufacturing type machines used primarily for quantity production of identical parts. Using face and shell end mills, and arbor-mounted cutters singly or in combination, these machines can be set up for a variety of milling operations. These machines have a fixed-table support or bed. They can be further subdivided into plain-milling, with one horizontal spindle, or duplex with two horizontal spindles located on opposite sides of the table. The headstock, together with the bed, forms the main frame of the machine. The spindle carrier slides on the vertical ways of the headstock and encloses the spindle, mounted in a quill, which provides cross-wise adjustment necessary for setting up the machine. The table guided in ways is provided on the bed. It moves longitudinally, or rotates, at right angles to the axis of rotation of the spindle. The working surface of the table has a series of T-slots. (See Fig. 7.3.)

In general, bed-type milling machines are semi- or fully-automatic and of simple, but sturdy, construction. There are several distinctive features: automatic cycle of approach of cutter and work relative to each other; rapid movement during noncutting part of the cycle; and selective spindle stops and speeds. Some cross and vertical adjustments are operated manually or semi-automatically depending upon the manufacturer. After the machine is set up, the operator is required only to load and unload the machine and to start the automatic cycle, which may be controlled by pre-set switches. Numerical control features can be added. Now consider estimating data for the general class of bed milling machines.

ESTIMATING DATA DISCUSSION

Data for setup are provided in Table 7.1. Most of the operation elements are also listed in Table 7.2. Because of basic machine differences, additional elements are listed for bed milling. For many values the elements are described similarly, but the times are different. Whenever elements are the same, refer to the estimating data discussion for Tables 7.1 and 7.2.

Entry variables for load and unload are weight and type of holding device. If the part requires a crane hoist, three choices are: trunnion and L-hooks, 3-claw chain, and plain chain. A trunnion has two projecting cylinders to provide a hook point for lifting and rotation. The hoist time is for both load and unload part.

Operation costs can be estimated directly for bed milling using Item 7.3 of Section IV. These data provide handling and machine manipulation only. See Item 7.1 for milling setup, Item 11.3 for machining, Item 11.4 for tool life, and Item 22.1 for inspection.

EXAMPLES

A. Estimate the finish mill operation of the top of a cylinder block. The block is 170–197 Bhn, and depth of cut is 1/16 in. The width of cut varies between 2 5/8 in. minimum and 7 1/2 in. maximum due to core openings. The length of the surface to be

FIGURE 7.3 Bed milling machine with two horizontal milling cutters. *(White-Sundstrand Machine Tool, Incorporated)*

milled is 31 1/4 in. Locating points are two crankshaft bearings at opposed ends. A 9-in. diameter 20-tooth carbide face mill for right-hand cutting is necessary to overlap on the 7 1/2-in. width of surface. The weight of the casting requires a crane hoist. The fixture has two sliding and tapered plugs and two loading rails. Determine the unit and shop estimate for a lot quantity of 675 units.

Table	Description	Time
7.3-1	Hook, hoist, load, and unload	1.44 min
7.3-1	Seat with mallet, 2 × .11	.22
7.3-2	Air cylinder	.07
8.2	Move table to approach at rapid traverse rate, 3.5 in. at 200 in./min	.02
11.3-1	Cutter approach, safety stock, and overtravel at end of cut = 2 + .17 + 2 = 4.17. Total length at feed = 4.17 + 31.25 = 35.42 in.	
11.3-2	Face mill. 35.42 in. × .19 (Use 8-in. diameter.)	6.73
8.2	Table travel after ending feed and rapid traverse back = 10 + 47 = 57 in.	.30
7.3-4	Change feed	.03
7.3-5	Blow fixture	.20
7.3-5	Adjust coolant	.05
7.3-5	Wipe locators	.05
11.4-2	Milling cutter replacement	1.00
22.1	Part inspection (during cutting time)	
	Unit estimate	10.11 min
	Shop estimate	5.9 pc/hr

B. Large hexagon nuts, alloy steel, 250–300 Bhn, have six surfaces to be milled. The depth of cut is 1/4 in. Width of cut is 3 7/16 in. along one of the six sides of the nut. The length of cut is 1 11/16 in. Locating is off a preturned hole. The six surfaces of the nut can be straddle milled, two at a time, and indexed twice. Cutters are side type with inserted blades of sintered carbide of a grade suitable for milling alloy steel. The cutters are 8 in. in diameter and the number of teeth is standard. Two surfaces are plunged in conjunction with indexing. The nut is placed and removed from the indexing fixture by hand and the fixture is hand operated. One turn of the index crank is equivalent to 60° rotation of the nut and brings a new pair of surfaces into position. A clearance of 12 in. is necessary for safe loading. The bed-type milling machine will have an automatic table cycle controlled by trip dogs. A machine sufficient in size for horsepower is identified. Each unit weighs 7.65 lb. A bed machine with specific performance capability is selected by the estimator. Find hr/100 units and shop time for 125 units.

Table	Description	Time	
7.1-1	Straddle mill with expanding plug	2.00	hr
7.1-2	Make parts, not allowed		
7.1-3	Commercial inspection, not allowed		
7.3-1	Load and unload	.22	min
7.3-1	Medium quick clamp	.05	
7.3-4	Start and stop spindle	.06	
8.2-1	Table travel to beginning of feed + travel at end of feed = 12 + 12 = 24 at rapid traverse rate of 150 in./min	.13	
11.3-3	Safety stock + approach + overtravel = .14 + .53 + .53 = 1.20 in. Straddle mill (1.20 + 1 11/16 = 2.89), 2.89 × .25	.72	
7.3-3	Index two times for new surfaces, 2 × .05	.10	
11.3-3	Straddle mill two additional times, .72 × 2	1.44	
	Unit estimate	2.70	min
	hr/100 units	4.500	
	Shop time	5.63	hr

C. Estimate unit cost for Example A with a base-cost approach. Include setup and optional cost for making part. It is more practical to estimate the $/100 units before setup conditions.

Item	Description	Cost
7.1	Setup	$ 13.79
7.1	2 × cycle cost = 2 × 1.45	2.90
	Setup subtotal	$ 16.69
7.3	Constant cycle cost	$ 7.85
7.3	Hoist	21.70
11.3	Face cast iron with carbide, 35.42 × 2.81	99.53
11.4	Tool replacement on estimate of 7 min, 7 × 2.24	15.68
	$/100 total	$144.76

TABLE 7.3 BED MILLING MACHINES

Setup See Table 7.1

Operation elements in estimating minutes

1. Pick up part, move and place; pick up and lay aside

	Weight						
Holding Device	5	10	15	25	35	45	60
Open vise; parallels; simple fixture without pins or stops	.13	.16	.19	.20	.22	.24	.26
Simple fixture with locating pins or blocks; between centers; V-blocks with stops	.14	.18	.21	.23	.25	.28	.31
Complex fixture with pins or blocks to fit piece; chuck or complex clamps	.16	.20	.24	.26	.27	.31	.35
Blind fixture with stops or pins; index plate with alignment; or align to mark or dial on fixture	.17	.22	.27	.29	.32	.37	.40

Position, hook hoist to parts on pallet, hoist part to holding device, aside hoist;
and remove part to pallet using:

Trunnion, L-hooks, or tongs	1.44
3-claw chain	1.55
Plain chain	1.89
Place cardboard, per layer, on skid	.12
Seat with mallet	.11
Wipe off parallels	.26
Straighten several loose parts in fixture or vise	.02
Check squareness and tap with mallet to align	.51
Level part	.18
Load and unload part to angle plate	1.01
Pry part out	.06
Use feeler or shim for locating	.18

2. Clamp and unclamp

Vise, ¼ turn	.05
Vise, 2 turns	.12
Medium V-quick clamp	.05
Large quick clamp	.06
Medium cam clamp, 90°–180° throw	.03
Large cam clamp	.04
Hand (star) wheel, 2 turns	.09
Thumb wheel or screw	.07
Position U-clamp/ea	.08
Allen screw (2 finger turns, 2 wrench turns)/ea	.18
Hex nut/ea	.21
Air clinder : 1 in., .06; 3 in. .07	
Operate foot-air clamp	.02

3. Part or part and fixture or attachment manipulation

	Weight				
Rotate, flip	10	20	30	45	60
90°	.05	.07	.09	.11	.13
180°	.06	.09	.11	.14	.16

Trunnion fixture

Rotate	90°	180°	270°
Min	.11	.13	.16

	Weight					
Turn part in vise	5	10	20	30	45	60
Min	.06	.07	.09	.13	.15	.21

4. Bed milling machine operation

Start or stop spindle	.03
Start and stop spindle	.06
Reverse spindle	.04
Spindle clamp, lock and unlock	.05
Start, advance work to cutter feed; after cut, retract for clearance and automatic stop	.12
Advance table transversly to stop and lock	.17
Unlock table, return transversly away from work	.10
Change feed or speed	.03
Adjust table dial to mark	.25

5. Cleaning, lubricating, or wiping

    Clean with air hose

        Small area 6 × 6-in. or under   .07

        12 × 12-in. area   .12

        12 × 12-in. to 12 × 24-in. area   .15

        12 × 24-in. to 18 × 48-in. area   .18

        Small fixture   .11

        Large fixture   .20

        Partial T-slots, add'l   .15

        Blow lube and chips from machined recess, add'l   .13

    Brush chips

        Small area and fixture   .12

        Medium area, fixture to 12 × 12 in.   .14

        Large area, fixture to 12 × 24 in.   .20

        Complex area and fixture   .26

    Lubricate tool or piece

        Oil tool or piece with brush   .07

        Adjust coolant or mist hose   .05

    Clean area, holding device

        Wipe locators with fingers   .04

        Wipe 6 × 6-in. area by hand   .05

        Wipe V-block or centers or attachment with rag   .15

        Wipe vise with rag   .12

6. Machining

    Face, side, slot, form, straddle, end or saw milling   See Table 11.3

    Drill, counterbore, or ream   See Table 11.2

7. Milling cutter replacement   See Table 11.4

8. Part inspection   See Table 22.1

9. Rapid traverse   See Table 8.2

7.4 Vertical-Spindle Ram-Type Milling Machines

DESCRIPTION

The design includes a knee and column support arrangement for the table. A saddle supporting the table provides in-and-out motions with respect to the column. The motor is mounted on the tool head supported by the overarm. A feature of this machine is the ram. The ram is a sliding element of the machines overarm and enables the spindle to move via hand crank or power, in and out, parallel to the movement of the saddle. Ram-type vertical mills can incorporate other motions. The entire ram overarm can pivot about the main upright axis to describe an arc over the worktable. Another motion is the ability to tilt the spindle axis off of vertical, either right or left, and forward or aft.

The machines operate at low horsepower and have a toolroom or light milling orientation. End mills are a common form of tooling but formed cutters for slotting and dovetailing and shell-type cutters for milling flat surfaces are suitable. These machines can also handle boring and tapping operations.

The turret model shown in Figure 7.4 has a 4 hp variable speed motor, 58-in. table length, 15-in. cross travel and a 15-in. vertical capacity.

ESTIMATING DATA DISCUSSION

Data for setup are listed in Table 7.1, and most of the operation elements are also listed in Table 7.2.

FIGURE 7.4 Vertical-spindle turret-type milling machine. *(Bridgeport Machines)*

Because of machine differences, additional elements are provided for vertical-spindle ram-type milling machines. In some cases, the elements are described similarly, but the times are different.

While Table 7.4 provides elements in terms of minutes, operational costs for this same machine can be estimated in $/100 units using Item 7.4 of Section IV. The entry variables are weight for the part and rehandling. The constant includes machine operation, clamping, and a proportionate cost for handling. The cost factor is for incremental handling and is related to weight. If the part has other surfaces that are milled, the constant cost is given again. If the part is removed, repositioned, and reclamped, the rehandling cost is given per occurrence. Item 7.4 does not include cutting, tool replacement, and inspection costs. Other operational cost items are used for those requirements.

EXAMPLES

A. An aluminum cast head is end milled. The bored hole is .750 in. OD and 2 in. deep. The depth of cut is 1/32 in. Length of cut is 2 in. The head weighs 6.28 lb. Fixture mounting is critical and tolerance checking is to be added to the estimate. Find the unit estimate, hr/unit, and the lot estimate for 87 units.

Table	Description	Time	
7.1-S1	Table setup	1.45	hr
7.1-S2	Make part, 2 × unit estimate	.04	hr
7.1-S3	Tolerance check, .001-in. depth tolerance	.13	hr
7.4-1	Load and unload part	.20	min
7.4-2	Clamp, 2 places 2 × .09	.18	
7.4-2	Pry part, add'l	.06	
7.4-4	Start and stop boring head	.06	
8.2-1	Rapid traverse ready to cut and retract	.16	
11.3-4	End mill opening, 2 × .01, ¾-in. cutter, HSS	.02	
7.4-5	Adjust mist	.05	
7.4-5	Blow chips	.15	
11.4-2	Tool wear out allowance	0	
22.1-3	Part inspection with depth micrometer, .001-in. tolerance	.29	
	Unit estimate	1.17	min
	hr/unit	.020	
	Lot estimate	3.317	hr

B. An aluminum cast head has a manifold area faced milled. Surface area is 8.25 × 2 in. overall with various cored areas. The head weighs 6.28 lb and tolerances are not critical. A previous fixture is used. An HSS 4-in. shell mill is used. Find pc/hr for the job.

Table	Description	Time
7.1-S1	Re-setup of previous operation	.75 hr
7.1-S2	Make part, not allowed	
7.1-S3	Tolerance check, not allowed	
7.4-1	Load and unload part	.20 min
7.4-2	2 star wheels 2 × .09	.18
7.4-4	Start and advance work to cutter feed	.12
	Cutter approach, safety stock allowance + overtravel = .27 + .11 = .38. Shell mill .38 + 8.25 = 8.63 in.	
11.1-3	Shell mill, 8.63 × .01	.08
7.4-5	Adjust mist hose	.05
7.4-5	Blow chips	.15
	Unit estimate	.78 min
	pc/hr	76

C. Find the base cost for Example A above using Items 7.4, 11.3, and 22.1. Find unit and lot cost for 90 units.

Item	Description	Cost
7.1	Setup constant	$13.79
7.1	Make part, 2 × unit cost, 2 × 17.39/100	.35
	Tolerance cost, estimate	5.00
	Setup subtotal	$19.14
7.4	Cycle constant	$12.40
7.4	Weight factor, 6.28 × .201	1.26
11.3	End mill, .357 × $\frac{1}{32}$	.01
22.1	Tolerance check for .001 in.	3.72
	$/100 units subtotal	$17.39
	Lot cost	$36.53
	Unit cost	$ .41

TABLE 7.4 VERTICAL-SPINDLE RAM-TYPE MILLING MACHINES

Setup   **See Table 7.1**

Operation elements in estimating minutes

1. Pick up part, move and place; pick up and lay aside

	Weight				
Holding Device	1.0	2.5	5	10	15
Open vise; parallels; simple fixture without pins or stops	.08	.10	.13	.16	.19
Simple fixture with locating pins or blocks; between centers; V-blocks with stops	.08	.11	.14	.18	.21
Complex fixture with pins or blocks to fit piece; chuck or complex clamps	.09	.12	.16	.20	.24
Blind fixture with stops or pins; index plate with alignment; or align to mark or dial on fixture	.10	.13	.17	.22	.27
Seat with mallet					.11
Wipe off parallels					.26

Check squareness and tap with mallet to align	.51
Place gage on surface and remove	.19
Level part	.18
Assemble split bushing or insert for holding and disassemble	.16
Load and unload part in collet	.24
Load and unload part to angle plate	1.01
Load and unload part in cup arbor	.48
Load and unload part in dividing head and tail stock	.39
Pry part out	.06
Use feeler or shim for locating	.18

2. Clamp and unclamp

Vise, ¼ turn	.05
Vise, 2 turns	.12
Small quick clamp	.04
Medium quick clamp	.05
Small cam clamp, 90°–180° throw	.02
Medium cam clamp, 90°–180° throw	.03
Hand (star) wheel, 2 turns	.09
Thumb wheel or screw, 2 turns	.07
Position U-clamp leach	.08
Allen screw (2 finger turns, 2 wrench turns)/ea	.18
Hex nut/ea	.21
Air cylinder: 1 in., .06; 3 in., .07	

3. Part or part and fixture or attachment manipulation

	Weight		
Rotate, flip	10	20	30
90°	.05	.07	.09
180°	.06	.09	.11

Trunnion fixture

Rotate	90°	180°	270°
Min	.11	.13	.16

Pin, unpin	.09

	Weight			
Turn part in vise	5	10	20	30
Min	.06	.07	.09	.13

Advance rotary table to work and return to load position. Each 4.5°	.01
Place and remove spacer block	.05

4. Turret milling machine operation

Start or stop spindle	.03
Start and stop spindle	.06
Reverse spindle	.04
Ram or headstock swivel clamp, lock and unlock	.19
Spindle clamp, lock and unlock	.05
Table clamp, lock and unlock	.07
Cross-slide, lock and unlock	.14
Start and advance work to cutter feed	.12
Trip lever, rapid traverse ready to cut, after cut retract for clearance and stop	.16
Jog table transversely to stop and lock	.17
Unlock, jog table transversely	.10
Raise, lower spindle, clamp, unlock	.21
Change feed or speed	.05

Adjust table dial to mark (horizontal)	.40
Adjust table dial to mark (vertical)	.28
Adjust cross feed dial to mark	.26
Adjust cutter or table to micrometer depth of cut	.20
Lower spindle 1 in.	.03
Lower spindle 1 in. and lock	.04
Raise spindle 1 in.	.02
Unlock and raise spindle	.04
Advance table and engage feed	.10
Return table	.08

5. Cleaning, lubricating or wiping

Clean with air hose	
Small area, 6 × 6-in. or under	.07
12 × 12-in. area	.12
12 × 12-in. to 12 × 24-in. area	.15
Small fixture	.11
Partial T-slots, add'l	.15
Blow lube and chips from machined recess, add'l	.13
Brush chips	
Small area and fixture	.12
Medium area, fixture to 12 × 12 in.	.14
Lube tool or piece with brush	.07
Adjust coolant or mist hose	.05
Clean area, holding device	
Wipe locators with fingers	.04
Wipe 6 × 6-in. area, by hand	.05
Wipe V-block or centers or attachment with rag	.15
Wipe vise with rag	.12

6. Machining

Face or end milling	See Table 11.3
Drill, counterbore, ream, or tap	See Table 11.2

7. Milling cutter replacement   See Table 11.4

8. Part inspection   See Table 22.1

7.5 Router Milling Machines

DESCRIPTION

Routers use high speeds, often in excess of 10,000 rpm, to face mill, profile, pocket, cut, or drill nonferrous metals and plastics. Routers can be classified as radial, profile, and shaper. The radial-type has a moveable head with the cutter in a vertical position mounted on hinged arms which allow motion over the table. A profile router has the cutter mounted in a rotating-spindle, fixed-position head stock. In this machine, profiling and pocketing is controlled by the movement of a pattern over a guide pin, while depth is controlled by vertical movement of head. In the shaper-type, the cutter head is mounted under the machine table and pro-

jects above surface. A guide is fastened to the table for positioning of the workpiece.

The router shown in Figure 7.5 has push-button controls, allows for interchanging heads, guide pin lock and release, handwheel for vertical table adjustment, and airfoot pedal for lowering and raising router head.

ESTIMATING DATA DISCUSSION

Data for setup are listed in Table 7.1, and most of the operation elements are also listed in Table 7.2. Because of machine differences, additional ele-

FIGURE 7.5 Milling router. *(Onsrud Division, Danly Machine Corporation)*

ments are provided for router machines. In some cases the elements are described similarly, but times may differ. For a description of the elements, see 7.2.

If you wish to estimate base cost directly, rather than minutes, Item 7.5 in Section IV can be used. These costs are for handling only. They are a condensation of Table 7.5, router data. Entry variables for Item 7.5 are weight and rehandling. The constant cost includes machine operation, clamping of part, and a proportionate cost for handling. The weight multiplies the factor and is for incremental handling. If the operation calls for other surfaces to be routed, and if the part is removed from a fixture, turned over, and reclamped, the rehandling cost is given per occurrence. Item 7.4 does not include cutting (see Item 11.3) or tool replacement (see Item 11.4) or inspection (see Item 22.1).

EXAMPLES

A. An aluminum alloy is routed in a pocket operation. A two-flute end mill, 3/4 in. diameter, is used to pocket an inside step. The shape of the pocket is controlled by movement of pattern over a guide pin. The aluminum part has holes drilled and reamed through the part for locating on the pattern. Two small quick clamps hold the part against the plate. The pocket is 21 in. long and the part weighs 2.4 lb. Find the unit estimate.

Table	Description	Time
7.1-S	Table setup	1.40 hr
7.5-1	Load and unload	.11 min
7.5-2	2 small quick-acting clamps	.08
7.5-4	Start and stop machine	.05
7.5-4	Lower and raise head 1 in.	.10
11.3-5	End mill with ¾-in. HSS 21 in., .01 × 21	.21
7.5-5	Blow off table top	.12
	Unit estimate	.67 min

B. A hydraulic automatic transmission valve body is face milled with a carbide 4-tooth 4-in. cutter. The body is 6-in. wide requiring two passes 8-in. long. The holding fixture is a vise with handle bars allowing the fixture and part to be hand fed under the cutter. A stock of 1/16 in. is removed. The body weighs 12.3 lb. Estimate the hourly production.

Table	Description	Time
7.1-S1	Vise with end-mill setup	1.45 hr
7.5-1	Load and unload part	.19 min
7.5-2	Two quick-acting clamps	.08
7.5-4	Start and stop spindle	.05
7.5-5	Adjust mist hose	.05
	Cutter approach + safety distance = .68 + .11 = .79 in. Total length per pass = 8.79	
11.3-1	Face mill 8.79 in two passes = 8.79 × .01 × 2 =	.18
7.5-5	Blow off chips	.15
	Unit estimate	.70 min
	pc/hr	86

C. Four .0625-in. plastic strips are clamped together and fed along a fence mounted to a table. Each 24-in. strip has several holes predrilled allowing location on a sliding fixture element with 2 pins. A 1-in. end mill, 2 flute, is used to edge the four parts. Find the lot estimate for 1250 units.

Table	Description	Time
7.1-S1	Table setup with end mill	1.55 hr
7.5-1	Load and unload 4 parts, 4 × .08	.32 min
7.5-2	Allen screws, 2 × .18	.36
7.5-4	Start and stop spindle	.05
11.3-4	Side mill 24 in. long plastic part, .05 × 24	1.20
7.5-5	Blow plastic chips	.28
	Four strip total estimate	2.21 min
	Unit estimate	.55 min
	Lot estimate	13.06 hr

D. Estimate Example A above using the base-cost methods. Information will be found in Items 7.1, 7.5, 11.3.

Item	Description	Cost
7.1	Setup constant	$17.56
7.5	Cycle constant	$10.60
7.5	Weight factor, 2.4 × .146	.35
11.3	End mill, 21 × .357	7.50
	$/100 units subtotal	$18.45
	Unit estimate (no setup costs)	$ .18
	Setup cost	$17.56
	Lot cost for 267 units	$66.82

TABLE 7.5 ROUTER MILLING MACHINES

Setup   **See Table 7.1**

Operation elements in estimating minutes

1. Pick up part, move and place; pick up and lay aside

		Weight			
Holding Device	1.0	2.5	5	10	15
Open vise; parallels; simple fixture without pins or stops	.08	.10	.13	.16	.19
Simple fixture with locating pins or blocks; between centers; V-blocks with stops	.08	.11	.14	.18	.21
Straighten several loose parts in fixture or vise					.02
Pry part out					.06
Unwrap and wrap part for protection					.12

2. Clamp and unclamp

Vise, ¼ turn	.05
Vise, 2 turns	.12
Small quick clamp	.04
Small cam clamp, 90°–180° throw	.02
Hand (star) wheel, 2 turns	.09
Position U-clamp	.08
Allen screw, (2 finger turns, 2 wrench turns)	.18
Hex nut/ea (2 finger turns, 2 wrench turns)	.21
Air cylinder 1-in. throw	.06

3. Part or part and fixture or attachment manipulation

	Weight		
Rotate, flip	10	20	30
90°	.05	.07	.09
180°	.06	.09	.11

Trunnion fixture

Rotate	90°	180°	270°
Min	.11	.13	.16

Pin, unpin   .09

	Weight			
Turn part in vise	5	10	20	30
Min	.06	.07	.09	.13

4. Router milling machine operation

Start and stop spindle	.05
Raise or lower head and cutter, 1 in.	.10
Handwheel adjustment of table, 1 in.	.30
Guide pin lock and release	.25
Change spindle speed	.14
Set depth stops	.35
Tilt table and lock	.50
Adjust table fence	.60
Brake air spindle	.05

5. Cleaning, lubricating or wiping

Clean with air hose	
Small area 6 × 6-in. or under	.07
12 × 12-in. area	.12
12 × 12-in. to 12 × 24-in. area	.15
12 × 24-in. to 36 × 48-in. table	.28
Add'l for excessive aluminum or plastic chips	.15
Small fixture	.11
Blow lube and chips from machined recess, add'l	.13
Brush chips from small area including fixture	.12
Adjust mist hose	.05
Wipe locators with fingers	.04

6. Machining

Face, end or engrave milling	See Table 11.3
Drill	See Table 11.2

7. Milling cutter replacement   See Table 11.4

8. Part inspection   See Table 22.1

7.6 Special Milling Machines

DESCRIPTION

The family of milling machine types is diversified and a great variety of models is available. To provide estimating data becomes cumbersome due to these distinctions. Thus, we have identified milling machines as standard and special. The standard milling machines are described elsewhere. The special machines are not divided into subgroups. Trade names abound, such as duplicators, panto mills, contour, planer, engravers, hydrotel, etc. Our purpose is to show estimating data for these special machines as a unit.

Figure 7.6 is a 40-in. Hydro-Tel Milling Machine with switchable computer NC and a universal electronic tracer. Three milling heads are found in this machine. Notice that this machine has a traveling planer bed. A follower is shown suspended from the crossrail on the right side.

ESTIMATING DATA DISCUSSION

Data for setup are listed in Table 7.1, and most of the operation elements are also listed in Table 7.2. Because of machine differences, additional elements are provided for special milling machines. In some cases the elements are described similarly, but the times may differ. For a description of the elements, see 7.2.

The estimate can also be figured in base cost, and the methods are easier than using time. For a base-cost estimate, use Item 7.6 of Section IV. Entry variables are pounds, rehandle, and hoist. The constant cost covers handling (partially), clamping, machine manipulation, and oiling. Additional handling is covered by the factor which relates to weight. Rehandle covers the work where the part is rearranged on the table. If a hoist is required, a cost is provided, but remember to include the constant cost also.

EXAMPLES

A. Keyways are milled simultaneously on two steel shafts placed abreast on the table of a rise-and-fall milling machine. The keyway is 1/4 in. wide × 11 in. long × .145 in. deep in a 1-in. OD soft-steel bar stock. The two shafts are placed in V-blocks, side by side against end stops, and are clamped with two hand clamps. Two HSS staggered tooth slotting cutters are spaced at a required distance on an arbor. The rise and fall feature engages the cutter into the bar stock with a minimum approach. Cutter size is 3-in. dia. Find lot size for 34 units.

FIGURE 7.6 Hydro-tel milling machine with switchable computer numerical control and universal electronic tracer. *(Cincinnati Milacron)*

Table	Description	Time
7.1-S1	Table setup with straddle mill	1.90 hr
7.1-S2	Make part time, 2 × .061	.12 hr
7.1-S3	Inspection, not allowed	
7.6-1	Load 2.5 lb stock in V-blocks, 2 × .14	.28 min
7.6-2	Small cam clamp, 2 × .02	.04
7.6-4	Start and stop spindle	.06
7.6-5	Adjust lubricant	.05
	Rapid traverse cutter to work + safety. Stock = .83 + .11 = .94	
11.3-3	Mill 11.94 in. of stock, 11.94 × .55	6.57
8.2-1	Rapid retract 12 in. at 80 in./min	.15
7.6-5	Blow off chips	.18
	Two-part estimate	7.33 min
	Unit estimate	3.67 min
	Lot estimate	4.10 hr

B. A pocket and a step operation is planned for a milling machine using a duplicating arm mechanism. The size of the reduction is 2 to 1. The end mill is 1/8 in. in diameter, 2 flute HSS. A slot 1/8 in. in width is milled 1/8 in. deep inside the edge of an aluminum extrusion 9.2-in. long. The step is 8.6 in. in length, and 1/16-in. wide and deep. Find the unit estimate.

Table	Description	Time
7.1-S1	Table setup with part length, 12 in. for end mill	1.60 hr
7.1-S2	Make part, 2 × .038	.08 hr
7.6-5	Clean nest with air	.15 min
7.6-1	Load and unload, 3.1 lb part	.13
7.6-2	2 thumbscrews	.14
7.6-5	Lubricate piece	.07
7.6-4	Start and stop spindle	.06
7.6-4	Position $1/8$-in. tool to work	.20
11.3-4	Mill $1/8$-in., 9.2 × .03	.28
7.6-5	Blow chips	.15
7.6-4	Start and stop spindle	.06
9.3-4	Key-chuck tool change	.30
7.6-4	Position $1/16$-in. tool to work	.20
7.6-4	Change speed	.07
11.3-4	Mill $1/16$-in., 8.6 × .04	.34
7.6-5	Blow chips	.15
	Unit estimate	2.30 min

C. Determine the base cost for Example A above using Items 7.6, 11.3 and 8.2. Lot size is 34 units. Assume 300-grade stainless steel. Usually cycle cost is determined prior to setup.

Item	Description	Cost
7.1	Setup for straddle mill	$ 22.58
	Make cost, 2 × unit cost, 2 × 1.17	2.34
	Setup subtotal	$ 24.92
7.6	Cycle constant	$ 14.70
7.6	Loading factor 2.5 × 2 × .059 (for two parts)	.30
11.3	Mill 11.94 × 18.2	217.32
8.2	Rapid retract 12 × .121	1.45
	$/200 units subtotal	$233.77
	$/100 units subtotal	$116.89
	Lot cost	$ 64.66

TABLE 7.6 SPECIAL MILLING MACHINES

Setup   **See Table 7.1**

Operation elements in estimating minutes

1. Pick up part, move and place; pick up and lay aside

				Weight			
Holding Device	5	10	15	25	35	45	60
Open vise; parallels; simple fixture without pins or stops	.13	.16	.19	.20	.22	.24	.26
Simple fixture with locating pins or blocks; between centers; V-blocks with stops	.14	.18	.21	.23	.25	.28	.31
Complex fixture with pins or blocks to fit piece; chuck or complex clamps	.16	.20	.24	.26	.27	.31	.35
Blind fixture with stops or pins; index plate with alignment; or align to mark or dial on fixture	.17	.22	.27	.29	.32	.37	.40

Position hook hoist to part on pallet, hoist, part to holding device, aside hoist; and remove part to pallet using trunnion, L-hooks, or tongs	1.44
3-claw chain	1.55
Plain chain	1.89
Seat with mallet	.11
Wipe off parallels	.26
Unwrap and wrap part for protection	.24
Straighten several loose parts in fixture or vise	.02
Check squareness and tap with mallet to align	.51
Place gage on surface and remove	.19
Level part	.18
Assemble split bushing or insert for hold and disassemble	.16
Load and unload part in collet	.24
Load and unload part in angle plate	1.01
Load and unload part in cup arbor	.48
Load and unload part in dividing head and tail stock	.39
Place on index head and tighten nut	.06
Pry part out	.06
Use feeler or shim for locating	.18
For engraver machine, slide small part to stops	.04
For engraved piece, fill character, clean off excess, per character	.01

2. Clamp and unclamp

Vise, ¼ turn	.05
Vise, 2 turns	.12
Small quick clamp	.04
Medium quick clamp	.05
Large quick clamp	.06
Small cam clamp, 90°–180° throw	.02
Medium cam clamp, 90°–180° throw	.03
Large cam clamp	.04
Hand (star) wheel, 2 turns	.09
Thumb wheel or screw, 2 turns	.07
Position U-clamp/ea	.08
Allen screw (2 finger turns, 2 wrench turns)/ea	.18
Hex nut/ea	.21
Air cylinder: 1-in. throw, .06; 3-in. throw	.07

3. Part or part and fixture or attachment manipulation

Rotate, flip	Weight				
	10	20	30	45	60
90°	.05	.07	.09	.11	.13
180°	.06	.09	.11	.14	.16

Trunnion fixture

Rotate	90°	180°	270°
Min	.11	.13	.16

Pin, unpin .09

Turn part in vise	Weight					
	5	10	20	30	45	60
Min	.06	.07	.09	.13	.15	.21

4. Special milling machine operation

Start or stop spindle	.03
Start and stop spindle	.06
Reverse spindle	.04
Spindle clamp, lock and unlock, raise	.24
Table clamp, lock and unlock	.08
Cross-slide, lock and unlock	.15
Swivel head, lock and unlock	.22
Start, advance work to cutter feed	.14
Advance table transversely to stop and lock	.19
Unlock table, return transversely	.12
Change feed or speed	.07
Adjust dial to mark	.35
Adjust cutter or table to micrometer depth of cut	.20
For each manual shift of tool	.06
For each manual shift of stylus on pattern	.18

5. Cleaning, lubricating or wiping

Clean with air hose	
Small area 6 × 6-in. or under	.07
12 × 12-in. area	.12
12 × 12-in. to 12 × 24-in. area	.15
12 × 24-in. to 18 × 48-in. area	.18
Small fixture	.11
Large fixture	.20
Partial T-slots, add'l	.15
Blow lube and chips from machined recess, add'l	.13
Brush chips	
Small area and fixture	.12
Medium area, fixture to 12 × 12 in.	.14
Large area, fixture to 12 × 24 in.	.20
Complex area and fixture	.26
Lubricate tool or piece	
Oil tool or piece with brush	.07
Adjust coolant or mist hose	.05
Clean area, holding device	
Wipe locators with fingers	.04
Wipe 6 × 6-in. area by hand	.05
Wipe V-block or centers or attachment with rag	.15
Wipe vise with rag	.12

6. Machining

Face, side, slot, form straddle, end, saw, or engrave milling	See Table 11.3
Drill, counterbore, ream, or tap	See Table 11.2

7. Milling cutter replacement   See Table 11.4

8. Part inspection   See Table 22.1

7.7 Hand Milling Machines

DESCRIPTION

Hand millers are a class of manually-fed machines where the table is controlled by the operator. The operator may use a hand-feed lever or a wheel. Customarily, the spindles are horizontal, and arbor-mounted cutters are common. The tables are about 30 in. in length, and width is approximately 10 in. T-slots are available for mounting light fixtures and attachments. Parts are loaded manually, and their size is small.

Figure 7.7 shows two milling machines where hand-lever controls feeds to head, saddle and table motion. Other models may have motorized feeds.

ESTIMATING DATA DISCUSSION

Data for setup are listed in Table 7.1, and most of the operation elements are also described in 7.2. Because of machine differences, additional elements are provided for hand miller machines. In

FIGURE 7.7 Hand-lever control feeding of small milling machines. (*Barker Milling Machine Company*)

212

some cases the elements are described similarly, but times differ.

Costs may be estimated for the hand miller using Item 7.7 of Section IV. This alternate method is faster than element estimating and is almost as accurate over a sample of estimates. The entry variables are part weight and a rehandle. The constant cost includes handling (partial), clamping, and machine manipulation. Additional handling cost is allowed by the weight factor. If the part is removed from the fixture and repositioned for another cut during the same operation, a rehandling cost per occurrence is included. Item 7.7 does not include cutting, tool replacement, or inspection costs. Other operational cost estimates are used for this work and are included to arrive at a cost per 100 units ($/100 units). Setup costs for the hand miller are included in Item 7.1.

EXAMPLES

A. Alloy steel rods are splined milled on two ends. Shafts, 14.65-in. long and 1/2 in. in diameter, weigh .8 lb. Inserted into a collet and indexed by a dividing head, each end has four splines milled a length of 1.215 in. by a specially-formed cutter 4 in. in diameter. However, it is similar to a plain cutter. Tolerances are commercial. Lot size is 125 units. Find unit and lot estimate.

Table	Description	Time
7.1-1S	Setup collet with indexing	1.25 hr
7.1-2S	Make part, 2 × unit estimate	.18 hr
7.1-3	Tolerance check, not allowed	
7.7-1	Load and unload part in collet	.24 min
7.7-4	Start and stop spindle	.06
7.7-4	Advance, ready to cut, retract	.09
11.3-3	Slot 1.215 in., 1.215 × .97	1.17
7.7-3	Rotate collet	.04
Repeat	Repeat 3 above elements for 3 more splines, 3 × (.09 + 1.17 + .04)	3.90
7.7-3	Turn end-for-end in collet	.09
Repeat	Repeat advance, slot and rotate, 4 × 1.30	5.20
	Unit estimate	10.79 min
	Lot estimate	23.91 hr

B. An aluminum extrusion having an irregular area but cutting length of .6 in. is sawed by a hand milling operation. The extrusion is 20 in. in length and pushed against a stop, followed by the sawing operation. For a large quantity, find hr/1000 units. The extrusion weighs 6.1 lb., and the cutter is a standard. Each extrusion yields 27 parts.

Table	Description	Time
7.7-1	Load extrusion	.14 min
7.7-2	Quick clamp	.04
7.7-4	Start and stop spindle	.06
Estimate	Push against stop	.02
11.3-5	Saw aluminum, .6 × .06	.04
Repeat	Repeat push and saw element 26 times, 26 × .06	1.56
7.7-1	Toss aside scrap	.03
7.7-5	Blow scrap	.15
	Extrusion estimate	2.04 min
	Unit estimate	.075 min
	hr/1000 units	1.259

C. Find the unit and lot cost for Example A above. Chip making cost uses Item 11.3. Eight splines are milled per unit.

Item	Description	Cost
7.1	Setup, use slotting costs	$ 17.56
	Setup subtotal	$ 17.56
7.7	Constant cost	$ 7.61
7.7	Weight constant, .8 × .266	.21
7.7	Rehandle end-for-end	5.47
11.3	Slot, 1.215 × 18.2	22.11
7.7	Rehandle, use for collet rotation, at 50%, .5 × 5.47 × 4	10.94
11.3	Mill 7 more splines, 7 × 22.11 (1.215 × 18.2)	154.79
	$/100 units subtotal	$201.13
	Lot cost for 125 units	$268.97

TABLE 7.7   HAND MILLING MACHINES

Setup   **See Table 7.1**

Operation elements in estimating minutes

1. Pick up part, move and place; pick up and lay aside

		Weight		
Holding Device	½	1	2 ½	5
Open vise; parallels; simple fixture without pins or stops	.06	.08	.10	.13
Simple fixture with locating pins or blocks; between centers; V-blocks with stops	.07	.08	.11	.14

Seat with mallet	.11
Wipe off parallels	.26
Straighten several loose parts in fixture or vise	.02
Check squareness and tap with mallet to align	.51
Load and unload part in collet	.24
Load and unload part in dividing head and tailstock	.39
Load and unload part in universal chuck	.32
Pry part out	.06
Use feeler or shim for locating	.18
Air eject, deduct	.04
Toss aside, deduct	.03

2. Clamp and unclamp

Vise, ¼ turn	.05
Small quick clamp	.04
Small cam clamp. 90°–180° throw	.02
Hand (star) wheel, 2 turns	.09
Thumb wheel or screw, 2 turns	.07
Position U-clamp	.08
Allen screw (2 finger turns, 2 wrench turns)	.18
Hex nut/ea	.21
Air cylinder, 1-in. throw	.06

3. Part or part and fixture or attachment manipulation

	Weight		
Rotate, flip	5	10	20
90°	.04	.05	.07
180°	.05	.06	.09

Trunnion fixture

Rotate	90°	180°	270°
Min	.11	.13	.16

Pin, unpin .09

Turn part in vise	Weight		
	5	10	20
Min	.06	.07	.09

In collet, end-for-end .09
Turn part, end-for-end, in dividing head and tail stock .25

4. Hand miller machine operation

Start or stop spindle .03
Start and stop spindle .06
Reverse spindle .04
Spindle clamp, lock and unlock .05
Table clamp, lock and unlock .07
Trip lever, advance ready to cut; after cut, retract for clearance and stop .09
Change speed or screw feed .07
Adjust cutter or table to micrometer depth of cut .20
Back work from cutter and stop machine .06

5. Cleaning, lubricating or wiping

Clean with air hose
    6 × 6-in. area or under .07
    12 × 12-in. area or under .12
    12 × 12-in. to 12 × 24-in. area .15
    Fixture in vise .11
    Partial T-slots, add'l .08
Brush area and fixture .12
Adjust coolant or mist hose .05
Wipe locators with fingers .04
Wipe 6 × 6-in. area with hand .05
Wipe V-block or centers or attachment with rag .15

6. Machining

Side, slot, form, straddle or saw milling   See Table 11.3

7. Milling cutter replacement   See Table 11.4

8. Part inspection   See Table 22.1

MACHINING CENTERS

8.1 Machining Centers

DESCRIPTION

Early design placed control units on existing machine tool structures to achieve numerical control. As experience expanded, the machine center evolved and a distinctive class of machine tools developed with generally two- to five-axis capability. Pallets for off-machine loading, shuttles, and a tool holder that can accommodate many tools are only a few of the special features available. While machining centers have a variety of configurations, they are basically chip removal structures with NC control. These data consider this class of machine similar to a general purpose mill able to mill, drill, bore, face, spot, counterbore, route, and more. Part positioning is a function of rotation, indexing, and table traversing at various rates. Figure 8.1 is a four-axis model that has a rotary table.

ESTIMATING DATA DISCUSSION

These data are for the estimating of machining center setup and the units are estimating hr. The values include the build-up and removal from the machine table and control unit parts, fixture, clamps, tape, etc. required to produce the part.

Job preparation includes these elements: punch in/out, receive instructions, tape, drawing, position tape in reader, get blocking, parallels, fixture, pins or other tooling, position machine to proper coordinates on X–Y axis using pin or piece as a "0" point, measure for clamp heights, adjust control boxes, start machine, check hole location on first piece and check drawing, position hoist or crane, and after lot is run, sweep off chips and clean area, and remove tape from machine.

Setup Element 2 uses entry variables of number of clamps and clamp height. This work may include using parallels, filler blocks, step blocks, straps, positioning and tightening threaded studs, etc. Teardown includes similar work except in reverse order.

Pin stop is for any dowel pin to locate piece or fixture as indicated by drawing or grid sketch. Element includes study grid sketch, mark hole for pin location, clean, and teardown.

Locator plug or fixture consists of obtaining plug or fixture, positioning on table. Plug or fixture is bolted to table, and teardown.

Adapter ring fits on holding fixture and is attached by threaded bolts. Set tooling involves obtain, assemble tool to adapter, load tool and adapter in tool matrix, and teardown. Some tools require miking for dimension or adjusting for dimension after trial cut.

Element 4 provides for the study of grid sketch for pin location, clean out holes, position dowel pins, align angle plate, tighten, and teardown. Element 5 deals with the optional inclusion of "make part." Certainly, it is necessary to finish a part before the setup is concluded, but this time is also included in the cycle time. Element 6 consists of exceptional tolerance requirements of a setup.

In cycle Element 1, there is a distinction of a single-

FIGURE 8.1 Four-axis machining center. *(White-Sundstrand)*

or double-table layout. The double layout uses two setups on the same table, or a second setup is on the pallet arrangement. The single layout involves loading, machining one piece to completion, and unload followed by another piece in the same fixture. Double layout consists of two setups on the grid table for machining one piece to completion, load second piece ready for machining during period of first part machining, machine second piece and simultaneously remove previous piece, and prepare next piece for loading.

Entry variables for using Table 8.1 are pin stops or locator plugs, weight, and part configuration. For weight under 45 lb, the work includes move piece from skid to grid table, align piece to pin stops or locator plug, and reset tape. After machining, remove piece to skid. An occasional mallet blow is included for seating or loosening. When weight exceeds 45 lb, a jib crane is used, and a part configuration is identified for entry. A part may be mostly circular and a 50-in. diameter is used to separate the selection of a time value. A bottom-area perimeter of 35 in. is used for selection when the configuration is mostly rectangular or square. In clamp and unclamp, the work involves the positioning of an end clamp over piece and stepblock, tighten, and aside wrench, done in reverse for teardown.

Element 4 involves a selection of machining-center operations. For automatic tool changes see Table 8.2 which is used for several tape-drive machines having automatic tool selection. A manual tool change is possible at the quill and a choice is provided.

Element 5, for practical purposes, can be done during the NC cycle, although location and fixture cleaning is done off the NC tape. The element that indicates piece involves locating to the origin point with a dial indicator, clear spindle of previous tool, position table, position spindle with correct tool to location, and check coordinates.

Costs for setup and 100 units can be determined using Item 8.1 of Section IV. Entry variables for setup are no. of clamps or bolts and the no. of tools that are set for this work. Some NC machines have standard tools that are garrisoned permanently in the magazine. This factor would not involve those tools unless they are removed and set or qualified for depth of cut. The $/100 units depends upon entry factors of no. of coordinate changes for machining cuts, hoist, and rehandle. The constant includes a manual load and unload, NC start, and minor machine control and part clamping. The number of discrete machine locations gives the number of coordinates or machine positioning for new cuts. The information does not include cost for cutting (see Item 11), tool change (see Item 8.2) or inspection (see Item 22.1).

218

EXAMPLES

A. A front-cover aluminum part is machined on a NC machining center. The part is loaded one at a time on a horizontal table. Ten tools are required and twenty position changes are necessary to machine the cover. Clamping in T-slots will be used. A tape is unavailable at the time of the estimate. The machining schedule is provided below. Find the unit and shop estimate.

Table	Description	Time
8.1-4	Start machine	.10 min
8.1-1	Load to pin stops	1.03
8.1-2	Tighten 3 clamps	1.50
8.2-1	Rapid traverse to and from part at 300 in./min for 25 in.	.16
8.2-2	Ten tool changes, magazine rate at .30	3.00
8.1-4	Coordinate changes, .08 × 20	1.60
11.2-4	Drill 1 hole, $^{19}/_{32}$-in. OD, .507-in. long, .08 × .507	.05
11.2-4	Flat-bottom drill, 1 hole, $^{19}/_{32}$-in. OD, .311-in. long, .08 × .311	.02
11.2-7	Ream 1 hole to .609 in., .507-in. long	.05
11.2-4	Countersink hole, .08 × .241	.02
11.3-4	End mill .062-in. radius to .312-in. dimension, .537-in. long, HSS, .03 × 1.6 in.	.05
11.3-4	Counterdrill .33-in. deep, 6 times, $^3/_8$-in. tool, .08 × .33 × 6	.16
11.3-4	Step drill .196-in. large OD, 6 times by .612-in. deep, .07 × .612 × 6	.26
11.3-4	Countersink 120° by .24-in. diameter by .151-in. deep 6 times, .07 × .24 × 6	.10
11.2-8	Tap 6 holes 19–32 UNF–3B × .435-in. deep, .13 × .435 × 6	.34
	Unit estimate	8.52 min
	Shop estimate	7 pc/hr

B. For Example A above, determine lot and unit cost using a base-cost approach. Lot quantity is 67. Use Items 8.1, 8.2, 11.2, and 11.3. The machining schedule uses the information from Example A.

Item	Description	Cost
8.1	Setup constant	$ 4.40
8.1	Clamp factor, 3 × 1.10	3.30
8.1	Ten tools, 10 × .55	5.50
	Setup subtotal	$ 13.20
8.1	Cycle constant	$ 64.40
8.1	Coordinate changes, 20 × 1.43	28.60
8.2	Rapid traverse, 25 × .121	3.03
8.2	Ten tool changes, 10 × 3.67	36.70
11.2	Drill $^{19}/_{32}$-in. hole, $^{19}/_{32}$ × .507 × 3.33 (1 hole)	1.00
11.2	Flat bottom drill, $^{19}/_{32}$ × .311 × 3.33 (1 hole)	.61
11.2	Ream, .507 × 1.61	.82
	Countersink, estimate	.50
11.3	End mill, 1.6 × .357	.57
11.2	Counterdrill, 6 × $^3/_8$ × .33 × 3.33 (use drilling)	2.47
11.2	Step drill, 6 × .192 × .612 × 6.62 (use drilling)	4.76
11.2	Countersink, 6 × .24 × .151 × 6.62	1.44
11.2	Tap, 6 × .435 × 2.47	6.45
	$/100 units subtotal	$151.35
	Lot cost for 67 units	$114.60

TABLE 8.1 MACHINING CENTERS

Setup in estimating hours

1. Job preparation, constant   .35

2. Tooling

Prepare clamps with locator plug

Clamp height	No. clamps					
	1	2	3	4	5	6
1	.05	.10	.15	.20	.25	.30
4	.06	.13	.19	.26	.32	.38
10	.08	.16	.23	.31	.39	.47
16	.09	.17	.26	.34	.43	.51
Add'l	.01	.01	.02	.03	.04	.04

Prepare clamps without locator plug

Clamp height	No. clamps					
	1	2	3	4	5	6
1	.09	.14	.20	.26	.31	.37
4	.10	.16	.24	.30	.36	.43
10	.11	.18	.26	.33	.41	.49
16	.12	.20	.29	.37	.46	.54
Add'l	.01	.02	.03	.04	.05	.06

Pin stop   .02/pin

C-clamp   .01/clamp

Locator plug or fixture

No. bolts	0	1	2	3	4
Under 45 lb	.02	.05	.08	.11	.15
Over 45 lb	.06	.09	.13	.16	.19

Adapter ring   .06

3. Set tools

Drilling	.02
Reaming	.04
Core-spade	.04
Boring	.11
Tapping	.04
Facing	.02
Presetting tool	.25
Load tool in turret or station	.17/tool

4. Angle block

With gage stop	.14
Without gage stop	.13

5. Make-piece (optional): $2 \times$ hr/per 1 unit

6. Tolerance checking (optional)

Tolerance	hr
$^1/_{64}$ −.011	.03
.01 −.0051	.05
.005 −.0031	.08
.003 −.0011	.10
.001 −	.13

Operation elements in estimating minutes

1. Pick up part, move and place; pick up and lay aside

Single-table layout

	Weight		
Position	To 45 lb	Over 45 lb to 50-in. Dia to 35-in. perm	Over 45 lb over 50-in. Dia over 35-in. perm
Align to pin stops	1.03	3.54	5.06
Align on locator plug	2.26	4.07	5.53

Double-table layout

	Weight		
Position	To 45 lb	Over 45 lb to 50-in. dia to 35-in. perm	Over 45 lb over 50-in. dia over 35-in. perm
Align to pin stops	.73	3.10	4.62
Align on locator plug	2.08	3.62	5.09

2. Clamp and unclamp

Tighten clamp or strap

No.	1	2	3	4	5	6	7
Min	.53	1.06	1.50	2.11	2.64	3.17	3.70

Set screw or C-clamp   1.19/ea
Adjustable bottle jack   .36/ea

3. Part and fixture manipulation

Shuttle   .90
Reposition   60% of basic time

4. Machining center operation

Start machine   .10
Rapid traverse   See Table 8.2
Automatic tool change   See Table 8.2
Manual tool change   .86
Keylock time   .17
Spindle on-time   .04
Tape reader factor   1.00
Table index
    Small machine, under 10 hp   .18
    Large machine   .30
Coordinate change   .08

5. Cleaning, lubrication or wiping

Clean area with air hose	.18
Large fixture, air hose	.20
Brush chips, complex area and fixture	.26
Lubricate tool or piece	.14
Adjust coolant hose	.10
Clean and wipe locators or pins	.08

6. Machining

Face, side, slot, form, straddle, end	See Table 11.3
Drill, counterbore, ream	See Table 11.2
Bore	See Table 11.1

7. Milling cutter replacement   See Table 11.4

8. Part inspection   See Table 22.1
Indicate piece   4.08

8.2 Rapid Travel and Automatic Tool Changer Elements

DESCRIPTION

Many machines have some form of rapid travel of a machine element and automatic tool changing. These data have been collected here because of convenience and the necessity of space reduction. For various reasons, other estimating data may have their own rapid travel and automatic tool changer data. For milling and machining centers, the data are compiled here, however.

ESTIMATING DATA DISCUSSION

The rapid traverse element consists of a pure machine element move. It is one direction only, and does not include any machine dwell, tarry, or stepping motor peculiarity. The entry variables are distance for the table, spindle, headstock, pallet, or other machine element. Velocity is expressed in minutes per inch (min/in.). The body of the table reads minutes per occurrence (min/occurrence). The time does not include provision for feeds or machining. The rapid-travel distance in elemental time value is calculated by assuming a distance from the loading position to the position where the machine feed starts. By applying the time values per inch from the chart, a total time value can be computed for the rapid travel "in." The specified rapid travel per inch is chosen by referring to the machine specification for the machine. The rapid travel "out" element for the estimate is found by applying the same per inch time value as used in the rapid travel "in" element. The total length of machine cut plus the original rapid travel in value is the distance used to compute the value.

Automatic tool changing varies machine to machine. Three situations are provided. "Prepositioned" involves tools that are accessible immediately for changing. Studies suggest that 10 hp is a convenient machine size to make another separation. Tool changing implies that the tool is removed from the spindle and another one inserted, which has been automatically preselected from the tool magazine.

If estimating is in dollars directly, Section IV approaches are applicable. Table 8.2 elements are also found as Item 8.2 in Section IV. Entry variables are inch for rapid travel of a machine component and number of automatic tool changes during an operation.

TABLE 8.2 RAPID TRAVEL AND AUTOMATIC TOOL CHANGER ELEMENTS

Operation elements in estimating minutes

1. Rapid traverse of machine table, spindle, headstock or pallet, or other machine element, min/occurrence

	Velocity, in./min						
Distance	25	50	100	150	200	300	400
1	.04	.02	.01	.01	.01	.003	.003
2	.08	.04	.02	.01	.01	.01	.01
4	.16	.08	.04	.03	.02	.01	.01
6	.24	.12	.06	.04	.03	.02	.02
8	.32	.16	.08	.05	.04	.03	.02
10	.40	.20	.10	.07	.05	.03	.03
15	.60	.30	.15	.10	.08	.05	.04
20	.80	.40	.20	.13	.10	.07	.05
25	1.00	.50	.25	.17	.13	.08	.06
30	1.20	.60	.30	.20	.15	.10	.08
40	1.60	.80	.40	.27	.20	.13	.10
50	2.00	1.00	.50	.33	.25	.17	.13
60	2.40	1.20	.60	.40	.30	.20	.15
100	4.00	2.00	1.00	.66	.50	.34	.26
200	8.00	4.00	2.00	1.33	1.00	.68	.50
300	12.00	6.00	3.00	2.00	1.50	1.00	.75
500	20.00	10.00	5.00	3.33	2.50	1.68	1.25

2. Automatic tool changing, min/occurrence

No. changes	Prepositioned	10 hp or less	Greater than 10 hp
1	.15	.30	.50
2	.30	.60	1.00
3	.45	.90	1.50
4	.60	1.20	2.00
5	.75	1.50	2.50
6	.90	1.80	3.00
7	1.05	2.10	3.50
8	1.20	2.40	4.00
9	1.35	2.70	4.50
10	1.50	3.00	5.00
11	1.65	3.30	5.50
12	1.80	3.60	6.00
13	1.95	3.90	6.50
14	2.10	4.20	7.00
15	2.25	4.50	7.50
16	2.40	4.80	8.00
17	2.55	5.10	8.50
18	2.70	5.40	9.00
19	2.85	5.70	9.50
20	3.00	6.00	10.00
Add'l	.15	.30	.50

9.1 Drilling Machines Setup and Layout

DESCRIPTION

Setup estimating data are provided for the several drilling machines. They are used for job-shop and moderate-run production. For long-term production, setup is often an indirect expense and may not be estimated; it is charged as overhead expense. Time observations were taken for the basic elements in the distinctive machine applications.

In setup, the operator may work partially with indirect labor. This has an influence on the amount of setup. Despite this effect, a setup consists of the following elements.

1. Punch in/punch out
2. Get tools, fixtures, and later return
3. Study drawing and other information
4. Get parts and arrange
5. Setup table, spindles, tooling, NC controls
6. Make part(s), (optional to include)
7. Inspection approval, but wait not included
8. Clean up table when parts are finished

ESTIMATING DATA DISCUSSION

For setup evaluation, there are four major considerations: machine, part configuration, method of tie-down for tooling, and part variables (tolerances, operations required). These variables are often known by the estimator.

In Element 1, a basic setup is provided but exclusive of 6 and 7 above. Additional time beyond the number of spindles provided by the machine (i.e., 1, 2, etc.) is given in Element 5.

For turret machines, NC or otherwise, Element 2 is applied and the entry variable is the number of

used turrets. The jigging and fixtures are averaged for the machine.

Multiple spindle or cluster drilling machines have as the entry variable the number of tool spindles. Special tooling for part handling accompanies this machine.

Element 5 provides optional selections such as piece part production and inspection. While piece part production of one, two, or three or more parts is necessary to effect a setup, the time for these setup units is also given in the operation elements. Inclusion in the setup is an optional choice by the estimator. Similarly, first part inspection may or may not be required for all parts. Exceptions may be critical-tolerance parts, parts with a history of being difficult, or expensive materials.

Element 6 is the setup and making of a drill templet. It is not included in any of the above elements. It includes study print; get equipment; figure hole locations; make templet blank; and locate, mark and drill holes.

Making of sheet metal templets for punching, notching, and blanking operations is estimated by Element 7. It includes study print; clean blank and paint; and scribe 2 lines center punch; and swing circle for each hole. For a notch or brake line, a line is scratched. Part is sheared to final size prior to this work.

Elements 8 and 9 are the layout of locations and a centerpunch for each hole on a part itself. It may be desirable to consider this work as an operation, since one or several parts may be produced in this fashion.

If faster estimating is desired, Item 9.1 of Section IV may be used. These data provide base-cost per setup occurrence. The entry variable for the upright, sensitive, and cluster machines depend upon the no. of spindles. A layout templet for drill press or punch press work is provided. The entry variables are no. of holes and lines, for which a factor is given. For notches, brake lines, shear edges, etc., the no. of separate lines is counted, and a factor is used as a multiplier.

EXAMPLES

These data are demonstrated with the drilling machine tables.

TABLE 9.1   DRILLING MACHINES SETUP AND LAYOUT

Setup in estimating hours

1. Sensitive drill press and upright drilling machines

Jig or fixture	No. of Spindles					
	1	2	3	4	5	6
On table or vise	.17	.26	.34	.41	.47	.54
Plate or sandwich	.19	.28	.36	.43	.48	.56
Box or collet	.24	.33	.41	.47	.54	.61
Air chuck, collet	.20	.29	.37	.44	.50	.57
Parallels, V-block	.19	.27	.35	.42	.48	.55

2. Turret drilling machines

No. turrets	1	2	3	4	5	6	7	8
Jig, fixture, vise, rails	.25	.33	.40	.47	.55	.62	.69	.76

3. Cluster spindle machine

No. tool spindles	1	2	3	4	5	6	7	8	9	10	Add'l
Hr	.08	.17	.25	.33	.42	.48	.58	.67	.75	.83	.08

Install jig or fixture on table, clean, align	1.00
Critical depth	.10/hole

4. Radial drill press machine

On table or vise or floor plates	.28
Angle plate	.45
Fixture	.40
Crane loading	.05

5. Miscellaneous elements

Piece production, 2 × unit time *cycle*	Optional
First part inspection	Optional
Constant	.03
Location coordinate	.02
Hole size	.003
Add'l hole sizes above number of spindles	.06/ea
Tap or magic chuck attachment	.02/ea
Depth on hole	.05/spindle

6. Lay out and make drill templet

No. lines	1	2	3	4	5	6	7	8	9	10	Add'l
Hr	.29	.31	.33	.35	.37	.39	.41	.43	.45	.47	.02

Lay out flat sheet and make sheet metal templet

No. holes	1	2	3	4	5	6	7	8	9	10	Add'l
Hr	.04	.06	.07	.08	.10	.11	.12	.13	.15	.16	.02

Lay out flat sheet for notches, brake lines, angles on templet

No. lines	1	2	3	4	5	6	7	8	9	10	Add'l
Hr	.01	.02	.03	.04	.05	.06	.07	.08	.09	.10	.01

Lay out flat parts and machine center-punch hole locations, per occurrence

No. holes	1	2	3	4	5	6	7	8	9	10	Add'l
Hr	.08	.10	.11	.13	.17	.18	.21	.23	.25	.27	.02

Lay out irregular shaped parts and machine center-punch hole locations, per occurrence

No. lines	1	2	3	4	5	6	7	8	9	10	Add'l
Hr	.13	.15	.18	.19	.22	.24	.27	.28	.31	.34	.03

9.2 Sensitive Drill Press Machines

DESCRIPTION

The sensitive drilling machine is a high-speed machine of simple construction similar to the upright drill press. Machines of this type are hand-fed, usually by means of a rack and pinion or involute spline drive on the sleeve holding the rotating spindle. These drills may be driven directly by a motor, belt, friction disk, etc. The machines may have from one to eight spindles. Gearing or belt cones may provide from 4 to 16 speeds.

In Figure 9.2, the motor is an enclosed direct drive, 4-speed motor. Speeds can be changed without stopping the motor.

ESTIMATING DATA DISCUSSION

Element 1 comprises the basic load and unload of the part. Entry variables are weight and type of holding device. Obviously, as the part becomes heavier or lighter, the type of handling is changed and this factor is evaluated in the data. If the part is disposed by a toss-aside, a deduction is provided. If additional parts are multiple-loaded, time for full handling is given for each part.

Once the part is loaded, Element 2 provides for tighten and untighten, and several conditions are specified. Element 3 deals with jib or part and jib manipulation.

The operation of the sensitive drill press is given in Element 4, and a variety of work is described. Once the part is loaded and clamped, it is positioned under the drill. Following the last hole, it is moved away from the spindle for part removal. Thus one hole less is required for hole to hole positioning. The selection of these elements depends upon whether the drill press is a single- or gang-spindle machine.

Element 5 deals with part, jig, or fixture and machine cleaning and lubricating by several methods.

In Element 6, the manual drilling elements are used as the sensitive drill press machine does not have power feed.

Base cost per 100 units can be estimated using "rules of thumb" provided by Item 9.2 of Section IV. These costs are related to Table 9.2 and Section II PHC for Chicago. Item 9.2 does not include any costs for setup drilling (see Item 11.2), drill replacement (see Item 11.4) or operator inspection (see Item 22.1). These costs are added from the use of those items. Entry variables for Item 9.2 are weight, number of rehandles, holes, and tools. The constant cost of $7.04 is always given for each operation. If the part or jig is turned over to position another side, a rehandle cost is added for each occurrence. The number of holes provides for raising and lowering spindle, and positioning hole to hole. The number of tools allows cost for changing drill bits, reamers, taps, etc., or moving spindle to spindle.

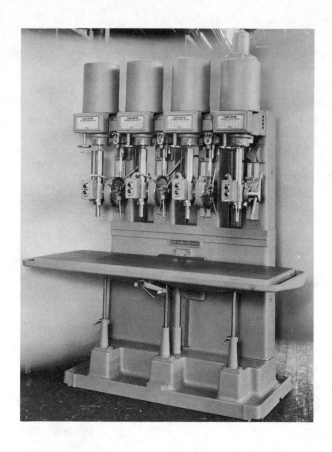

FIGURE 9.2 Four-spindle sensitive drilling machine. *(Leland-Gifford Company, Division of Fayscott, Incorporated)*

EXAMPLES

A. A 3-in. long, 1/2-in. OD low-carbon steel pin has a 1/16-in. OD cross-hole drilled through. A jig is used. Tolerances are commercial. The part weighs .2 lb. Find the min/unit.

Table	Description	Time
9.2-1	Pick up part and lay aside	.05 min
9.2-2	Two thumb screws	.12
9.2-4	Raise and lower spindle	.02
11.2-1	Drill 1 hole, $\frac{1}{16}$-in. OD $\times$ $\frac{1}{2}$ in. deep	.14
9.2-6	Blow jig clean	.06
9.2-6	Oil tool	.05
	Unit estimate	.44 min

B. An aluminum fitting, 2 3/4 in. in diameter, has 16 pilot holes, 0.098 in. in diameter, for a distance of 3/16 in. The part weighs less than 1 lb. A fixture with locating pins is used. Estimate the small lot unit time, hr/100 units, and shop time.

Table	Description	Time
9.2-1	Pick up part and lay aside	.08 min
9.2-2	Quick-acting clamp	.05
9.2-4	Position work under drill	.04
11.2-1	Drill 16 holes, 16 $\times$ .10	1.60
9.2-4	Raise tool, position hole to hole, 15 times	.99
9.2-4	Clear drill from work	.04
9.2-5	Blow jig, medium area	.11
	No checking time for pilot holes	0
	No drill life and replacement	0
	Unit estimate	2.91 min
	hr/100 units	4.85
	Shop time	20.60 pc/hr

C. A two-spindle sensitive drill press is used to drill and tap an irregular steel casting. One spindle is used for drilling, and the second is used for tapping. One 1/4-20 hole is drilled and tapped for a 1/2-in. depth while two 3/8-in. holes are drilled only. A standard drill jig is used. Weight is 8.2 lb. One reposition of tool and part is necessary. Find the lot time for 18 parts.

Table	Description	Time
9.1-S1	Setup two spindles	.33 hr
9.2-1	Pick up part and lay aside	.18 min
9.2-2	Toggle clamp	.05
9.2-4	Raise and lower spindle for first hole	.02
9.2-4	Add'l spindle operator reposition	.01
9.2-4	Change tool, quick acting collet	.09
11.2-1	Drill ¼-in. holes, ½ in. deep	.81
11.2-1	Drill 2⅜-in. holes, ½ in. deep, 2 × .96	1.92
9.2-3	Reposition tool and part	.02
9.2-4	Position hole to hole, 4 times	.26
Estimate	Tap ¼-20, ½ × .15	.08
9.2-5	Brush chips for medium area	.24
9.2-5	Blow out chips from casting cavity	.11
11.4-3	Tool wear out	.05
	Unit estimate	3.84 min
	Lot estimate	1.48 hr

D. Find the base cost for Example B above using operational costs. A lot quantity is 85 units. A one-spindle sensitive drill press is used. Use Items 9.1, 9.2, and 11.2.

Item	Description	Cost
9.1	Setup constant	$ 2.13
9.1	One spindle	.88
	Setup subtotal	$ 3.01
9.2	Cycle constant	$ 7.04
9.2	Weight factor, 1 × .142	.14
9.2	One tool	1.58
9.2	16 holes, 16 × 1.11	17.76
11.2	Drill holes 16 (14.6 × .187 + 4.17 × .098)	50.22
	$/100 units subtotal	$76.74
	Lot cost for 85 units	$68.24

TABLE 9.2 SENSITIVE DRILL PRESS MACHINES

Setup   See Table 9.1

Operation elements in estimating minutes

1. Pick up part, move and place, pick up and lay aside

	Weight					
Holding Device	.5	1.0	2.5	5.0	10.0	15.0
Table, parallels, open vise, simple fixture	.05	.07	.09	.12	.14	.17
V-block, table between hold-down clamps, fixture with locating pins or blocks, between centers	.06	.08	.10	.13	.16	.19

Holding Device	Weight					
	.5	1.0	2.5	5.0	10.0	15.0
Chuck, complex clamping, or fixture with locating pins or blocks to fit part	.07	.08	.11	.14	.18	.22
Blind fixture with locating pins or blocks or stops, index plate with alignment, or align to mark in fixture	.07	.09	.12	.15	.20	.24

Deduct for toss aside .... .02

For additional part for handling in Element 1

Weight	2	5	10	15
Min	.05	.07	.08	.10

Pry or tap part out .... .06

2. Clamp and unclamp

Vise, ¼ turn .... .05
Vise, full turn .... .08
Toggle or quick-acting clamp .... .05
Cam clamp .... .03
Star wheel .... .07
Thumb screw .... .06
Air cylinder .... .05
U-clamp with hex nut .... .26
C-clamp with hex nut .... .32
C-clamp with thumb screw .... .21
Strap clamp with hex nut .... .31
Add'l nut .... .05

3. Part or part and jig manipulation

Rotate part or part and fixture

Rotate, flip	Weight			
	10	20	30	45
90°	.01	.02	.03	.04
180°	.02	.04	.05	.07

Trunnion fixture

Rotate	90°	180°	270°
Min	.07	.08	.10

Pin, unpin .... .07
Turn part in vise .... .10

4. Sensitive drill press machine operation

Start or stop spindle, clutch type .... .03
Start or stop spindle, button or pull type .... .01
Raise and lower spindle .... .02
Spindle clamp, lock and unlock .... .05
Bushing, place and remove .... .11
Bushing, shift hole-to-hole .... .08

Change pulley belt speed   .30
Set depth pointer or dial marker   .04
Table clamp, lock and unlock   .07
Rotate table on column   .05
Walk back to first spindle (for progressive spindles)   .01

Change tools	1	2	3	4	5	Add'l
Quick-change collets	.09	.18	.27	.36	.45	.09
Keyed-drill chuck	.30	.60	.90	1.20	1.50	.30
Taper shank with drift	.35	.70	1.05	1.40	1.75	.35

Position work under drill, adjust coolant, advance drill to work, align to work or bushing, raise spindle after machining

Weight	5	10	30	45
Min	.04	.05	.06	.07

Raise tool, position work hole-to-hole, advance tool to work

Holes	Min	Holes	Min	Holes	Min	Holes	Min
1	.07	6	.40	11	.73	16	1.06
2	.13	7	.46	12	.79	17	1.12
3	.20	8	.53	13	.86	18	1.19
4	.26	9	.59	14	.92	19	1.25
5	.33	10	.66	15	.99	Add'l	.06

5. Cleaning, lubricating, or wiping

   Clean with air hose
       Small area up to 6 × 6   .06
       Medium area to 12 × 12   .11
       Large area to 12 × 24   .14
       Small fixture   .10
       Complex large fixture   .18
   Brush chips
       Small area up to 6 × 6   .11
       Medium area to 12 × 12   .13
       Large area to 12 × 24   .18
       Fixture   .24
   Lubricate tool or piece
       Oil tool or piece with brush   .05
       Dip tool in compound   .02
   Adjust coolant hose   .04
   Clean area, holding device, or hole
       Wipe locators with fingers   .03
       Wipe 6 × 6-in. area with hand   .04
       Wipe V-block or centers with rag   .11
       Wipe vise with rag   .10
   Blow lube and chips from hole

Holes	1	2	3	4	5	6	8	9	10	Add'l
Min	.06	.08	.11	.13	.15	.17	.21	.24	.26	.02

6. Machining

   Drill, counterbore, ream, or tap   See Table 11.2

7. Drill replacement   See Table 11.4

8. Part inspection   See Table 22.1

9.3 Upright Drilling Machines

DESCRIPTION

Upright drilling machines have power feeding mechanisms (and non-powered, as well) for the rotating drill. They are designed for heavier work than the sensitive drilling machines. The column is box-type, and it is more rigid than a round column machine. When the uprights can be grouped on a single table, it is called a gang drill. Tapping can be handled as well.

In the model shown in Figure 9.3, the maximum capacity is 7 1/2 hp. Eight quick-change gears are available and the machine can be ganged in 2 to 6 spindles. Various gear speeds are available, anywhere from 32 to 708 for gear feeds ranging from .005 to .085 ipr.

Now consider estimating data for the broad class of upright drilling machines.

ESTIMATING DATA DISCUSSION

Many elements are common in the upright drilling machine and the sensitive drill press machine.

Entry variables for Element 1 are weight and type of holding device. But, the weight range is higher than was found in Table 9.2 as these machines do drilling of larger parts, although small work is possible. Element 2 is for tighten and untighten and is per occurrence.

Some of the elements of machine operation depend upon the particular machine being estimated. The selection of drill, counterbore, ream, or tap will use power feeds of Table 11.2.

Costs for upright drilling machines can be estimated using Item 9.3 of Section IV. This approach is faster than the techniques suggested by the elemental approach, though for an individual determination, it is not as accurate. The data for Item 9.3 are consolidated from Table 9.3. Entry variables are weight, rehandle, and number of tools and holes. A constant cost is always given. Some handling effort is included in the constant, but a variable cost de-

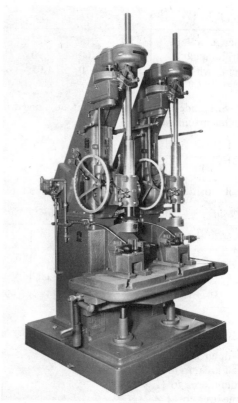

FIGURE 9.3 Two-spindle upright drilling and tapping machine with 7½ hp capacity. (*Barnes Drill*)

pends upon weight. If the part (and a fixture or jig also) is turned over, a rehandle cost is added for each surface other than the initial surface. The number of holes are counted and multiplies a cost factor. This covers movement of the part between holes and raising and lowering of the drill bit. The changing of drill bits, reamers, etc., or the use of different spindles for various tools, is covered by the tool factor. See Item 11.2 for machining and 22.1 for inspection costs, which are added to the costs found from Item 9.3.

EXAMPLES

A. An aluminum casting has four holes drilled. Part weight is 25 lb, and a fixture with locating pins and 2 star clamps are required. The drill schedule is given below. The part is not considered critical in inspection. A 4-spindle machine is used. Find the unit estimate showing a fuller extension of the elements.

Table	Description	Time
9.1-S1	Box jig and three active spindles	.41 hr
9.1-5	Piece production, first-part inspection	Not allowed
9.3-4	Start and stop, push button	.01 min
9.3-1	Fixture with locating pins	.23
9.3-2	2 star clamps	.18

232

Table	Description	Time
9.3-4	Position under drill, first hole	.09
11.2-4	Drill one $\frac{3}{16}$-OD hole $\times \frac{3}{4}$ in. deep, $\frac{3}{4} \times .07$ (L includes lead and break through)	.05
9.3-4	Position to next hole, advance drill	.11
11.2-4	Drill 2nd $\frac{3}{16}$-OD hole $\times \frac{1}{4}$ in. deep	.02
9.3-4	Raise tool into clear, and reposition, advance tool	.11
9.3-5	Blow chips, small area	.06
9.3-3	Tumble jig, 45 lb or less	.07
9.3-4	Install and remove a slip bushing	.08
11.2-4	Drill $\frac{1}{4}$ in. through $\frac{3}{16}$-in. deep	.05
9.3-4	Raise drill, position hole-to-hole, advance drill	.11
11.2-4	Drill $\frac{7}{8}$-in. hole to depth of $1\frac{1}{2}$ in., $1.5 \times .10$	.15
9.3-4	Raise drill into clear, move work into clear	.09
9.3-5	Blow jig clean to receive next load	.10
9.3-5	Blow table clean to receive next load	.11
22.1-3	Unit time to check part	Not allowed
11.4-3	Unit time to sharpen drills, $.01 + .01$	.02
	Unit estimate	1.64 min

B. A large stainless steel valve stem is loaded between centers, and a drilling cap is clamped on. A 2-spindle upright drilling machine is used to drill and ream 4 holes and drill and tap 3 holes. Weight is 12 lb, and the part is expected to cause some difficulty. Find the lot estimate for 163 parts.

Table	Description	Time
9.1-S1	Setup 2 spindle, 12 lb, estimate as value not given for between centers	.30 hr
9.1-S5	Piece production	Not allowed
9.1-S5	First-part inspection for 4 reamed holes, $.03 + 4 \times .02 + 4 \times .003$	.12 hr
9.3-4	Start and stop	.03 min
9.3-1	Load and unload part between centers	.19
9.3-2	2 U-clamps	.52
9.3-4	Position under drill, adjust coolant, advance drill to work, first hole	.09
9.3-4	Raise tool, hole-to-hole, advance tool, 13 times $\times .11$	1.43
11.2-4	Drill four .730-in. holes $\times$ 2.62-in. deep, lead and break through $= .39 \times \frac{2}{3} = .26$, total $L = 2.62 + .26 = 2.83$, $4 \times .49 \times 2.88$	5.64
11.2-7	Ream 4 holes .75-OD, $4 \times .55 \times 2.62$	5.76
11.2-4	Tap drill three $\frac{21}{64}$ in.-holes, 1.5-in. deep, $3 \times .39$ ($1.5 + \frac{2}{3} \times .18$) in.	1.90
11.2-8	Tap $\frac{3}{8} = 24$, 2.5-in. deep, $3 \times .30 \times 1.5$	1.35
9.3-4	Change 3 tools on one spindle, 3 times, $3 \times .09$	.27
9.3-4	Change speed on one spindle, 3 times, $3 \times .02$	.06
9.3-4	Change feed, 3 times, $3 \times .04$	.12
9.3-4	Clear drill after drilling and tapping	.09
9.3-3	Roll stem over, 3 times, $3 \times .04$	.12
9.3-5	Lubricate drill, average of 4 times, $4 \times .05$	.20
9.3-5	Lubricate tap, $3 \times .05$	.15
9.3-5	Blow jig and piece clean, $.11 + .10$	.21
22.1-3	Unit time to check piece, 4 holes with .002-OD tolerance, go, no-go, $4 \times .16\frac{1}{5}$	.13
11.4-3	Drill sharpen allowance	
	.730-in. drill, 5.64 min	.44
	.750-in. reamer, 5.76 min	.44
	$\frac{21}{64}$-in. drill, 1.90 min	.17
	$\frac{3}{8}$-24 tap, 1.35 min	.17
	Unit estimate	19.48 min
	Lot estimate	53.34 hr

C. Estimate the cost of Example A above using a base-cost approach and Items 9.1, 9.3, 11.2, and 11.4. A lot quantity is 365.

Item	Description	Cost
9.1	Setup constant	$ 2.13
9.1	3 active spindles, 3 × .878	2.63
	Setup subtotal	$ 4.76
9.3	Cycle constant	$11.50
9.3	Weight factor, 25 × .979	24.48
9.3	Tumble jig, rehandle	1.00
9.3	Holes, 4 × 2.19	8.76
9.3	Tools, 4 × 2.19	8.76
11.2	Drill $\frac{3}{16}$ × $\frac{3}{4}$ × 6.62	.93
11.2	Drill $\frac{3}{16}$ × $\frac{1}{4}$ × 6.62	.31
11.2	Drill $\frac{1}{4}$ × $\frac{3}{16}$ × 6.62	.31
11.2	Drill $\frac{7}{8}$ × 1.5 × 1.65	2.17
11.4	Drill life, estimate about .25 min of drill time, .25 × 2.41	.60
	$/100 units subtotal	$58.82
	Lot cost	$219.45
	Unit cost	$ .60

TABLE 9.3   UPRIGHT DRILLING MACHINES

Setup   **See Table 9.1**

Operation elements in estimating minutes

1. Pick up part, move, and place; pick up and lay aside

		Weight					
Holding Device		5	10	15	25	35	45
Table, parallels, open vise, simple fixture		.12	.14	.17	.18	.20	.22
V-block, table between hold-down clamps, fixture with locating pins or blocks, between centers		.13	.16	.19	.21	.23	.25
Chuck, complex clamping, or fixture with locating pins or blocks to fit part		.14	.18	.22	.23	.26	.28
Blind fixture with locating pins or blocks or stops, index plate with alignment, or align to mark on fixture		.15	.20	.24	.27	.28	.33

Deduct for toss aside   .03

For additional part

Weight	5	10	15	30
Min	.07	.08	.10	.13

Pry or tap part out   .07

2. Clamp and unclamp

Vise, ¼ turn	.06
Vise, full turn	.09
Toggle or quick-acting clamp	.06
Cam clamp	.04
Star wheel	.09
Thumb screw	.09
Air cylinder	.05
U-clamp with hex nut	.26
C-clamp with hex nut	.32
Clamp with thumb screw	.21
Strap clamp with hex nut	.31
Add'l nut	.08
Operate foot air clamp	.02

3. Part or part and jig manipulation

Rotate part or part and fixture

	Weight				
Rotate, flip	10	20	30	45	60
90°	.01	.02	.03	.04	.05
180°	.02	.04	.05	.07	.08

Trunnion fixture

Rotate	90°	180°	270°
Min	.07	.08	.10

Pin, unpin	.07
Turn part in vise	.10

4. Upright drilling machine operation

Start or stop spindle, clutch type	.03
Start or stop spindle, button or pull type	.01
Reverse spindle, friction clutch	.02
Reverse spindle, positive clutch	.01
Reverse spindle, motor clutch	.01
Raise or lower spindle	.03
Spindle clamp, lock and unlock	.05
Change speed, single lever	.02
Change speed, double lever	.05
Change feed, single lever	.04
Change feed, double lever	.06
Engage feed, clutch type	.01
Engage feed, hand-feed lever type	.01
Set depth pointed or dial marker	.04
Spindle clamp, lock and unlock	.05
Table clamp, lock and unlock	.07
Walk back to first spindle	.01

Change tools	1	2	3	4	5	Add'l
Quick-change collets	.09	.18	.27	.36	.45	.09
Keyed-drill chuck	.30	.60	.90	1.20	1.50	.30
Taper shank with drift	.35	.70	1.05	1.40	1.75	.35

Bushing, place and remove: .11, shift hole-to-hole	.08
Position work under drill, adjust coolant, advance drill to work, first hole, or reverse	.09

Raise tool, position work hole-to-hole, advance tool to work:

Holes	Min	Holes	Min	Holes	Min
1	.11	5	.55	9	.99
2	.22	6	.66	10	1.10
3	.33	7	.77	11	1.21
4	.44	8	.88	Add'l	.11

5. Cleaning, lubricating, or wiping

Clean area with air hose
    Small area up to 6 × 6   .06
    Medium area to 12 × 12   .11
    Area to 12 × 24   .14
    Large area to 18 × 36   .25
    Small fixture   .10
    Complex large fixture   .18
Brush chips
    Small area up to 6 × 6   .11
    Medium area to 12 × 12   .13
    Area to 12 × 24   .18
    Large area to 18 × 36   .31
    Fixture   .24
Lubricate tool or piece
    Oil tool or piece with brush   .05
    Dip tool in compound   .02
    Adjust coolant hose   .04
Clean area, holding device or hole
    Wipe locators with fingers   .03
    Wipe 6 × 6-in. area with hand   .04
    Wipe V-blocks or centers with rag   .11
    Wipe vise with rag   .10
Blow lube and chips from hole

Holes	1	2	3	4	5	6	7	8	9	10	Add'l
Min	.06	.08	.11	.13	.15	.17	.19	.21	.24	.26	.02

6. Machining

Drill, counterbore, ream, or tap   See Table 11.2

7. Drill replacement   See Table 11.4

8. Part inspection   See Table 22.1

9.4 Turret Drilling Machines

DESCRIPTION

The outstanding characteristic here is the turret. Anywhere from six- to ten-spindle turret head drilling machines are available. Control of the turret, meaning "index, advance, and after drilling, retracting" can be manual or automatically controlled.

These machines, if NC or hydraulically or stepped controlled, provide directional positioning in the plane of the table. Z-axis feed and depth control are available. A DC motor provides individual, per spindle, infinitely variable feed rates for the Z-axis.

FIGURE 9.4 NC turret drill press. (*Burgmaster*)

The feed rates, rapid approach points, and depth stops are adjustable. A separate cam for each spindle selects the point at which the tool goes from rapid approach to the desired preset feed rate.

Numerical control is a feature frequently found with these machines. The NC often uses 1-in. wide, 8-channel tape using word address and variable length block format. The positioning control is two-axis simultaneous open loop.

Figure 9.4 is an example of an all-electric, automatic, NC turret machine designed for production drilling, tapping, and boring. The table size is 24 × 40 in., and it is a bed-type allowing for heavy shuttle tables.

ESTIMATING DATA DISCUSSION

While elements are common in all drilling machines, distinctions in time are required in turret drilling machines because of differences in the mode of machine control, whether it has manual, semiautomatic, or numerical control. Additionally, table size and the convenience or inconvenience of NC controls affect handling.

Element 1 deals with handling and intends to move the part from a tote box, or skid, to the table or holding device, and then return it. For a flat stack item there is a deduction to be made from the table values, while for additional nonstacked parts, there is a lower handling time.

Once the part is loaded in or on the holding device, several methods of clamping and unclamping are listed in Element 2. Part or part and jig manipulation has entry variables: weight, degree rotation, and type of fixture. Elements 1, 2, and 3 are usually under non-NC machine control and are done during operator control of the machine.

Machine operation is considered by Element 4. Change tool deals with removing and inserting tool in a turret station holder during a stop in the cycle. If a drilling machine has two turret heads, movement of the table is considered. The element raise tool, position to new hole, and advance does not include any drilling time and Table 11.2 is used. For sensitive turret drilling machines, Elements 1 and 2 are used. For powered turret drilling machines, the other elements of Table 11.2 are considered. Element 5 considers cleaning, lubricating, or wiping of the table, tool, or fixture.

If it is desired to estimate cost directly rather than in minutes, Item 9.4 of Section IV can be applied. These costs are a condensation of Table 9.4 data. The information to estimate $/100 units using Item 9.4 are weight of the part, number of part rehandles, holes, and tools. The constant cost is always used. A weight factor provides additional cost beyond a residual handling cost which is included in the constant. The handling places the part on the coordinate table. If additional surfaces are to be drilled, a rehandling is provided for each surface beyond the first one. Hole cost provides for advance and retract of the tool and table position to a new coordinate position. The number of turrets is also a factor.

EXAMPLES

A. An aluminum flat part is stacked drilled in 37 locations. Each part weighs 2.7 lb and is 1/8-in. thick and loaded against a rail clamp-type fixture. The stack height is 7/8-in. thick. Four turret stations are used in the NC turret drilling machine. Locations and hole sizes are not critical. A lot quantity of 600 parts is to be estimated for unit, hr/100 units, and pc/hr.

Table	Description	Time
9.1-S1	Turret drilling machine setup	.47 hr
9.1-S1	Piece production, first-part inspection	Not allowed
9.4-4	Start tape	.02 min
9.4-1	Load on table, between hold downs, .13, but deduct for flat part .03 = .10, 7 parts are loaded	.70
9.4-2	2 clamp screws, .21 × 2	.42
9.4-7	Rapid traverse at 200 ipm, 8 in.	.04
9.4-4	Index 2 blank turret stations	.06
11.2-4	Drill twelve .187-in. holes, distance = .10 + .875 = .975 in., drill time for 12 holes = 12 × .09 × .975	1.05
11.2-4	Drill three .4375-in. holes, distance = .24 + .875 = 1.12-in., drill time for 3 holes = 3 × .09 × 1.12	.30
11.2-4	Drill seven .516-in. holes, distance = .28 + .875 = 1.16-in., drill time for 7 holes = 7 × .08 × 1.16 in.	.65
11.2-4	Drill fifteen ⅛-in. holes, distance = .07 + .875 = .95 in., drill time for 15 holes = 15 × .07 × .95	.99
9.4-4	Position hole-to-hole 36 times, 36 × .06	2.16
11.4-3	Drill replacement	
	¼ in. or less, drill time = 1.05 + .99	.15
	¼ + to ½ in., drill time = .3	.02
	½ + to ¾ in., drill time = .65	.03
	Stack estimate	6.59 min
	Unit estimate	.94 min
	hr/100 units	1.57
	Shop estimate	63 pc/hr

B. A gray cast iron 125 psi 4-in. tee casting has a 6-hole bolt circle drilled and tapped on 3 flange faces. The turret drilling machine has the fixture positioned and mounted on the table. Two turrets are used. Location and hole size are ordinary. The tee casting weighs 18 lb. The fixture is indexed twice to present 2 other flanges. Find the unit estimate.

Table	Description	Time
9.1-S2	Turret drilling machine setup	.33 hr
9.1-S5	Tap attachment for turret	.02 hr
9.4-1	Load and unload to indexing fixture with alignment	.27 min
9.4-2	2 cam clamps	.06
9.4-4	Start tape	.02
8.2-1	Rapid traverse 8-in. to first position	.04
11.2-4	Drill 1-in. hole, 6 locations on 1 flange, distance = .53 + 1.25 = 1.78 in., time = $6 \times 1.78 \times .27$	2.88
9.4-4	Index 1 station	.03
9.2-6	Tap 6 holes, 8 threads/in., $6 \times 1.25 \times .32$	2.40
9.4-4	Raise tool, position hole-to-hole, advance tool to work for 12 drilled and tapped holes	.66
	Index empty turrets in above element	
8.2-1	Rapid traverse 200 ipm 8 in. to clear turret for indexing of fixture and tape stops	.04
9.4-3	Index fixture to present new flange	.05
Repeat	Machine second flange face using above 8 elements	6.22
Repeat	Machine third flange	6.22
9.4-5	Blow off table	.25
11.4-3	Drill replacement	
	1-in. drill, $2.88 \times 3 = 8.64$, .25 + .20	.45
	1-in. tap, $2.40 \times 3 = 7.20$, .25 + .15	.40
	Unit estimate	19.79 min

C. Estimate the base cost of Example A above using several items of Section IV. A lot quantity is 600 units.

Item	Description	Cost
9.1	Setup constant	$ 2.13
9.1	2 turrets, $2 \times .878$	1.76
	Setup subtotal	$ 3.89
9.4	Turret constant	$ 9.76
9.4	Loading factor $2.7 \times 7 \times 1.28$	24.19
9.4	2 indexes, 2×1.85	3.70
8.2	Rapid traverse, in and out, $2 \times 8 \times .121$	1.94
11.2	Drill 27 holes, $27 \times 1 \times .975 \times 6.62$	174.27
11.2	Drill 9 holes, $9 \times 1.15 \times 3.33$	34.47
9.4	Move 36 holes, 36×1.24	44.64
9.4	2 turret index, 2×1.85	3.70
11.4	Drill replacement, assume 3 min of drilling, 3×2.41	7.23
	$/100 units subtotal	$ 303.90
	Lot cost for 600 units	$1827.29
	Unit cost	$ 3.05

TABLE 9.4 TURRET DRILLING MACHINES

Setup   **See Table 9.1**

Operation elements in estimating minutes

1. Pick up part, move, and place; pick up and lay aside.

Holding Device	Weight					
	1.0	2.5	5.0	10	15	25
Table, parallels, open vise, simple fixture	.07	.09	.12	.14	.17	.18
V-block, table between hold-down clamps, fixture with locating pins on blocks, between centers	.08	.10	.13	.16	.19	.21

Holding Device	Weight					
	1.0	2.5	5.0	10	15	25
Chuck, complex clamping or fixture with locating pins or blocks to fit part	.08	.11	.14	.18	.22	.23
Blind fixture with locating pins or blocks or stops, index plate with alignment, or align to mark on fixture	.09	.12	.15	.20	.24	.27

Deduct for flat stack parts .03
Deduct for toss aside .02
For additional part (nonstacked)

Weight	2	5	10	15	25
Min	.05	.07	.08	.10	.12

Pry or tap part out .07

2. Clamping and unclamping

Vise, ¼ turn .05
Vise, full turn .08
Toggle or quick-acting clamp .05
Cam clamp .03
Star wheel .07
Thumb screw .06
Air cylinder .05
U-clamp with hex nut .26
C-clamp with hex nut .32
C-clamp with thumb screw .21
Strap clamp with hex nut .31
Add'l nut .05
Operate foot air clamp .02

3. Part or part and jig manipulation

Rotate part or part and fixture

Rotate, flip	Weight			
	10	20	30	45
90°	.01	.02	.03	.04
180°	.02	.04	.05	.07

Trunnion fixture

Rotate	90°	100°	270°
Min	.07	.08	.10

Pin, unpin .07
Turn part in vise .10
Index of fixture .15/stop
Rotation of rotary table: 90°, .07; 180°, .12

4. Turret drilling machine operation

Change tool .06
Move part turret to turret, for multiple turret model .06
Semiautomatic jog table .01/in.
Start machine or start tape .02
Raise tool, position work to new X–Y coordinate hole, advance
    tool to work

240

Holes	Min	Holes	Min	Holes	Min	Holes	Min
1	.06	6	.33	11	.61	16	.88
2	.11	7	.39	12	.66	17	.94
3	.17	8	.44	13	.72	18	.99
4	.22	9	.50	14	.77	19	1.05
5	.28	10	.55	15	.83	Add'l	.06

Turret	1	2	3	4	5	6	7	8
Index	.03	.06	.09	.12	.15	.18	.21	.24
Retract, index, advance tool	.09	.18	.27	.32	.45	.54	.63	.72

5. Cleaning lubricating or wiping

Clean area with air hose
- Small area up to 6 × 6   .06
- Medium area up to 12 × 12   .11
- Area up to 12 × 24   .14
- Large area up to 18 × 36   .25
- Small fixture   .10
- Complex large fixture   .18

Brush chips
- Small area up to 6 × 6   .11
- Medium area up to 12 × 12   .13
- Area up to 12 × 24   .18
- Large area up to 18 × 36   .31
- Fixture   .24

Lubricate tool or piece
- Oil tool or piece with brush   .05
- Dip tool in compound   .02
- Adjust coolant hose or mist   .04

Clean area, holding device or hole
- Wipe locators with fingers   .03
- Wipe 6 × 6-in. area with hand   .04
- Wipe V-blocks or centers with rag   .11
- Wipe vise with rag   .10

Blow lube and chips from hole

Holes	1	2	3	4	5	6	7	8	9	10	Add'l
Min	.06	.08	.11	.13	.15	.17	.19	.21	.24	.26	.02

6. Machining

Drill, counterbore, ream, tap   See Table 11.2

7. Rapid traverse   See Table 8.2

8. Drill replacement   See Table 11.4

9. Part inspection   See Table 22.1

9.5 Cluster Drilling Machines

DESCRIPTION

Sometimes called multi-spindle drilling, this method can have a special drilling attachment which fits to the spindle quill. Multi-spindle drilling machines are also available. The attachment spindles are driven through universal joints and telescoping splined shafts. Various speeds for drilling, reaming, and tapping can be adapted in the headstock by pickoff change gears. Slip spindles handle either drilling or

FIGURE 9.5 Multi-spindle drilling machine outfitted with rotary work table and part holding fixture. (*National Automatic Tool Company, Incorporated*)

tapping. Cams control rapid traverse and feed length.

A cluster spindle machine shown in Figure 9.5 has a maximum feedstroke of 18 in. and feeding pressure of 16,500 lb. The range of feeding is 1–20 ipm. The number, speed, and feed of the drills depend upon the material being drilled and the particular model.

ESTIMATING DATA DISCUSSION

Handling is listed by Element 1 and is explained under sensitive drilling machines. Element 2 covers clamping and unclamping and is per occurrence. If a rotary table is used, Element 3 would be used. The operation of the multi-spindle machine is treated in Element 4. Rapid-traverse of the headstock or table is found in Table 8.2. The selection of the various elements in Element 4 depends on the automatic cycles incorporated in the machine. Inasmuch as several drills, taps, or reamers are working simultaneously, machine time is different than for one tool working, and multi-spindle machine time is given in Table 11.2, Element 5. Drill replacement and part inspection are calculated. They depend upon cutting time, hole location, and size tolerance.

If a simpler approach is desired to Table 9.5, Item 9.5 of Section IV can be employed. This item provides base cost for handling and certain machine elements. Other items are used for machining, tool replacement, inspection, and setup. Item 9.5 is composed of three costs. Always provide the constant cost. With the weight known, multiply the cost factor by the weight to find additional handling costs. If the part is removed from the jig or table clamps and flipped over for another set of holes, a rehandle cost can be added. The sum of these costs is called $/100 units. It does not include cluster drilling, however.

EXAMPLES

A. A plate approximately 4-in. wide × 8-in. long and 3/8-in. thick is commercial yellow brass. Drill ten 3/16-in. holes through 2 plates loaded in a simple locating fixture, but the fixture has locating bushings. Tolerances are commercial and operating checking allowance is not required. Find unit time.

Table	Description	Time
9.1-S3	Setup multiple-spindle drilling attachment	.83 hr
9.1-S1	Install fixture on table	1.00 hr
9.5-1	Plate weighs 3.70 lb and is loaded to simple fixture	.12 min
9.5-1	Second plate	.07
9.5-2	3 thumb screws	.18
9.5-4	Position under drills and advance drills to work	.08
9.5-4	Start machine, stop	.02
11.2-5	Drill 10 holes (.75 in. length of cut)	.12
9.5-4	Position drills into clear and move jig into clear	.08
9.5-5	Clean jig to receive next load	.10
9.5-5	Clean table to receive next load	.14
11.4-3	Drill replacement	
	Ten $\frac{3}{16}$-in. drills, 1.20 min of drilling	.10
	Stack estimate	1.01
	Unit estimate	.51

B. A turned part is placed on a V-type holding fixture. The fixture holds 4 parts. The parts are manually transferred from station to station being relocated radially in each position. Parts are automatically clamped by spring-loaded pressure pads mounted below the slip spindle plate. A hanging bushing plate is located by 2 guide pins. Material is CRS and weighs under 3 lb ea. A total of 7 holes are simultaneously drilled in the 4 parts with a head-feed multiple-spindle drilling machine. Find unit time and pc/hr.

Table	Description	Time
9.1-S3	Multiple-spindle drilling machine setup	.58 hr
9.1-S3	Install fixture on table	1.00 hr
9.1-S3	3 holes have critical depth	.30 hr
9.5-1	Remove last piece, and load first piece	.12 min
9.5-1	Transfer 3 pieces to next station, 3 × .07	.21
9.5-2	Clamping automatic, foot air clamp	.02
Estimate	Palm button start and automatic return	.04
9.5-5	Start oiling with coolant hose	.04
8.2-7	Head rapid traverse 8 in. at 150 ipm	.05
11.2-5	Drill 7 holes, maximum depth $1\frac{1}{8}$ in., 1.125 × .47	.53
9.5-5	Blow off fixture	.18
11.4-3	Drill replacement	
	1⅛-in. diameter, .53 min	.10
	2¼-in. diameter, 1.06 min	.26
	4 .27-in. diameter, 2.12 min	.26
22.1-3	Part inspection	
	Go, no-go 4 holes, .005-in. tolerance, .15/5 × 4	.12

Table	Description	Time
8.2-1	Head rapid traverse 8 in. up	.05
	Unit estimate	1.92 min
	Shop estimate	31 pc/hr

C. Using a base-cost approach, estimate the following example. The lot quantity is 1750 and 20 releases are scheduled each year. Determine annual cost for this operation.

Item	Description	Cost
9.1	Setup constant	$ .63
9.1	Seven spindles, 7×1.00	7.00
9.1	Complicated fixtures, estimate	9.41
	Setup subtotal	$ 17.04
9.5	Cycle constant	11.70
9.5	Weight factor, 2 parts, $2 \times 3 \times .148$	.89
8.2	Rapid traverse, in and out, $2 \times 8 \times .121$	1.94
11.2	Constant for drilling, mild steel	4.36
11.2	Depth factor, 1.125×4.55	5.12
11.4	Drill wear (estimate roughly 1 min of drill time)	2.41
22.1	Part inspection, 4 holes at .005 in. tolerance, $4 \times .615$	2.46
	$/100 units subtotal	$ 28.88
	Lot cost for 1750 units	$ 522.44
	Annual cost for 20 orders	$10,448.80

TABLE 9.5   CLUSTER DRILLING MACHINES

Setup   **See Table 9.1**

Operation elements in estimating minutes

1. Pick up part, move, and place; pick up and lay aside

	Weight					
Holding Device	1.0	2.5	5.0	10	15	25
Table, parallels, open vise, simple fixture	.07	.09	.12	.14	.17	.18
V-block, table between hold-down clamps, fixture with locating pins or blocks, between centers	.08	.10	.13	.16	.19	.21
Chuck, complex clamping or fixture with locating pins or blocks to fit part	.08	.11	.14	.18	.22	.23
Blind fixture with locating pins or blocks or stops, index plate with alignment, or align to mark on fixture	.09	.12	.15	.20	.24	.27

For additional part

Weight	2	5	10	15	25
Min	.05	.07	.08	.10	.12

Pry or tap part out	.07
Dial or magazine part	.05

2. Clamp and unclamp, ea

    Toggle or quick-acting clamp   .05
    Cam clamp   .03
    Star wheel   .07
    Thumb screw   .06
    Air cylinder   .05
    U-clamp with hex nut   .26
    C-clamp with hex nut   .32
    C-clamp with thumb screw   .21
    Strap clamp with hex nut   .31
    Add'l nut   .05
    Operate foot air clamp   .02

3. Part or part and jig manipulation

    Rotate part and fixture horizontally   .06
    Pin and unpin   .07
    Rotation of rotary table, 90° .07; 180°   .12
    Index fixture 90°   .05

4. Cluster machine operation

    Start or stop machine, push button   .01
    Start or stop machine, palm-operated push button   .04
    Raise or lower table, clamp and unclamp   .12
    Raise or lower headstock   .10
    Foot operated treadle switch   .02
    Shift lever for 2-speed control   .06
    Position drill into clear and move jig to clear   .08

5. Cleaning, lubricating, or wiping

    Clean area with air hose
        Small area up to 6 × 6   .06
        Medium area up to 12 × 12   .11
        Area up to 12 × 24   .14
        Large area up to 18 × 36   .25
        Small fixture   .10
        Complex large fixture   .18
    Brush chips
        Small area up to 6 × 6   .11
        Medium area up to 12 × 12   .13
        Area up to 12 × 24   .18
        Large area up to 18 × 36   .31
        Fixture   .24

    Lubricate tools or piece

Oil tools	1	2	3	4	5	6	Add'l
Min	.05	.09	.12	.14	.15	.16	.01

    Wipe locators with fingers   .03

6. Drill, counterbore, ream, or tap   See Table 11.2

7. Rapid traverse   See Table 8.2

8. Drill replacement   See Table 11.4

9. Part inspection   See Table 22.1

9.6 Radial Drilling Machines

DESCRIPTION

The radial drilling machine is suitable for large work where it may not be feasible to move the unit around if several holes are to be drilled. The vertical column supports an arm which carries the drilling head. The arm may be swung around to any position over the workbed, and the drilling head has radial adjustment along this arm. Drilling in the vertical plane is common but on some machines the head may be swiveled to drill holes at various angles in a vertical plane.

Figure 9.6 is an example of a 3-ft radial drilling machine with a 2 1/2-in. drill capacity in mild steel, 12 spindle speeds, and 9 power feeds.

ESTIMATING DATA DISCUSSION

Handling for radial drill work is similarly arranged as in other drilling machines although time values may differ. Alignment requirements of rough or irregular castings and forgings, shimming, and jacking are additional for Element 1.

Clamping and unclamping, Element 2, are similar to other drilling machines except for the differences in time.

Radial drilling machine operation, Element 4, is composed of elements which have been recombined to allow for easy use. For instance, raise spindle (.05), move arm and head hole-to-hole, and lower spindle (.05) have been combined with an average distance between holes and the number of holes. Other elements have been joined to facilitate speed.

The approach provided by Table 9.6 provides min/unit. Using Item 9.6 of Section IV, one can estimate cost per 100 units ($/100 units), and the two sets of data are indirectly related. To use Item 9.6, determine the weight of the part, the number of

FIGURE 9.6 A 3-ft radial drill press. (*Clausing Corporation*)

surfaces requiring machining, tools, and holes. A constant cost is the first value used. A manual weight factor provides for additional handling cost. A hoist cost may be used if a jib or overhead crane is required. In this situation, the additional manual cost for handling would not be used. If the part is turned over or on its side, a rehandle cost per side beyond the initial surface is added. The number of different tools and holes allows for tool changing, moving the radial arm, lowering, and raising the tool.

EXAMPLES

A. A 78-in. long × 21 in.-wide × 12 in.-thick annealed aluminum plate is drilled with six 1/2-in. holes and twenty-six 1 1/2-in. holes. Locating bump pins are used with screw-down clamps, and a plate fixture is overlaid having holes for bushings. Five parts are to be estimated for lot time.

Table	Description	Time
9.1-S4	Fixture on floor plates	.28 hr
9.1-S4	Crane loading	.05 hr
9.6-1	Load and unload part with hoist	.95 min
9.6-1	Align part	.27
9.6-1	Shim low points, estimate 2	1.14
9.6-2	Clamp using planer-type T-bolts, 6 necessary, 6 × .34	2.04

Table	Description	Time
9.6-2	Plier assist, 6 × .07	.42
9.6-1	Load plate fixture over aluminum stock, 60 16, crane loading	.95
9.6-2	Lock fixture to plate, 6 C-clamps, 6 × .15	.09
9.6-4	Pull radial arm from clear position	.10
9.6-4	Change speed lever, 2 times, 2 × .04	.08
9.6-4	Change feed lever, 2 times, 2 × .03	.06
9.6-4	Start and stop machine	.14
9.6-4	Install tool, 2 tools, 2 × .09	.18
9.6-4	Raise drill, move head hole-to-hole, and lower drill for six ½-in. holes, average distance apart 10 in.	1.16
9.6-4	Bushing, place and remove for ½-in. hole, 6 × .14	.84
11.2-4	Drill six ½-in. holes, 2-in. deep, lead and break through = .26, distance = 2.26, machine time = 6 × 2.26 × .09	1.22
9.6-4	Raise drill, move arm and head hole-to-hole, and lower drill for twenty-six 1½-in. holes with 5-in. average distance apart, 1.63 + 16 × .16	4.19
9.6-4	Bushing, place and remove, 26 × .14	3.64
11.2-4	Drill twenty-six 1½-in. holes, drill point, and breakthrough = .79, total distance = 2.70, total time = 26 × 2.79 × .10	7.25
9.6-5	Oil tool, each time, 32 × .09	2.88
9.6-5	Clean floor plates, 2 × .25	.50
9.6-5	Blow off fixture, 2 × .21	.42
9.6-5	Blow off chips off part, every 5th hole .25 × 32 × $\frac{1}{5}$	1.60
9.6-4	Push arm into clear position	.08
11.4-3	Drill replacement	
	½-in. drill, 1.22 min	.07
	1½-in. drill, 7.25 min	.21
22.1-3	Hole size inspection	
	½-in. size, .005-in tolerance, .07/5	.02
	1½-in. size, fractional tolerance	No time
	Unit estimate	30.50 min
	Lot estimate	2.87 hr

B. Estimate the part shown in Figure 9.6. The cast iron part weighs 14.2 lb and one 2-in. hole is drilled 3/4 in. through, followed by a reaming operation. Find unit time.

Table	Description	Time
9.6-1	Load part onto side-hole locator	.22 min
9.6-1	Insert and remove back locating pin	.32
9.6-2	Tighten U-clamp from hole, star wheel	.18
9.6-4	Lower drill from clear position	.05
9.6-4	Change speed lever	.04
9.6-4	Bushing, place and remove	.11
11.2-4	Drill 2-in. hole, lead and breakthrough = 1.05 in., L = 180 in., drill time = 1.8 × .44	.79
9.6-4	Raise drill 3 in.	.05
9.6-4	Bushing, place and remove	.11
9.6-4	Change speed and feed lever	.07
9.6-4	Lower drill 3 in.	.05
11.2-7	Ream hole, .3 × .75	.23
9.6-4	Raise reamer 3 in.	.05
9.6-5	Blow off fixture	.21
11.4-3	Tool replacement	
	2-in. drill, .79 min	.05
	2-in. reamer, .23 min	.03
22.1-3	Part inspection	
	1-in., .003-in. tolerance hole, plug gage, .15/5	.03
	Unit estimate	2.59 min

C. Find base cost for Example B above using operational costs of Section IV. A lot quantity of 315 is released every 3 months. Find cost of lot quantity.

Item	Description	Cost
9.1	Radial drill setup constant	$ 12.54
9.1	Complicated fixture, estimate	9.41
	Setup subtotal	$ 21.95
9.6	Cycle constant	$ 21.48
9.6	Weight factor, 14.2 × .105	1.49
9.6	Tool factor, 2 × 4.99, 2 tools	9.98
9.6	Holes, 2 × 3.49	6.98
11.2	Drill, 2 × 1.8 × 4.13	14.87
11.2	Ream, .75 × 5.32	3.99
11.4	Tool replacement (assume 1 min of cutting)	2.41
22.1	Part inspection, .003-in. hole tolerance	3.72
	$/100 units subtotal	$ 64.92
	Lot cost	$226.45
	Annual cost, 4 releases	$905.79

TABLE 9.6   RADIAL DRILLING MACHINES

Setup   **See Table 9.1**

Operation elements in estimating minutes

1. Pick up part, move, and place; pick up and lay aside.

			Weight			
Holding device	15	25	35	45	60	Hoist
Floor plates, parallels, table, open vise, simple fixture	.22	.23	.25	.26	.28	.95
V-block, table between hold-down clamps, fixture with locating pins or blocks	.24	.26	.27	.30	.33	1.05
Chuck, complex clamping, or fixture with locating pins, or block to fit part	.26	.28	.30	.33	.36	1.11
Blind fixture with locating pins or blocks or stop, or align to make on fixture	.20	.31	.34	.38	.42	1.23

Add for irregular casting or forging	1.00
Align part with rule or level	.27
Insert and remove locating pin	.32
Align part on table or floor plates with square	.82
Shim part	.57
Set jack	.17

2. Clamp and unclamp

Vise, full turn, hammer to seal	.70
Toggle or quick-acting clamp	.07
Cam lever	.10
Star wheel	.18
Thumb screw	.08
Air cylinder	.08
U-clamp with hex nut	.28

248

C-clamp with hex nut, small, .15, large   .34
C-clamp with thumb screw   .23
Strap clamp with hex nut   .33
Add'l nut   .23
Plier assist   .07

3. Part or part and jig manipulation

Turn part in vise

Weight	15	35	60
Min	.10	.17	.26

Tumble jig

Weight	15	35	60
Min	.08	.14	.18

Turn part over on table

Weight	15	35	60
Min	.07	.14	.21

4. Radial drilling machine operation

Pull radial arm from clear position   .10
Push away radial arm to clear position   .08
Change speed lever   .04
Stop, start, or reverse spindle lever   .04
Change feed lever   .03
Start or stop machine   .14
Lock or unlock radial arm or spindle   .03

Change tools	1	2	3	4	5	Add'l
Quick-change	.09	.18	.27	.36	.45	.09

Install tool in quick-change chuck, move arm from clear into position,
   advance tool to work   .24
Raise spindle, (average of 3 in.)   .05
Raise spindle, move arm and head hole-to-hole, and lower spindle, given
   distance and hole

| Distance | Holes | | | | | | | | | | |
	1	2	3	4	5	6	7	8	9	10	Add'l
1–3	.15	.30	.46	.61	.76	.91	1.06	1.22	1.37	1.52	.15
4–9	.16	.33	.49	.65	.82	.98	1.14	1.30	1.47	1.63	.16
10–19	.19	.39	.58	.77	.97	1.17	1.35	1.54	1.74	1.93	.19
20–29	.21	.42	.63	.84	1.05	1.26	1.47	1.68	1.89	2.10	.21
Add'l in.											.01

Raise spindle, change tool, change feed and speed, position arm and head
   hole-to-hole, lower spindle

| Distance | Holes | | | | | | | | | | |
	1	2	3	4	5	6	7	8	9	10	Add'l
1–3	.31	.62	.94	1.25	1.56	1.87	2.18	2.50	2.81	3.12	.31
4–9	.32	.65	.97	1.29	1.62	1.94	2.26	2.58	2.91	3.23	.32
10–19	.35	.71	1.06	1.41	1.77	2.12	2.47	2.82	3.18	3.53	.35
20–29	.37	.74	1.11	1.48	1.85	2.22	2.59	2.96	3.33	3.70	.37
Add'l in.											.01

Raise spindle, change tools, exchange slip bushings, and lower spindle
(no reposition)

Bushings	1	2	3	4	5	6	7	8	10	Add'l
Min	.33	.67	1.00	1.34	1.67	2.00	2.34	2.67	3.34	.33

Bushing, place and remove   .11
Bushing, shift hole-to-hole   .14

Move radial arm or headstock hole-to-hole

Distance	1–3	4–5	10–19	20–29	Add'l
Min	.04	.05	.08	.10	.01

5. Cleaning, lubricating, or wiping

Clean area with air hose
    Medium area up to 12 × 12   .11
    Area up to 12 × 24   .14
    Large area up to 18 × 36   .25
    Fixture   .21
Brush chips
    Area up to 12 × 12   .15
    Large area up to 18 × 36   .31
    Fixture   .27
    Vise   .18
Lubricate tool or piece
    Oil tool   .09
    Adjust coolant hose   .06

6. Machining

    Drill, counterbore, ream, tap   See Table 11.2

7. Rapid traverse   See Table 8.2

8. Drill replacement   See Table 11.4

9. Part inspection   See Table 22.1

10.1 Horizontal Milling, Drilling, and Boring Machines

DESCRIPTION

The horizontal milling machine, also known as the horizontal bar, keeps the work stationary while the tool is rotated. It is adapted to the machining of horizontal holes or milling of surfaces. The horizontal spindle for holding the tool is supported and controlled by the headstock. The headstock can be moved vertically. The table has longitudinal and crosswise movements. A rotary table can be mounted. Instead of a table, floor plates may be used, and the column is then mounted on ways for movement along the floor plates. Configurations can include palleted auxiliary tables, tool changing, and work-handling carousel pallet shuttles, preselected positioning, automatic slope machining, etc. Now consider estimating data for the general class of horizontal bars. (See Figure 10.1.)

ESTIMATING DATA DISCUSSION

The basic time is required and includes job preparation chores such as punch in/out, study print and process sheet, and remove chips. Elements 1 through 9 are expressed in setup hours per occurrence (hr/occurrence).

Element 2 includes: get angle plate, transport to machine, secure with 2 strap clamps, move spindle to angle plate and align angle plate with spindle, and reverse the work.

Element 2 involves a hoist hookup, transport to machine table or floor ways, position, unhook, secure with 3 or 4 strap clamps, and reverse the work.

Element 3 involves a move—either by hand or power—of a fixture, secure with straps or bolts, align fixture to spindle, and reverse the work. Element 5 involves the installation and removal of a block in the floor plates using the overhead crane. The installation of a rotary table, turntable, index table, Element 5, includes the hoist pickup and move, and securing the rotary table to the machine table. It also includes the positioning of a rotary table on an index table and reverse the work.

Element 6 involves screws (before loading parallel blocks), shims, or jack screws (before loading piece), and reverse the work. The inspector checks process sheet for machining operation and drawings for inspections, picks up measuring tools, and inspects the requested dimensions.

Now consider the cycle elements. The manual load and unload includes walking to pallet, pickup, transport to table and position, and reverse the work. A jib or crane is similar except a hoist and sling is used. Entry variable is weight. A bridge or bay crane may be required for heavier parts. Element 2 involves the work to secure and release part. Various holding devices are suggested. The bottle jack is used for leveling piece. A double stud strap or hairpin is clamped to the T-studs. Washers are included.

Element 3 is used to zero in machine. Work includes: study of the machining location, determine coordinates, and use first tool and align piece with spindle to X and Y coordinates per location. Finally, the readout is set. The dial indicate element includes

FIGURE 10.1 Table type horizontal milling, drilling and, boring machine. *(Giddings and Lewis Machine Tool Company)*

work to indicate piece, table, or fixture, and lock headstock and/or table, and reverse the work. The work included with the tables involves retracting tool away, loosening nuts to unlock table, turn table, relock, and position spindle to piece for machining.

Element 4 involves much of the same work except for different tools. One example is select tool and position into spindle, retract spindle, remove tool from spindle with drift key or draw bar, and clean off tool. A stub bar for a first bore will include position adapter to spindle for solid tools, remove solid tool adapter before assembling stub bar, pick up stub bar, position in spindle and position to piece, and retract bar, remove bar from spindle and set aside. An in-line bar for a fixture involves (a) assemble clutch adapter to spindle, (b) position headstock for spindle to accept boring bar, lock, (c) pick up bar with hoist and position bar through fixture and piece and unhook hoist, (d) turn fixture 90° to spindle and secure index table, (e) and reverse the work.

Element 5 deals with assembling of cutter to various tools, securing, and reversing the work. It can include the assembly of a cutter to slot in bar and securing, and reversing.

Element 6 is for advance and retract a tool from the cut. Thus, this element includes the necessary manipulation of levers to engage and disengage the tool to the cut.

For a fraction tolerance, the operator sets the depth of cutting tool and aligns to piece and retracts the tool. For a decimal tolerance, set depth of cutting tool and advance to cut, pick up gage and gage depth and retract cutting tool. The trial portion of this work depends upon the tolerance. The decimal tolerance is given more trials expressed in the time. Distinctions are made for a single- or double-edge cutter.

Element 7 is the weighed average of moving a table, saddle, headstock, column, spindle, or combination to a readout coordinate. Thus, a rapid traverse time is covered by this time rather than Table 8.2.

The data in Table 10.1 have been summarized in Item 10.1 of Section IV. Using a Section IV approach, estimates can be determined in $/100 units and $/setup occurrence. The setup provides a constant cost and an addition for a plate, table, or fixture or other auxiliary. The cycle time requires several entry variables. A constant cost is always included. If a hoist is necessary, a cost for loading and unloading is provided. The number of clamps are estimated. A cost factor is multiplied by the number. A factor is available for the number of installing and removing of tools and cutters. The line bar inserted through a fixture or part is separated for special treatment. Installation and removal of cutters can be evaluated. The advance and retract of the cutter is dependent upon a fractional or decimal tolerance. Travel between holes and surfaces is estimated based on linear X–Y distances measured in inches. Item 10.1 does not include any machine time or tool replacement because of tool wear. (It is included in Item 11.4.)

A. Load and unload the work.

Table	Description	Time
10.1-1	Crane load	8.59 min
10.1-2	Strap clamps, 4	5.84
		14.43 min

B. Center drill, drill and tap two 4 1/2 NC holes.

Table	Description	Time
10.1-4	Position and remove, 3 × .57	1.71 min
10.1-3	Start and stop, 3 × .40	1.20
10.1-3	Change feed, speed 2 × .34	.68
10.1-6	Advance and retract tool, 3 × .18	.54
10.1-6	Center drill	.49
11.2-4	Drill 1 $\frac{25}{32}$-Dia × 2-in. deep, .444 × 2	.88
11.2-8	Tap, .38 × 2	.76
		6.26 min

C. Core drill and line bore 2.75-in. hole inside of casting, decimal hole.

Table	Description	Time
10.1-4	Position and remove tool	.57 min
10.1-3	Start and stop, 2 × .40	.80
10.1-3	Change feed and speed, 2 × .34	.68
10.1-5	Position and remove cutter	2.15
10.1-6	Advance and retract core drill	.18
11.2-4	Core drill 2.55-in. hole, 2-in. deep, .51 × 2	1.02
11.1-3	Rough bore, .10 × 2, carbide	.20
10.1-6	Advance, retract	1.48
10.1-5	Position and remove boring cutters	2.15
11.1-3	Finish bore, .13 × 2, carbide	.26
10.1-6	Advance and retract in-line bar	2.63
		12.12 min

D. Estimate the base costs for the work patterns, A, B, and C as shown above.

Item	Description	Cost
10.1	Crane load	$139.00
10.1	4 strap clamps, 4 × 57.3	229.20
	$/100 units for A-pattern	$368.20
10.1	Tools, 3 × 48.4	$145.20
11.1	Start drill, steel	19.20
11.2	Drill, 1 $\frac{25}{32}$ × 2 × 3.33, mild steel	11.86
11.2	Tap, 2 × 5.69	11.38
	$/100 units for B-pattern	$187.64

EXAMPLES

A complicated gear box having box dimensions of 29 × 40 × 17 has many line bores, counter bores, backfaces, taps, and drilled holes. The material is gray cast iron, ferritic ASTM A 48, class 20, and weighs about 715 lb. For a part of the work, find typical element patterns, and show the time required.

Item	Description	Cost
10.1	Tools, 3 × 48.4	$145.20
10.1	Cutter changes, 3 × 37.4	112.20
10.1	Decimal hole	85.70
11.2	Core drill 2.55 × 2 × 3.45, cast iron	17.60
11.1	Rough bore, 3.66 × 2.75 × 2, HSS	20.13
11.1	Finish bore, 5.23 × 2.75 × 2, HSS	28.77
	$/100 units for C-pattern	$409.60

TABLE 10.1 HORIZONTAL MILLING, DRILLING, AND BORING MACHINES

Setup in estimating hours

1. Base time .31

2. Angle plate
   Angle plate, load manually .25
   Second angle plate .22
   Crane lift or hoist lift of angle plate
       3 hold downs .37
       4 hold downs .44
   Second angle plate
       3 hold downs .34
       4 hold downs .41

3. Fixture load and unload

	Strap hold downs			Bolt hold downs		
	2	3	4	2	3	4
Hand carry	.27	.35	.42	.17	.20	.22
Hoist lift	.36	.44	.51	.26	.29	.31

4. Center plug
   Less than 6 in., .02; more than 6 in. .07

5. Block or table
   Floor plate block .27
   Install rotary table .49

6. Prepare strap clamp for holding piece .10
   Prepare stop block for holding piece .05
   Prepare bolt, slot block, set screw or .01
       adjustable for setting piece .02

7. Select sleeve, assemble to tool and disassemble .01

8. Inspection
   Fractional tolerance .01
   Decimal tolerance .02

9. Piece production (optional), 2 × hr per 1 unit

Operation elements in estimating minutes

1. Handling
   Load and unload manually 1.74

   Jib or crane

Weight	500	1000	2000
Load, Unload	7.22	8.59	9.21
Reposition	4.33	5.15	5.53

2. Clamp and unclamp piece

Number	1	2	3	4	Add'l
Strap clamp	1.46	2.92	4.38	5.84	1.46
Set screw or C-clamp	1.19	2.37	3.56	4.74	1.19
Adjust bottle jack	.36	.73	1.08	1.44	.36
Double stud strap	7.93	15.87	23.79	31.72	7.93

3. Machine operation, ea occurrence
  Change speed   .18
  Change feed   .16
  Start and stop   .40
  Readout per location   2.79
  Dial indicate   5.34
  Manually index rotary table 4.31
  Power-turn rotary table   1.70

4. Install and remove tool, ea
  Center, drill, or tap   .57
  Spot face or back face   .87
  Core drill or ream   1.31
  Stub bar for first bore   2.05
  Stub bar for bore, ream, or face 1.35
  Stub bar for back face   3.15
  Stub bar for milling   2.61
  In-line bar through piece   3.94
  In-line bar through fixture 19.47
  In-line bar and relocate in fixture 18.73

5. Install and remove cutter, ea occurrence
  Stub bar with chamfer and spot face 1.01
  Stub bar bore and ream   1.52
  Stub bar with back face   2.53
  Bar in-line for chamfer or ream 1.73
  Bar in-line for bore, spot face, or back face 2.15

6. Advance and retract tool, ea occurrence
  Center drill, drill, tap, or end mill .18
  Core drill or reamer   .60
  Spot face and back face   .73
  Spot face and backface, decimal tolerance 1.82
  Face mill
    Fraction tolerance   1.20
    Finish decimal tolerance   2.69
    Same depth, different location .70
  Stub bar
    Single edge cutter, fractional tolerance 1.40
    Single edge cutter, decimal tolerance 6.19
    Double edge cutter, fractional tolerance .44
    Double edge cutter, decimal tolerance 1.97
  Bar, in-line
    Single edge cutter, fractional tolerance 1.48
    Single edge cutter, decimal tolerance 7.01
    Double edge, fractional tolerance .52
    Double edge, decimal tolerance 2.63

7. Machine travel, ea occurrence

Distance	Min	Distance	Min	Distance	Min
10	.10	30	.30	85	.85
12	.12	35	.35	90	.90
14	.14	40	.40	95	.95
16	.16	45	.45	100	1.00
18	.18	50	.50	105	1.05
20	.20	55	.55	110	1.10
22	.22	60	.60	120	1.20
24	.24	65	.65	130	1.30
26	.26	70	.70	140	1.40
28	.28	75	.75	150	1.50
30	.30	80	.80	Add'l	.01

8. Machining
   Bore, thread, start drill   See Table 11.1
   Drill, counterbore, ream or tap   See Table 11.2
   Face mill   See Table 11.3

9. Tool life and replacement   See Table 11.4

10.2 Boring and Facing Machines

DESCRIPTION

Boring and facing machines are designed for close tolerance boring. Machines have a minimum of two boring heads and can handle boring, facing, and turning elements. They have hydraulically-operated tables and are semiautomatic. The sequence is controlled by adjustable stop dogs. (See Figure 10.2.)

ESTIMATING DATA DISCUSSION

Entry variables for setup are the number of boring heads and tolerance. The handling elements depend upon part size. A small part may be handled with one hand. Medium parts do not weigh over 3 lb; large parts do not exceed 8 lb. In these data, heavy parts are 15 lb. or less. These four categories are for fixture loading. Loading and unloading to an angle plate or machinist vise are additional methods. A variety of devices are provided for in clamping. If a cam lever is used to tighten, the time also includes unclamp. Similarly, a pry part includes the work to obtain and set aside a screwdriver.

If the estimator wishes to use rule-of-thumb approaches, Item 10.2 of Section IV can be used. This cost is for handling and loading/unloading for each boring station. A boring station may have one or two boring heads machining simultaneously, but machining cost is provided by Items 11.1 and 11.2.

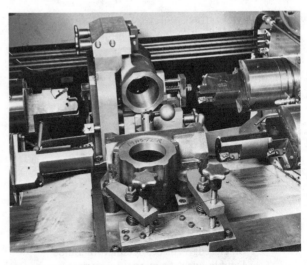

FIGURE 10.2 Boring and facing machine working on a hydraulic power component. *(Ex-Cell-O Corporation.)*

EXAMPLES

A. Ductile-iron power-steering gear bodies are to be bored and faced square to the bore. The castings are to be processed on a 4-spindle machine. The part is rough bored, counterbored, and chamfered. The main bore is machined in the front station and reloaded into the rear station for simultaneous small bore machining. The machining schedule is given below. Find the unit time and lot time for a quantity of 1800.

Table	Description	Time
10.2-S	4 boring heads, .60 + 3 × .35	1.65 hr
10.2-S	Exceptional tolerances, 4 heads	.80 hr
10.2-1	Load part, get, dispose	.17 min
10.2-2	Clamping plates, 2	.20
10.2-2	Hand knob, 2	.16
10.2-2	Cam lever	.05
10.2-3	Blow off fixture	.07
10.2-3	Air blow part	.12
10.2-4	Machine operation	.02
10.2-4	Longitudinal distance	.18
11.1-3	Rough bore 10 in.-long, 4-in. OD, carbide .21 × (10 + .25)	2.15
	Counterbore 4.5 in., ½-in. long in front station, .27 (.5 + .25) = .20	
11.1-2	Face 5 in.-OD × ½-in. long, .19 × − .10 (but this simo to rough boring operation)	
Repeat	Load, clamp, unclamp, unload for back station handling	.97
11.1-3	Rough machine cross bores simultaneously to front station machine time, no time	0
	Unit estimate	4.09 min
	Lot time	125.15 hr

B. Estimate the cost of Example A above using a base-cost approach.

Item	Description	Cost
10.2	Setup constant	$ 3.02
10.2	4 boring heads, 4 × 4.23	16.92
	Setup subtotal	$ 19.94
10.2	4 boring stations, 4 × 12.3	$ 49.20
11.1	Longest cut, 10 × 4 × .972, use cast iron, carbide and boring	38.88
	$/100 units subtotal	$ 88.08
	Lot cost for 1800 units	$1605.38

TABLE 10.2   BORING AND FACING MACHINES

Setup

First boring head	.60 hr
Each add'l boring head	.35 hr
Exceptional tolerance per head	.20 hr

Operation elements in estimating minutes

1. Handling part

	Small	Medium	Large	Heavy
Get and dispose	.04	.06	.10	.14
Load and unload	.04	.05	.07	.10

Angle plate, load and unload, clamp, unclamp	1.20
Vise for up to 5 lb.	.40
5–25 lb	.60

2. Clamp and unclamp
   Cam lever .05
   Position and remove swing or slide clamp .04
   Place and remove clamping plate .10
   Place and remove nut or bolt .04
   Operate air clamp .03
   Tighten and loosen nut using wrench .17
   Tighten and loosen hand knob or wing nut .08
   Pry part out of fixture .06

3. Cleaning
   Blow off fixture .07
   Wash part .08
   Air blow part, small, .06; large .12

4. Machine operation
   Engage feed .02
   Longitudinal feed, rapid traverse to work and return, per cut .09
   Cross feed .09/in.

5. Machining
   Face See Table 11.3
   Drill See Table 11.2
   Bore See Table 11.1

6. Tool wear and replacement See Table 11.4

7. Part inspection See Table 22.1

MACHINING and TOOL REPLACEMENT

11.1 Turn, Bore, Form, Cutoff, Thread, Start Drill, and Break Edges

DESCRIPTION

These data are for pure machine time and are appropriate for various metal-cutting machines. Their location within the databook is centralized, thus encouraging ease of application. While primarily to be used with turning machines, other data related to milling and drilling are nearby. Some machines have their machine times integral with handling in a single table such as sawing, hobbing, etc.

ESTIMATING DATA DISCUSSION

These data are used whenever the machine is in a cutting-feed mode. A length of cut is composed of the drawing length plus a safety distance, approach, and overtravel. The entry variable for Element 1 is the diameter of the feature being machined. Element 1 is called safety stock, and provides for that small distance when there is no chips or cutting from the point of conclusion of rapid traverse velocity to cutting. This small length is affected by age of the machine and part tolerance. The total length of cutting is used to multiply the minutes per inch for various types of machining. The length of cut is multiplied by the factor given in Element 2.

Several factors affect the time to turn stock. Diameter, material of part, tool geometry, overhang, material, and sharpness, feed, depth of cut, machine stiffness, and horsepower are essential considerations. Despite the difficulty of precisely defining these machinability factors, the estimator is required to pick a time value in advance of production. Published information and general recommendations often provide ranges for surface-cutting velocity and feed from 300 to 500%, and the estimator is to pick a value. In this book, however, specific time values, minutes per inch (min/in.), are provided for a variety of diameters, materials, and machine cuts.

The factor is "minutes per inch" rather than inch per minute because it is more convenient for estimating. The practice of "min/in." is followed throughout this book. The guide value is multiplied by length of cut resulting in minutes for the machining element.

Some companies follow a procedure to match the estimated rpm to available machine rpm's. While this may be useful, the step may not be worth the effort. The table values provided in this databook are keyed to significant diameters; and many modern machines provide infinite rpm drive cutters. This matching results in negligible improvement over a number of estimates. We recommend using table values, or the next highest value if a specific diameter is unavailable.

Entry variables for Element 2, turn, are tool material, part material and bar diameter. Time values are min/in. and with the length of cut found, the element time is the arithmetic product. The top and lower value are for rough and finish turning. For a two-pass plan of rough and finish, the two values may be added. For a roughing depth of cut in excess of 0.3 in., increase time by 25%. Cutting speed and feed values for selected materials are as follows:

| Material | Bhn | Turning | | | |
| | | High speed steel | | Carbide | |
		Rough	Finish	Rough	Finish
Low-carbon steel, free machining	170	(160,.015)	(210,.007)	(500,.020)	(700,.007)
Low-carbon steel	150	(120,.015)	(160,.007)	(400,.020)	(600,.007)
Medium-carbon steel	215	(190,.015)	(125,.007)	(325,.020)	(400,.007)
Stainless steel, 300	170	(100,.015)	(125,.007)	(300,.015)	(400,.007)
Stainless steel, 400	195	(150,.015)	(160,.007)	(350,.015)	(350,.007)
Steel castings, forging	225	(95,.015)	(125,.007)	(360,.020)	(475,.007)
Cast iron, gray	150	(145,.015)	(185,.007)	(500,.020)	(675,.010)
Aluminum	100	(600,.015)	(800,.007)	(800,.020)	(1200,.010)
Copper alloys		(275,.015)	(350,.007)	(550,.020)	(650,.007)
Plastic		(300,.010)	(300,.005)	(500,.010)	(500,.005)

$$\text{min/in.} = \frac{\pi \, Dia}{12 f V} \quad \text{where } Dia = \text{diameter, in.}$$

$$f = \text{feed in./rev.}$$

$$V = \text{cutting velocity, fpm.}$$

For instance, for free-machining low-carbon steel with an HSS rough speed of 160 and a 0.015 ipr, the 3-in. diameter calculates to give a min/in. of 0.33. Obviously other values for V and f can be substituted and differing values computed.

Cutting velocities and feeds, other than those given above, for some harder materials are as follows for carbide tools:

Material	Roughing		Finishing	
Hastelloy	40,	.021	75,	.007
Inconel	80,	.021	160,	.007
Rene 41	35,	.021	85,	.007
J-1570	40,	.021	100,	.007

Thus, if a 3-in. OD bar of hastelloy was to be turned, the value of V and f could be used, or a ratio of $\dfrac{.33 \times 160 \times .015}{40 \times .021}$ to give 0.94 min/in. The idea of forming a ratio of the products of $V \times f$ multiplied by the tabular value is quick.

Entry values for boring Element 3 are tool and part material, and diameter of the feature being machined. Basic turning velocities and feeds were reduced for boring. The diameter is chosen before stock removal; and the practice of selecting the next-higher diameter from the table is preferred, especially if interpolation between neighboring values leads to negligible results over a number of estimates.

The basic turning velocities and feeds were reduced for forming and cutoff, Element 4. The maximum diameter of the feature to be formed is the entry variable and the length of cut is measured as the radial distance moved of the form cutter.

The entry variables for single-point threading, Element 5, are no. of threads per in. and material. The value given by the intersection is multiplied by the product of the length of thread by nominal diameter. Data used in the construction of the table are the following:

Material	Cutting Velocity	Passes
Steel (mild, free-machining)	25	5
Steel (hard, stainless)	10	8
Cast iron	25	6
Brass	30	3
Aluminum	30	4
Plastic	50	5

The estimating formula is (no. of passes) $\times$ (threads per in.) $\div$ 3.82 V and the factor in the table is multiplied by the product of L and Dia. For example, assume a threaded Dia of 6 in., $L = 1\,1/4$ in., and there are 5 threads per in. for an aluminum casting. The time = .17 $\times$ 6 $\times$ 1.25 = 1.28 min. The time factor includes only threading, as positioning, set depth, etc., are found in other tables. In self-opening die threading, the entry variables are similar to 5, and the factor is multiplied by the $L \times Dia$. The diameter is the nominal size of the thread. The L is full distance of the thread. Tapping time is found in Table 11.2.

The time to start-drill is related to the diameter of the hole being drilled and material. Break edges include the pickup of the file, etc., deburr corner of rotating edges, and lay tool aside. The entry variables are number of inside and outside diameters.

Direct labor cost can be estimated using Item 11.1 of Section IV. These costs are for pure machining and they are added to part handling, machine operation, and inspection as given by other items. These cost data are a reduction of Table 11.1 and are over a number of estimates; the two alternative methods in finding direct-labor efforts are similar. The cost values are dollars per 100 units ($/100 units). It is necessary to multiply the factor by the machining requirements. For turning and boring, each cell provides an upper rough cost and a lower finishing cost. Form or cutoff has one value. Each of these three machining types is identified by high-speed steel or carbide tool material selections. Turning, boring, form, or cutoff cost factors are multiplied by the total distance. For threading, multiply the factor by length × diameter × threads per in. (*f*actor × *L* × *Dia* × threads/in.). The start drill element is dependent upon the diameter of the hole to be drilled. Hand file edges, also called "break edges", has a cost factor relating to the number of internal and external diameters.

EXAMPLES

Examples for estimating direct-labor time applying to these data are found elsewhere, notably the turning and boring machines.

TABLE 11.1 TURN, BORE, FORM, CUTOFF, THREAD, START DRILL, AND BREAK EDGES

Setup **See other tables**

Operation elements in estimating minutes

1. Safety stock, min/occurrence

Dia	¾	1	1¾	2
Min	.01	.03	.05	.09 max

CAN AND SHOULD MAKE THIS ADJUSTMENT INTO THE ~~DIAMETER~~ LENGTH OF PC.

2. Turn, min/in.
   or FACE
   High-speed steel

Per in per pass

Material	Diameter ¼	½	¾	1	1¼	1½	1¾	2	2¼	2½	2¾	3	4	5	6	7	8	9	10	
	.03	.05	.08	.11	.14	.16	.19	.22	.25	.27	.30	.33	.44	.55	.65	.76	.87	.98	1.09	ROUGHING
Low-carbon steel, free-machining	.04	.09	.13	.18	.22	.27	.31	.30	.40	.45	.49	.53	.71	.89	1.07	1.25	1.42	1.60	1.78	FINISHING
	.04	.07	.11	.15	.18	.22	.25	.29	.33	.36	.40	.44	.58	.73	.87	1.02	1.16	1.31	1.45	
Low-carbon steel	.06	.12	.18	.23	.29	.35	.41	.47	.53	.58	.64	.70	.93	1.17	1.40	1.64	1.87	2.10	2.34	
	.05	.10	.15	.19	.24	.29	.34	.39	.44	.48	.53	.58	.78	.97	1.16	1.36	1.55	1.75	1.94	
Medium-carbon steel	.07	.15	.22	.30	.37	.45	.52	.60	.67	.75	.82	.90	1.20	1.50	1.80	2.09	2.39	2.69	2.99	
	.04	.09	.13	.17	.22	.26	.31	.35	.39	.44	.48	.52	.70	.87	1.05	1.22	1.40	1.57	1.75	
Stainless steel, 300	.07	.15	.22	.30	.37	.45	.52	.60	.67	.75	.82	.90	1.20	1.50	1.80	2.09	2.39	2.69	2.99	
	.03	.06	.09	.12	.15	.17	.20	.23	.26	.29	.32	.35	.47	.58	.70	.81	.93	1.05	1.16	
Stainless steel, 400	.06	.12	.18	.23	.29	.35	.41	.47	.53	.58	.64	.70	.93	1.17	1.40	1.64	1.87	2.10	2.34	
	.05	.09	.14	.18	.23	.28	.32	.37	.41	.46	.51	.55	.73	.92	1.10	1.29	1.47	1.65	1.84	
Steel castings, forgings	.07	.15	.22	.30	.37	.45	.52	.60	.67	.75	.82	.90	1.20	1.50	1.80	2.09	2.39	2.69	2.99	
	.03	.06	.09	.12	.15	.18	.21	.24	.27	.30	.33	.36	.48	.60	.72	.84	.96	1.08	1.20	
Cast iron, gray	.05	.10	.15	.20	.25	.30	.35	.40	.45	.51	.56	.61	.81	1.01	1.21	1.42	1.62	1.82	2.02	
	.01	.01	.02	.03	.04	.04	.05	.06	.07	.07	.08	.09	.12	.15	.17	.20	.23	.26	.29	
Aluminum	.01	.02	.04	.05	.06	.07	.08	.09	.11	.12	.13	.14	.19	.23	.28	.33	.37	.42	.47	
	.02	.03	.05	.06	.08	.10	.11	.13	.14	.16	.17	.19	.25	.32	.38	.44	.51	.57	.63	
Copper alloy	.03	.05	.08	.11	.13	.16	.19	.21	.24	.27	.29	.32	.43	.53	.64	.75	.85	.96	1.07	
	.02	.04	.07	.09	.11	.13	.15	.17	.20	.22	.24	.26	.35	.44	.52	.61	.70	.79	.87	
Plastics	.04	.09	.13	.17	.22	.26	.31	.35	.39	.44	.48	.52	.70	.87	1.05	1.22	1.40	1.57	1.75	

Carbide

Material	¼	½	¾	1	1¼	1½	1¾	2	2¼	2½	2¾	3	4	5	6	7	8	9	10
Low-carbon steel, free-machining	.01	.01	.02	.03	.03	.04	.05	.05	.06	.07	.07	.08	.10	.13	.16	.18	.21	.24	.26
	.01	.03	.04	.05	.07	.08	.09	.11	.12	.13	.15	.16	.21	.27	.32	.37	.43	.48	.53
Low-carbon steel	.01	.02	.02	.03	.04	.05	.06	.07	.07	.08	.09	.10	.13	.16	.20	.23	.26	.29	.33
	.02	.03	.05	.06	.08	.09	.11	.12	.14	.16	.17	.19	.25	.31	.37	.44	.50	.56	.62
Medium-carbon steel	.01	.02	.03	.04	.05	.06	.07	.08	.09	.10	.11	.12	.16	.20	.24	.28	.32	.36	.40
	.02	.05	.07	.09	.12	.14	.16	.19	.21	.23	.26	.28	.37	.47	.56	.65	.75	.84	.93
Stainless steel, 300	.01	.03	.04	.06	.07	.09	.10	.12	.13	.15	.16	.17	.23	.29	.35	.41	.47	.52	.58
	.02	.05	.07	.09	.12	.14	.16	.19	.21	.23	.26	.28	.37	.47	.56	.65	.75	.84	.93
Stainless steel, 400	.02	.03	.05	.06	.08	.09	.11	.12	.14	.16	.17	.19	.25	.31	.37	.44	.50	.56	.62
	.03	.07	.10	.13	.17	.20	.23	.27	.30	.33	.37	.40	.53	.67	.80	.93	1.07	1.20	1.34
Steel castings, forgings	.01	.02	.03	.04	.05	.05	.06	.07	.08	.09	.10	.11	.15	.18	.22	.25	.29	.33	.36
	.02	.04	.06	.08	.10	.12	.14	.16	.18	.20	.22	.24	.31	.39	.47	.55	.63	.71	.79
Cast iron, gray	.01	.01	.02	.03	.03	.04	.05	.05	.06	.07	.07	.08	.10	.13	.16	.18	.21	.24	.26
	.01	.02	.03	.04	.05	.06	.07	.08	.09	.10	.11	.12	.16	.19	.23	.27	.31	.35	.39
Aluminum	.01	.01	.01	.02	.02	.02	.03	.03	.04	.04	.04	.05	.07	.08	.10	.11	.13	.15	.16
	.01	.01	.02	.02	.03	.03	.04	.04	.05	.05	.06	.07	.09	.11	.13	.15	.17	.20	.22
Copper alloys	.01	.01	.02	.02	.03	.04	.04	.05	.05	.06	.07	.07	.10	.12	.14	.17	.19	.21	.24
	.01	.03	.04	.06	.07	.09	.10	.12	.13	.14	.16	.17	.23	.29	.35	.40	.46	.52	.58
Plastics	.01	.03	.04	.05	.07	.08	.09	.10	.12	.13	.14	.16	.21	.26	.31	.37	.42	.47	.52
	.03	.05	.08	.10	.13	.16	.18	.21	.24	.26	.29	.31	.42	.52	.63	.73	.84	.94	1.05

3. Bore, min/in.

High speed steel

Material	¼	½	¾	1	1¼	1½	1¾	2	2¼	2½	2¾	3	4	5	6	7	8	9	10
Low-carbon steel, free-machining	.04	.09	.13	.18	.22	.27	.31	.36	.40	.45	.49	.53	.71	.89	1.07	1.25	1.42	1.60	1.78
	.06	.12	.18	.25	.31	.37	.43	.49	.55	.62	.68	.74	.99	1.23	1.48	1.73	1.97	2.22	2.46
Low-carbon steel	.06	.12	.18	.23	.29	.35	.41	.47	.53	.58	.64	.70	.93	1.17	1.40	1.64	1.87	2.10	2.34
	.08	.16	.24	.32	.40	.49	.57	.65	.73	.81	.89	.97	1.29	1.62	1.94	2.26	2.59	2.91	3.24
Medium-carbon steel	.07	.15	.22	.30	.37	.45	.52	.60	.67	.75	.82	.90	1.20	1.50	1.80	2.09	2.39	2.69	2.99
	.10	.21	.31	.41	.52	.62	.72	.83	.93	1.04	1.14	1.24	1.66	2.07	2.48	2.90	3.31	3.73	4.14
Stainless steel, 300	.07	.15	.22	.30	.37	.45	.52	.60	.67	.75	.82	.90	1.20	1.50	1.80	2.09	2.39	2.69	2.99
	.10	.21	.31	.41	.52	.62	.72	.83	.93	1.04	1.14	1.24	1.66	2.07	2.48	2.90	3.31	3.73	4.14
Stainless steel, 400	.06	.12	.18	.23	.29	.35	.41	.47	.53	.58	.64	.70	.93	1.17	1.40	1.64	1.87	2.10	2.34
	.08	.16	.24	.32	.40	.49	.57	.65	.73	.81	.89	.97	1.29	1.62	1.94	2.26	2.59	2.91	3.24
Steel casting, forgings	.07	.15	.22	.30	.37	.45	.52	.60	.67	.75	.82	.90	1.20	1.50	1.80	2.09	2.39	2.69	2.99
	.10	.21	.31	.41	.52	.62	.72	.83	.93	1.04	1.14	1.24	1.66	2.07	2.48	2.90	3.31	3.73	4.14
Cast iron, gray	.05	.10	.15	.20	.25	.30	.35	.40	.45	.51	.56	.61	.81	1.01	1.21	1.42	1.62	1.82	2.02
	.07	.14	.21	.28	.35	.42	.49	.56	.63	.70	.77	.84	1.12	1.40	1.68	1.96	2.24	2.52	2.80
Aluminum	.01	.02	.04	.05	.06	.07	.08	.09	.11	.12	.13	.14	.19	.23	.28	.33	.37	.42	.47
	.02	.03	.05	.06	.08	.10	.11	.13	.15	.16	.18	.19	.26	.32	.39	.45	.52	.58	.65
Copper alloys	.03	.05	.08	.11	.13	.16	.19	.21	.24	.27	.29	.32	.43	.53	.64	.75	.85	.96	1.07
	.04	.07	.11	.15	.18	.22	.26	.30	.33	.37	.41	.44	.59	.75	.89	1.04	1.18	1.33	1.48
Plastics	.04	.09	.13	.17	.22	.26	.31	.35	.39	.44	.48	.52	.70	.87	1.05	1.22	1.40	1.57	1.75
	.06	.12	.18	.24	.30	.36	.42	.48	.54	.60	.66	.72	.97	1.21	1.45	1.69	1.93	2.17	2.42

Carbide

Material	¼	½	¾	1	1¼	1½	1¾	2	2¼	2½	2¾	3	4	5	6	7	8	9	10
											Diameter								
Low-carbon steel, free-machining	.01	.03	.04	.05	.07	.08	.09	.11	.12	.13	.15	.16	.21	.27	.32	.37	.43	.48	.53
	.02	.04	.06	.07	.09	.11	.13	.15	.17	.18	.20	.22	.30	.37	.44	.52	.59	.67	.74
Low-carbon steel	.02	.03	.05	.06	.08	.09	.11	.12	.14	.16	.17	.19	.25	.31	.37	.44	.50	.56	.62
	.02	.04	.06	.09	.11	.13	.15	.17	.19	.22	.24	.26	.35	.43	.52	.60	.69	.78	.86
Medium-carbon steel	.02	.05	.07	.09	.12	.14	.16	.19	.21	.23	.26	.28	.37	.47	.56	.65	.75	.84	.93
	.03	.06	.10	.13	.16	.19	.23	.26	.29	.32	.36	.39	.52	.65	.78	.91	1.04	1.16	1.29
Stainless steel, 300	.02	.05	.07	.09	.12	.14	.16	.19	.21	.23	.26	.28	.37	.47	.56	.65	.75	.84	.93
	.03	.06	.10	.13	.16	.19	.23	.26	.29	.32	.36	.39	.52	.65	.78	.91	1.04	1.16	1.29
Stainless steel, 400	.03	.05	.08	.11	.13	.16	.19	.21	.24	.27	.29	.32	.43	.53	.64	.75	.85	.96	1.07
	.04	.07	.11	.15	.18	.22	.26	.30	.33	.37	.41	.44	.59	.74	.89	1.04	1.18	1.33	1.48
Steel castings, forgings	.02	.04	.06	.08	.10	.12	.14	.16	.18	.20	.22	.24	.31	.39	.47	.55	.63	.71	.79
	.03	.05	.08	.11	.14	.16	.19	.22	.25	.27	.30	.33	.44	.54	.65	.76	.87	.98	1.09
Cast iron, gray	.01	.02	.03	.04	.05	.06	.07	.08	.09	.10	.11	.12	.16	.19	.23	.27	.31	.35	.39
	.01	.03	.04	.05	.07	.08	.09	.11	.12	.13	.15	.16	.21	.27	.32	.38	.43	.48	.54
Aluminum	.01	.01	.02	.02	.03	.03	.04	.04	.05	.05	.06	.07	.09	.11	.13	.15	.17	.20	.22
	.01	.02	.02	.03	.04	.05	.05	.06	.07	.08	.08	.09	.12	.15	.18	.21	.24	.27	.30
Copper alloys	.01	.03	.04	.06	.07	.09	.10	.12	.13	.14	.16	.23	.29	.35	.40	.46	.48	.52	.58
	.02	.04	.06	.08	.10	.12	.14	.16	.18	.20	.22	.32	.40	.48	.56	.64	.70	.72	.80
Plastics	.03	.05	.08	.10	.13	.16	.18	.21	.24	.26	.29	.31	.42	.52	.63	.73	.84	.94	1.05
	.04	.07	.11	.14	.18	.22	.25	.29	.33	.36	.40	.43	.58	.72	.87	1.01	1.16	1.30	1.45

4. Form or cutoff, min/in.

High speed steel

Material	¼	½	¾	1	1¼	1½	1¾	2	2¼	2½	2¾	3	4	5	6	7	8	9	10
											Diameter								
Low-carbon steel, free-machining	.09	.18	.27	.36	.45	.55	.64	.73	.82	.91	1.00	1.09	1.45	1.82	2.18	2.55	2.91	3.27	3.64
Low-carbon steel	.12	.24	.36	.48	.61	.73	.85	.97	1.09	1.21	1.33	1.45	1.94	2.42	2.91	3.39	3.88	4.36	4.85
Medium-carbon steel	.16	.32	.48	.65	.81	.97	1.13	1.29	1.45	1.62	1.78	1.94	2.59	3.23	3.88	4.52	5.17	5.82	6.46
Stainless steel, 300	.15	.29	.44	.58	.73	.87	1.02	1.16	1.31	1.45	1.60	1.75	2.33	2.91	3.49	4.07	4.65	5.24	5.82
Stainless steel, 400	.10	.19	.29	.39	.48	.58	.68	.78	.87	.97	1.07	1.16	1.55	1.94	2.33	2.71	3.10	3.49	3.88
Steel castings, forgings	.15	.31	.46	.61	.77	.92	1.07	1.22	1.38	1.53	1.68	1.84	2.45	3.06	3.67	4.29	4.90	5.51	6.12
Cast iron, gray	.10	.20	.30	.40	.50	.60	.70	.80	.90	1.00	1.10	1.20	1.60	2.01	2.41	2.81	3.21	3.61	4.01
Aluminum	.02	.05	.07	.10	.12	.15	.17	.19	.22	.24	.27	.29	.39	.48	.58	.68	.78	.87	.97
Copper alloys	.05	.11	.16	.21	.26	.32	.37	.42	.48	.53	.58	.63	.85	1.06	1.27	1.48	1.69	1.90	2.12
Plastics	.07	.15	.22	.29	.36	.44	.51	.58	.65	.73	.80	.87	1.16	1.45	1.75	2.04	2.33	2.62	2.91

Carbide

Material	¼	½	¾	1	1¼	1½	1¾	2	2¼	2½	2¾	3	4	5	6	7	8	9	10
								Diameter											
Low-carbon steel, free-machining	.02	.04	.07	.09	.11	.13	.15	.17	.20	.22	.24	.26	.35	.44	.52	.61	.70	.79	.87
Low-carbon steel	.03	.05	.08	.11	.14	.16	.19	.22	.25	.27	.30	.33	.44	.55	.65	.76	.87	.98	1.09
Medium-carbon steel	.03	.07	.10	.13	.17	.20	.23	.27	.30	.34	.37	.40	.54	.67	.81	.94	1.07	1.21	1.34
Stainless steel, 300	.05	.10	.15	.19	.24	.29	.34	.39	.44	.48	.53	.58	.78	.97	1.16	1.36	1.55	1.75	1.94
Stainless steel, 400	.04	.08	.12	.17	.21	.25	.29	.33	.37	.42	.46	.50	.66	.83	1.00	1.16	1.33	1.50	1.66
Steel castings, forgings	.03	.06	.09	.12	.15	.18	.21	.24	.27	.30	.33	.36	.48	.61	.73	.85	.97	1.09	1.21
Cast iron, gray	.02	.04	.07	.09	.11	.13	.15	.17	.20	.22	.24	.26	.35	.44	.52	.61	.70	.79	.87
Aluminum	.01	.03	.04	.05	.07	.08	.10	.11	.12	.14	.15	.16	.22	.27	.33	.38	.44	.49	.55
Copper alloys	.02	.04	.06	.08	.10	.12	.14	.16	.18	.20	.22	.32	.40	.48	.56	.64	.68	.71	.79
Plastics	.04	.09	.13	.17	.22	.26	.31	.35	.39	.44	.48	.52	.70	.87	1.05	1.22	1.40	1.57	1.75

5. Threading

Threading, single-point; factor $\times L \times Dia$ = min

Material	4	5	6	7	8	9	10	11	12	14	16	18	20	24	28	32
							Threads per in.									
Steel (mild), free-machining	.21	.26	.31	.37	.42	.47	.52	.58	.63	.73	.84	.94	1.05	1.26	1.47	1.68
Steel (hard), stainless	.84	1.05	1.26	1.47	1.69	1.88	2.09	2.30	2.51	2.93	3.35	3.77	4.19	5.03	5.86	6.70
Cast iron	.25	.31	.38	.44	.50	.57	.63	.69	.75	.88	1.01	1.13	1.26			
Brass	.10	.13	.16	.18	.21	.24	.26	.29	.31	.37	.42	.47	.52	.63	.73	.84
Aluminum	.14	.17	.21	.24	.28	.31	.35	.38	.42	.49	.56	.63	.70	.84	.98	1.12
Plastic	.10	.13	.16	.18	.21	.24	.26	.29	.31	.37	.42	.47	.52	.63	.73	.84

Threading self-opening die; factor $\times L \times Dia$ = min

Material	4	5	6	7	8	9	10	11	12	14	16	18	20	24	28	32
							Threads per in.									
Steel (mild), free-machining	.04	.05	.06	.07	.08	.09	.10	.12	.13	.15	.17	.19	.21	.25	.29	.34
Steel (hard), stainless	.10	.13	.16	.18	.21	.24	.26	.29	.31	.37	.42	.47	.52	.63	.73	.84
Cast iron	.04	.05	.06	.07	.08	.09	.10	.12	.13	.15	.17	.19	.21	.25	.29	.34
Brass, Aluminum	.03	.04	.05	.06	.07	.08	.09	.10	.10	.12	.14	.16	.17	.21	.24	.28
Plastic	.02	.03	.03	.04	.04	.05	.05	.06	.06	.07	.08	.09	.10	.13	.15	.17

6. Start drill, min[1]

Steel	Dia	¼	5/16	½	1	2	3	
	Min	.02	.03	.05	.11	.35	.66	

Steel (medium) Cast iron	Dia	¼	5/16	½	¾	1	1½	3
	Min	.03	.04	.07	.12	.14	.25	.83

Steel (alloy) Forgings Stainless	Dia	¼	⅜	⅝	1	2	3	
	Min	.04	.07	.13	.22	.70	1.31	

Steel (high tensile) Titanium	Dia	¼	⅜	⅝	1	2		
	Min	.07	.12	.21	.37	1.16		

Aluminum, brass, magnesium, plastic	Dia	¼	⅜	½	1	1½	2	3
	Min	.01	.02	.05	.05	.08	.14	.26

[1] *Dia* is for hole to be drilled.

7. Break edges, min

	No. of Outside Diameters									
No. of Inside Dia	0	1	2	3	4	5	6	7	8	9
0	0	.06	.11	.14	.17	.19	.22	.24	.26	.29
1	.06	.08	.12	.16	.16	.20	.23	.25	.28	.30
2	.08	.11	.14	.18	.20	.23	.25	.28	.30	.31
3	.10	.12	.16	.19	.22	.24	.26	.29	.31	.32
4	.11	.13	.17	.20	.23	.25	.28	.29	.32	.34
5	.12	.14	.18	.22	.24	.26	.29	.31	.34	.35

11.2 Drill, Ream, Counterbore, Countersink, Tap, and Microdrill

DESCRIPTION

These data are for pure machine time and are appropriate for operations involving drilling, counterboring, spotfacing, countersinking, reaming, and tapping, especially with various drilling, turning, and milling machines. The location of this information is centralized to facilitate its use.

Not all drilling machining times are included in this section. But machining for gun drilling, core drilling, taper reaming, and pipe threading can be judged and estimated using a similar context from these and other drilling data.

ESTIMATING DATA DISCUSSION

For Element 1, the entry variables are depth of material to be drilled, diameter of drill, and material. The drilling is sensitive, i.e., manual, using a sensitive drill press. For sensitive drilling no approach or breakthrough distance is added to the stock depth; use the depth only. The time is min per hole. Multiply the hole time by the number of holes for that size. The materials are soft steel, hard steels implying stainless grades and tool steels, brass implying brass, cast and soft bronzes, and aluminum. To expedite table usage, the upper values may be selected to avoid tabular interpolation.

In sensitive reaming, Element 2, which differs from power reaming, only length and ream diameter are evaluated. Material distinctions were overlooked, since they are averaged jointly for the data.

For Element 4, entry variables are drill diameter and five classes of raw material. The basic formula for:

$$\text{min/in.} = \frac{\pi \, Dia}{12 \, Vf}, \text{ where } V = \text{surface cutting velocity, ft/min, and}$$
$$f = \text{in. per rev}$$

The min/in. value from Elements 4, 6, 7, and 8 require that they be multiplied by L, or length, which may be longer than the depth shown by the drawing. For drilling length, we add for drill point, and the following table is used.

The tabular values provide drill point and breakthrough length as related to drill diameter. Using the

Drill-point lead and breakthrough in.

Drill Dia	Distance	Drill Dia	Distance	Drill Dia	Distance
.019	.01	.416	.22	1⅛	.59
.038	.02	.454	.24	1¼	.66
.057	.03	.5	.26	1½	.79
.076	.04	.53	.28	1⅝	.86
.095	.05	.57	.30	1¾	.93
.113	.06	.61	.32	2	1.05
.132	.07	.64	.34	2⅛	1.12
.151	.08	.68	.36	2¼	1.19
.170	.09	.72	.38	2⅜	1.26
.189	.10	.75	.39	2½	1.32
.208	.11	.79	.42	2⅝	1.39
.227	.12	.83	.44	2¾	1.45
.25	.13	.87	.46	2⅞	1.52
.265	.14	.91	.48	3	1.59
.284	.15	.95	.50	3⅛	1.65
.303	.16	.98	.52	3¼	1.72
.322	.17	1.00	.53	3⅜	1.78
.340	.18	1.02	.54	3½	1.85
.359	.19	1.06	.56		
.378	.20	1.10	.58	Add'l	.53

118° included angle of the drill point, the approach and break-through distance is given above. For example, with a .5-in. drill, the value of .26 in. is added to the drilling length. For stainless steel, the drill point is flatter, so multiply the tabular value by 0.6. Whenever power drilling time is computed, add to the design drill distance, the distance for drill-point lead and breakthrough. Each drilling rate, *i.e.,* min/in., is multiplied by this total length.

Despite the realization that power drilling is done for a variety of machines where rpm may be fixed rather than infinitely variable, the data are associated directly to velocity without an rpm correction, as rpm adjustment is not worth the effort in estimating. The minimum diameter is 1/4 in. as smaller diameters have the same min/in. due to the compensating feed and diameter in the formula.

Material	Velocity
Aluminum and alloys	250
Brass and bronze (ordinary)	250
Die castings (zinc base)	250
Iron, cast (soft)	80
Magnesium and alloy	250
Plastics or similar material	250
Steel	
Mild, .2 to .3 carbon	100
Hard, .4 to .5 carbon	80
Forgings	50
High tensile (heat treated)	30
Stainless steel	50
Titanium alloys	30

Feeds used for Element 4 are as follows:

Dia	Feed	Dia	Feed	Dia	Feed
1/16	.001	3/8	.005	1½	.015
1/8	.002	1/2	.006	1¾	.015
5/32	.0025	5/8	.008	2	.015
3/16	.003	3/4	.008	2½	.016
1/4	.004	1	.012	3	.018
5/16	.0045	1¼	.014		

These speeds and feeds for Element 4 are based upon high-speed steel, and if carbide is used, the rates can be decreased 15 to 30%. If necessary, the estimator can adjust the values for min/in. for other requirements. Remember to multiply the min/in. by the length or depth of the hole. This length may include an addition for point and breakthrough as shown by the above table. For deep holes, raise and lower spindles to relieve chips as necessary.

The Element 5 entry variable for multi-spindle or cluster power-feed drilling is metal length and two types of material. In this type of drilling, several different diameters may be simultaneously working, thus, maximum metal length is selected as the entry variable rather than a drill diameter. No drill point and breakthrough distance is added to metal length, as that consideration is a part of the information used to construct the table.

In counterbore machining, an end-cutting tool having two or more cutting edges is used in producing holes of more than one single diameter. If the counterbore depth is shallow, the operation may be spot facing. Speeds and feeds are slightly less than power drilling to allow for chip discharge caused by the packing during end cutting. These values can be used for counterdrilling and counterskinking. This work is considered powered.

In reaming, Element 7, we estimate the reaming element at slower fpm but higher feed rates than drills of corresponding diameter under power-feeding conditions. For high-speed steel reamers, the following conditions were used to construct the tabular entry.

	Feed ipr				
	Steel (mild)	Steel (medium)	Steel (alloy)	Steel (high tensile)	Aluminum, brass, mag.
fpm Dia	75	85	40	30	140
⅛	.005	.004	.004	.003	.006
½	.010	.007	.007	.005	.012
1	.016	.012	.012	.008	.020
2	.026	.020	.020	.013	.032
2½	.035	.028	.028	.018	.043
3	.045	.035	.035	.023	.056

Solid and carbide-tipped reamers may be operated at speeds up to 150% of HSS reamers. This work is considered powered. The table may be used for tapered reaming as well as straight reaming.

In Element 8 on tapping, the entry variables are no. of threads and material. Feed is not specified for tapping since it is dependent upon thread pitch. The time is for tap, dwell, and reverse out. If an automatic reverse is not available, a time to stop and start the machine and reverse spindle speed is necessary. The times are for min/in. of depth.

Microdrilling is the name for miniature-hole machining, and the diameter is generally considered to be .020 in. or less. However, data for small holes are extremely variable. Depth-to-diameter ratios are high as well. Tool life and clearing of chips present special problems. Specialized microdrilling machines may be hand-fed sensitive units. In automatic operations, a spindle head is fed forward for a predetermined distance and retracted quickly; then the cycle is repeated. Some production reports indicate that drills need regrinding after every 150 holes, although in one instance, several thousand holes were drilled in half-hard brass with a single HSS drill. Carbide and HSS steels are both used, but the data makes no distinction for drill material differences. The element data averages drill material and types of machine, either hand sensitive or automatic.

The values of Table 11.2 have been summarized in Item 11.2 of Section IV. Dimensions are dollars per 100 units ($/100 units). The Section-IV approach is faster, and the data are labor cost adjusted to the Chicago base area. Item 11.2 has entry information of type of operation, depth and diameter in. Item 11.2 is for machining only. It is added to part handling and machine manipulation as obtained by other items.

EXAMPLES

The application of these data is found through the drilling, turning, milling, machining center, and other machine applications.

TABLE 11.2   DRILL, REAM, COUNTERBORE, COUNTER-SINK, TAP, AND MICRODRILL

Setup   **See other tables**

Operation elements in estimating minutes

1. Sensitive drilling, min per hole

		Drill Dia									
Depth	Material	.093	.125	.156	.187	.25	.375	.5	.675	.75	1.0
.093	Soft steel					.08	.25	.42			
	Hard steel	.03	.08	.12	.17	.27	.47	.66			
	Brass	.03	.05	.06	.08	.11	.18	.24	.33		
	Aluminum	.05	.05	.06	.07	.08	.11	.14	.18	.19	.25
.156	Soft steel					.10	.27	.44			
	Hard steel	.06	.11	.16	.21	.31	.50	.70			
	Brass	.05	.07	.09	.10	.13	.20	.26	.36		
	Aluminum	.07	.08	.09	.09	.11	.13	.16	.20	.22	.27

Depth	Material	\ Drill Dia .093	.125	.156	.187	.25	.375	.5	.675	.75	1.0
.187	Soft steel					.13	.30	.46			
	Hard steel	.10	.15	.20	.25	.35	.54	.73			
	Brass	.07	.09	.11	.12	.16	.22	.29	.38		
	Aluminum	.10	.10	.11	.12	.13	.16	.19	.23	.24	.30
.25	Soft steel				.09	.17	.34	.51			
	Hard steel	.18	.23	.28	.32	.42	.62	.81			
	Brass	.12	.14	.15	.17	.20	.27	.33	.42		
	Aluminum	.14	.15	.16	.17	.18	.21	.24	.28	.29	.35
.312	Soft steel			.09	.13	.22	.39	.55			
	Hard steel	.25	.30	.35	.40	.50	.69	.89			
	Brass	.16	.18	.20	.21	.24	.31	.39	.47		
	Aluminum	.19	.20	.21	.21	.23	.26	.28	.32	.34	.40
.375	Soft steel		.09	.14	.18	.26	.43	.60			
	Hard steel	.33	.38	.43	.47	.57	.77	.96			
	Brass	.21	.22	.24	.26	.29	.35	.42	.51		
	Aluminum	.24	.25	.26	.26	.28	.31	.33	.37	.39	.45
.5	Soft steel	.14	.18	.23	.27	.35	.52	.69			
	Hard steel	.48	.53	.58	.63	.72	.92	1.11			
	Brass	.30	.31	.33	.34	.38	.44	.52	.60		
	Aluminum	.34	.35	.35	.36	.38	.40	.43	.47	.49	.54
.675	Aluminum	.48	.48	.49	.50	.51	.54	.57	.61	.62	.68
.75	Aluminum	.54	.54	.55	.56	.57	.60	.63	.67	.68	.74
1.00	Aluminum	.73	.74	.74	.75	.77	.79	.82	.86	.88	.93

2. Sensitive reaming, min per hole

Depth	\ Ream Dia .1	.2	.3	.4	.5	.6	.7
.05			.04	.06	.08	.10	.12
.1		.02	.04	.07	.09	.11	.13
.2		.03	.05	.08	.10	.12	.14
.3		.04	.06	.09	.11	.13	.15
.4	.03	.05	.07	.10	.12	.14	.16
.5	.04	.06	.08	.11	.13	.15	.17
.6	.05	.07	.09	.12	.14	.16	.18
.7	.06	.08	.10	.13	.15	.17	.19
.8	.07	.09	.11	.14	.16	.18	.20
.9	.08	.10	.12	.15	.17	.19	.21
1.0	.09	.11	.13	.16	.18	.20	.22

3. Sensitive countersinking   .03/ea

4. Power drilling, min/in.

Drill Dia	Steel (mild)	Steel (medium), cast iron	Steel (alloy), forgings, stainless	Steel (high tensile), titanium	Aluminum, brass, magnesium, plastic
$1/4$	.16	.20	.33	.55	.07
$5/16$	.18	.23	.36	.61	.07
$3/8$	.20	.25	.39	.65	.08
$1/2$	.22	.27	.44	.73	.09

Drill Dia	Steel (mild)	Steel (medium), cast iron	Steel (alloy), forgings, stainless	Steel (high tensile), titanium	Aluminum, brass, magnesium, plastic
⅝	.20	.26	.41	.68	.08
¾	.25	.31	.49	.82	.10
1	.22	.27	.44	.73	.09
1¼	.23	.29	.47	.78	.09
1½	.26	.33	.52	.87	.10
1¾	.31	.38	.61	1.02	.12
2	.35	.44	.70	1.16	.14
2½	.41	.51	.82	1.36	.16
3	.44	.55	.87	1.45	.17

5. Cluster power drilling, min

Metal depth	Steel (mild)	Soft nonferrous
.2	.28	.08
.3	.30	.08
.4	.33	.09
.5	.36	.10
.6	.38	.10
.7	.40	.11
.8	.43	.12
.9	.45	.12
1.0	.47	.13

6. Counterboring, spotfacing, and countersinking, min/in.

Dia	Steel (mild)	Iron, steel (medium)	Steel (hard)
¼	.24	.31	.55
⅜	.27	.35	.61
½	.29	.37	.65
¾	.36	.47	.82
1	.36	.47	.82
1½	.55	.70	1.23
2	.58	.75	1.31

7. Power reaming, min/in.

Ream Dia	Steel (mild)	Steel (medium), cast iron	Steel (alloy), forgings, stainless	Steel (high tensile), titanium	Aluminum, brass, magnesium
⅛	.09	.10	.20	.36	.04
½	.17	.22	.47	.87	.08
1	.22	.26	.55	1.09	.09
2	.27	.31	.65	1.34	.12
2½	.25	.27	.58	1.21	.11
3	.23	.26	.56	1.14	.10

8. Tapping, min/in.

Threads/in.	Steel	Stainless steel	Aluminum	Brass	Plastic
56	.24		.13	.12	.14
48	.18		.13	.11	.12
40	.16	.38	.12	.10	.11
32	.18	.33	.13	.11	.12
24	.17	.30	.14	.10	.13
20	.15	.30	.12	.10	.12
16	.19	.33	.15	.11	.14
13	.23	.39	.18	.13	.15
11	.26	.39	.18	.13	.16
10	.32	.48	.21	.16	
9	.32	.48	.21	.16	
8	.32	.48	.21	.16	
7	.32	.48	.22	.16	
6	.34	.51	.22	.17	
5	.34	.51	.23	.17	
4	.38	.57	.24	.19	

9. Microdrilling, min per hole

Brass

	Dia	.005	.020	.040
	.10	.003	.025	
Depth	.20	.066	.050	.036
	.30		.075	.053
	.40			.070

Cast iron

	Dia	.020	.040
	.10	.050	.036
Depth	.20	.100	.073
	.30		.100
	.40		.145

Stainless Steel

	Dia.	.040
Depth	.10	.05
	.20	.10

11.3 Face, Side, Slot, Form, Straddle, End, Saw, and Engrave Milling

DESCRIPTION

These data are for pure machine cutting time and are suitable for milling operations. Their locations are centralized, thus facilitating their greatest use.

Not all rotating-tool machining times are included in this section, particularly those more closely identified with turning, drilling, hobbing, gear cutting, etc.

ESTIMATING DATA DISCUSSION

The length of cut is the total distance the machine is operating at the cutting feed. The length is found by adding the approach, safety, blueprint length of cut and overtravel, if required. This distance is multiplied by the time per in. specified for the type and material of cutter and material of part.

The approach for side milling recognizes that when the cutter first touches the material it is not at full depth. Once the vertical centerline of the cutter is over the initial line of material, the approach distance is determined. Entry variables for periphery cutting are diameter of cutter and depth of cut values for approach or overtravel are given below for peripheral cutters.

A different approach or overtravel is necessary for a face or shell end mill approaching a flat surface.

Cutter approach or overtravel—helical, side, saw and key slot cutter, in.

Dia of cutter, in.	Depth of cut								
	$1/16$	$1/8$	$1/4$	$1/2$	$3/4$	1	2	3	4
$1\frac{1}{4}$	.27	.37	.50	.61					
$1\frac{1}{2}$	.30	.41	.56	.71	.75				
$1\frac{3}{4}$	.32	.45	.61	.79	.87				
2	.35	.48	.64	.87	.97	1.00			
$2\frac{1}{2}$	.39	.54	.71	1.00	1.15	1.22			
$2\frac{3}{4}$	.41	.57	.79	1.06	1.22	1.32			
3	.43	.60	.83	1.12	1.30	1.41			
$3\frac{1}{4}$	.45	.63	.87	1.17	1.37	1.50			
$3\frac{1}{2}$	.46	.65	.91	1.22	1.44	1.58			
$3\frac{3}{4}$	.48	.67	.93	1.28	1.50	1.66			
4	.49	.70	.97	1.32	1.56	1.73	2.00		
$4\frac{1}{4}$	.51	.72	1.00	1.37	1.62	1.80	2.12		
$4\frac{1}{2}$	.53	.74	1.03	1.41	1.67	1.87	2.24		
$4\frac{3}{4}$	.54	.76	1.06	1.46	1.73	1.93	2.35		
5	.56	.78	1.09	1.50	1.79	2.00	2.45		
$5\frac{1}{2}$	.58	.82	1.14	1.58	1.89	2.12	2.64		
6	.61	.86	1.20	1.66	1.98	2.24	2.83	3.00	
7	.65	.93	1.30	1.80	2.17	2.45	3.16	3.46	
8	.71	.99	1.39	1.94	2.33	2.65	3.46	3.87	4.00
9	.75	1.05	1.48	2.06	2.49	2.83	3.74	4.24	4.47
10	.79	1.11	1.56	2.18	2.63	3.00	4.00	4.58	4.90
11	.83	1.17	1.64	2.29	2.77	3.16	4.24	4.89	5.29
12	.86	1.22	1.72	2.40	2.91	3.32	4.47	5.19	5.65

Entry variables are cutter diameter and width of work piece. Another case where data are not given is for milling a flat in a round piece of stock. A formula for this condition is $L = 2(Dia \cdot d - d^2)^{1/2}$ where L = length of cut, Dia = diameter of work piece, and d = depth of cut.

Cutter approach or overtravel—face, shell and end milling cutters, in.

Dia of cutter, in.	Width of cut										
	1	2	3	4	5	6	7	8	9	10	12
1	.50										
2	.27	1.00									
3	.09	.38	1.50								
4		.27	.68	2.00							
5		.21	.50	1.00	2.50						
6		.17	.40	.76	1.34	3.00					
7			.34	.63	1.05	1.70	3.50				
8				.53	.88	1.35	2.06	4.00			
10					.76	1.00	1.43	2.00	2.82	5.00	
12						.80	1.03	1.53	2.03	2.68	6.00
14							.88	1.26	1.64	2.10	3.38
16								1.07	1.38	1.76	2.71
18									1.20	1.52	2.29
20											2.00

A safety length is added for a short distance before the cutter enters the material.

Safety distance, in.

Cutter dia	4	4 + to 8	8 + to 12	12 +
Distance, in.	.11	.14	.17	.20

Elements 1 through 6 are the machining times for milling machines and machining centers. Their application depends upon the selection of milling machine initially. The machine times are related to the in. of milling or the no. of characters. The machine times have been determined using practical chip load per tooth, and periphery cutting velocity for either high-speed steel (HSS) or carbide types of cutters. The basic relationship is

$$\text{min/in.} = \frac{\pi Dia}{12 f_t n V},$$ where Dia = cutter dia, in.

f_t = chip load per tooth, in. per tooth,
n = number of teeth in cutter,
V = cutter speed, fpm.

Standard cutter sizes and teeth were adopted. Obviously, differing variables using other approaches to determine cutting times are possible but many of their effects tend to offset each other. V is chosen to allow most any practical depth of cut and f_t will allow a commercial surface finish. The hardnesses for the selected materials are as follows:

Material	Bhn
Low-carbon steel, free-machining	170
Low-carbon steel	150
Medium-carbon steel	215
Stainless steel, austenitic 300	170
Stainless steel, martensite 400	196
Steel castings	230
Aluminum	

While there are thousands of materials, these are a good representation. For other difficult materials the estimator makes comparative estimates.

The tables do not indicate the rpm that might be used. Sometimes the cutting velocity, tool, etc., are matched to the particular machine. For example, the cutting velocity may lead to an rpm that is unavailable on the machine. While a downward adjustment can be made to accommodate, it is not recommended at the time of estimate because rpm adjustment is only one of many factors that is difficult to foresee. Nor are distinctions made for cutting tool grades, lubrication, horsepower required, vertical or horizontal cutting setups in these data. These refinements, while oftentimes necessary, are too involved at the time of estimating. Thus, we choose min/in. of cut because that is easiest to use. On balance, this approach provides for consistency, ease, and accuracy.

Element 1, face milling, has the cutter axis perpendicular to the surface, and cuts along the periphery of individual teeth and the surface of the face cutting edges. The machined surface per cutter pass may equal the whole width of the face of the cutter or any fraction of the diameter. Thus, the entry variables are cutter and work piece material and cutter diameter. Overlap between adjacent passes is an assumption the estimator makes. For nonrigid setups, or parts prone to chatter, increase time by 30%.

Element 2, side milling, is different than Element 3 even though the cutter may be identical. Standard side-milling cutters are used for both applications. Convex or concave milling would use Element 3.

In end milling, Element 4, if the ratio of load length to diameter exceeds 3:1, increase the time 25%. (For roughing end mills, reduce the time 15%.) A four-fluted standard end mill is adopted. Other specialized end mill styles, while not true end mills, such as a T-slot or dovetail, will use this element.

Element 5, saw milling, adopts standard metal slitting saws. Distinctions whether the slitting saws are plain or have side chip clearance with or without staggered teeth do not influence the data very much.

Element 6, engraving, includes machine time and reposition tool to next character. The element would adopt the end-milling principles, but geometry, no. of flutes, and tool pointing are different. Engraving data are based upon time-study observations.

Direct-labor cost for general milling-machining can be estimated using Item 11.3 of Section IV. These values are expressed in $/100 units. Item 11.3 is for milling machining only, and other items are necessary to complete an operational cost estimate. The information necessary to find pure milling time is type of material being cut, material of cutter, and length of cut. The length of cut is determined using print dimensions, knowledge of cutter, and approach/overtravel adjustments.

EXAMPLES

Examples using these data are found with various machines, especially the milling and machining center.

TABLE 11.3   FACE, SIDE, SLOT, FORM, STRADDLE, END, SAW, AND ENGRAVE MILLING

Setup   **In other tables**

Operation elements in estimating minutes

1. Face milling, min/in.

Material	HSS Dia					Cutter Dia				
	2	3	4	5	6	3	4	5	6	8
Low-carbon steel, free-machining	.08	.09	.10	.11	.12	.03	.04	.04	.05	.05
Low-carbon steel	.18	.22	.24	.26	.27	.08	.11	.10	.12	.13
Medium-carbon steel	.27	.33	.36	.39	.41	.12	.16	.15	.18	.19
Stainless steel, 300	.55	.65	.73	.78	.82	.13	.17	.16	.19	.20
Stainless steel, 400	.36	.44	.48	.52	.55	.12	.16	.15	.18	.19
Steel castings, forgings	.36	.44	.48	.52	.55	.13	.17	.16	.19	.20
Aluminum	.01	.01	.01	.02	.02	.01	.01	.01	.01	.01
Copper alloys	.03	.03	.04	.04	.04	.02	.02	.02	.02	.02
Plastics	.05	.06	.06	.07	.07	.03	.03	.03	.03	.03
Cast iron	.31	.37	.42	.45	.47	.12	.16	.15	.18	.19

2. Side milling, min/in.

Material	HSS Dia						Carbide Dia				
	2	3	4	5	6	8	3	4	5	6	8
Low-carbon steel, free-machining	.07	.10	.11	.13	.14	.16	.05	.07	.06	.06	.07
Low-carbon steel	.14	.18	.22	.24	.26	.30	.10	.14	.13	.12	.15
Medium-carbon steel	.31	.41	.48	.55	.59	.67	.17	.23	.22	.21	.25

Material	HSS Dia						Carbide Dia				
	2	3	4	5	6	8	3	4	5	6	8
Stainless steel, 300	.31	.41	.48	.55	.59	.67	.17	.23	.22	.21	.25
Stainless steel, 400	.37	.49	.58	.65	.71	.81	.17	.23	.22	.21	.25
Steel castings, forgings	.93	1.23	1.45	1.64	1.78	2.01	.30	.40	.37	.36	.43
Aluminum	.01	.02	.02	.02	.02	.03	.01	.01	.01	.01	.01
Copper alloys	.07	.09	.10	.12	.13	.14	.06	.08	.08	.08	.09
Plastics	.04	.05	.06	.07	.08	.09	.04	.04	.04	.04	.04
Cast iron	.50	.65	.78	.87	.95	1.40	.22	.29	.27	.26	.32

3. Slot, form and straddle milling, min/in.

Material	HSS Dia						Carbide Dia				
	2	3	4	5	6	8	3	4	5	6	8
Low-carbon steel, free-machining	.10	.14	.17	.19	.21	.24	.04	.09	.08	.10	.11
Low-carbon steel	.42	.55	.65	.73	.79	.90	.14	.18	.17	.20	.22
Medium-carbon steel	.62	.82	.97	1.09	1.19	1.34	.26	.35	.33	.39	.42
Stainless steel, 300	.62	.82	.97	1.09	1.19	1.34	.26	.35	.33	.39	.42
Stainless steel, 400	.75	.98	1.16	1.31	1.43	1.61	.26	.35	.33	.39	.42
Steel castings, forgings	1.25	1.64	1.94	2.18	2.38	2.69	.30	.40	.37	.45	.48
Aluminum	.03	.04	.05	.05	.06	.07	.02	.02	.02	.02	.02
Copper alloys	.13	.18	.21	.23	.25	.29	.08	.11	.10	.13	.13
Plastics	.08	.11	.13	.15	.16	.18	.05	.08	.08	.10	.13
Cast iron	1.00	1.31	1.55	1.75	1.90	2.15	.38	.51	.47	.57	.61

4. End milling, min/in.

Material	HSS Dia				Carbide Dia			
	1/8	1/4	1/2	1	1/8	1/4	1/2	1
Low-carbon steel, free-machining	.10	.10	.06	.10	.03	.03	.02	.02
Low-carbon steel	.18	.18	.12	.18	.05	.05	.03	.04
Medium-carbon steel	.68	.55	.27	.36	.11	.14	.07	.07
Stainless steel, 300	.41	.55	.33	.36	.07	.07	.04	.06
Stainless steel, 400	.55	.65	.65	.36	.07	.07	.04	.06
Steel castings, forgings	.82	1.09	.65	.55	.12	.15	.07	.09
Aluminum	.03	.03	.01	.01	.01	.01	.01	.01
Copper alloys	.16	.18	.13	.12	.04	.04	.02	.03
Plastics	.05	.05	.04	.05	.03	.03	.02	.02
Cast iron	.74	.74	.40	.48	.12	.14	.07	.08

5. Saw milling, min/in.

Material	HSS Dia, blade < 1/8 in.					HSS Dia, blade ≥ 1/8 in.				
	2 1/2	3	4	5	6	2 1/2	3	4	5	6
Low-carbon steel, free-machining	.27	.31	.34	.38	.44	.14	.15	.17	.19	.22
Low-carbon steel,	.52	.58	.65	.73	.83	.26	.29	.32	.36	.42
Medium carbon steel	1.30	1.45	1.62	1.82	2.08	.78	.87	.97	1.09	1.25

Material	HSS Dia, blade < $\frac{1}{8}$ in.					HSS Dia, blade $\geq$ $\frac{1}{8}$ in.				
	2 ½	3	4	5	6	2 ½	3	4	5	6
Stainless steel, 300	1.30	1.45	1.62	1.82	2.08	.78	.87	.97	1.09	1.25
Stainless steel, 400	1.56	1.75	1.94	2.18	2.49	.93	1.05	1.16	1.31	1.50
Steel castings, forgings	1.95	2.18	2.42	2.73	3.12	1.17	1.31	1.45	1.64	1.87
Aluminum	.08	.09	.10	.11	.12	.04	.04	.05	.05	.06
Copper alloys	.17	.19	.21	.23	.27	.08	.09	.10	.12	.13
Plastics	.17	.19	.22	.24	.28	.10	.12	.13	.15	.17
Cast iron	1.56	1.75	1.94	2.18	2.49	.93	1.05	1.40	1.31	1.50

6. Engraving, min per character

Material	Height of character							
	$\frac{1}{8}$	$\frac{5}{32}$	$\frac{3}{16}$	$\frac{1}{4}$	$\frac{5}{16}$	$\frac{3}{8}$	$\frac{7}{16}$	$\frac{1}{2}$
Steel	.15	.16	.17	.18	.19	.19	.21	.22
Brass	.13	.14	.15	.16	.17	.18	.19	.19
Aluminum	.12	.13	.14	.15	.15	.16	.17	.18
Plastic	.07	.07	.08	.08	.09	.10	.12	.12

11.4 Tool Life and Replacement

DESCRIPTION

Cutting tools become dull as usage continues and their effectiveness drops. At some point in time it is necessary to resharpen, index, or replace the tool. The span of usefulness, from sharpness to dullness, is defined as tool life. The quantity tool life varies with the quality of the cutting materials operating in different materials as well as with many other variables.

When tools become dull, direct-labor time is required to replace them with sharp ones. Not all tools are sharpened by the operator, such as reamers, milling cutters, and gear hobs. While drills can be sharpened, the sharpening can also be done by the tool crib, and this is a discretionary selection by estimators. The time required to keep cutting tools operable is prorated over units produced during the tool life. The following data estimate that time.

These data provide a time to prorate the removal, also possibly resharpening, and replacement of the tool in the machine. The prorated time is added to the operation estimate. Operations related to turning, milling, hobbing, and drilling are historically handled by tool life and replacement as provided here.

ESTIMATING DATA DISCUSSION

The assumptions for tool life and replacement for turning elements are:

Material	HSS	Carbide
Soft steel	160 min	425 min
Medium steel, cast iron	120 min	360 min
Hard steel, stainless	90 min	225 min

The time to replace a turning, boring, etc., type of tool is 2 min. Entry variables are cutting time, type of material, and tool. Inasmuch as there may be several or more turning tools, the cutting time is total machining time for the operation, and the minutes are the prorated life for several tools for one unit. Even though turning operations may include drilling, simply sum all the machining time as the entry variable. Thus, expediency is used for this estimate because of the involved nature of tool life.

Element 2 deals with milling tool life. The first subpart provides an estimate whenever the tool edge is an indexable carbide point. Entry variables are cutting time and part-material. The basic time to index and qualify an insert point is 1.00 min.

In the second subpart of Element 2, the time, as read from the chart, is the prorated unit time for removal and replacement of small tools. For this element, small tools are those having shanks for insertion in the end of the milling machine spindle, those having a center hole for arbor mounting, or those having the cutter back recessed for a single-bolt. Single-bolt mounted face cutters are 6-in. or less. The basic time is 3 min.

Large tools are those face cutters having a multiple-bolt mounting, or face cutter 8-in. or greater. These sizes have a bolt-circle and not single-point mounting. Large tool replacement time is 10 min.

The tool life, in min, of the tool for Element 2 is as follows:

Material	HSS	Carbide
Soft steel	45 min	120 min
Medium steel	30 min	90 min
Cast iron	30 min	90 min
Stainless steel	15 min	60 min

The Taylor tool life equation for cast iron is $VT^{0.12} = 225$ and $VT^{0.43} = 3000$, for HSS and carbide respectively.

Element 3 deals with tool life for drills and drill-type tools. Entry variables are drill dia, total drill min corresponding to the diameters and part ma-terial. The time to remove drill, regrind, and replace is 3 min, and it is this time that is prorated to the job. The tool life for the variables is given below.

Dia (in.)	Stainless, cast steel, forgings, tool steels	Steel (medium, hard)	Steel (mild), cast iron	Aluminum brass, magnesium
¼	25	30	30	60
¼ to ½	35	35	35	75
½ to ¾	40	40	45	90
¾ to 1	40	50	60	105
1 in. +	50	55	60	120

For SAE 1020 steel, if for a 5/8-in. OD drill there is a cycle time of 1.20 min for drilling, then $45/1.20 = 37.5$ parts are drilled, and the resharpen time $= 3/37.5 = 0.08$ min which is about 7% in this example.

An alternate approach to this detailed method of estimating tool life is given by Item 11.4 of Section IV. Its dimensions are $/100 units. The entry factor is min of metal cutting within the operation. With this value known or reasonably estimated, a selection of the process, turning, milling, or drilling, and tool material will facilitate choosing the cost factor. Multiply the cost factor and min to give the estimated base cost for tool life and replacement.

EXAMPLES

A. A turret lathe uses 7 tools including start drill, drill, boring bar, reamer, recessing-type tool, tap, and cutoff. The total machine time is 7.62 min. Find the time for tool life to add to the unit estimate.

Table	Description	Time
11.4-1	Tool life for 7 tools for carbide machining of medium-hardness steel	.04 min
	Unit estimate	.04 min

B. A 9-in. face mill made for right-hand cutting and having 20 teeth is used to mill the top of a cylinder block on a vertical knee-and-column milling machine. The cast iron is 170–197 Bhn, length of cut is 31 1/4 in. The cutting time including cutting, approach, overtravel, and safety stock is 2.19 min. Find the time to add to the unit estimate for indexable inserts, or remove and replace a large tool.

Table	Description	Time
11.4-2	Unclamp, reposition, qualify, and clamp inserts, 20 × .03	.60 min
	Unit estimate	.60 min

Table	Description	Time
11.4-2	Unbolt worn cutter and rebolt new cutter	.28 min
	Unit estimate	.28 min

C. An NC machining center drills 18 holes in a steel forging according to the schedule below. Presuming that the NC tape is interrupted to allow tool changing within the tool storage, what time would be added to the unit estimate?

No.	Dia	Cycle time	No.	Dia	Cycle time
3	F	.06	1	1.0	.72
2	$^{25}/_{64}$	.19	4	.875	.27
2	$^{33}/_{64}$	.23	2	#45	.08
4	.75	.26			

Table	Description	Time
11.4-3	Two drills are less than $\frac{1}{4}$ in., and total cycle time = .34 min	.06 min
11.4-3	One drill is less than $\frac{1}{2}$ in., and total cycle time = .38 min	.04
11.4-3	Two drills are less than $\frac{3}{4}$ in., and total cycle time = 1.50 min	.15
11.4-3	One drill is less than 1 in., and total cycle time = 1.08 min	.15
11.4-3	One drill exceeds 1 in., and total cycle time = .72 min	.06
	Unit estimate	.46 min

The drill life and replacement time is added to the unit estimate for the machine, and the estimate is 11% of the total drilling time.

TABLE 11.4 TOOL LIFE AND REPLACEMENT

Setup   Not applicable

Operation elements in estimating minutes

1. Turning tool life, min per operation

Operation cutting time	Soft steel		Medium steel, cast iron		Stainless steel	
	HSS	Carbide	HSS	Carbide	HSS	Carbide
.3			.01		.01	
.4	.01		.01		.01	
.5	.01		.01		.01	.004
.6	.01	.003	.01	.003	.01	.01
.7	.01	.003	.01	.004	.02	.01
.8	.01	.004	.01	.004	.02	.01
.9	.01	.004	.02	.01	.02	.01
1.2	.02	.01	.02	.01	.03	.01
1.5	.02	.01	.03	.01	.03	.01
1.8	.02	.01	.03	.01	.04	.02
2.2	.03	.01	.04	.01	.05	.02
2.5	.03	.01	.04	.01	.06	.02
3.0	.04	.01	.05	.02	.07	.03
3.5	.04	.02	.06	.02	.08	.03
4.0	.05	.02	.07	.02	.09	.04
4.5	.06	.02	.08	.03	.10	.04
5.0	.06	.02	.08	.03	.11	.04
5.5	.07	.03	.09	.03	.12	.05
6	.08	.03	.10	.03	.13	.05
7	.09	.03	.12	.04	.16	.06
8	.10	.04	.13	.04	.18	.07
9	.11	.04	.15	.05	.20	.08
10	.13	.05	.17	.06	.22	.09
12	.15	.06	.20	.07	.27	.11

Operation cutting time	Soft steel		Medium steel, cast iron		Stainless steel	
	HSS	Carbide	HSS	Carbide	HSS	Carbide
14	.18	.07	.23	.08	.31	.12
16	.20	.08	.27	.09	.36	.14
18	.23	.08	.30	.10	.40	.16
20	.25	.09	.33	.11	.44	.18
25	.31	.12	.42	.14	.56	.22
30	.38	.14	.50	.17	.67	.27
35	.44	.16	.58	.19	.78	.31
40	.50	.19	.67	.22	.89	.36

2. Milling tool life, min per operation

Index a throwaway insert, min per insert on tool. <u>Multiply by no. of inserts.</u>

Operation cutting time	Soft steel	Medium steel, cast iron	Stainless steel
.8	.01	.01	.01
1.0	.01	.01	.02
1.2	.01	.01	.02
1.4	.01	.02	.02
1.5	.01	.02	.03
2.0	.02	.02	.03
2.5	.02	.03	.04
3.0	.03	.03	.05
3.5	.03	.04	.06
4.0	.03	.04	.07
4.5	.04	.05	.08
5	.04	.06	.08
6	.05	.07	.10
7	.06	.08	.12
8	.07	.09	.13
9	.08	.10	.15
10	.08	.11	.17
12	.10	.13	.20
15	.13	.17	.25
20	.17	.22	.33
25	.21	.28	.42

Remove and replace small tool, min per operation

Cutting time	Soft steel		Medium steel, cast iron		Stainless steel	
	HSS	Carbide	HSS	Carbide	HSS	Carbide
.2	.01	.01	.02	.01	.04	.01
.4	.03	.01	.04	.01	.08	.02
.6	.04	.02	.06	.02	.12	.03
.8	.05	.02	.08	.03	.16	.04

Cutting time	Soft steel		Medium steel, cast iron		Stainless steel	
	HSS	Carbide	HSS	Carbide	HSS	Carbide
1.0	.07	.03	.10	.03	.20	.05
1.2	.08	.03	.12	.04	.24	.06
1.4	.09	.04	.14	.15	.28	.07
1.5	.10	.04	.15	.05	.30	.08
2.0	.13	.05	.20	.07	.40	.10
2.5	.17	.06	.25	.08	.50	.13
3.0	.20	.08	.30	.10	.60	.15
3.5	.23	.09	.35	.12	.70	.18
4.0	.27	.10	.40	.13	.80	.20
4.5	.30	.11	.45	.15	.90	.23
5	.33	.13	.50	.17	1.00	.25
6	.40	.15	.60	.20	1.20	.30
7	.47	.18	.70	.23	1.40	.35
8	.53	.20	.80	.27	1.60	.40
9	.60	.23	.90	.30	1.80	.45
10	.67	.25	1.00	.33	2.00	.50
12	.80	.30	1.20	.40	2.40	.60
15	1.00	.38	1.50	.50	3.00	.75
20	1.33	.50	2.00	.67	4.00	1.00
25	1.67	.63	2.50	.83	5.00	1.25

Remove and replace large tool, min per operation

Cutting time	Soft steel		Medium steel, cast iron		Stainless steel	
	HSS	Carbide	HSS	Carbide	HSS	Carbide
.2	.04	.02	.07	.02	.13	.03
.4	.09	.03	.13	.04	.27	.07
.6	.13	.05	.20	.07	.40	.10
.8	.18	.07	.27	.09	.53	.13
1.0	.22	.08	.33	.11	.67	.17
1.2	.27	.10	.40	.13	.80	.20
1.4	.31	.12	.47	.16	.93	.23
1.5	.33	.13	.50	.17	1.00	.25
2.0	.44	.17	.67	.22	1.33	.33
2.5	.56	.21	.83	.28	1.67	.42
3.0	.67	.25	1.00	.33	2.00	.50
3.5	.78	.29	1.17	.39	2.33	.58
4.0	.89	.33	1.33	.44	2.67	.67
4.5	1.00	.38	1.50	.50		.75
5	1.11	.42	1.67	.56		.83
6	1.33	.50	2.00	.67		1.00

Cutting time	Soft steel		Medium steel, cast iron		Stainless steel	
	HSS	Carbide	HSS	Carbide	HSS	Carbide
7	1.56	.58	2.33	.78		1.17
8	1.78	.67	2.67	.89		1.33
9	2.00	.75	3.00	1.00		1.50
10	2.22	.83	3.33	1.11		1.67
12	2.67	1.00		1.33		2.00
15	3.33	1.25		1.67		2.50
20	4.44	1.67		2.22		3.33
25	5.56	2.08		2.78		4.17

3. Drilling tool life, min per operation

Remove drill, grind or replace, and install drill

Drill Dia	Total drill cutting time per unit	Stainless, cast steel, forgings, tool steels	Steel (medium, hard)	Steel (mild), cast iron	Aluminum, brass, magnesium
¼	.10	.01	.01	.01	.01
	.20	.02	.02	.02	.01
	.50	.06	.05	.05	.03
	1.0	.12	.10	.10	.05
	2.0	.24	.20	.20	.10
	3.0	.36	.30	.30	.15
	4.0	.48	.40	.40	.20
	5.0	.60	.50	.50	.25
¼+ to ½	.10	.01	.01	.01	
	.20	.02	.02	.02	.01
	.50	.04	.04	.04	.02
	1.0	.09	.09	.09	.04
	2.0	.17	.17	.17	.08
	3.0	.26	.26	.26	.12
	4.0	.34	.34	.34	.16
	5.0	.43	.43	.43	.20
½+ to ¾	.10	.01	.01	.01	
	.20	.02	.02	.01	.01
	.50	.04	.04	.03	.02
	1.0	.08	.08	.07	.03
	2.0	.15	.15	.13	.07
	3.0	.23	.23	.20	.10
	4.0	.30	.30	.27	.13
	5.0	.38	.38	.33	.17

Drill Dia	Total drill cutting time per unit	Stainless cast steel, forgings, tool steels	Steel (medium, hard)	Steel (mild), cast iron	Aluminum, brass, magnesium
¾ + to 1	.10	.01	.01	.01	
	.20	.02	.01	.01	.01
	.50	.04	.03	.03	.01
	1.0	.08	.06	.05	.03
	2.0	.15	.12	.10	.06
	3.0	.23	.18	.15	.09
	4.0	.30	.24	.20	.11
	5.0	.38	.30	.25	.14
1+	.10	.01	.01	.01	
	.20	.01	.01	.01	.01
	.50	.03	.03	.03	.01
	1.0	.06	.05	.05	.03
	2.0	.12	.11	.10	.05
	3.0	.18	.16	.15	.08
	4.0	.24	.22	.20	.10
	5.0	.30	.27	.25	.13

BROACHING

12.1 Broaching Machines

DESCRIPTION

Broaching is the process whereby a cutter, called a broach, is used to finish internal or external surfaces such as holes, squares, irregular sections, keyways, teeth of internal gears, splines, and flat surfaces. The broach is an elongated tool having a number of successive teeth of increasing size cutting in a fixed path. A part is often completed in one pass, where the last teeth on the broach conform to finished dimension. The work being broached is usually held in a fixed position and the tool travels through or over the work. The tool, after completing the cut, is returned to the start position, thus completing the cycle. Internal broaches start where the hole has been drilled, reamed or bored, or cored, or stamped or hot pierced.

A broaching machine consists of the tool, work-holding fixture, drive, and frame. The machines may either pull or push the tool through the work. Varieties of models include horizontal surfacing, single-ram vertical, double-ram vertical, large pull down, vertical pull-up electric, and horizontal hydraulic broaching. Even manual small-size presses can be used to push broaches through a hole.

Figure 12.1 is a single-ram broaching machine with variable velocity for surface broaching. This machine has tipdown tables for easier loading. Shuttle tables are optional. Surface velocities range from 5.35 fpm and a return speed of 70 fpm.

Some machines have automatic broach bar engagement while in others, the broach must be retrieved from the inner floor of the machine. In some machines, after disassembly of piece, pushing of a power lever returns the broach bar to the starting position.

FIGURE 12.1 Single-ram vertical broaching machine. (*Ex-Cell-O Machine Tool Products*)

ESTIMATING DATA DISCUSSION

Setup hours include the standard setup and tear-down of the machine, cleaning of fixtures, broaches, guides, gages, etc. used on the job. Distinction is provided for machine and line-up for fixed or loose broaches. The operation elements are for a variety of machines, and the estimator needs to be able to identify machine features.

Pick up, place in position to hold, and remove and place aside may be determined using Element 1 of Table 12.1. Fixtures may be unnecessary, as in the case of a simple nesting die, and various tool designs will have clamping distinctions. If the broach machine is semiautomatic, this element is unnecessary, because the machine has automatic pull or push heads. If additional passes are required, shims of the desired thickness are used, and the time per pass is obtained from Element 4. Inspection and deburring, Elements 6 and 7, may be handled during machining cycle of previous passes, if time is available.

Machining time is found using this relationship:

$$\text{Machine time} = \frac{L \text{ of stroke}}{\text{cutting speed}} + \frac{L \text{ of stroke}}{\text{return speed}}$$

and the estimates of fpm are provided for four material classes. The data are based on a return velocity of 2:1, even though some machines have fixed return velocities. Corrections can be made using the formula if considered important. In duplex broaching machines, it may not be necessary to allow a return stroke, and this time must be deducted from the estimate. Also, the fixture may be loaded during one of the machine cycles, thus the estimate will be machine time only. In the absence of specific knowledge about broach length, assume the length of the broach for one pass as:

Type	Equation
Splines	Broach length = −5 + 15 (part Dia) + 8 (part L)
Internal keyways	Broach length = 20 + 40 (key width) + 85 (key depth)
Round holes	Broach length = 6 + 6 (Dia + 6) part L

For a six-spline having a nominal diameter of 2 in. and a part length of 5 in., the approximate broach length is 62 in.

Speed and ease of application can be increased by avoiding calculation or interpolation if the next higher Table 12.1 values are used.

Operational costs for broaching can be determined using Item 12.1 of Section IV. The entry variable is broach length, as the materials are averaged. The constant cost is always provided. The final value is setup dollars and dollars per 100 units ($/100 units).

EXAMPLES

A. Estimate the time to broach a lot of 18,000 automotive front-gear blanks where the gear has 39 internal involute spline teeth. The work will be done on a 50-ton pull-down broaching machine with 42-in. stroke. Two splines must be square with the two faces within 0.003 in. total indicator reading. Before broaching, the faces are ground and the hole is precision-bored with the faces. The part is 4140 material and weighs 7.5 lb. The broach is estimated to be 30-in. long.

Table	Description	Time	
12.1-S	Setup	.5	hr
12.1-1	Handle at 7.5 lb	.17	min
12.1-1	Tip over discharge	−.02	
12.1-2	Location on hole and face in nest	.04	
12.1-4	Engage power lever	.03	
12.1-5	Apply oil	.04	
12.1-8	Machine and retract broach	.58	
	Unit estimate	.84	min
	Total lot estimate	252.5	hr

B. Re-estimate Example A above using a base-cost approach. Find lot cost.

Item	Description	Cost
12.1	Setup	$ 7.49
	Setup subtotal	$ 7.49

Item	Description	Cost
12.1	Cycle constant	$ 11.10
	Length of broach, 30 × .228	6.84
	$/100 units subtotal	$ 17.94
	Lot cost	$3236.69

TABLE 12.1 BROACHING MACHINES

Setup

Single-ram machine	.5 hr
Double-ram machine	.6 hr
Horizontal machine	.7 hr

Operation elements in estimating minutes

1. Pick up part and put aside

From tote pan or small carton   .05

From pallet or skid,

Weight	2–6	7–10	11–15
Min	.11	.17	.25

Chain hoist	.74
Less for tilt discharge	.02

2. Assemble and disassemble from fixture

Locate from 1 hole	.03
Locate from 2 holes	.03
Locate from 1 hole and 1 edge	.04
Locate from 1 hole and 2 edges	.03
Open and close hinge or swinging clamp	.06
or wing screw or nut	.04
or palm grip knobs	.08
or thumbscrew	.06
or wedge	.10
or hold-down bar with 2 nuts	.04

3. Assemble part over tail end of broach   .04

Assemble broach through port to pull head	.02
Assemble part over shank of bar and assemble broach to pull head	.18
Disassemble broach from pull head	.08

4. Shim for additional cut, per pass   .05

Direct oil to part	.02
Start and stop	.03
Engage power lever	
No disassemble of broach	.03
Disassemble broach	.02
Engage and disengage ram	.05

5. Wire brush broach bar   .15

Clean fixture with brush	.04
Apply oil to broach with brush, 1 per 5	.04

6. Inspection

Go/no-go plug gage	.07
Spline gage	.05
Inside micrometer	.10
Scale rule	.08

7. File burrs off part

.07

8. Machine time, min per operation

Broach L	Brass, bronze, cast iron	Mild steel	Cast iron, medium steel	Hard steel
6.0	.03	.03	.09	.11
8.8	.04	.05	.13	.16
10.0	.04	.05	.15	.18
11.0	.05	.06	.17	.20
12.1	.05	.06	.18	.22
13.3	.06	.07	.20	.25
14.6	.06	.08	.22	.27
16.1	.07	.08	.24	.30
17.7	.07	.09	.27	.33
19.5	.08	.10	.29	.36
21.4	.09	.11	.32	.39
23.6	.10	.12	.35	.43
25.9	.11	.14	.39	.48
28.5	.12	.15	.43	.53
31.4	.13	.17	.47	.58
34.5	.15	.18	.52	.64
38.0	.16	.20	.57	.70
41.8	.18	.22	.63	.77
45.9	.19	.24	.69	.85
50.5	.21	.27	.76	.93
55.6	.23	.29	.83	1.02
61.2	.26	.32	.92	1.13
67.3	.28	.35	1.01	1.24
74.0	.31	.39	1.11	1.36
fpm	35.	28.	18.	8.
return fpm	70.	56.	36.	16.

GRINDING MACHINES

13.1 Cylindrical Grinding Machines

DESCRIPTION

This machine is used primarily for grinding external cylindrical surfaces, tapered and simple-formed surfaces, and shoulder faces. These data cover axial traverse and plunge grinding. Special single-purpose machines can be rough-estimated, using these data, if machine knowledge is available.

Plain cylindrical grinding machines have swings from 6 to 24 in., and center distances from 18 to 120 in. The power of the wheel motor of regular machines varies from 5 to 25 hp.

Figure 13.1 is a center-type grinding machine with a swing-down internal grinding head. It has an infinitely variable table traverse speed from 2 to 240 ipm and infinite selection for headstock speeds. Pick feed amounts from .0002 to .0016 in. (diameter reduction) in eight steps are available for traverse grinding. Now, consider estimating data for the class of cylindrical grinding machines.

ESTIMATING DATA DISCUSSION

In addition to usual operator, machine, and part instruction chores involved in a setup for cylindrical grinding machines, special considerations can be given to grinding wheel diameter and tolerance requirements. Setup includes the installation of work-holding devices, setting of feed and traverse rates, limit positions for rapid approach, and power infeed and initial truing of installed grinding wheel. The setup values, as given in Table 13.1, are not for semi- or fully automatic operations, since that time

may be from 1 to several hr. The setup data are based upon two factors, wheel diameter and tolerance. The total tolerance, or sum of bilateral tolerance values, are used.

The operational elements are composed of handling, machine operation, grinding, and tolerance control of the part. Handling time is composed of elements to pick up and unload part; and then to mount it in a collet, chuck, face plate, dog, arbor, or mandrel; and if not already secured to machine, then mount the part between centers. Machine operation includes the position of the work for traverse or plunge grinding.

Element 4 provides time for traverse grind, dwell, and sparkout. Entry variables are total stock, material, work velocity, and wheel traverse feed. The relationship used for traverse time is

$$\text{time} = \frac{L \times T_s \times Dia}{(WP)2f_i \pi V}$$

where L = length of part grind, T_s = total stock removed from diameter, Dia = original diameter, W = width of grinding wheel, P = traverse for each work revolution in fraction of wheel width, f_i is the infeed of wheel per pass, and V = workpiece peripheral velocity.

If there are no interfering shoulders with a larger diameter than the diameter to be ground, there is no adjustment to part length. An overlap or one-half of the wheel width or 1/2 in. is adequate. If one shoulder prevents wheel overlap, the wheel grinds to that surface.

FIGURE 13.1 Center-type grinding machine with a swing-down internal grinding head feature. *(Cincinnati Milacron)*

The symbol W is wheel width, 1-in., 2-in., . . ., and corresponds to the machine specification being estimated. The symbol P is the traverse for each work revolution in fractions of wheel width, and is given later in the information. The infeed rates, f_i, refer to the penetration of the grinding wheel into the work. The diameter is reduced by twice the amount of wheel advance. Note that some cylindrical grinding machines have cross-slide hand wheels with graduations indicating double the amount of actual wheel advance. This calculation is performed twice, once for rough-grind and finish grind, and is

summed in the table values. A stock of .002 in. is allowed for each finish grind. The estimating approach assumes a two-infeed and two-traverse feed operation.

In cylindrical traverse grinding, the table values are multiplied by $L \cdot Dia / W$ after the entry values are chosen and determined from the drawing.

For traverse cylindrical grinding and dwell, incremental values for stock removal above .040 in. are given in units of .001 in. Add the additional times to the upper table values and multiply by $L \cdot Dia / W$ or Dia.

Representative material	Material condition	V, velocity fpm	f_i = infeed, in. per pass		P = traverse for each work revolution in fractions of wheel width	
			Rough	Finish	Rough	Finish
1. Tool steel	Hardened	50	.001	.0002	$1/4$	$1/8$
2. Tool steel	Annealed	60	.001	.0004	$1/2$	$1/6$
3. Plain carbon steel, alloy steel	Hardened	70	.001	.0004	$1/4$	$1/8$
	Hardened	70	.001	.0004	$1/4$	$1/8$
4. Plain carbon steel, alloy steel, copper alloys	Annealed	100	.001	.0004	$1/2$	$1/6$
	Annealed	100	.001	.0004	$1/2$	$1/6$
	Annealed or cold drawn	100	.001	.0004	$1/3$	$1/6$
5. Aluminum alloys	Cold drawn Solution-treated	150	.001	.0005	$1/3$	$1/6$

Dwell, or tarry, in traverse grinding refers to the controlled delay of the table at the end of the traverse. This delay extends the engagement time of the wheel with the surface at the end position of the traverse. Dwell is used for areas which are not con-

tacted twice during to-and-fro movements of the table, and whenever grinding is close to a shoulder. Entry variables are stock removal and material. Dwell time is multiplied by part diameter, *Dia*.

Sparkout overcomes part or machine deflections

during grinding and also to improve finish. Sparkout occurs after the part has attained final size by discontinuing infeed and making passes. A pass is one movement across the face of the wheel in one direction, and three finish grind passes are used. For sparkout time, the entry variable is material or velocity, V. Sparkout times are multiplied by the ratio $L \cdot Dia / W$.

For Element 5, plunge grinding, the feed rates per revolution are less than traverse grinding. On the other hand, infeed during plunge grinding is continuous. Infeed rates used by the table are:

Work material	Infeed per rev	
	Rough	Finish
Steel, soft	.0005	.0002
Plain carbon steel, hardened	.0002	.00005
Alloy and tool steel, hardened	.0001	.000025

The resultant reduction of work diameter is twice the amount of cross-slide movement causing wheel infeed.

Entry variables for Element 5 are typical material, diameter, and total stock removed. Incremental additions are possible for increases in diameter and stock removal beyond those shown. A two-feed plunge grind is calculated for the table, an approach allowance constant of .008 in., and 4 rev for sparking out are included.

For the dress wheel, Element 6, truing of the wheel is necessary and the interval depends on performance and wear of the wheel and accuracy-finish requirements of the operation. For a 20-in. wheel, 6500 fpm, and a traverse feed rate of .003 in. per wheel rev, a travel rate of 3.720 in./min axially is used, which is prorated over 20 parts.

In hand-controlled operations, gaging or operator-inspection. Element 7, is necessary. Micrometer, snap gages, air gages, or electronic devices are used. Automatic size control, which concludes the grind operation when a preset size is reached, virtually requires no time, and is not shown.

Another approach can use Item 13.1 of Section IV to estimate a cylindrical grinding cost. The $/100 units are called base cost. Entry variables are similar to the information needed for Table 13.1. The grinding estimate is dependent upon traverse stock removal, length and diameter of grind surface, width of wheel, dwell, sparkout, plunge, and hoist, if necessary. Not all terms have to be used. The first term of the constant is always included. The second term is multiplied by stock removal, length, and diameter of grind and divided by wheel width to give cost for traversing. The third term accounts for dwell cost, and the factor is multiplied by stock removal and diameter. The fourth term allows cost for sparkout and is multiplied by $L \cdot Dia / W$. The parenthesis is for plunge grinding. Two entry variables are necessary for plunge or diameter and stock removal.

EXAMPLES

A. An alloy steel shaft turned to 1.512/1.515-in. *Dia* 13-in. long is to be traverse ground to 1.4982/1.4987 in. diameter. There is sufficient material on one end to use a driving dog and give sufficient wheel clearance. Wheel diameter is 24 in. and width is 2 in. A lot of 210 is planned. Find the unit and lot estimate.

Table	Description	Time
13.1-S	Wheel diameter	.75 hr
13.1-S	Tolerance of .0005 in	.20 hr
13.1-1	Pick up part, aside, 6.5 lb	.07 min
13.1-2	Load, unload in dog	.13
13.1-2	Mount in centers	.10
13.1-2	Grease centers	.08
13.1-3	Operate machine, start, stop	.05
13.1-3	Change speed	.01
13.1-3	Position wheel to work	.16
13.1-4	Traverse grind .017, $V = 70$, $P = \frac{1}{4}$ and $\frac{1}{8}$, $L \cdot Dia / W = 13 \times$ 1.5/2, and .25 $\times$ 13 $\times$ 1.5/2	2.44
13.1-5	Dress wheel	.20
13.1-6	Inspection, 3 places	.15
	Unit estimate	3.39 min
	Lot estimate	12.81 hr

B. The shank of a hardened carbon steel component is plunge ground to a 1.625-in. *Dia* and length of 1 3/4 in. with a 2-in. wide wheel. The work will be held by a collet.

A grinding allowance of .012/.015 in. is expected for a lot of 2000 parts. Find the unit, lot, and shop estimate.

Table	Description	Time
13.1-S	Setup .50 + .05	.55 hr
13.1-1	Pick up part	.07 min
13.1-1	Load, unload in collet	.09
13.1-3	Operate machine	.05
13.1-3	Move wheel to work	.07
13.1-4	Plunge grind	.39
13.1-6	Dress wheel	.20
13.1-7	Electronic check	.06
	Unit estimate	.93 min
	Lot estimate	31.55 hr
	Shop estimate	64.5 pc/hr

C. Re-estimate Example A above using a base-cost approach.

Item	Description	Cost
13.1	Setup	$ 8.69
13.1	Tight tolerance	3.34
	Setup subtotal	$ 12.03
13.1	Cycle constant	$ 15.40
13.1	Traverse grind, .017 × 13 × 1.5/2 × 158	26.19
13.1	Sparkout, 13 × 1.5/2 × 2.01	19.60
13.1	Dwell, 1.5 × .002 × 80.3	.24
22.1	Inspection, .0005 in. dimension	9.34
	$/100 units subtotal	$ 70.82
	Lot cost	$160.75

D. Find the cost directly of the part estimated by Example B above. Apply base-cost values.

Item	Description	Cost
13.1	Setup constant	$ 8.69
	Setup subtotal	$ 8.69
13.1	Cycle constant	$ 15.40
13.1	Plunge, 5.75 × 1.625 + 643 × .015	18.99
22.1	Tolerance, .001 in.	3.72
	$/100 units subtotal	$ 38.11
	Lot cost	$770.89

TABLE 13.1   CYLINDRICAL GRINDING MACHINES

Setup

Wheel diameter to 12 in.	.25 hr
to 20 in.	.50 hr
to 30 in.	.75 hr
Tolerance .005+	.05 hr
.004 to .001	.15 hr
.0009 to .00025	.20 hr

Operation elements in estimating minutes

1. Pick up and aside part

Small, 0 to 5 lb	.05
Medium, 5+ to 13 lb	.07
Large, 13+ lb	.09
Chain hoist	.74

2. Load and unload part

Collet	.09
Chuck	.36
Face plate	.66
Dog	.13
Quick-acting dog	.08
Expanding arbor	.10
Press on-and-off mandrel	.24
Between and remove from centers	.10
Grease centers	.08

3. Operate machine

Start and stop	.05
Change speed	.01
Move wheel to-and-from work	.07
Position wheel to work and feed depth of grind,	
Manual	.16
Automatic	.03
Against shoulder for plunge, manual	.30
Open and close guard cover	.05
Turn coolant on and off	.04

4. Traverse grind, dwell, and sparkout

Grind stock	Representative material	Time per work rev in fractions of wheel width			Dwell	Sparkout
		$^1/_4$ & $^1/_8$	$^1/_3$ & $^1/_6$	$^1/_2$ & $^1/_6$		
.020	Hardened tool steel	.48	.36	.30	.15	.13
.020	Annealed tool steel	.30	.22	.17	.10	.10
.020	Hardened carbon and alloy steel	.25	.19	.15	.09	.09
.020	Annealed steels, copper alloys	.18	.13	.10	.06	.06
.020	Aluminum	.11	.08	.06	.04	.04
.025	Hardened tool steel	.55	.41	.33	.17	.13
.025	Annealed tool steel	.35	.26	.20	.12	.10
.025	Hardened carbon and alloy steel	.30	.22	.17	.10	.09
.025	Annealed steels, copper alloys	.21	.16	.12	.07	.06
.025	Aluminum	.13	.10	.07	.05	.04
.030	Hardened tool steel	.61	.45	.37	.20	.13
.030	Annealed tool steel	.40	.30	.23	.14	.10
.030	Hardened carbon and alloy steel	.35	.26	.19	.12	.09
.030	Annealed steels, copper alloys	.24	.18	.14	.09	.06
.030	Aluminum	.15	.11	.08	.06	.04
.040	Hardened tool steel	.74	.55	.43	.25	.13
.040	Annealed tool steel	.51	.38	.28	.19	.10
.040	Hardened carbon and alloy steel	.44	.33	.24	.16	.09
.040	Annealed steels, copper alloys	.31	.23	.17	.11	.06
.040	Aluminum	.20	.15	.11	.07	.04
Add'l .001	Hardened tool steel	.013	.009	.007	.004	0
	Annealed tool steel	.011	.009	.006	.005	0
	Hardened carbon and alloy steel	.010	.007	.005	.004	0
	Annealed steels, copper alloys	.008	.005	.004	.003	0
	Aluminum	.005	.003	.003	.002	0
Multiply table's value by . . . . . . L = grind length, Dia = diameter, W = wheel width		$L \cdot Dia / W$	$L \cdot Dia / W$	$L \cdot Dia / W$	Dia	$L \cdot Dia / W$

5. Plunge grind, min

Dia	Aluminum, annealed steels, copper alloys				Hardened carbon and alloy steels				Tool steels			
	Total stock removed				Total stock removed				Total stock removed			
	.010	.020	.030	Add'l .001	.010	.020	.030	Add'l .001	.010	.020	.030	Add'l .001
1	.04	.07	.09	.003	.16	.26	.35	.01	.37	.58	.80	.02
1.5	.06	.10	.14	.005	.25	.39	.53	.01	.55	.88	1.20	.04
2	.08	.14	.19	.007	.33	.52	.70	.02	.73	1.17	1.61	.04
3	.13	.20	.28	.008	.49	.77	1.05	.03	1.10	1.75	2.41	.06
4	.17	.27	.38	.010	.66	1.03	1.41	.03	1.47	2.34	3.21	.09
5	.21	.34	.47	.013	.82	1.29	1.76	.04	1.83	2.92	4.01	.11
6	.25	.41	.57	.016	.99	1.55	2.11	.06	2.20	3.51	4.82	.13
Add'l	.04	.06	.09		.16	.26	.35		.37	.58	.81	

6. Dress wheel

1-in. wheel, 1.93 min; per part .... .10
2-in. wheel, 3.86 min; per part .... .20
Add'l in., 1.93 min; per part .... .10

7. Inspection

Micrometer 3 places .... .15
Micrometer 2 places .... .10
Electronic check .... .06
Other inspection .... See Table 22.1

13.2 Centerless Grinding Machines

DESCRIPTION

Centerless grinders are designed to support and feed the stock by using two wheels and a workrest. The wheels, turning in the same direction, are the grinding and regulating wheels. The regulating wheel is smaller and provides pressure. Its tilted angular position forces stock to move atop a workrest while the part is being ground. The rate at which parts move through the machine is governed by the speed and angle of the regulator wheel. The width of the grinding wheel is from 4 in. to 20 in. for larger size machines. Work diameters can be from 1/4 in. or less to 6 in. or 10 in., depending on the machine. The two types of centerless grinding estimating data considered here are the through-feed method for straight cylindrical surfaces without interfering shoulders, and the infeed method for parts that have a shoulder. With the through-feed method, the work traverses through the machine. The infeed method is similar to plunge grinding with the cylindrical-type grinder.

The process does not require center drilling of ends, and loading is simple. Both short and large quantity runs are common.

One centerless grinding machine is shown in Figure 13.2. This machine has a 30-hp spindle drive motor and can accommodate wheels up to 10-in. wide and 24-in. in diameter. The hydraulic truing unit is mounted to the bed. A V-bar grinding attachment allows the OD grinding of bar stock up to 1.5-in. OD by 100-in. long.

ESTIMATING DATA DISCUSSION

The data given for setup are considered average as changes from through-feed to infeed or vice versa, and installation of chutes affects the estimate. A complete wheel change requires about 15 min if an extra spindle is available, while 45 min is required using the same wheel.

Operation elements are provided for infeed grinding. Handling includes loading and unloading part to work blade. If the work is ejected by wheel

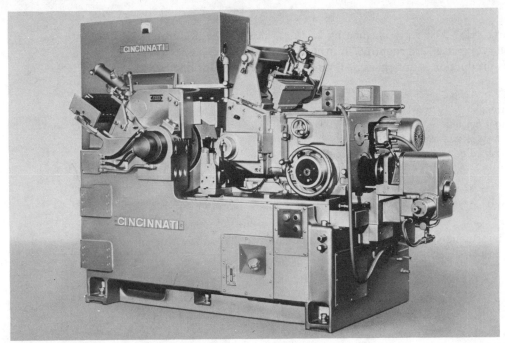

FIGURE 13.2 Centerless grinding machine. (*Cincinnati Milacron*)

retraction, .01 min is deducted. Although stock affects time to grind, the estimate is related to diameter, that being chosen for ease of application reasons as the principal time driver. The time is for one-plunge. The threshold time is for a diameter of .4 in. or less; for diameters in excess of 1 1/2 in., add .28 min/in. For instance, a 2-in. part would be allowed .38 min. Tolerance checking is based upon a frequency of 50 pc between micrometer checkings. For other frequencies, the micrometer check-time can be divided by typical shop practice. Wheel dress time is related to 400 grinds, but this depends upon part shape, material, machine, grind stock available, and other factors.

For through-feed grinding, the handling time is compared to grind time. If handling time is smaller,

usual practice is to overlook it in the estimate. If the load time is greater, the difference is added to the estimate. Through-feed grind time is for one pass. While practices vary, some companies establish a manufacturing specification of roughing out of .008 to .010 in. and a finishing or sparkout of .0005 in. to .002 in. The grind time is related to length of grind diameter for one pass. If the grind time is sufficient, other elements can be assumed to take place during this period.

Centerless ground parts can also be estimated using Item 13.2 of Section IV. Distinction is made between through-feed and infeed methods. The entry variable for infeed is part diameter, while for through-feed, the entry requires knowledge of part length. The grinding time is per pass.

EXAMPLES

A. Free-machining steel parts, 6-in. long, have a 1.125-in. long shoulder, leaving 4.75 in. of .547-in. *Dia* stock. Stock removal to finish dimension is .010 in. to be removed in two grinds, .008 in., and a .002-in. cleanup to final tolerance of ± .001. A moderate lot quantity of 350 is required and the infeed method of centerless grinding is planned. Part weight is .48 lb. Estimate total lot time for two grinds combined as one operation.

Table	Description	Time	
13.2-S	Setup	1.2	hr
13.2-1	Load and unload part, 2 × .03	.06	min
13.2-1	Deduct for chute ejection, 2 × .01	−.02	
13.2-2	Wheel to work, 2 × .04	.08	
13.2-3	Two infeed grinds, 2 × .10	.20	
13.2-4	Move wheel back from work, 2 × .05	.10	
13.2-8	Check tolerance for rough	0	
13.2-8	Check tolerance for finish	.005	
13.2-9	Dress wheel for rough	0	
13.2-9	Dress wheel for finish	.01	
	Unit estimate	.435	min
	Lot estimate	3.74	hr

B. Stainless steel parts, AISI 303, 8.318-in. long by 1.316 ± .002-in. *Dia* are ground using through-feed, and two passes are required to bring the stock to finish specification. Nearly continuous production is anticipated. Estimate the unit time for one pass.

Table	Description	Time	
13.2-5	Load part via trough	.01	min
13.2-5	Remove part from machine	0	
13.2-6	Through-feed one pass and use 10.7 in.	.14	
Note:	Handling time can be done during machine time		
13.2-7	Gather parts	.005	
13.2-8	Check tolerances	.005	
13.2-11	Dress wheel	.005	
	Unit estimate	.155	min

C. Using Section IV information, find the base-cost of a lot quantity of 350. The diameter is 1.125 in. and there are two passes.

Item	Description	Cost
13.2	Setup	$14.77
	Setup subtotal	$14.77
13.2	Infeed constant	$ 3.18
13.2	Pass factor, 1.125 × 2 × 2.61	5.87
22.1	Tolerance, .001 in.	3.72
	$/100 units subtotal	$12.77
	Lot cost	$59.47

TABLE 13.2 CENTERLESS GRINDING MACHINES

Setup   **1.2 hr**

Operation elements in estimating minutes

1. Handle part to grinder, infeed grinding

Weight	3	5	12
Min	.03	.04	.05

Deduct for chute ejection   .01

2. Bring wheel to work, infeed grinder   .04

3. Infeed grind, one plunge

Dia	Min
.4	.09
.6	.10
.7	.12
.9	.14
1.1	.16
1.2	.18
1.3	.21
1.5	.24
Add'l in.	.28

4. Move wheel back from work, infeed grinding   .05

5. Through-feed grinding

Load part from tote pan to grinder   .04
Fill gravity trough, .19/occurrence   .01   prorated
Remove part from machine   0

6. Through-feed grind, one pass

L	Min
.5	.02
1.1	.03
2.0	.04
3.2	.05
4.9	.07
7.3	.10
10.7	.14
15.4	.20
Add'l	.012

7. Gather parts, place in tote pan   .005

8. Check tolerances, .18/occurrence, prorated   .005

9. Dress wheel, 4.00/occurrence, prorated   .005

13.3 Honing Machines

DESCRIPTION

Honing is a low-velocity abrading process. Since material removal is accomplished at lower cutting speeds than in grinding, heating and pressure are less, resulting in size control. Abrasives are aluminum oxide, silicon carbide, or diamond. The grits, bonded together, are formed into sticks. Honing, depending on the machine, may be done on internal or external surfaces. There are manual honing units and fixtured honing tools. Size control is managed by gaging the tool or bore. Tools for honing may be mounted on a variety of machines—drill press, electric drill, or any tool that will rotate and reciprocate and allow a floating abrading action. Honing is possible for a wide variety of metallics, ceramics, fiberglass, tool steels, etc. A machine for power stroking is shown in Figure 13.3. Bore diameters from 0.060 in. to 3.75 in. are possible. Other machines are capable up to 12 in. diameter.

ESTIMATING DATA DISCUSSION

Some machines have automatic cycle start and shut-off. Spindle speed selection, stroking rates, universal fixtures, gages, and diamond dressing affect the operation elements. The honing Element 7 is for a variety of materials, ranging from soft steel to hard tool steel using aluminum oxide, diamond, or

FIGURE 13.3 Power-stroked honing machine. (*Sunnen Products Company*)

silicon carbide abrasives. The range of stock removal is for final sizing, cleanup, or rework of bore diameters. Thus, Element 7 is a general purpose honing element. The entry is based upon diameter and .001 in. of stock removal (meaning final bore diameter minus initial bore diameter).

Element 7 also provides for honing cylinders where larger-stock removal is emphasized for mild steel. The distinction between the entries depends on whether the abrasive is either diamond or aluminum oxide. A bore of 2⅜-in. OD × 11⅛-in. length having .030-in. stock removal would find the factor as .25 for diamond-imbedded grinding stones (going to the next larger diameter to avoid tabular interpolation), and a time of 2.78 min ($=.25 \times 11.125$).

For large diameter or long-length bores, the operator may be working on a different machine simultaneously because of the opportunity to do other work. This ''sharing of time'' between two or more operations allows a reduction of time opportunity by the estimator.

Item 13.3 of Section IV may be used for quick estimates of honing. Entry variables for Item 13.3 are bore circumference, stock removal expressed in .001 in., and length of honed bore. The constant is always used.

EXAMPLES

A. Estimate the time to hone a bushing, D3 steel, 58 Rockwell C, 2.16-in. long, .6425/.6250-in. bore. The previous operation was reaming. Mean stock removal from the diameter is .005 in. A lot of 1400 is required.

Table	Description	Time
13.3-S	Setup	.30 hr
13.3-1	Handle	.09 min
13.2-2	Start and stop	.04
13.3-3	Set honing dial	.06
13.3-5	Install fixture	.25
13.3-7	Hone, .68 × 2.16	1.47
	Hone life, 1400 × .66 sq in. = 928 sq in.	
	Unit estimate	1.19 min
	Lot estimate	44.87 hr

B. For Example A above, find base-cost using Item 13.3 of Section IV. Find lot and unit cost.

Item	Description	Cost
13.3	Setup	$ 2.89
	Setup subtotal	$ 2.89
13.3	Cycle constant	$ 4.82
13.3	Circumference = 2.02 in., L = 2.16 in., 2.02 × 2.16 × 1.25	5.45
13.3	Stock removal = .005 in. .005 × 2.16 × 2314	24.99
	$/100 units subtotal	$ 35.26
	Lot cost	$ 496.55
	Unit cost	$ .35

TABLE 13.3 HONING MACHINES

Setup .3 hr

Operation elements in estimating minutes

1. Load and unload part on tray
   Light .09
   25 lb + .16

2. Start and stop .04

3. Set honing dial .06

4. Air-clean part .13
   Cloth clean part .17
   Wipe part with hand .05
   Wipe off excess oil or grease .49

5. Place part on mandrel and remove, manual honing   .08
   25 lb +   .19
   Install fixture to hold part for power honing and remove   .25

6. Micrometer check ± .0001 in.   .48
   Go/no-go gage   .08

7. Honing

Honing (per in. of bore L), maintenance or cleanup

Bore Dia	Stock removal				
	.001	.002	.003	.004	.005
.32	.08	.15	.30	.45	.60
.5	.08	.19	.34	.49	.64
.64	.08	.23	.38	.53	.68
.95	.17	.32	.47	.62	.77
1.27	.25	.40	.55	.70	.85
2.	.43	.58	.73	.88	1.03
3.	.68	.83	.90	1.13	1.28
4.	.95	1.09	1.24	1.39	1.54

Additional: sq in. of surface area   .08
Per ea mil of stock removal   .15
Hone life: 3800 sq in. of surface area
     Replace set of stones   1.00

Honing (per in. of bore L), mild steel with diamond-imbedded stones

Bore Dia	Stock removal					
	.010	.020	.030	.040	.050	.100
2	.16	.19	.21	.24	.26	.39
3	.17	.21	.25	.28	.32	.51
4	.18	.23	.28	.33	.38	.64
5	.20	.26	.32	.38	.45	.76
6	.21	.28	.36	.43	.51	.88

Honing (per in. of bore L), mild steel with aluminum oxide stones

Bore Dia	Stock removal					
	.010	.020	.030	.040	.050	.100
2	.17	.22	.27	.32	.37	.63
3	.19	.27	.34	.42	.50	.89
4	.22	.32	.42	.52	.62	1.14
5	.24	.37	.50	.62	.75	1.39
6	.27	.42	.57	.72	.88	1.64

8. Hand file edge of bore

Material	Bore Dia				Add'l per in. of circumference
	.32	.64	.95	1.27	
Soft	.05	.07	.09	.11	.018
Rockwell C 20–35	.06	.08	.10	.12	.021
Rockwell C 35+	.07	.10	.12	.14	.024

13.4 Surface Grinding Machines

DESCRIPTION

The grinding of flat or plane surfaces is defined as surface grinding. The machines considered in this estimating guide are the planer with a reciprocating table and a rotating table. Each type has the potential variation of the grinding-wheel spindle in either a horizontal or vertical position. Magnetic chucks are a feature of this machine. Heavy or light stock removal, finish, and tolerance are the usual advantages claimed for these machines. Surfaces need not be regular (i.e., unbroken areas) to accomplish surface grinding. Straight or recessed wheels grinding on the outside face or circumference and segmental or ring-shaped wheels are the wheel designs. In rotary-surface grinding, a vertical spindle can be tilted to reduce the wheel area in contact with the work to allow greater depths, less heating, and higher utilization or available horsepower. For finish grinding, the spindle is returned to a perpendicular position which presents a flat grinding surface to the workpiece.

Horizontal-spindle, reciprocating-table surface grinders include small grinders, die-block grinders, and large grinders. The machines are rated by width × height adjustment × length, and range from 12 × 16 × 36 in. to 48 × 36 × 240 in. Table feeds are hydraulic, with speeds up to 125 fpm. Wheel head is power raising and lowering on larger models and manual on the lighter and smaller machines. Wheel crossfeed is hydraulic transverse, with feeds vari-able up to the width of the wheel. Electronic reversing controls are available. On the smaller machines the grinding wheels may be 20 in. in diameter with a 3-in. face or smaller. On larger machines, typical diameters may be 20, 28, 32, or 36 in. with a 6-in. face. A 12-in. wide table horizontal grinder is shown in Figure 13.4A.

Vertical-spindle, rotary-table surface grinding machines include models having table diameters ranging from less than 30 in. to 168 in. Table speed ranges may be fixed or have variable rpm within a range. Spindle horsepower, depending on the model, can range up to 300 hp. Wheel head feeds are continuous or rachet, depending on the manufacturer, and are hand- or automatic-fed, variable from 0.005 to .165 in./min. Feed wheels may be graduated in steps of .001 in. Tiltable spindles for rough grinding allow for grain penetration. Automatic electronic gaging gives continuous measurement of the work during the cutting cycle. Figure 13.4B is a 300-hp machine with a 72-in. magnetic worktable.

ESTIMATING DATA DISCUSSION

The setup is listed as .6 hr and includes ordinary machine chores. It does not include a wheel change, which is an optional part of the run time. If estimating practice is to include a wheel change, Element 12 is added to .6 hr for a total of .9 hr.

FIGURE 13.4A Horizontal reciprocating table grinder. *(Mattison Grinder)*

FIGURE 13.4B Heavy rotary table, vertical spindle grinder. *(Mattison Grinder)*

The initial listed element is for load and unload, where the entry variable is part weight. Two conditions are given: from table for small and medium sized parts, and from the floor for larger parts. Loading may also refer to fixtures; holding bars, for nonmagnetic workpieces; for bracing; or leveling. The time is found in Element 3.

In rotary grinding, the chuck is positioned under the wheel. For planer-type grinders, the table is positioned for grinding, then Element 4 is used. The number of pieces in the fixture or on the chuck is the entry variable for Element 4 and is determined from knowledge of the part surface area, packing on the table, and the developed area of a fixture, if used. Specific machine table areas must be known.

Grinding times are calculated using Elements 5 (traverse grind), 6 (plunge grinding), and 7 (rotary table grinding). Entry variables for traverse and plunge grinding for planer-type grinding are stock width, depth of grind, and machine grind-wheel width. For plunge grinding they are depth of grind and grinding velocity. For rotary-table grinding, entry variables are depth of grind and material grinding rate.

Stock width is maximum dimension required for grinding. The part width dimension is used directly, as an overlap of one-wheel face width is already included in the calculations. If a stock width other than those shown is required, the "Add'l 1" can be added or subtracted from table values and an approximation will result. Naturally, if stock width is less than wheel width, the plunge grinding data are used. Otherwise, for stock widths greater than wheel widths, traverse grinding is employed. Obviously, the estimator will have in mind a particular machine where wheel width is known.

Depth of grind is the deliberate overstock remaining from a previous operation. Stock allowances for a grinding approach and material irregularities are included in the calculations, though they are not specifically shown as depth of grind. For instance, a .005-in. grind stock assumes a .005-in. stock allowance for approach and irregularities, and thus there is a .010 total amount for grind removal. Also, for .020-in. stock, there is a stock approach of .008 in. which provides a total of .028-in. stock. The minimum and maximum stock allowance for approach and irregularities are .005 and .008 in. The maximum .008 in., is provided once .020-in. stock is reached. Additional or lesser stock allowances can be calculated for depth of grind or for approach irregularities using the "Add'l .001 in." number.

The table time to traverse grind is for 1 in. of length per a surface velocity of 1 fpm. Once entry values of stock width, stock depth, and wheel width are known and a value selected, the tabular factor is multiplied by the ratio L/V. Determination of length

(L) starts with knowledge of maximum part grind and then an approach and overtravel length is added. This approach-overtravel length may be 1 wheel dia. The length dimension is in in.

The time values are based upon 90% of total stock being rough ground, leaving 10% for finish grind in a two-phase operation. A sparkout of four passes over all area is included in the calculations of Element 5.

Downfeed and crossfeeds assumed for each wheel width within the calculations are:

Wheel width	1½	3	6	Plunge
Crossfeed, rough, in.	¾	1½	3	
Crossfeed, finish, in.	⅜	¾	1½	
Downfeed, rough, in.	.0009	.001	.001	.0008
Downfeed, finish, in.	.00045	.0005	.0005	.0004

Selection of the entry value of surface velocity for plunge grinding is necessary. Adjustments to table values are possible in the "Add'l 1" surface velocity rpm, if improved estimating accuracy is thought necessary. Suggested grinding velocities (V) are given as:

Material	Cast iron	Soft steels	Hard steels
Traverse velocity, fpm	80	80	90
Plunge velocity, fpm	60	70	80

In the 5 to 12 hp planer-type grinder machines, the common rate of stock removal is 1/4 to 2 cu in./min; in 3 1/2 to 5 hp it is 1 cu in./min in cast iron, and 10 hp removes 1 cu in./min in steel. Deflection or rigidity, broken or continuous surface area, and wet or dry grinding can affect these values.

For traverse and plunge grinding, the tabular value is multiplied by L/V and L respectively. L is the length in in. of the part plus a distance for approach and overtravel, perhaps approximated by a wheel dia. V is selected from the above tabular values.

Rotary table grinding time, Element 7, is calculated differently from planer-type grinding. The material removal rate is related to grinding-head hp available, type of material, and the nature of the surface. The hp required per cu in. of material per min is given as:

Area, sq in.	300	600	1000	2000
		Cast Iron		
Continuous	5	6	7	8
Broken up	4	5	6	6
		Steel		
Continuous	7	8	9	10
Broken up	6	7	8	9

Thus, for cast iron, if the developed area is about 550 sq in., and is unrelieved and continuous, the required hp/cu in./min = 6; if that area is broken up the requirements are less, or 5 hp/cu in./min, because chip clearance is increased. The aluminum rate is 4 hp/cu in./min. Having a depth of grind, and a material grinding rate, the tabular value from Element 6 is multiplied by the ratio of *Area/hp$_m$*, where the hp_m is the machine-grinding head horsepower. Area is that which is seen by the segmented wheel and may be larger than the calculated and apparent area.

Element 8, dwell or sparkout, is for high-tolerance grinding. Elements 5 and 6 include four sparkout passes and are for commercial tolerances. Tolerances for tenths or rotary-table grinding may require sparkout.

If the work is hidden, i.e., prevented from being checked, such as for rotary surface grinding, it is necessary to expose the work for dimension checking and Element 9 is applied.

The rotary-table segmented grinding is self-dressing, but the planer-type horizontal wheels are dressed via a diamond point. Element 12 accounts for both dressing and wheel changing. Wheel wear is contingent upon several factors, and one rule is .015 in. of grinding wheel reduction per .125 in. removed for cast iron, and .050 in. per .125 in. for steel. Thus, it is possible to estimate the proportion of wheel change time.

Item 13.4 of Section IV can be used to estimate costs for large singular parts that are to be surface ground. Patterned along the lines of Table 13.4, the approach of Item 13.4, however, is simpler and is similar when group values are compared. Entry variables to find cost are traverse stock width, grind depth, and length. For plunging, the entry variable is grind depth by length. For rotary grinding, three grades of materials are provided, and the entry value is cu in. The constant cost is used for single large parts. However, for small parts, the constant is overlooked. A hoist time is provided if weight exceeds manual handling. The handling is common among the various methods of grinding.

EXAMPLES

A. Estimate the time to surface grind 4 sides of AISI 6150 steel index dogs having irregular dimensions, but an overall dimension of $3/4 \times 2\ 3/8 \times 5/8$ in. The dogs are to be loaded 384 at a time on a 35 hp planer-type surface grinder with a 20- $\times$ 6-in. grinding wheel where table width is 30 in. Stock removal is .010 in. per side. Determine unit time for a large quantity.

Table	Description	Time
13.4-1	Load and unload from table, 1 unit	.07 min
	Load 32 across for a 20-in. stock width, and 12 along the traverse length for 31.5-in. of metal	
13.4-5	Traverse grind 1 side, 20×31.5 in. Overtravel and approach = 10 in. for a length of 41.5 in. Velocity = 90 fpm. Time = (23.7 × 41.5/90)/384	.03
13.4-10	Check with gage, .17/384	0
13.4-11	Wash grinding grits, .69 + .004 (384 − 69)/384	.005
13.4-12	Dress wheel, 2.00/384	.005
Repeat	Duplicate above elements for 3 other sides	.33
	Unit estimate	.44 min
	hr/100 units	0.733

B. Leaded steel plates having dimensions of 11 1/4-in. long by 2 1/2-in. wide and 1-in. thick are rough ground 7 at a time to remove .016 in. per side using a planer-type surface grinder. The operation is plunge grinding using a 3-in. wheel. Determine lot time for 120 pc.

Table	Description	Time
13.4-S	Setup	0.6 hr
13.4-1	Load and unload, 2.9 lb	0.10 min
13.4-6	Plunge grind at 80 fpm	
	Approach and overtravel distance of 14 in. is assumed for a total length of 92.75 in. Unit time = (92.75 × .044)/.7	.59
13.4-10	Check sample with depth gage, .60/7	.09
13.4-11	Wash grits off parts, .44/7	.06
13.4-11	Clean table, .37/7	.05
13.4-12	Dress wheel, .63/7	.09
Repeat	Duplicate above elements for second side	.98
	Unit estimate	1.96 min
	Lot estimate	4.52 hr

C. Estimate a rotary-grinding job of a $60 \times 60 \times 3$-in. 1020 steel plate, where stock removal is 1/8 in. from each side. Stock removal is 450 cu in. per side. Assume a 200 hp spindle motor machine is available for the job. The area is 3600 sq in. per side. Find the unit time in min and hr/1 unit.

Table	Description	Time
13.4-1	Load and unload, crane	5.00 min
13.4-4	Position chuck, 1 pc	.31
13.4-7	Use 10 hp/cu in./min, and factor of 1.25 is read, multiply	
	$(1.25) \times (3600)/200$	22.50
13.4-8	Sparkout, $1.93 + (3600 - 1148)\ .0015$	5.61
13.4-9	Expose work	.13
13.4-10	Check size thickness	.60
13.4-11	Wash part	.37
Repeat	Part is turned over and above elements are repeated for second side	34.52
	Unit estimate	69.04 min
	hr/1 unit	1.51

D. Find the base-cost of 1 unit for Example A above. Load 384 on table. Each part weighs .3 lb.

Item	Description	Cost
13.4	Constant for small multiple parts	$0
13.4	Load factor, $.3 \times .111$	.033
13.4	Traverse length = 41.5 in.	
	Stock width = 20 in.	
	Stock removal = .01 in.	
	Formula, $\{.958 \times 20 + 464 \times .01\} \times 41.5/384$	2.572
13.4	Repeat above for 3 other sides, 3×2.605	7.815
	$/100 units	$10.420

E. Estimate base-cost for Example B above. Each part weighs 2.9 lb.

Item	Description	Cost
13.4	Setup subtotal	$ 8.02
13.4	Cycle constant	$ 25.80
13.4	Load factor, seven at once, $2.9 \times 7 \times .111$	2.25
13.4	Plunge grind, $.016 \times 92.75 \times 50.1$	74.35
22.1	.005-in. tolerance	.62
Repeat	Duplicate above 4 elements for second side (103.02×1)	103.02
	$/700 units subtotal	$206.04
	$/100 units	$ 29.43
	Unit cost	$ .29
	Lot cost	$ 43.34

TABLE 13.4 SURFACE GRINDING MACHINES

Setup   **0.6 hr**

Operation elements in estimating minutes

1. Load and unload part or fixture onto magnetic chuck, lb

From table	From floor	Min	From table	From floor	Min
3.6		.07	36.0	19.3	.21
5.3		.08	41.0	24.0	.24
7.3		.09	46.5	29.1	.26
9.4		.10	52.5	34.7	.28
11.7		.11		40.9	.31
14.3		.12		47.7	.34
17.1	1.7	.13		55.2	.38
				Add'l 1	.004
20.2	4.6	.15		Add'l 1	.005
23.6	7.7	.16	Electric hoist		1.12
27.4	11.2	.18	Hand double-chain hoist		4
31.5	15.1	.19	Bay crane		5–20

2. Tighten part in fixture

      Nut, washer or strap   .55

      Loosen and tighten nut only   .27

      Index chuck while tightening   .04

3. Position and remove holding bars on magnetic chuck

No. of bars	Min	No. of bars	Min
2	.06	11	.78
3	.14	12	.86
4	.22	13	.94
5	.30	14	1.02
6	.38	15	1.10
7	.46	16	1.18
8	.54	17	1.26
9	.62	18	1.33
10	.70	Add'l	.08

4. Position chuck under grinding wheel

No. pc	Min.
3	.31
6	.32
9	.33
12	.34
15	.35
18	.37
21	.38
24	.39
27	.40
30	.41
Add'l	.004

5. Traverse grind[1]

Stock width	Depth of grind	Min to grind width for 1 in. of length per 1 fpm		
		Wheel width		
		1½	3	6
3	.005	11.9	8.3	
	.010	16.5	11.4	
	.015	21.1	14.6	
	.020	25.7	17.7	
	.025	29.5	20.3	
	.030	33.3	22.8	
	Add'l .001	.75	.50	
6	.005	20.8	12.8	8.3
	.010	28.8	17.2	11.4
	.015	36.9	21.8	14.6
	.020	45.0	26.5	17.7
	.025	51.7	30.3	20.3
	.030	58.3	34.3	22.8
	Add'l .001	1.42	.75	.50
10	.010	45.3	24.8	15.3
	.015	58.0	31.6	19.4
	.020	70.7	38.3	23.6
	.025	91.8	49.5	30.4
	.030	112.8	60.7	37.3
	Add'l .001	2.17	1.17	.67

Stock Width	Depth of grind	Min to grind width for 1 in. of length per 1 fpm		
		Wheel width		
		1½	3	6
20	.010	86.6	43.9	23.7
	.020	134.9	67.7	38.3
	.030	175.1	87.5	49.5
	.040	215.3	107.3	60.7
	.050	255.6	127.2	71.9
	Add'l .001	4.00	2.00	1.08
Add'l 1		6.83		
30	.010		60.2	34.3
	.020		91.4	53.0
	.030		125.6	68.5
	.040		154.0	84.0
	.050		182.4	99.5
	Add'l .001		2.92	1.58
Add'l 1			4.00	
40	.010			43.9
	.020			67.7
	.030			87.5
	.040			107.3
	.050			127.2
	Add'l .001			2.00
Add'l 1				1.58

[1] Multiply table time by L/V to obtain min.
$L = $ in., $V = $ fpm

6. Traverse plunge grind[2]

Depth of grind	Min to grind 1 in. L					
	Grinding velocity, fpm					
	30	50	60	70	80	Add'l 1
.005	.059	.035	.029	.025	.022	−.0003
.006	.063	.038	.032	.028	.024	−.0003
.007	.068	.041	.034	.029	.026	−.0003
.008	.073	.043	.037	.031	.027	−.0003
.009	.077	.046	.038	.033	.029	−.0003
.010	.086	.052	.043	.037	.033	−.0004
.011	.091	.054	.045	.039	.034	−.0004
.012	.095	.058	.048	.041	.036	−.0004
.013	.100	.060	.050	.043	.038	−.0004
.014	.104	.063	.053	.045	.039	−.0005
.015	.113	.068	.057	.048	.043	−.0005
.016	.118	.071	.059	.051	.044	−.0005
.017	.123	.073	.062	.053	.046	−.0006
.018	.128	.077	.063	.054	.048	−.0006
.019	.132	.079	.066	.057	.049	−.0006
.020	.142	.084	.071	.061	.053	−.0007

Depth of grind	Min to grind 1 in. L					
	Grinding velocity, fpm					
	30	50	60	70	80	Add'l 1
.022	.150	.090	.075	.064	.057	−.0007
.024	.159	.096	.080	.068	.060	−.0008
.025	.163	.098	.082	.070	.062	−.0008
.028	.178	.107	.088	.076	.067	−.0008
.030	.187	.112	.093	.080	.070	−.0008
Add'l .001	.004	.003	.003	.002	.001	

[2] Multiply table time by length + approach and overtravel, or L, to obtain min, L is in.

7. Rotary table grind [3]

Depth of grind	Material grinding rate, hp/cu in./min								
	4	5	6	7	8	9	10	20	Add'l 1
.010	.04	.05	.06	.07	.08	.09	.10	.20	.01
.015	.06	.08	.09	.10	.12	.13	.15	.30	.015
.020	.08	.10	.12	.14	.16	.18	.20	.40	.02
.025	.10	.13	.15	.17	.20	.22	.25	.50	.025
.030	.12	.15	.18	.21	.24	.27	.30	.60	.03
.040	.16	.20	.24	.28	.32	.36	.40	.80	.04
.050	.20	.25	.30	.35	.40	.45	.50	1.00	.05
.060	.24	.30	.36	.42	.48	.54	.60	1.20	.06
.070	.28	.35	.42	.49	.56	.63	.70	1.40	.07
.080	.32	.40	.48	.56	.64	.72	.80	1.60	.08
.090	.36	.45	.54	.63	.72	.81	.90	1.80	.09
.100	.40	.50	.60	.70	.80	.90	1.00	2.00	.10
.125	.50	.63	.75	.87	1.00	1.12	1.25	2.50	.13
.150	.60	.75	.90	1.05	1.20	1.35	1.50	3.00	.15
.175	.70	.88	1.05	1.27	1.40	1.57	1.75	3.50	.18
.200	.80	1.00	1.20	1.40	1.60	1.80	2.00	4.00	.20
.250	1.00	1.25	1.50	1.75	2.00	2.25	2.50	2.75	.25
Add'l .001	.004	.005	.006	.007	.008	.009	.01	.02	

[3] Multiply table time by A/hp_m to obtain min, A = sq. in.

8. Dwell or sparkout

Area	Min
20	.21
53	.26
96	.32
149	.40
215	.51
298	.63
402	.79
531	.99
692	1.23
894	1.54
1148	1.93
Add'l 1	.0015

9. Expose work for dimension checking

No. pc on chuck	Min
7	.13
14	.14
21	.15
28	.16
35	.17
42	.19
49	.20
Add'l 1	.002

10. Check with profile gage or scale .17
    Check sample with depth micrometer .60

11. Wash grinding grit off parts with coolant

No. pc on chuck	Min
3	.41
9	.44
15	.46
21	.49
27	.51
33	.54
39	.56
45	.59
51	.62
57	.64
63	.67
69	.69
Add'l 1	.004

Clean chuck or table or single large part .37

12. Change wheel or dress wheel
    Change wheel 16.00
    Dress wheel (traverse and plunge)

Wheel width	1½	3	6
Rough grind	.47	.63	1.00
Finish grind	.92	1.28	2.00

(Prorate over no. of pc.)

13.5 Internal Grinding Machines

DESCRIPTION

Internal grinding machines operate with rapidly rotating grinding wheels, and in the majority of machines, the workpiece is also rotated. Additionally, a traverse movement will bring the wheel into the work area and retract the wheel at the end of the operation. Wheel retraction may also be needed for wheel dressing, gaging, etc. A transverse movement has the dual role of the wheel approach to the surface of the work, which in some cases may be in a recessed location, and secondly, a feed movement during stock removal. The feed may be at different rates for roughing and finishing.

Internal grinders range from machines having a minimum capacity of about 1 mm to about 32+in. maximum hole diameter. Hole lengths vary up to 24 in. Features of some manufacturers' models include diamond and electronic sizing, automatic dressing with counter for frequency of dressing, and automatic compensation. A typical grinder is shown in Figure 13.5.

Planetary internal grinders and grinders where the workpiece is rotated by rolls are not considered in these data. Now, consider estimating data for the general class of internal grinding machines.

ESTIMATING DATA DISCUSSION

A value of 0.7 hr is considered average for small- and large-size internal grinders. Operational elements are similar to external cylindrical grinding.

Internal grinding time calculations are similar to those of external machines. The basic formula for traverse grinding is used, but velocities and feeds are reduced. A distinction is made for large and small (smaller than 1 in.) bores or slender holes where length to diameter ratios require less grinding wheel pressure. Hardened alloy and tool steel materials, if velocity requirements are considered similar, can be estimated as small holes.

For internal grinding, the following parameters were adopted:

	Traverse regular bores	Traverse small holes	Plunge
Velocity, fpm	60	30	40
Infeed, rough	.0006	.0006	.0004
Infeed, finish	.0002	.0002	.0001

Table values are multiplied by the ratio $L \cdot dia/W$, where L = in.-length of grind, accounting for shoulders or hole bottom; D = in.-internal diameter; and W = in.-width of grind wheel. If wheel width is wider than hole stroke, the internal grind is considered a plunge grind, even though some machines impart a slight oscillation to the grinding stone. For longer holes, having lengths which are a multiple of the wheel width, the general practices of traverse grinding are observed. Sparkout assumes four dead passes to obtain final finish and tolerance. A stock allowance for runout and approach, initially at .004 for the .010-in. total stock, is gradually increased to .008 in. for .024-in. and higher stock allowances. The runout and approach values are included in the calculations and need not be added to the stock allowance, which is determined by subtraction of initial and final diameters. In traverse and plunge grinding, the practice of allotting 10% of the total

FIGURE 13.5 Internal chucking grinder. *(Hermes Machines Tool Company, Inc.)*

stock for a finish grind stock allowance is observed by the data.

Inspection times are indicated as per piece, following the description, and then are prorated over 10 units.

Internal grinding can be estimated in cost-dollars directly by Item 13.5 of Section IV. The cost depends upon the entry variables of traverse grind stock removal, length, diameter, wheel width, stock diameter for plunge grinding, and use of a hoist. The constant cost is always given. Traverse grinding cost, or the second term, is multiplied by the stock removal in thousandths, length and diameter, and divided by wheel width. This calculation is similar to Table 13.5. The third term is for plunge grinding. The cost factor is multiplied by the stock diameter. The final term is for handling by a hoist, if the part is too heavy or awkward for manual loading. The final run-time cost is expressed as $/100 units.

EXAMPLES

A. A workpiece is to be ground internally and final bore dimensions are 7 in., 2.5-in. length, and the material is fully heat treated to give an R_c value between 59–62. The wheel chosen for the job is 4.5-in. diameter and 1.25-in. wide. Grinding allowance is .030 in. Estimate the floor to floor time.

Table	Description	Time
13.5-1	Chain hoist	.74 min
13.5-2	Load and unload part	.14
13.5-3	Start and stop work	.03
13.5-3	Guard cover	.05
13.5-3	Start and stop grind wheel	.02
13.5-4	Traverse grind, .67 × 2.5 × 7 ÷ 1.25	9.52
13.5-4	Sparkout (.06 × 2.5 × 7 ÷ 1.25)	.84
13.5-6	Dress wheel, 2 times	.14
13.5-7	Inspection, electronic	.01
	Unit estimate	11.49 min

B. Estimate the total lot time for grinding an .867-in. ID by 1-in. long spacer. Material is soft steel, and the amount of stock is .010 in. Lot quantity is 861, wheel diameter is 5/8 in., and the length of the wheel is 2 in. Assume dry grinding conditions.

Table	Description	Time
13.5-S	Setup	.6 hr
13.5-1	Pick up small part	.05 min
13.5-2	Load and unload	.09
13.5-3	Operate machine	.03
13.5-5	Plunge grind	.19
13.5-6	Dress wheel	.07
13.5-7	Air gaging	.01
	Unit estimate	.44 min
	Lot estimate	6.91 hr

C. Estimate base-cost for Example A above with a quantity of 20.

Item	Description	Cost
13.5	Setup subtotal	$ 8.02
13.5	Cycle constant, stock removal = .030 in.; length = 2.5 in.; diameter = 7; and wheel width = 1.25	$ 11.00
13.5	Stock removal, (.030 × 2.5 × 7 ÷ 1.25) × 733	307.86
13.5	Hoist	16.40
	$/100 units subtotal	$335.26
	Lot cost	$ 75.07

TABLE 13.5 INTERNAL GRINDING MACHINES

Setup .6 hr

Operation elements in estimating minutes

1. Pickup and aside part
   - Small, 0–5 lb .05
   - Medium, 5+ –13 lb .07
   - Large, 13+ lb .09
   - Chain hoist .74

2. Load and unload part
   - Collet .09
   - In chuck jaws .07
   - Align part in fixture .14

3. Operate machine
   - Start and stop workhead .03
   - Change workhead speed .002
   - Start and stop grind wheel .02
   - Engage and disengage table speed lever .04
   - Open and close workhead guard cover .05
   - Move truing lever to-and-from position .04
   - Operate runout treadle .01

4. Traverse grind—internal

Total stock	Regular holes and bores	Small and slender holes
.005	.12	.23
.010	.24	.49
.012	.28	.56
.014	.33	.66
.016	.39	.77
.018	.42	.84
.020	.48	.95
.022	.51	1.01
.024	.56	1.13
.026	.60	1.20
.028	.64	1.26
.030	.67	1.34
.032	.71	1.41
.034	.74	1.49
Add'l .001	.02	.05
Sparkout	.06	.13
Multiply table values	$\dfrac{L \cdot Dia}{W}$	$\dfrac{L \cdot Dia}{W}$

5. Plunge grind—internal

Dia	Total stock removed					Add'l .001
	.005	.010	.015	.020	.030	
1	.11	.19	.26	.34	.47	.01
1.5	.18	.28	.40	.50	.71	.01
2	.24	.38	.54	.67	.93	.02
3	.35	.57	.80	1.01	1.40	.04
4	.48	.75	1.07	1.34	1.87	.06
5	.59	.95	1.33	1.69	2.33	.07
6	.71	1.13	1.61	2.03	2.80	.08
Add'l 1.0	1.3	.19	.26	.33	.47	

6. Dress wheel   .07

7. Inspection
    Plug gaging, manual, .20 min   .02
    Inside micrometer, .46 min   .016
    Mechanical dial indicators, .15 min   .015
    Rear-inserted power-operated plug, .04 min   .004
    Air or electronic indicators, .10 min   .01

13.6 Free Abrasive Grinding Machines

DESCRIPTION

Free abrasive grinding machines produce almost geometrically true surfaces on parts, correct minor surface imperfections, and improve dimensional accuracy to provide a very close fit between two contacting surfaces. Although free abrasive grinding is a material-removing operation, it is not always economical for that purpose. The method is used on flat, cylindrical, or specially formed surfaces. The part surfaces are in contact with an abrasive in such a way that fresh abrasive contacts are being made. Consider the estimating data for the general case of semiautomatic free abrasive grinding machines of external flat surfaces.

Machines are available which provide up to four rings. Rings may range in internal diameter (ID) from 4½ in. to 36 in. Figure 13.6 is a 4-ring machine. As the rotating table turns, it carries the abrasive grains across the surface of each part; the pressure plate is above the ring.

ESTIMATING DATA DISCUSSION

Handling is for one-hand or two-hand held loading of parts. It is possible to load on a separate table during grinding time, in which case only the first rings are considered for the estimate. Subsequent retaining rings are loaded during the lapping time. For elements performed during machine lapping,

FIGURE 13.6 Free abrasive grinding machine. *(Speedfam)*

the estimated time is zero, except whenever off-loading elements exceed the abrasive time.

A small part is easily held with one hand, while a large part requires two hands. Turnover may be during lapping time. For some machines which may have automatic handling provisions, turnover is mechanical, that is, free of operator involvement. However, this automatic turnover element does interrupt machine operation and 0.75 min per ring is required.

If work is done during the abrasive grinding element, additional time is zero. Parts can be loaded into spare rings and subsequently eased onto the lapping table. Some machines, however, may be stopped during turnover.

A start and stop element is required. For lapping machines which have a free weight, a time is provided to clean, place, and remove weight for each ring. On some other machines, the backing plate is lowered under machine control. A release of pressure plate per ring is also available.

The unit estimate depends upon the number of parts loaded into each retaining ring. The abrasive action is performed simultaneously on several or many parts. The number of parts per ring is given below.

No. parts per ring

Ring Dia, in.	Part Dia, in.								
	.2	.4	.8	1	2	4	6	9	10
6¾	950	220	55	32	7	1	1		
9		380	100	60	15	3	1	1	
18			400	260	66	25	5	1	1
24			750	480	115	28	11	3	4
32				875	210	50	21	9	8

Stock removal rates are expressed as min/in. For example, if a medium hardness steel (40–45 Rc) requires an 8-surface roughness requirement, and 0.002 in. metal removal is necessary, the time for each side is .002 × 12,000 = 24 min. This time is divided by the number of rings and the number of parts loaded into each ring.

If you wish to estimate direct-labor cost, use Item 13.6 of Section IV. The constant cost is always used. The second term is applied for each side abrasively ground. Multiply this number by the number of thousandths. For instance, if .003 in. is to be abrasively ground, multiply by 3. For two sides, multiply again by 2. The final number is divided by the number of parts abrasively ground simultaneously on all rings.

EXAMPLES

A. A flat cylindrical surface must have free abrasively ground sides in a vertical machine. A ring fixture with 12 openings is loaded. The part material is alloy steel and has been previously rough ground, but 0.003 in. per side stock removal is required. Find the lot time for 8,000 units. The machine has four rings. Ring loading is not available during lapping.

Table	Description	Time	
13.6-S	Setup	.5	hr
13.6-1	Load and unload	.12	min
13.6-1	Turn over for second side	.05	
13.6-2	Start and stop, .05 ÷ 12 (4)	.001	
13.6-2	Clean rings twice, 2 (.30 ÷ 12)	.05	
13.6-3	Free abrasive grind, 8 surface finish, 12,000 × .003 ÷ 4 (12)	.75	
13.6-3	Free abrasive grind, second side	.75	
	Unit estimate	1.721	min
	hr/100 units	2.869	
	Lot estimate	230	hr

B. A 1-in. OD ½ in. ID soft steel washer must have .003 in. per side removed for a 16 RMS finish on both sides. A free abrasive grinding machine with 4 rings is available. Loading is unavailable during grinding time. Machine control of pressure plates is an available machine feature. A 9-in. ring size machine is assumed. Find the unit estimate.

310

Table	Description		Time	
13.6-S	Setup		.5	hr
13.6-1	Load and unload small part		.03	min
13.6-1	Turn over for second side		.01	
13.6-2	Start and stop, .05 (2 ÷ 240)		0	
13.6-3	Lap first side: 5000 (.003 ÷ 240)		.063	
13.6-3	Lap second side		.063	
13.6-2	Lower backup wheels, release		0	
	Unit estimate		.166	min

C. Re-estimate Estimate B using Item 13.6 of Section IV. Find $/100 unit cost. Two sides are free abrasively ground, and a total of 60 units are loaded in 9-in. rings.

Item	Description	Cost
13.6	Constant	$1.13
13.6	Lap, 2 sides, .003 in. each side (161 × 2) ÷ (3 × 60)	1.79
	$/100 units	$2.92

TABLE 13.6   FREE ABRASIVE GRINDING MACHINES

Setup .5 hr

Operation elements in estimating minutes

1. Handling

Load and unload small part	.03
Load and unload medium part	.07
Load and unload large part	.12
Turn over for other side,	
small	.01
medium	.03
large	.05
Turn over ring and all parts automatically	.75
Preload parts into spare retaining rings	0
Slide ring with parts onto table	.10
Remove retaining ring	.08
Sandwich-turn parts	.15

2. Machine operation

Start and stop	.05
Clean, place and remove weight per lapping ring	.38/no. pcs
Lower backup wheel, per ring	.03
Release pressure plate, per ring	.02
Clean ring, each occurrence	.30

3. Free abrasive grinding

Stock removal rates,[1] min/in.

Material	Surface Finish				
	4	6	8	16	25
Aluminum				1,500	600
Cast iron		12,000	7,500	5,000	3,300
Glass				600	400
Nickel		30,000			6,000
Sintered iron				6,000	1,875
Steel (soft)			10,000	5,000	3,000
Steel (medium)	20,000		12,000	7,500	5,000
Steel (hard)	30,000		15,000	7,500	

[1] Multiply by stock removal in thousandths thickness and divide by no. parts in ring.

4. Miscellaneous elements, per occurrence

Insert in envelope for protection	.09
Inspect thickness or finish	.14
Wipe small part	.03

13.7 Disk Grinding Machines

DESCRIPTION

Disk grinding consists of grinding a side of a workpiece on the flat side or face of an abrasive grinding disk. The grinding disk is mounted on a steel wheel which is attached to a motorized spindle assembly.

To remove stock or material from the parallel faces of a part, a double disk grinding machine is used. The machine has two power driven spindles, and each supports an abrasive disk. The spindles are mounted so that the abrasive disks are opposite each other, (see Figure 13.7A). Thus, as the work is carried between the opposed abrasive disks during the grinding operation, the disks can grind opposite and parallel sides or faces.

Flat surfaces offer possibilities for disk grinding, especially parallel flat surfaces that permit grinding the faces simultaneously.

The advantage in double disk grinding is with a part with two faces that are approximately equal in area. It is more economical to finish two surfaces or faces in one operation. This combines high production while generating a size tolerance, flat and parallel surfaces, and a required surface finish.

Figure 13.7B is a double-disk grinding machine. Machines can be equipped with a variety of fixtures to meet special needs or greater production. An oscillating arm fixture contains an opening where individual parts are loaded and unloaded. Rotary-type fixtures are for medium or small sized parts where high production and accuracy are required. A through-feed type fixture is also possible. Feeding methods range from manual to automatic. Parts feeder and conveyor unloading are also possible.

Some machines may have only single-sided disk grinding.

ESTIMATING DATA DISCUSSION

Setup conditions relate closely to production quantity. For long runs there is the necessity to clean the machine, perhaps at the beginning of each shift. For short runs where there are changes in fixtures, materials, and grinding requirements, other conditions are provided.

Element 1 deals with disk grinding. The data analysis averaged a variety of feeding conditions ranging from individual loading to automatic feeding. If the loading is completely automatic and a tender is unnecessary, then direct labor time is zero. These estimates then indicate the production rate.

The estimating "driver" is the outside area multiplied by the stock removal. Outside area is the maximum x-y part envelope. Stock removal is for both sides and per pass. If only one disk grinder wheel is available, the amount of stock removal is also less.

When the material is aluminum, we use the part area, stock removal, and width of the part. The lookup procedure for the table needs three pieces of information. The area of the part uses the major x-y dimensions as if the part is a rectangle. If the width is over 5 in., or if the width is over 3 in. and has a total indicator reading for flatness of $\pm.005$, use the column designated "W > 5 in." Otherwise use the column "W < 5 in." Table lookup rules may be used to facilitate speed. For example, if the area and total stock

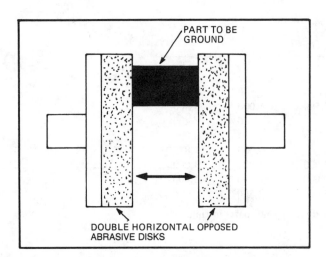

FIGURE 13.7A The operation of abrasive disks during the grinding process.

FIGURE 13.7B Double disk grinding machine (Bendix-Besly).

removal are not listed, the estimator may want to jump up to higher value. For ceramic parts, the stock removal is .005 in., and represents high-volume experiences.

$$\text{No. of passes} = 1 + \frac{\text{Total mat'l to be removed} - \text{Finish cut}}{\text{Mat'l removed per pass (see table below)}}$$

Size of Part	Rough Cut	Finish Cut	Material
Round 0–1 Dia	.010	.010	Bronze, aluminum, brass
Round 0–1 Dia	.005	.002–.003	Stainless steel, hardened steel
Round 1–1½ in. Dia	.003	.0015–.002	Stainless steel, hardened steel
	.010	.005	Bronze, aluminum, brass

Irregular shapes can be estimated by figuring on the longest dimension as compared to the diameters, as figured above.

By referring to Item 13.7 of Section IV the estimator can determine direct labor cost. Steel, cast iron, and aluminum are the three materials that can be determined. For each material, it is necessary to find the product of surface area and stock removal. The area is found from the maximum x-y dimensions and is sq in. The stock removal is per pass and measured in thousandths. Operation estimates are based upon the Chicago Productive Hour Cost.

EXAMPLES

A. A SAE 5130 Rockwell 45 pinion gear is to be disk ground using a double disk grinding machine. Stock removal is .009 in. and a flatness of .0005 in. and parallelism of .0005 in. is required. A finish of 20 RMS is necessary. The pinion gear has a 1.323-in. pitch diameter and a width of .75 in. Find the unit estimate. Assume a very long run.

Table	Description	Time
13.7-1	Area of face ≈ 1.368 sq in.; stock removal = .009 in.; 1.368 × .009 = .012	.038 min
	Unit estimate	.038 min

B. A double horizontal wet disk grinder with a hydraulically driven oscillating fixture is to be estimated for a gray cast iron valve body. A total of .093-in. stock removal is necessary. The area of the value body faces is irregular, but the maximum x-y dimensions are 2½ × 3⁵⁄₁₆ in. A quantity of 5500 units is planned.

Table	Description	Time
13.7-S	Setup	3.0 hr
13.7-1	Outside area = 8.3 sq in.; stock removal = .093 in.; 8.3 × .093 = .77	.25 min
	Unit estimate	.25 min
	Hr/100 units	.417
	Lot estimate	25.94 hr

C. An aluminum part having major dimensions in the x-y plane is 3.7 × 5.9 in. Stock removal is .015 in. Each blank is later sheared into two pieces. A quantity of 80 blanks is planned. Find the cycle time, unit estimate, hr/100 units, and lot time.

Table	Description	Time
13.7-S	Setup basic	.75 hr
13.7-1	Area = 21.83 sq in.	.51 min
	Cycle estimate	.51 min
	Unit estimate	.255 min
	Hr/100 units	.425
	Lot estimate	1.43 hr

D. A ceramic ring has an order of 200,000 units. The tolerances are ±.0005 in. and the OD is 1.5 in. Find the time for the lot.

Table	Description	Time	
13.7-S	Change wheels	4.0	hr
13.7-S	Adjust wheels	.2	
13.7-S	Dress wheels	3.4	
	Total setup	7.9	hr
13.7-1	Disc grind ceramic part	.015	min
	Unit estimate	.015	min
	Hr/10,000 units	2.500	
	Lot estimate	57.9	hr

E. Re-estimate Example A for direct-labor cost. While the operation is automatic loading and unloading, a machine tender does standby and incurs direct-labor cost. Find $/100 units.

Item	Description	Cost
13.7	Setup subtotal	$11.57
13.7	Cycle constant	$ .56
	Grind area = 1.368 sq in.; stock = .009 sq in.	
13.7	1.368 × .009 × 2.699	.032
	$/100 units	$ .592

F. Find the direct labor cost for Example B. Use Item 13.7 of Section IV for a rough estimate.

Item	Description	Cost
13.7	Constant	$ .56
13.7	Stock removal × area = .772; .772 × 4.02	3.103
	$/100 units	$3.663

TABLE 13.7   DISK GRINDING MACHINES

Setup

Dress wheel and reset machine	.75 hr
Change abrasive wheels (each material change)	4.0 hr
Dress wheel (every 3 hours of operation)	.2 hr
Remove, replace feed wheels	1.0–6.0 hr
Change bushings of feedwheel	2.0 hr

Operation elements in estimating minutes

1. Disk grind

   Steel:

Outside area × stock removal	.001	.003	.005	.01	.02	.03
Min	.035	.036	.036	.037	.038	.040

Outside area × stock removal	.04	.05	.06	.07	.08	.09
Min	.042	.043	.045	.047	.048	.050

Outside area × Stock removal	.1	.2	.3	.4	.5	Add'l .1
Min	.052	.069	.085	.10	.12	.016

Cast iron:
>   Piston rings, 2–6-in. *Dia,* .0057-in. max
>   Stock removal   .0035 ea

Outside area × stock removal	.5	1.0	2.0	3.0	5.0	10
Min	.12	.25	.50	.75	1.25	2.50

Aluminum:

	Stock Removal, in.									
	.006		.012		.015		.018		.024	
Area	W < 5	W > 5	W < 5	W > 5	W < 5	W > 5	W < 5	W > 5	W < 5	W > 5
3	.09		.09		.20		.20		.21	
9	.10		.10		.22		.23		.24	
15	.13	.27	.14	.28	.27	.41	.28	.42	.31	.45
21	.19	.34	.20	.35	.34	.49	.36	.51	.39	.54
27	.19	.34	.21	.36	.36	.51	.39	.54	.43	.58
33	.19	.34	.21	.36	.38	.53	.43	.56	.46	.61
39	.20	.35	.22	.37	.40	.55	.44	.59	.49	.64
47	.20	.35	.23	.38	.42	.57	.47	.62	.54	.69
57		.37		.40		.62		.67		.75
69		.38		.43		.68		.73		.84
84		.40		.45		.73		.79		.92
100		.42		.48		.79		.86		1.01
120		.44		.52		.86		.95		1.12

Ceramic:

Dia	.5	.8	1	1.1	1.3	1.5	1.8
Min	.007	.008	.009	.010	.011	.015	.024

2. Wheel dressing
>   Automatic from microprocessor control   0
>   Manual, prorated   .002/unit

13.8 Vertical Internal Grinding Machines

DESCRIPTION

The grinding of internal bores, cams, and other contoured surfaces can be done on a vertical internal grinding machine. Parts are loaded on a horizontal rotating table and chucking is possible. Some vertical grinding wheel spindles can rotate up to 60,000 rpm while the worktable revolves at speeds between 30 and 100 rpm. To permit grinding of contoured surfaces, the worktable is attached to a master cam, which is an enlarged concentric version of the ID to be ground. This master cam rotates against two fixed rolls spaced 90° apart on the cam housing.

An axial traverse motion brings the grinding wheel into the work area, which also allows for vertical traverse grinding. A crossfeed motion brings the grinding wheel into contact with the workpiece and then continues to feed into the piece until the necessary stock has been removed. Maximum stock removal is about .035 in. on the diameter. Feed rates differ between rough and finish grinding.

Due to the size of the machine considered, the outside diameter of the workpiece does not exceed 6 in. Part height is also limited.

ESTIMATING DATA DISCUSSION

The general setup includes adjustments for feed rates, wheel approach, diamond wheel dressing, sparkout, and test cycles. The time needed to change a machine cam is also included under setup. This element is not required if the same cam ID is required in subsequent part lots. Setup values are listed in hours.

The operation elements are composed of part handling, machine start and stop, rough grinding with sparkout, wheel dressing, finish grinding with sparkout, and grinding wheel changes. Part handling consists of loading and unloading the machine, with variations allowed if the machine work fixture is removed for loading. Since part size is limited to objects with 6-in. *Dia* or less, this factor is considered constant in the estimating table. Machine start and stop includes the time to push the start button, as well as the automatic machine operations of opening and closing the door, and starting and stopping the coolant flow.

The grinding cycles are more complicated due to the number of variables. These include workspeed variations, part diameter, part length, spindle diameter and length, grinding wheel and part material, revolutions for sparkout, and the amount of stock removed. For these estimations, it is assumed that 90% of the stock is removed during rough grinding. The rough sparkout varies with the required finish. For parts with tight tolerances, it is not uncommon to have the sparkout last for over a half minute. One minute is the maximum. After the wheel is dressed the final 10% of stock is removed in the finish grind cycle, with application of the finish sparkout as above. For ideal grinding, the grinding wheel diameter should roughly equal .75 *Dia,* where *Dia* = equivalent bore diameter of the cam. Also, for these estimates, the infeed is .0003 in. for rough grinding and .0001 in. for finish grinding.

In internal grinding there are two possibilities. If the spindle is shorter than the length of the part, a traverse grinding operation is necessary. For rough grinding, the axial wheel advances 75% of the grinding wheel width per workpiece revolution. One quarter of the nominal width is also allowed for overlap. For finish grinding, the axial wheel advances only 25%. The values given in the table must be multiplied by the quantity

$$\frac{L \times Dia}{W}$$

where L = length of part, in.;
Dia = equivalent bore diameter (adjusted from cam ID); and
W = width of grinding wheel, in.

This computed value will be the estimated time in minutes. If the grinding wheel width is wider than the part length, a plunge grinding operation is necessary. These values can be taken from the element table for plunge grinding. To find work surface speed from rpm, use the following equation:

$$V = \pi DR / 12$$

Due to grinding wheel wear, the wheel will have to be changed or dressed periodically. Since available grinding wheel abrasives differ as widely as material hardnesses, this value is prorated for a quantity, specifically 40 parts per grinding wheel. Finally, operator inspection of parts is done internal to the grinding element, therefore no additional time is allotted for this activity.

Internal grinding costs can be estimated directly by a rule of thumb estimating equation located in Section IV. The cost depends on the entry variables of stock removal, part height, grinding wheel width, and worktable revolutions. The cycle constant is always used. Traverse grinding cost (the second term in the equation) is calculated by multiplying the stock removed (in.) by the part height (in.), and divided by wheel width and table rpm. Plunge grinding cost is calculated by dividing the stock removed by the table rpm. The final run-cost is expressed in $/100 units.

EXAMPLES

A. A lot of 200 pump liners is to be ground. The equivalent cam diameter is .80 in., and the height is 1.20 in. The part is loaded directly into the machine so the fixture need not be removed. The grinding wheel is 2-in. long and revolves at 60,000 rpm. The worktable rotates at 40 rpm. The total stock to be removed is .015 in. on the radius. Find unit and lot estimates.

Table	Description	Time
13.8-S	General setup	1.3 hr
13.8-1	Load and unload	.46 min
13.8-2	Start and stop	.13
13.8-4	Rough grind (plunge) .014 in. stock	1.17
13.8-5	Rough sparkout	.50
13.8-6	Dress wheel	.06
13.8-4	Finish grind (plunge) .001 in. stock	.25

Table	Description	Time
13.8-5	Finish sparkout	.58
13.8-8	Change grinding wheel	.15
	Unit estimate	3.30 min
	Lot estimate	12.30 hr
	Hr / 100 units	5.50

B. A lot of 30 parts with internal cam ID's is to be ground. The equivalent cam diameter is 3 in., and the height of the part is also 3 in. Work rotates at 30 rpm and the spindle width is 2 in. A total of .013 in. of stock is to be removed. Find unit and lot estimates.

Table	Description	Time
13.8-S	Setup	1.3 hr
13.8-1	Load and unload fixture	1.66 min
13.8-2	Start and stop	.13
13.8-3	Rough grind (traverse) .012 in. stock .47 × 3 × 3/2	2.11
13.8-5	Rough sparkout	.50
13.8-6	Dress wheel	.06
13.8-3	Finish grind (traverse) .0010 in. stock .35 × 3 × 3/2	1.57
13.8-5	Finish sparkout	.58
	Unit estimate	6.61 min
	Lot estimate	4.60 hr
	Hr / 100 units	11.01

C. An internal cam ID is to be ground with an equivalent diameter of .9 in., and height of 3.25 in. The master cam must be changed since this cam differs in shape from that of the last lot run. Spindle width is 2 in., and the worktable rotates at 45 rpm. Stock removal is .015 in. Lot size is 80. Find unit and lot estimates for the total grinding process.

Table	Description	Time
13.8-S1	Setup, 2 times	2.6 hr
13.8-S2	Master cam change, 2 times	3.8 hr
13.8-1	Load and unload, 2 times	.92 min
13.8-2	Start/stop, 2 times	.26
13.8-3	Rough grind (traverse) .014 in. stock 1.63 × 9 × 3.25/2	2.38
13.8-3	Rough grind (traverse) .010 in. stock 1.16 × .9 × 3.25/2	1.70
13.8-5	Rough sparkout, 2 times	1.00
13.8-6	Dress wheel, 2 times	.12
13.8-3	Finish grind (traverse) .001 in. stock 1.05 × .9 × 3.25/2	1.54
13.8-3	Finish grind (traverse) .001 in. stock 1.05 × .9 × 3.25/2	1.54
13.8-8	Change grinding wheel	.15
	Unit estimate	9.61 min
	Hr / 100 units	16.35
	Lot time for 80 units	16.01 hr

D. Re-estimate Example A as given above. Use Item 13.8 of Section IV. Find the lot cost.

Table	Description	Cost
13.8	Setup subtotal	$ 20.04
13.8	Cycle constant	41.82
13.8	Plunge grind, .015-in. removal, 40 rpm 80,000 × .015/40	30.00
	$/100 units	$ 71.82
	Lot total for 20 units	$163.68

TABLE 13.8   VERTICAL INTERNAL GRINDING MACHINES

Setup

Basic	1.3 hr
Master cam change	1.9 hr

Operation elements in estimating minutes

1. Handle part

Removable fixture	1.66
Machine fixture	.46

2. Start and stop   .13

3. Traverse grinding[1]

Total stock removed	Work surface velocity (fpm)					
	10	20	30	40	50	100
Rough						
.005	.59	.29	.19	.15	.12	.07
.010	1.16	.59	.39	.29	.23	.12
.012	1.40	.69	.47	.35	.28	.13
.014	1.63	.81	.55	.41	.32	.16
.016	1.87	.93	.61	.47	.39	.19
.018	2.09	1.04	.69	.52	.41	.21
.020	2.32	1.16	.77	.57	.47	.23
Finish						
.0010	1.05	.52	.35	.26	.21	.10
.0012	1.26	.63	.42	.31	.25	.13
.0015	1.57	.78	.52	.39	.31	.16
.0020	2.09	1.05	.70	.52	.42	.21

[1] Multiply by $L(Dia)/W$, L = length of part, Dia = bore diameter, W = wheel width.

4. Plunge grinding

Total stock removed	Work table rpm					
	30	40	50	60	70	100
Rough						
.005	.55	.42	.33	.28	.24	.17
.010	1.11	.83	.67	.55	.48	.33
.012	1.33	1.00	.80	.67	.57	.40
.014	1.55	1.17	.93	.78	.67	.47
.016	1.78	1.33	1.07	.89	.76	.53
.018	2.00	1.50	1.20	1.00	.80	.60
Finish						
.0010	.33	.25	.20	.17	.14	.10
.0012	.40	.30	.24	.20	.17	.12
.0015	.50	.37	.30	.25	.21	.15
.0020	.67	.50	.40	.33	.28	.20

5. Sparkout
       Rough grind   .50
       Finish grind   .58

6. Diamond dress wheel   .06

7. Inspection   0

8. Grinding wheel change = 6 min/40 parts   .15

GEAR CUTTING

14.1 Gear Shaper Machines

DESCRIPTION

The cutter gear generating process for cutting involute gears uses the principle that any two involute gears of the same pitch will mesh together. If one gear behaves as a cutter and is given a reciprocating motion, as in a gear shaper machine, it will be capable of generating conjugate tooth forms in a gear blank. A gear shaper cutter that provides this action is shown, mounted in a gear shaper, in Figure 14.1. In operation, the cutter and the blank rotate at the same pitch line velocity. In addition, a reciprocating motion is given to the cutter. A rotary feed mechanism is arranged to have the cutter automatically feed to the desired depth while both cutter and work are rotating. Internal and external teeth can be shaped.

Figure 14.1 is a machine that cuts spur, helical or herringbone gears, internal or external, and other noninvolute shapes up to a 40-in. pitch diameter and a 6-in. face width. Now consider estimating data for the general class of gear shaper machines.

ESTIMATING DATA DISCUSSION

Element 1, handling, includes both loading and unloading to the shaper table. Entry variable is weight. Table clamps, fixture, or chuck conditions are provided. Chip removal, part cleaning, and clamping is included in the handling element.

Element 2 includes machine start, position, and engage. The constant time of .25 min is always provided. In addition to the constant time, machine time

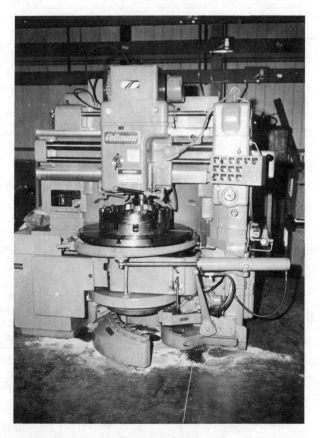

FIGURE 14.1 A gear shaper machine capable of shaping internal and external gears up to 36 pitch diameter (PD). (Fellows Corporation)

includes infeed time and rotary feed time for rough and finish cut.

The materials, their Brinell hardness number and cutting velocity, follow:

Material	Bhn	fpm
Low-carbon steel, free machining	170	93
Low-carbon steel	150	81
Medium-carbon steel	215	47
Stainless steels	180	55
Steel castings	230	43
Cast iron	soft	67
Cast iron	medium	51
Brass		100

The steps for estimating machining time involve finding the strokes per minute, infeed time, and rotary feed time. The equation for spm is

$$N = \frac{12 \times \text{fpm}}{2 \times \text{stroke length}}$$

Stroke length is related to face width plus approach and overtravel. For a helix gear, multiply N by the factor. Infeed time has the equation $\frac{D + .030}{.002 \times N}$, where D is tooth depth and .002 in./stroke is the feed rate. Rotary feed time is $\frac{PD \times \pi}{.020 \times N}$, where PD is the pitch diameter.

The rotary feed per stroke will vary with material, number of cuts, and finish required. The value .020 is adopted. Other values may be chosen by the estimator and by ratio; the tabular value can be adjusted. For instance, if .030 is preferred, the table value is multiplied by ⅔. The number of cuts may be 1, 2, or 3. This depends upon diameter pitch (PD) and its relationship to rotary feed per stroke. But .020 in. per stroke is an average value and can be used if other information is unavailable.

Strokes Per Minute (spm) For Straight Spur Gears

Material				Face width				
	½	1	1½	2	2½	3	3½	4
Low-carbon steel, free-machining	992	510	336	251	203	168	144	127
Steel, low-carbon	864	444	293	219	177	147	125	110
Steel, medium	501	258	170	127	103	85	73	64
Stainless steels	586	302	199	149	120	100	85	75
Steel casting	458	236	155	116	94	78	67	59
Cast iron, Soft	714	367	242	181	146	121	104	91
Medium	544	280	184	138	111	92	79	69
Brass	1066	548	361	270	218	181	155	136
Helix angle, degrees				15	30	45	60	
Factor				.97	.87	.71	.50	

Multiply spm for helical gears by factor.

Diametral pitch	No. cuts	Roughing	Semifinishing	Finishing
24–64	1	.014	.012	.004
	2	.012/.020	.012/.020	.006
	3		.012/.020/.020	.008
10–24	1	.030	.020	
	2	.015/.030	.030/.045	.025/.040
	3		.030/.030/.045	.030/.030
7–10	1	.020		
	2		.030/.040	.020/.035
	3		.030/.030/.040	.025/.025/.035
4–7	1	.015		
	2		.020/.030	.020/.025
	3		.020/.020/.030	.020/.020/.025

More than one machine may be tended by the operator, so the unit time is divided by the number of machines to approximate the direct-labor effort.

After finding the strokes per minute (spm) Element 3 is used and the nearest entry values are adopted.

Item 14.1 of Section IV can be used as an alternate method for the estimating of direct-labor cost. A summarization of the elemental approach as described here, Table 14.1, should be understood before applying Item 14.1. The cost is affected by the whole depth, D, of the gear. An approach of .030 is added to D. Stroke length, L, is the face width of gears and ⅛ in. is added for approach and overtravel. Finally the pitch diameter of the work, PD, must be available from the drawings. The PD is used for rotary feed time, and one or more passes may be necessary. The PD appears in the fourth term. If the gear blank is too heavy for manual loading, a jib cost is added, in which case the cost as related to weight is overlooked. The constant cost is always given. The sum of the several costs is $ / 100 units. Cost due to tool wear and its consequent delays for tool replacement are covered by Item 11.4.

EXAMPLES

A. A steel forging, 7 pitch, 80 teeth, .257-in. depth of tooth, and a length of face of 3 ⅝ in. is to be estimated with gear shaping. Weight is 32 lb. Two cuts are anticipated. Find the lot time for 272 units. Two machines are tended by one operator.

Table	Description	Time	
14.1-S	Setup for spur gear	.6	hr
14.1-S	Fixture	.3	hr
14.1-1	Handle	1.11	min
14.1-2	Machine time constant	.25	
	Strokes per minute, 59	—	
14.1-3	Using $N = 61$ and $DP = 8$, infeed	2.48	
14.1-4	Rough rotary feed, $N = 61, DP = 8$	20.8	
22.1-3	Check gear over pins	.20	
14.1-4	Finish rotary feed, $N = 61, DP = 8, 20.8 \times .020/.030$	13.85	
22.1-3	Check gear over pins	.20	
11.4-2	Tool wear and replacement for 35 min	2.34	
	Floor-to-floor time	41.23	min
	Unit estimate	20.62	min
	Lot estimate	95.39	hr

B. Find the base cost of Example A above using Item 14.1 of Section IV. Weight is 32 lb and overtravel is .125 in. Total stroke distance = 3.75 in.

Item	Description	Cost
14.1	Setup subtotal	$ 12.40
14.1	Cycle constant	$ 18.90
14.1	Weight factor, $32 \times .649$	20.77
14.1	Infeed time, $3.48 (.257 + .03) \times (3.625 + .125)$	3.75
14.1	Rotary time, $7 \times 3.75 \times 10.9$	286.13
14.1	Rotary time, finish	286.13
22.1	Check gear, 2 times $\times$ 9.34, for .0005 in.	18.68
11.4	Tool wear for 30 minutes, 30×2.24, HSS	67.20
	$ / 100 units subtotal	$701.56
	Direct labor 2 machines reduction	$350.78
	Lot cost, $12.48 + 272/100 \times 350.78$	$966.60

TABLE 14.1 GEAR SHAPER MACHINES

Setup   **.6 hr**

  Helical gears   1.0

      For .001 total composite error or less, add   .2

      For fixture, add   .3

Operation elements in estimating minutes

1. Handling

Manual load and unload blank

Weight	1	5	25	50
To table clamps	.68	1.14	1.97	3.14
To fixture	.40	1.03	.78	1.11
To chuck	.52	1.06	.98	2.54

Jib load   4.00

Turnover   65% of basic handling

2. Start, position, engage   .25

3. Infeed shape, min

	Diametral pitch and whole depth									
spm	2 1.08	3 .72	4 .54	8 .27	12 .18	18 .12	24 .09	30 .07	36 .06	40 .05
50	11.09	7.49	5.69	3.00	2.10	1.50	1.20	1.02	.90	.84
55	10.08	6.81	5.18	2.72	1.91	1.36	1.09	.93	.82	.76
61	9.16	6.19	4.70	2.48	1.73	1.24	.99	.84	.74	.69
67	8.33	5.63	4.28	2.25	1.58	1.13	.90	.77	.68	.63
73	7.57	5.12	3.89	2.05	1.43	1.02	.82	.70	.61	.57
81	6.88	4.65	3.53	1.86	1.30	.93	.74	.63	.56	.52
89	6.26	4.23	3.21	1.69	1.18	.85	.68	.58	.51	.47
97	5.69	3.84	2.92	1.54	1.08	.77	.62	.52	.46	.43
107	5.17	3.49	2.66	1.40	.98	.70	.56	.48	.42	.39
118	4.70	3.18	2.41	1.27	.89	.64	.51	.43	.38	.36
130	4.27	2.89	2.19	1.16	.81	.58	.46	.39	.35	.32
143	3.89	2.63	2.00	1.05	.74	.53	.42	.36	.32	.29
157	3.53	2.39	1.81	.95	.67	.48	.38	.32	.29	.27
173	3.21	2.17	1.65	.87	.61	.43	.35	.30	.26	.24
190	2.92	1.97	1.50	.79	.55	.39	.32	.27	.24	.22
209	2.65	1.79	1.36	.72	.50	.36	.29	.24	.22	.20
230	2.41	1.63	1.24	.65	.46	.33	.26	.22	.20	.18
253	2.19	1.48	1.13	.59	.41	.30	.24	.20	.18	.17
278	1.99	1.35	1.02	.54	.38	.27	.22	.18	.16	
306	1.81	1.22	.93	.499	.34	.24	.20	.17		
336	1.65	1.11	.85	.45	.31	.22	.18	.15		
370	1.50	1.01	.77	.40	.28	.20	.16	.14		
407	1.36	.92	.70	.37	.26	.18	.15	.13		
448	1.24	.84	.64	.33	.23	.17	.13	.11		
492	1.13	.76	.58	.30	.21	.15	.12			
542	1.02	.69	.53	.28	.19	.14	.11			
596	.93	.63	.48	.25	.18	.13	.10			

324

4. Rotary feed shape, min

Pitch diameter and circumference

spm	1 3.14	1½ 4.7	2 6.3	2½ 7.9	3 9.4	3½ 11.0	4 12.6	5 15.7	8 25.1	10 31.4	15 47.1
50	3.14	4.71	6.28	7.85	9.4	11.0	12.6	15.7	25.1	31.4	47.1
55	2.86	4.28	5.71	7.14	8.6	10.0	11.4	14.3	22.8	28.6	42.8
61	2.60	3.89	5.19	6.49	7.8	9.1	10.4	13.0	20.8	26.0	38.9
67	2.36	3.54	4.72	5.90	7.1	8.3	9.4	11.8	18.9	23.6	35.4
73	2.15	3.22	4.29	5.36	6.4	7.5	8.6	10.7	17.2	21.5	32.2
81	1.96	2.93	3.90	4.88	5.9	6.8	7.8	9.8	15.6	19.5	29.3
89	1.77	2.66	3.55	4.43	5.3	6.2	7.1	8.9	14.2	17.7	26.6
97	1.61	2.42	3.22	4.03	4.8	5.6	6.4	8.1	12.9	16.1	24.2
107	1.47	2.20	2.93	3.66	4.4	5.1	5.9	7.3	11.7	14.7	22.0
118	1.33	2.00	2.66	3.33	4.0	4.7	5.3	6.7	10.7	13.3	20.0
130	1.21	1.82	2.42	3.03	3.6	4.2	4.8	6.1	9.7	12.1	18.2
143	1.10	1.65	2.20	2.75	3.3	3.9	4.4	5.5	8.8	11.0	16.5
157	1.00	1.50	2.00	2.50	3.0	3.5	4.0	5.0	8.0	10.0	15.0
173	.91	1.37	1.82	2.28	2.7	3.2	3.6	4.6	7.3	9.1	13.7
190	.83	1.24	1.65	2.07	2.5	2.9	3.3	4.1	6.6	8.3	12.4
209	.75	1.13	1.50	1.88	2.3	2.6	3.0	3.8	6.0	7.5	11.3
230	.68	1.03	1.37	1.71	2.1	2.4	2.7	3.4	5.5	6.8	10.3
253	.62	.93	1.24	1.55	1.9	2.2	2.5	3.1	5.0	6.2	9.3
278	.57	.85	1.13	1.41	1.7	2.0	2.3	2.8	4.5	5.7	8.5
306	.51	.77	1.03	1.28	1.5	1.8	2.1	2.6	4.1	5.1	7.7
336	.47	.70	.93	1.17	1.4	1.6	1.9	2.3	3.7	4.7	7.0
370	.42	.64	.85	1.06	1.3	1.5	1.7	2.1	3.4	4.2	6.4
407	.39	.58	.77	.96	1.2	1.4	1.5	1.9	3.1	3.9	5.8
448	.35	.53	.70	.88	1.1	1.2	1.4	1.8	2.8	3.5	5.3
492	.32	.48	.64	.80	1.0	1.1	1.3	1.6	2.6	3.2	4.8
542	.29	.43	.58	.72	.9	1.0	1.2	1.4	2.3	2.9	4.3
596	.26	.40	.53	.66	.8	.9	1.1	1.3	2.1	2.6	4.0

5. Tool wear and replacement   See Table 11.4

6. Inspection   See Table 22.1
   Indicate surface and true up gear blank   1.20

14.2 Hobbing Machines

DESCRIPTION

Hobbing is defined as a generating process consisting of a rotating and advancing fluted steel worm cutter which passes a revolving blank. In this process all motions are rotary, with no reciprocating or indexing movements. In the actual process of cutting, the gear and the hob rotate together as in mesh.

Figure 14.2 is a hobbing machine with radial feed, axial feed, automatic double cut, and automatic double cut with crown. Also included are variable speeds and feeds, differential, and automatic hob shift.

ESTIMATING DATA DISCUSSION

Element 1 deals with handling elements. The estimator will know whether one part or several are simultaneously hobbed. If a gear blank is arbor

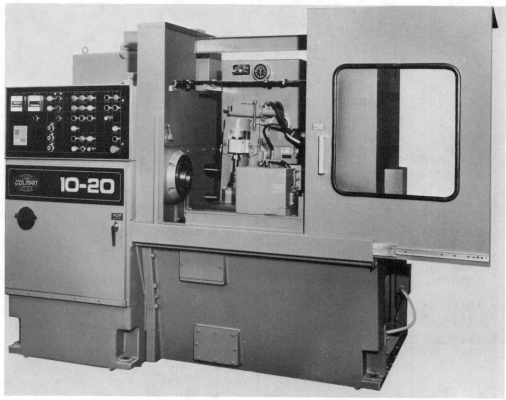

FIGURE 14.2 Hobbing machine. (Barber Colman)

loaded, tightening and loosening of nuts is also appropriate.

The hob to use for spur gears depends upon the pitch of the teeth and number of teeth; but for helical gear, the hob is selected with consideration for tooth profile of lead angle, normal diametrical pitch, and cutter diameter. The entry variable is diametral pitch and hob diameter, and the formula for approach and overrun is

$$\{WD\,(HD - WD)\}^{1/2} + \tfrac{1}{8}, \text{ where } WD$$
$$= \text{whole depth of gear tooth}$$

HD = hob diameter, and the $\tfrac{1}{8}$ in. accounts for safety stock. This distance can be used for spur gears or splines or where hob swivel is less than 5°. This table is shown on the next page, and it is used to adjust the length of hob machining.

The hob has a high angle setting for gears having a helix angle. The entry factors are hob diameter, work diameter, swivel angle of the hob, and diametral pitch. The formula depends upon these four variables. This is shown on the following page.

Overrun distance for gears having a helix angle is also shown. The top value is for the $14\tfrac{1}{2}°$ involute system. (This is shown on the following page.)

For Element 3, the entry variables are material, hob diameter, and swivel. The factor is multiplied by the number of teeth and length of cut which includes the distance between the face of the gear and the approach. A swivel angle is used for helical gears. The "0" is selected for straight spur gears. If a multiple thread hob is used, divide by the number of threads. Normally the thread number is one. The hob diameters are roughly matched to diametral pitch. For hob diameters not shown, interpolate values. If two arbors for one machine are available, the loading of arbors is done during machine time. Some companies may have two or more machines tended by a single operator, in which case the estimated unit time is divided by the number of machines tended by the operator. Spur gears and spline hobbing require an approach and overrun distance to be added to the drawing length of the part.

Hobbing may also be estimated in dollars using Item 14.2 of Section IV. This approach, while faster, may not be as accurate for individual gears when compared to the elemental estimates method; but the originating information for both methods is similar. Entry variables depend upon knowledge of gear design or number of gear teeth, N, face width, L, and approximate hob diameter. An approximate to the approach distance depends upon hob diameter. For helix gears, double the approach. The face width is multiplied by the number of gear blanks mounted on the arbor. Tool wear and hob replacement are found using Item 11.4.

326

Approach and overrun for spur gear and spline hobbing, in.

Diametral pitch	1⅞	2½	3	3½	4	4½	5	6	7
								Hob Dia	
1									3.36
1¼									3.14
1½									2.95
1¾								2.55	2.69
2								2.43	2.65
2¼								2.32	2.53
2½							2.01	2.23	2.43
2¾							1.94	2.15	2.33
3					1.66	1.77	1.88	2.07	2.25
4			1.28	1.39	1.49	1.59	1.68	1.84	1.99
5			1.18	1.28	1.37	1.45	1.53	1.67	1.81
6			1.10	1.19	1.27	1.34	1.42	1.55	1.67
7			1.04	1.12	1.19	1.26	1.33	1.45	1.56
8			.98	1.06	1.13	1.19	1.26	1.37	1.47
9			.94	1.01	1.07	1.14	1.19	1.30	1.40
10			.90	.97	1.03	1.09	1.14	1.24	1.34
12			.87	.93	.99	1.04	1.10	1.19	1.28
14			.84	.90	.95	1.01	1.06	1.15	1.23
16	.64	.73	.79	.84	.89	.94	.99	1.07	1.15
18	.61	.69	.74	.80	.84	.89	.93	1.01	1.08
20	.58	.66	.71	.76	.81	.85	.89	.97	1.03
24	.56	.63	.68	.73	.77	.81	.85	.92	.99
28	.53	.59	.64	.68	.72	.76	.79	.85	.91
32	.50	.56							
36	.47	.53							
40	.44	.49							

Finishing only   .13

Approach where hob is swiveled, in.

	Hob Dia	2½						3½					
	Work Dia	2			3			3			4½			6		
	Swivel angle	15°	30°	45°	15°	30°	45°	15°	30°	45°	15°	30°	45°	15°	30°	45°
Diametral pitch	4	1.5	1.7	2.1	1.5	1.7	2.2	1.8	2.0	2.5	1.8	2.1	2.7	1.5	1.9	2.7
	6	1.5	1.6	1.9	1.5	1.7	2.0	1.8	2.0	2.3	1.8	2.0	2.5	1.5	1.8	2.4
	10	1.5	1.6	1.8	1.5	1.6	1.9	1.8	1.9	2.2	1.8	2.0	2.2	1.6	1.7	2.1
	14	1.5	1.6	1.7	1.6	1.6	1.8	1.8	1.9	2.1	1.9	1.9	2.1	1.6	1.7	2.0
	18	1.6	1.6	1.7	1.6	1.6	1.7	1.9	1.9	2.0	1.9	1.9	2.1	1.6	1.7	1.9
	24	1.6	1.6	1.7	1.6	1.6	1.7	1.9	1.9	2.0	1.9	1.9	2.0	1.6	1.6	1.8

Overrun where hob is swiveled, in.

Swivel angle	Helix angle 15°			Helix angle 30°			Helix angle 45°		
	15°	30°	45°	15°	30°	45°	15°	30°	45°
4	.3	.6	1.1	1.2	.5	.9	.2	.4	.8
	.2	.4	.7	.8	.4	.7	.1	.3	.5
6	.2	.4	.7	1.1	.3	.6	.1	.3	.5
	.1	.3	.5	.8	.2	.4	.1	.2	.3
10	.1	.3	.4	1.0	.2	.4	.1	.2	.3
	.1	.2	.3	.7	.2	.3	.1	.1	.2
14	.1	.2	.3	1.0	.2	.3	.1	.1	.2
	.1	.1	.2	.7	.1	.2		.1	.2
18	.1	.1	.2	1.0	.1	.2		.1	.2
		.1	.2	.7	.1	.1		.1	.1
24	.1	.1	.2	1.0	.1	.2		.1	.1
	.1	.1	.1	.7	.1			.1	.1

Left axis label: *Diametral pitch*

(Top value = 14½° involute.)
(Lower value = 20° involute system.)

EXAMPLES

A. Nine gear blanks are loaded on an arbor. The gears are 45-tooth, 16-pitch mild steel spur gear having a face width of ½ in. A 16-pitch gear will use a 2½ in. hob. Use 1 arbor. Find unit time.

Table	Description	Time
14.2-S	Setup	.54 hr
14.2-1	Load and unload 9 gears	.99 min
14.2-1	Set nut and tighten, release	.29
14.2-2	Advance carriage	.14
14.2-2	Lower or raise work spindle	.14
14.2-2	Start machine	.05
14.2-3	Machine 9 gears. Approach is .73 in. Length of cut is .73 + 9 × .5 = 5.2. Machine time is 5.2 × 45 × .07	16.38
14.2-2	Clear carriage	.15
14.2-2	Check work	0
11.4-2	Tool wear allowance, 1.31 min/unit, large tool	.31
	Total estimate	18.45 min
	Unit estimate	2.05 min

B. A spur gear made of medium-carbon alloy steel and 3 gears are loaded on an arbor for cutting. The gear is 24 *DP*, 51 teeth, 20° full depth involute and a face width of 0.438 in. Find the lot time for 18 units. A 3-in. hob is chosen.

Table	Description	Time
14.2-S	Setup	.54 hr
14.2-1	Pick up part and install 3 × .11	.33 min
14.2-1	Set nut, tighten, loosen	.29
14.2-2	Advance steady rest and tighten	.23
14.2-2	Start machine	.05
14.2-2	Advance carriage	.14
14.2-2	Engage feed	.02
14.2-3	Machine time. Approach, .68 in., 3 × .438 = 1.31, machine distance = 1.99. Machine time = 1.99 × 51 × .13	13.19
	Total time	14.22 min
	Unit estimate	4.74 min
	Lot estimate	1.92 hr

C. Find the base-cost for Example A above using Items 14.2 and 11.4 of Section IV.

Item	Description	Cost
14.2	Setup subtotal	$ 8.74
14.2	Constant cost	$ 9.98
14.2	Hobbing, $1.75 \times 45 \times (5.2 + .07 + 3.12 \times 2.5)$	1,029.26
11.4	Tool allowance, 15 min. estimated for blanks, 15×2.24	33.60
	$ / 900 units	$1,072.84
	$ / 100 units	$ 119.20
	Unit cost	$ 1.19

TABLE 14.2   HOBBING MACHINES

Setup

Spur gears, splines	.54 hr
Helical gears	1.04
For .001 total composite error or less, add	.24

Operation elements in estimating minutes

1. Handling

Chuckgear blanks	
Small, .09; large,	.15
Chuck shaft and lay aside	.37
Load and unload gear on arbor	.11
Set nut on work arbor and tighten, release	.29
Mark gears	.30
Load spline shaft or pinion	.60

2. Machine operation

Start machine	.05
Advance carriage manually	.14
Engage feed	.02
Lower or raise work spindle	.14
Clear carriage	.15
Advance steady rest and tighten in position	.23
Indicate part for alignment	.40

3. Hobbing. min = no. teeth $\times L \times$ table value

	Hob Dia											
	1⅞				2½				3			
	Swivel angle											
Material	0°	30°	45°	60°	0°	30°	45°	60°	0°	30°	45°	60°
Steel, free-machining	.04	.05	.06	.08	.07	.08	.10	.14	.07	.08	.10	.14
Steel, low-carbon	.05	.06	.07	.10	.07	.08	.10	.14	.08	.09	.11	.16
Steel, medium-carbon	.08	.09	.12	.16	.11	.13	.15	.22	.13	.16	.19	.27
Stainless, 300 series	.07	.08	.10	.14	.09	.11	.13	.19	.11	.13	.16	.23
Stainless, 400 series	.06	.07	.08	.12	.08	.09	.11	.16	.09	.10	.13	.18
Carbon steel castings	.12	.14	.17	.24	.16	.19	.23	.32	.25	.28	.35	.49
Gray iron	.20	.23	.28	.40	.26	.31	.37	.53	.12	.13	.16	.23
Aluminum	.05	.06	.07	.10	.06	.07	.09	.13	.03	.03	.04	.06
Brass	.06	.07	.08	.12	.08	.09	.11	.16	.03	.04	.05	.06

	Hob Dia											
	4				5				6			
Material	Swivel angle											
	0°	30°	45°	60°	0°	30°	45°	60°	0°	30°	45°	60°
Steel, free-machining	.12	.13	.16	.23	.15	.17	.21	.29	.23	.27	.33	.47
Steel, low-carbon	.12	.14	.17	.23	.15	.17	.21	.29	.23	.27	.33	.47
Steel, medium-carbon	.19	.22	.27	.39	.24	.28	.34	.48	.39	.45	.55	.78
Stainless, 300 series	.19	.21	.26	.37	.23	.27	.33	.46	.37	.43	.53	.74
Stainless, 400 series	.14	.16	.20	.28	.18	.20	.25	.35	.28	.33	.40	.57
Carbon steel castings	.37	.43	.52	.74	.46	.53	.65	.92	.74	.85	1.04	1.48
Gray iron	.15	.17	.21	.30	.19	.22	.27	.38	.30	.35	.43	.60
Aluminum	.03	.04	.05	.07	.04	.05	.06	.08	.07	.08	.09	.13
Brass	.04	.04	.05	.08	.05	.06	.07	.10	.08	.09	.11	.16

THREAD CUTTING and FORM ROLLING

15.1 Thread Cutting and Form Rolling Machines

DESCRIPTION

Rotating spindle with stationary work held by vise grips is the type of thread cutting described here. A universal threading machine can be furnished with one or more spindles. Self-opening die heads are assembled tools incorporating inserted cutting components called chasers, the cutting edges not being integral with the tool body. Figure 15.1 is an example of a two-spindle threading machine.

Threads can be rolled in any material sufficiently plastic to withstand the forces of cold working. Factors that influence a material's resistance to deformation are material hardness, internal friction, yield point, and work hardening. Rolling methods are infeed, automatic continuous, and forced-through feed. Roll burnishing can be done on form rolling machines. These machines can be equipped with an automatic parts feeder.

ESTIMATING DATA DISCUSSION

Small handheld parts are covered by these data. Handling as described for Element 1 visualizes a one-spindle machine. On two or more spindles, the handling may be done during a machining cycle.

Entry variables for Element 1 are material and threads per in. To obtain minutes, multiply the factor by the diameter $\times$ length of thread ($Dia \times L$). Surface velocities for the materials are:

Material	Cutting Velocity
Steel, mild	25–50
Steel, hard	10–35
Malleable iron	30–60
Brass	45–70
Aluminum	50–80

The lower values of the cutting velocity range are assigned to the larger thread pitches while the higher end of the range is appropriate to the finer threads per inch.

In form rolling, the manual operation includes labor loading and rolling, and one machine is assumed. For automatic feed, an operator will watch one or more machines. One unit time may be divided by the number of machines being tended by the operator to get an estimate of direct labor time.

It may be desirable to estimate cost directly. Item 15.1 of Section IV can be used for thread cutting and form rolling. The entry variable for thread rolling is thread diameter by length. Form rolling has two options: manual or automatic rolling. The base cost per 100 units is for one machine. For multiple machine operation, divide the cost by the number of machines handled.

FIGURE 15.1 Double-spindle thread cutting machine. (*Teledyne Landis Machine*)

EXAMPLES

A. An instrument case having a 6¼-in. 18-pitch, 7/16-in. long external thread and a mating case cover with 6¼-in., 18-pitch, ½-in., long internal thread is made of cold rolled steel. A double-spindle thread cutting machine is selected. Find the sets per hour (sets / hr).

Table	Description	Time
15.1-1	Pick up external case and load	.08 min
15.1-1	Advance work to die	.04
15.1-2	Thread, $12 \times \frac{7}{16} \times 6\frac{1}{4}$	.33
15.1-1	Release and aside of part	.09
	For 2nd spindle, some work can be done during machining cycle of other part	
Repeat	Handling from above	.21
15.1-2	Thread, $12 \times \frac{1}{2} \times 6\frac{1}{4}$	.38
	Effective time per set = machine time	.71 min
	and 20% interference time	.14
	Unit estimate	.85 min
	Sets/hr	70

B. An Acme thread stem, 1⅜-in. diameter, 4-pitch, 3G Acme, 4½-in. long is made of cold rolled steel. A single spindle machine is used. Find the unit time.

Table	Description	Time
15.1-1	Pick up piece	.08 min
15.1-1	Advance	.04
15.1-2	Thread, $.05 \times 4.5 \times 1.375$	.31
15.1-1	Release and aside	.09
	Unit estimate	.52 min

C. A 15-in. long automobile upper control suspension control arm has two ends automatically rolled with 1-in. long ⅝-in. dia 18-pitch threads. The parts are fed automatically and deposited onto a conveyor belt. Find the cycle time and pc/hr.

Table	Description	Time
15.1-3	Total thread length for ⅝ in. diameter	.0182 min
	Unit estimate	.0182 min
	Shop estimate	3297 pc/hr

D. For the instrument case described in Example A above, estimate the base cost.

Item	Description	Cost
15.1	Constant for cycle	$ 2.60
15.1	External thread, $\frac{7}{16} \times 6.25 \times 1.73$	4.73
15.1	Constant for internal part	2.60
15.1	Internal thread, $\frac{1}{2} \times 6.25 \times 1.73$	5.41
	$/ 100 sets	$15.34

E. Find the base cost for rolling a thread on the suspension arm of Example C.

Item	Description	Cost
15.1	Automatic thread rolling	$0.281
	$/ 100 units	$0.281

TABLE 15.1 THREAD CUTTING AND FORM ROLLING MACHINES

Setup .5 hr

Operation elements in estimating minutes

1. Thread cutting

Pick up part and load in vise	.08
Advance work to die	.04
Clear work from die head	.02
Release part from vise	.04
Aside of part	.05
Bulk load container per quantity	2.00 / no.
Bulk unload container per quantity	1.00 / no.

2. Thread cutting, min = table value $\times L \times Dia$

	Threads per inch													
Material	5	6	7	8	9	10	12	14	16	18	20	24	28	32
Steel (mild) free machining	.05	.05	.06	.07	.08	.09	.10	.10	.12	.12	.12	.14	.15	.17
Steel (hard), stainless	.13	.13	.15	.17	.16	.17	.17	.18	.14	.13	.15	.18	.21	.24
Malleable cast iron	.04	.05	.06	.07	.06	.07	.08	.08	.09	.09	.09	.10	.12	.14
Brass	.03	.03	.04	.05	.05	.06	.06	.07	.08	.09	.09	.10	.10	.12
Aluminum, plastic	.03	.03	.04	.04	.04	.05	.05	.06	.06	.07	.07	.08	.09	.10

3. Form rolling

Manual feed, min / ea

	Diameter		
Length	5/8	3/4	1
.5	.0176	.0216	.0296
.75	.0178	.0218	.0298
1	.0180	.0220	.0300
1.5	.0184	.0224	.0303
2	.0188	.0228	.0307
3	.0196	.0236	.0315

Automatic feed, min. / ea

	Diameter					
Length	1/8	3/16	1/4	3/8	1/2	5/8
.5	.0064	.0078	.0091	.0019	.0146	.0173
.75	.0066	.0079	.0093	.0120	.0147	.0175
1	.0067	.0081	.0094	.0122	.0149	.0176
1.5	.0070	.0084	.0097	.0125	.0152	.0179
2			.0100	.0128	.0155	.0182
3					.0161	.0188

4. Tool replacement   See Table 11.4

WELDING and JOINING

16.1 Shielded Metal-Arc, Flux-Cored Arc, and Submerged Arc Welding Processes

DESCRIPTION

Shielded metal-arc welding (SMAW) is effected by melting with the heat of an arc between a coated metal electrode and the base metal. Flux-cored arc welding (FCAW) produces coalescence by heating with an arc between a continuous, consumable electrode and the work. Submerged arc welding (SAW) is a process wherein coalescence is produced by heating an arc between a bare metal electrode and the work. The arc is shielded by a blanket of loose granular fusible material deposited on the work in advance of the arc. Pressure is not used in any of these methods and filler is obtained from the electrode. While these three methods are dissimilar, many work features are common; thus, permitting their grouping.

SMAW, frequently called "stick electrode," is a common method of welding though its prominence in production is challenged by other methods. In this process, the arc is stuck between the electrically ground work and a 9- to 18-in. length of covered metal rod clamped to a holder. These estimating data cover manual SMAW. As the covered rod becomes shorter, the welder stops the process to replace the stub with a new electrode. The versatility of SMAW and the low cost and simplicity of equipment are important advantages to some production people.

FCAW involves an electrode with self-shielding characteristics in coil form and feeding it mechanically to the arc. These wires contain the flux in the core. With the press of a trigger, the operator feeds the electrode to the arc. The operator uses a gun instead of an electrode holder. Manual FCAW means operator manipulation of the gun while automatic FCAW is more mechanized, especially in gun control.

The SAW process differs from other arc welding processes in that a blanket of fusible, granular material (or flux) shields the arc and molten metal. The arc is struck between the workpiece and a bare wire electrode tip is submerged in the flux. As the arc is completely covered by the flux, it is not visible and the weld is run without the flash, spatter, and sparks that characterize the open arc processes.

Now consider the estimating data for the general class of arc welding processes.

ESTIMATING DATA DISCUSSION

These estimating data cover sheet metal, plate, or other weldment materials, notably carbon and low-alloy steels. Those data are for commercial welding. Code welding, implying various specifications and certified welds, are not covered, unless the estimator extends the information by judgmental processes.

These data are developed with a general approach to the elements, especially the handling and jigging. If a more convenient approach to estimating is desired, the handling data of Resistance Spot Welding (RSW) machines can be used especially for sheet metal work. For lighter or medium weight weldments, the handling information and approach

FIGURE 16.1A Self-shielded flux-cored electrode process for welding snowplow blades. *(The Lincoln Electric Company)*

used by Gas Metal-Arc Welding (GMAW) can be substituted. If the handling elemental substitution with RSW or GMAW for estimating is used, the estimator should consistently follow that plan. Note that heavy welding is only covered in Table 16.1, and the process elements are from the table.

Selection of the elements of the operation begins

FIGURE 16.1B Typical gun for semiautomatic submerged-arc welding with the gun designed for fluidized flux feeding. *(The Lincoln Electric Company)*

with handling the weldment base which is positioned for welding. Another part is fitted, clamped or jigged, if necessary, and tack welded or welded in place. This procedure may be repeated until the welding is completed. Or, the part may be progressively assembled and tacked until the weldment is fully assembled, and then the assembly finished welded. There are variations to this element pattern.

Entry variables for the pickup elements are length and width or weight. For sheet metal gage work, use the maximum X and Y coordinate dimension. As parts are joined, these entry variables increase, and as required, the entry variables become larger when using the table. The estimates are one-worker. If a welder and helper are used, double the appropriate elemental time.

The pickup, or get time, for sheet metal is used in a number of contexts. If weldment weight exceeds plant safety requirements, various hoist times are available and are listed. Depending upon hoist facilities, it may be necessary to add for C-clamps or pressure clamps, etc.

Element 2 deals with position materials. Simple position to a line or line with one or more closed ends are provided.

Element 3 deals with clamps of various kinds and includes the get, open, close, remove, and aside time. Fitup time depends upon previous operation, tolerances, and condition of the material.

Element 4 is for part weldment motion before and during welding. A variety of degrees and positionable devices are provided.

Element 5 is for work supporting arc time. The change electrode includes pushing helmet up, flip electrode butt aside, assemble new electrode to holder, and flip helmet down. These motions are identified and listed separately.

Element 6 covers tack time. Welding times are covered by Elements 7 through 9. Any interruptible element that may occur is not included. While entry variables for welding could be size of rod, fillet size, amperage, joint design, or ac vs. dc, we have based the entry variable upon method of welding, thickness, and type of joint as the estimator is more assured of this information at the time of the estimate.

The material is assumed to be carbon or low-alloy steel. Welding is for one side, one fillet, and no gap between butt joints unless exception is given in the remarks column. The welding time may involve multiple passes to fill a joint, but the welding time is simply weld length multiplied by minutes per inch ($L \times$ min/in.) The estimator does not multiply this time by the passes. Joint preparation is not covered here unless gouging by the welder is assumed, and judgment using welding effort for gouging is required.

In these joints, the flat condition is used unless

exceptions are noted in the remarks column. Vertical time would be more as overhead welding, which is not common in industrial welding. Penetration, of course, varies, but this information is averaged for the data.

For the SAW process, a backing strip between a gapped joint may be used, and this backing bar may be welded to the assembly. Whether a backing strip is used depends upon the weld design.

In manual welding for SMAW, FCAW, and SAW, the tack time includes raise and lower helmet, strike and break or stickout, and tack.

The welding time is the weld length multiplied by the factor expressed as min/in. It is arc time only. Judgment for materials other than carbon and low-alloy steel is necessary.

As we assume no shielding gas for FCAW, weld cleaning is necessary to remove the flux and splatter for the three methods. Element 10 covers the possibilities.

Direct labor costs can be estimated using Item 16.1 of Section IV. These costs are related to Table 16.1 and similar entry variables are applied. The first term deals with manual handling, positioning, and clamping. It is applied for each fitted part. For heavy parts, a hoist cost is available whenever required. If during welding the article calls for a turnover, a reposition cost can be added. The welding processes are identified as SMAW, FCAW, and SAW (manual or automatic). Weld thickness multiplied by weld length is, in turn, multiplied by the cost factor for the process. The entry variable for chipping and brushing is weld length. All dimensions are in inches.

EXAMPLES

A. Determine direct labor time to fabricate a section of a hopper car using a manual and automatic SAW. Six $\frac{3}{4}$-in. plates (three 40 × 80 in., two 60 × 80 in., and one 18 × 64 in.) are installed over frames. The welding schedule follows:

   a. Weld three 40 × 80 in. SAW automatic, butt welds, two fillets
   b. Weld two 60 × 80 in. SAW manual, tee weld vertical
   c. Weld one 18 × 64 in. SAW manual, butt weld, two fillets

All plate welds have no gap, and weld length is full perimeter. Assume power hoist hand-traverse material handling. Two fillets implies one fillet per side. As each hopper car requires a setup, the unit time is the setup and cycle time total. Only the material is taken to the hopper car, and only when the hopper car is completed is it disposed.

Table	Description	Time	
16.1-S	Setup manual SAW	.5	hr
16.1-S	Setup automatic SAW	2.0	hr
16.1-1	Pick up 6 plates, 6 × .54	3.24	min
16.1-1	Add for 12 C-clamps, 12 × .47	5.64	
16.1-2	Position material, jiggle hoist, 24 times for fitup, 24 × .25	6.00	
16.1-3	Open and close toggle clamps, 4 per plate, 4 × 6 × .08	1.92	
16.1-3	Raise and lower helmet, two sides, 48 edges (2 × 6 × 4), 48 × .02	.96	
16.1-9	Weld 3 40 × 80-in. plates, automatic 3 × 240 × .10	72.00	
16.1-9	Weld 2 60 × 80-in. plates, manual 2 × 280 × .23	128.80	
16.1-9	Weld 1 18 × 64-in. manual butt, 1 × 164 × .10	16.40	
16.1-10	Pick up air hammer, assume 2 times per edge, and per side, or 2 × 6 × 4 × 2 (2 times) (6 plates) (4 edges) (2 sides) x .04	3.84	
16.1-10	Air-hammer chip flux on top of weld for linear perimeter distance of weld, or		
	a. 1440 × .01	14.40	
	b. 560 × .01	5.60	
	c. 164 × .01	1.64	
16.1-10	Wire brush weld surface for linear perimeter distance of weld, or		
	a. 1440 × .01	14.40	
	b. 560 × .01	5.60	
	c. 164 × .01	1.64	
16.1-10	Push broom clean of welding area, and hopper area where welding conducted, or 120 sq ft or .01 × 120	1.20	
	Unit estimate	283.28	min
	Total direct labor for 1 hopper car	7.22	hr

B. Estimate the time to weld 6 (six) ½-in. gussets to a hopper car. The gussets are 8 lb/ea and are located on 3-ft centers. The gusset is clamp-held in position and tack welded in six locations, followed by 14 in. of weld. Manual FCAW is used. Include the setup as a part of the unit time, assuming the setup is required for each hopper car.

Table	Description	Time	
16.1-S	Setup	.4	hr
16.1-1	Pick up 6 gussets, 6 × .08	.48	min
16.1-2	Position 1 part to line, 2 ends are closed, 6 × .05	.30	
16.1-3	Apply and remove 2 C-clamps, 6 × 2 × .23	2.76	
16.1-5	Ground cables, 6 × .19	1.14	
16.1-5	Pick up, aside electrode gun, 2 × 6 × .08	.96	
16.1-5	Put on, take off gloves, 1 × .14	.14	
16.1-6	Tack weld, 6 × 6 × .09	3.24	
16.1-7	Butt weld, 6 × 14 × .28	23.52	
Judgment	Operator position between gussets, 6 × 1.00	6.00	
16.1-10	Pick up and aisde wire brush, 6 × .04	.24	
16.1-10	Brush welds, 6 × 14 × .01	.84	
	Unit estimate	39.62	min
	Total direct labor for 1 hopper car	1.06	hr

C. A box beam is composed of 4 rectangular $^3/_{16}$-in. plates internally stiffened by cross bracing at open ends. Each end has a platform welded to the beam. SMAW welding is used with 9-in. rods. A locating fixture is designed to weld 2 plates, then 3 plates, and finally 4, and will rotate easily. The fixture, built at bench height, is also designed for welding the internal end stiffeners and platforms. The schedule of parts and welds is as follows:

   a. $4^3/_{16}$-in. plates, 16 × 36 in., corner or butt welded
   b. 4¼-in. stiffeners, 4 × 15½ in., butt welded
   c. 2½-in. floor plates, 20 × 20 in., butt welded

The clean steel plates have been oxygen-fuel cut and kerf edge is fair. Lot size is 180. Find setup and hr/100 units. The units are for commercial service and weld quality requirements are good.

Table	Description	Time	
16.1-S	Setup for manual SMAW	.3	hr
16.1-1	Pick up two 16 × 36 × $^3/_{16}$-in plates, 30.6 lb., 2 × .09	.18	min
16.1-2	Position part to nest fixutre, wrench two times, 2 × .07	.14	
16.1-3	Open and close 3 toggle clamps, 3 × .06	.18	
16.1-3	Use hammer to force position, two times	.66	
16.1-6	Manual tack first corner internally, 3 × .09	.27	
16.1-7	Weld 36-in. of length corner internally, 36 x .07	2.52	
16.1-5	Electrode requirement is 0.102 lb/ft, using E7024 rods, ⅛ in. × 14-in. long, so rod changes are about 3 per ft.		
	Change electrodes, 9 x .09	.81	
16.1-4	Rotate fixture easily by hand	.03	
Repeat	Use appropriate elements above to tack and corner weld third plate	4.67	
16.1-1	Pick up fourth $^3/_{16}$-in. plate	.09	
16.1-2	Position part to nest fixture, wrench two times, 2 × .07	.14	
16.1-2	Open and close 3 toggle clamps 3 × .06	.18	
16.1-3	Hammer to force position	.66	
16.1-6	Manual tuck fourth corner external	.27	
16.1-7	Weld 36 in. of length, butt external, 36 × .12	4.32	
16.1-5	Change electrodes, 9 × .09	.81	
16.1-1	Load 2 stiffeners, 4.39 lb/ea, 2 × .07	.07	
16.1-2	Position parts to edge, 4 edges, 4 × .04	.16	
16.1-2	Apply square, two times	.42	
Judgment	Clamp and unclamp 4 special clamps (use C-clamps), 4 × .23	.92	
16.1-7	Weld each end of stiffener, use butt time, 4 × 17 × .4 ends	2.72	
	Replace electrodes 5 times	.45	

Table	Description	Time
Repeat	Use above 6 elements for second end	4.74
16.1-4	Rotate part 90°	.03
16.1-1	Pick up floor plate, chain hoist	.90
16.1-2	Position material to corner, jiggle hoist	.25
16.1-2	Apply and remove square	.21
16.1-3	Open and close toggle clamps, $2 \times .06$	
16.1-6	Tack each edge twice, four edges, $2 \times 4 \times .09$	.72
16.1-4	Rotate part 90°, 4 times	.12
16.1-5	Replace rods twice	.18
16.1-7	Weld corner external, ½-in. plate, $4 \times 16 \times .10$	4.80
16.1-5	Rod replacement estimated 4 per ft, $4 \times 4 \times .09$	1.44
Repeat	Use above 10 elements for second floor plate	8.76
16.1-11	Weldment aside, bridge crane	1.01
16.1-5	Pick up and aside electrode holder. Estimate 1 per tack, 2 per weld, each part, each reposition during welding, start and stop, etc. approximately 75 times, $75 \times .08$	6.00
	Unit estimate	49.94 min
	Shop estimate	1.2 pc/hr
	hrs/100 units	83.233
	Lot estimate	150.12 hr

D. Find the base cost for Example B above using Item 16.1 of Section IV. Combine setup and unit cost for one-part lot cost.

Item	Description	Cost
16.1	Setup manual subtotal	$ 5.26
16.1	Six gussets and hopper car is 7 pieces, 7×15.8	$110.60
16.1	36 tacks, 36×2.81	101.16
16.1	FCAW manual, $6 \times 14 \times \frac{1}{2} \times 8.78$, $L = 14$ in., thk $= \frac{1}{2}$ in.	368.76
16.1	Clean $6 \times 14 \times .210$	17.64
	$/100 cost subtotal	$598.16
	Lot cost if lot $= 1$ unit	$ 11.24

TABLE 16.1   SHIELDED METAL-ARC, FLUX-CORED ARC, AND SUBMERGED ARC WELDING PROCESSES

Setup

Shielded metal arc	.3 hr
Flux-cored arc, manual	.4 hr
Flux-cored arc, automatic	2–4.0 hr
Submerged arc, manual	.5 hr
Submerged arc, automatic	2–4.0 hr

Operation elements in estimating minutes

1. Pick up material

Pick up sheet metal, also reverse or turnover, or aside, each piece

					Length				
Width	3	6	9	12	24	36	48	72	96
3	.03	.03	.04	.04	.06	.07	.08	.11	.13
6		.04	.05	.05	.06	.08	.09	.13	.15
12				.06	.08	.09	.12	.15	.17
24					.09	.11	.12	.16	.18
36						.13	.15	.18	.20
48							.18	.22	.24

Pick up part, less than 7 lb   .07
Pick up part, between 7–13 lb   .08
Pick up part, greater than 13 lb   .09

Chain hoist   .89
Power hoist, hand traverse   .54
Power bridge crane   1.01
  Add'l for C-clamp   .47/ea
  Add'l for pressure clamp   .06/ea

2. Position material

Position sheet metal in fixture or jig, also relocate, 1 piece

					Length				
Width	3	6	9	12	24	36	48	72	96
3	.03	.03	.03	.04	.04	.05	.06	.08	.10
6		.03	.03	.04	.05	.06	.07	.09	.11
12				.04	.06	.06	.07	.09	.12
24					.06	.07	.08	.13	.15
36						.08	.10	.15	.17
48							.12	.17	.19

Position one part to line or edge (no mechanical aids)

Weight	0–7	7–13	13+	Hoist
Min	.04	.05	.06	.08

Position one part to line (1 end closed)

Weight	0–7	7–13	13+	Jiggle Hoist
Min	.03	.04	.04	.25

Position one part to line (2 ends closed)

Weight	0–7	7–13	13+	Jiggle Hoist
Min	.03	.05	.06	.25

Position one part to corner

Weight	0–7	7–13	13+	Jiggle Hoist
Min	.03	.04	.05	.25

Position one part to nest fixture, using wrench   .07
Apply and remove square or rule   .21

3. Clamp and unclamp; lock and unlock parts in fixture

	Small	Large
Open and close 1 toggle clamp	.06	.08
Apply and remove 1 vise grip or 1 quick-action clamp	.08	.13
Apply and remove 1 C-clamp	.23	.44
Apply and remove bar clamp	.19	.24
Apply and remove collar and wing nut	.10	.15
Use hammer to force position	.12	.33

4. Reposition weldment or fixture

For sheet metal, use Element 1
Apply and remove spacer   .14
Turn part 90°

Weight	0–7	7–13	13+
Min	.03	.04	.08

Chain hoist   .58
Power hoist, hand traverse   .41
Power bridge crane   .79
Add'l for C-clamp, pressure clamp

Turn part 180° or over

Weight	0–7	7–13	13+
Min	.06	.07	.13

Chain hoist   .88
Power hoist, hand traverse   .58
Power bridge crane   1.08
Add'l for C-clamps, pressure clamp
Mechanically rotated fixture by operator
Wheel or roller type: 90°, .03; 180°, .06

Degrees	45°	90°	180°
Min	.05	.08	.13

Crank-type fixture

Degrees	15°	30°	45°	60°	75°	90°
Min	.19	.33	.47	.62	.76	.92

5. Equipment operation

Attach and remove ground cables   .19
Pick up and lay aside electrode holder   .08
Change electrodes   .09
Flip electrode aside   .02
Pick up and lay aside face shield, helmet   .10
Open and close goggles   .06
Raise and lower helmet   .02
Put on, take off gloves   .14
Stamp   .12

6. Post-welding

Manual tack   .09/ea
Preheat   Use welding specifications
Postheat   Use welding specifications

7. Shielded metal-arc welding, manual, min/in.

Joint	Gage				
	18	16	14	12	10
Butt	.05	.04	.04	.05	.06
Corner	.07	.07	.06	.05	.06
Tee			.08	.07	.07
Lap	.05	.05	.05	.06	.07
Edge	.02	.03	.03	.03	.03

Joint	Plate							
	$3/16$	$1/4$	$5/16$	$3/8$	$1/2$	$5/8$	$3/4$	1
Butt	.12	.17	.22	.27	.35	.44	.53	.70
Corner	.07	.07	.07	.08	.10	.16	.23	.34
Tee	.07	.08	.08	.08	.10	.21	.30	.47

8. Flux-cored arc welding, manual, min/in.

Joint	Gage		Remarks
	12	10	
Butt		.05	Gap, 30° sloping sides
Tee	.04	.05	Flat
Tee	.04	.04	Vertical
Lap	.01	.02	Flat

Joint	Plate								Remarks
	$3/16$	$1/4$	$5/16$	$3/8$	$1/2$	$5/8$	$3/4$	1	
Butt	.07	.09	.14	.16	.28	.38	.51	.77	Gap, 30°, sloping sides
Butt				.34	.48				J-grooved, gap
Butt				.99	1.27	2.04	2.25	3.50	Gap, overhead
Tee	.95	.97			.15	.22	.34		Flat
Tee	.04	.06							Vertical
Lap	.03	.05	.07	.10					Flat

Flux cored arc welding, automatic, min/in.

Joint	Gage						Remarks
	18	16	14	12	10	$3/16$	
Butt		.005	.008	.009	.01	.01	No gap
Butt	.005	.006	.008	.01	.01	.02	Gap
Corner		.007	.009	.01	.01	.01	
Lap		.006	.008	.01	.01	.01	

Joint	Plate		Remarks
	$3/4$	1	
Butt	.19	.23	Gap, vertical with shoe

9. Submerged arc, manual, min/in.

Joint	Gage			Remarks
	14	12	10	
Butt	.02	.03	.03	Gap
Butt		.05	.05	No gap, two fillets
Tee	.03	.02	.02	
Lap	.02	.02	.02	

Joint	3/16	1/4	5/16	3/8	1/2	5/8	3/4	1	Remarks
Butt	.04	.07	.08	.10					Gap
Butt	.05	.06	.07	.08	.11	.14	.19	.35	Two fillets
Tee	.04	.04	.05	.06	.08	.14	.23		
Tee	.04	.05	.06	.07	.10				Two fillets
Lap	.03	.04	.05	.07					

Submerged arc welding, automatic, min/in.

Joint	16	14	12	10	Remarks
Butt	.01	.01	.02	.02	Gap, steel backing
Tee		.01	.01	.01	
Tee				.02	Two fillets
Corner	.007	.01	.01	.01	Backing plate
Edge	.007	.01	.01	.01	

Joint	3/16	1/4	5/16	3/8	1/2	5/8	3/4	Remarks
Butt	.02	.03	.04	.05	.07			Gap, steel backing
Butt		.03	.04	.05	.07	.10	.10	Two fillets
Tee	.02	.02	.03	.04	.07	.10	.14	
Tee	.03	.04	.05					Two fillets
Lap	.02	.03	.04	.05				

10. Cleaning

Pickup and aside chipping hammer, air hammer, hose or brush	.04
Manually chip weld	.02/in.
Air-hammer chip weld	.01/in.
Blow off weld, in.	.006/in.
Wire brush, in.	.01/in.
Push broom area	.01/sq ft

11. Weldment aside

For sheet metal, Use Element 1

Weight	0–7	7–13	13+
Min	.07	.08	.09

Chain hoist	.89
Power hoist, hand traverse	.54
Power bridge crane	1.01
Add'l for C-clamp, pressure clamp	

16.2 Gas Metal-Arc and Gas Tungsten-Arc Welding Processes

DESCRIPTION

Gas Metal-Arc Welding (GMAW) produces coalescence by heating with an arc between a continuous and consumable filler metal electrode and the work. Shielding is obtained entirely from an externally-supplied gas. Sometimes this method is called MIG (metal inert gas).

Gas Tungsten-Arc Welding (GTAW) produces coalescence by heating with an arc between a non-consumable tungsten electrode and the work. Shielding is obtained from a gas. A filler may or may not be used. This process is frequently called TIG (tungsten inert gas). Welding is possible in almost all positions. Slag removal is unnecessary. These processes are used with the commercially-important metals. Continuous joint or tack welding methods also are possible.

Figure 16.2A is a GMAW process. Here, 11-gage, 316-stainless steel is joined to 3/16-in. carbon steel using an average travel speed of 16 ipm and an argon CO_2 gas mixture. Figure 16.2B is a GTAW process, where 3-in. aluminum pipes are being joined with a filler metal. GMAW is used for spotwelding two materials from one side. (See Figure 16.2C.)

The estimating data is now considered for the general class of GMAW and GTAW processes.

ESTIMATING DATA DISCUSSION

Four possibilities exist for an approach to handling. A simple consolidated approach uses the inches of weld plus the number of tacks as the entry variable to determine handling time. On the basis of time-study observations, the number of joined compo-

FIGURE 16.2A Gas metal-arc welding (GMAW) process joining 316 stainless steel to 3/16 in. carbon steel. (*Union Carbide Corporation*)

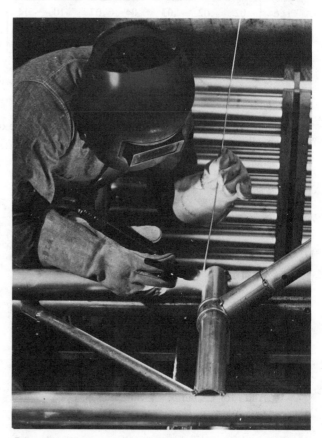

FIGURE 16.2B Gas tungsten-arc welding (GTAW) using filler metal to weld aluminum piping. (*Union Carbide Corporation*)

344

FIGURE 16.2C Gas metal-arc welding (GMAW) used in spot welding two materials. *(Union Carbide Corporation)*

nents, fixturing, jigging, clamps, etc., is related to this driver. Either the welded inch length or the number of tack welds may be zero ("0") or a positive (+) number. This element is complete, as it includes pickup materials, clamp, unclamp, fit, and aside welded components. The data are based on aluminum structural materials which, after assembly, is too heavy for operator handling.

The second approach to handling is for sheet metal materials and is a *get* table, move one part to the welding table. The same element would be used for subsequent parts. This table is also used for relocate and aside.

A girth approach ($= L + W + H$) for sheet metal is given in Resistance Spot Welding (RSW). For heavy welding, the data as given by Table 16.1 must be used.

Element 3 is welding time, expressed in min/in. for GMAW and GTAW. The time is total, as multiple passes are averaged in the data. This is especially true for thicker materials where multiple passes are required. The weld time is pure arc weld. Interruptions are itemized as separate elements. Tackweld includes: pickup of gun, tack 1 in., gun aside, and tilt helmet.

Entry variables for welding time are either GMAW or GTAW, material, joint, and thickness. Materials are considered clean, and welded quality is commercial. Code quality characteristics are not considered. A spotweld value for carbon steel involves position between GMAW spots and spot.

While slag chipping and clean up are not an element, blow off, clean, or wipe includes pickup of air hose, etc.

An alternate method to estimating time is given in Section IV. These items provide cost in terms of base $/100 units. Item 16.2 provides a version for GMAW and GTAW. Handling costs are based upon the length of weld and the number of spot welds. It is similar to Element 1 of Table 16.2. A variety of materials for GMAW and GTAW are given. The entry variable is the product of thickness by weld length.

EXAMPLES

A. Estimate the unit and lot time to weld 76 in. of 1/4-in. aluminum using the GMAW process. Blow off and a stamp to certify the weld are necessary. Lot size is 200 parts.

Table	Description	Time	
16.2-S	Setup	.4	hr
16.2-1	Handle components for 76 in. of weld	4.23	min
16.2-2	Attach cable	.19	
16.2-2	Pick up, lay aside gun, estimate 8 times for 4 components	.64	
16.2-2	Gloves	.14	
16.2-2	Stamp	.12	
16.2-4	Butt weld 1/4-in. aluminum plate, 76 × .10	7.60	
16.2-6	Blow off, .28 + (76-48) .0047	.41	
	Unit estimate	13.33	min
	Lot estimate	44.833	hr
	Shop estimate	4.5	pc/hr

B. Estimate the direct-labor time to weld 22 in. and tack 6 times with GMAW on a 3/8-in. aluminum plate. The lot quantity for this minor assembly is 150.

Table	Description	Time	
16.2-S	Setup	.44	hr
16.2-1	Weld in. + no. of tacks, 22 + 6 = 28	1.97	min
16.2-4	Fillet weld, 22 × .05	1.10	

Table	Description	Time
16.2-3	Tack weld, 6 × .09	.54
16.2-2	Attach cable	.19
16.2-2	Pick up gun, 4 times, 4 × .08	.32
16.2-6	Blow off	.23
	Unit estimate	4.35 min
	Lot estimate	11.275 hr

C. Estimate the base cost of Example A above using Item 16.2 of Section IV. Weld length = 76 in. and there are no tacks.

Item	Description	Cost
16.2	Setup subtotal	$ 4.21
16.2	Cycle constant	16.30
16.2	Handling factor, 76 × .842	63.99
16.2	GMAW ¼ in. aluminum 76 in. long, ¼ × 76 × 9.52	180.88
	$/100 units	$261.17
	Lot estimate	$526.55

TABLE 16.2   GAS METAL-ARC AND GAS TUNGSTEN-ARC WELDING PROCESSES

Setup   **.4 hr**

Operation elements in estimating minutes

1.   Handling components

Weld in. plus no. of tacks	Min	Weld in. plus no. of tacks	Min
1.0	.76	39.4	2.39
2.8	.84	45.0	2.62
4.8	.92	51.2	2.82
6.9	1.01	58.0	3.17
9.3	1.11	65.5	3.49
12.0	1.22	73.8	3.84
14.8	1.35	82.8	4.23
18.0	1.48	92.8	4.65
21.5	1.63	103.8	5.11
25.4	1.79	115.8	5.62
29.6	1.97	129.1	6.19
34.3	2.17	Add'l	.042

Get 1 sheet and load on table, also for relocate, dispose

	Length							
Width	3	6	9	12	18	36	60	84
3	.02	.03	.04	.04	.05	.07	.09	.12
6		.04	.05	.05	.06	.08	.10	.13
12				.06	.07	.09	.14	.16
18					.07	.09	.14	.17
36						.12	.16	.20

2.   Equipment operation

Attach, remove ground cable	.19
Pick up, lay aside gun	.08
Raise and lower helmet	.02
Put on, take off gloves	.14
Stamp	.12

3. Welding

Manual tack	.09/ea
Preheat	Use welding specifications for time
Postheat	Use welding specifications for time

4. Gas metal-arc welding, min/in.

ALUMINUM

Joint	Thickness								Remarks
	$1/8$	$3/16$	$1/4$	$3/8$	$1/2$	$5/8$	$3/4$	1	
Butt	.04	.09	.10	.13	.15	.19	.19		No gap, flat
Butt					.32		.49	.77	Gap, 70° V, two sides
Butt	.09	.09	.10						Gap, horizontal two sides
Butt				.17	.21		.31	.64	Gap, 70° V, horizontal, two sides
Fillet			.04	.05	.19				Horizontal

COPPER

Thk	$1/8$	$1/4$	$3/8$	$1/2$
Butt	.04	.12	.16	.21

STAINLESS STEEL

Joint	Thickness					Remarks
	$1/16$	$1/8$	$1/4$	$3/8$	$1/2$	
Butt		.06	.12	.14	.29	60° V, backing plate
Tee, lap	.06	.08				

CARBON STEEL

Thk	$1/8$	$3/16$	Remarks
Butt	.06	.10	Spray transfer

Spot weld and position	.17/spot

5. Gas tungsten-arc welding, min/in.

ALUMINUM

Thk	$1/32$	.050	$1/8$	$1/4$	$1/2$	$3/4$	Remarks
Butt	.02	.03	.04	.05	.05	.17	No filler rod

COPPER

Thk	$1/6$	$1/8$	$3/16$	$1/4$
Butt, corner	.10	.11	.12	.13
Fillet, lap	.12	.13	.14	.16

6. Blow off.

Weld in. + no. of tacks	Min	Weld in. + no. of tacks	Min
3	.07	26	.18
7	.09	35	.23
12	.12	48	.28
18	.15	Add'l	.0047

16.3 Resistance Spot Welding Machines

DESCRIPTION

Resistance Spot Welding (RSW) has two or more sheets of metal held between metal electrodes. A welding cycle is started with the electrodes contacting the metal under pressure before the current is applied for a period known as squeeze time. A low voltage current of sufficient amperage is passed between the electrodes causing the metal in contact to be rapidly raised to welding temperatures. As soon as the temperature is reached, the pressure between the electrodes squeezes the metal together and completes the weld. A pressure dwell completes the cycle. A nugget cools and forms the weld.

A picture of a stationary single-spot welding machine is shown in Figure 16.3. But these estimating data are intended for the general class of RSW machines.

ESTIMATING DATA DISCUSSION

Element 1 includes loading the major part from a skid, box, bear cage, etc. to a table. Following the final weld, it also includes remove subassembly aside. The time includes, both for replacement and removal, some occasional clamp and fixturing time. The independent variable is girth, $L + W + H$, and girth is the smallest-sized box of $L + W + H$ in. dimensions which will enclose any shape. In the case of a sphere, girth is the sum of three diameters. Girth is an easy calculation, and spot welded parts are reasonably correlated to girth. Element 2 is for loading component parts from skid, cage, tote box, etc. It includes moving major parts where occasional clamps or fixtures are necessary for positioning. The time variable also depends upon girth. The estimator, in order to expedite application, may want to use the higher table value rather than interpolate values. For instance, if $L + W + H = 26$, use .43 min.

Repositioning of the welded part may be required during spot welding. A 90°-reposition is a corner turn; 180° implies a roll over of the narrow dimension, while end-for-end is a flip of the longer dimension. Spot welding is covered for aluminum and steel, and several gages were a part of the observations. For an assembly exceeding $L + W + H = 80$, the table includes two operators. Spot-weld time must be doubled for two operators. The distance between spots and metal thickness are average for Element 4. Occasional clean tips is also included.

Base costs for spot welding can be estimated directly using Item 16.3 of Section IV. The entry variables for run cost per 100 units are girth $L + W + H$ and number of spots. Girth $L + W + H$ is calculated visualizing the smallest sized box that will fit the part. It is an easy calculation to make. Run cost depends upon the major part, and component parts that may be spot welded to the major part. If spots are off the original plane, a reposition cost is provided. The constant cost is always used.

FIGURE 16.3 Single-spot welding machine joining unalloyed annealed titanium. (*Sciaky Brothers, Inc.*)

348

EXAMPLES

A. Two sheets of .010-in. Titanium 4901 material are to be spot welded. The major part, an unusual configuration, has a minimum girth of 69 in. The secondary part has a girth of 27.3 in. and 23 in-line spots are required. A holding fixture with level clamps positions both parts relative to each other. Commercial tolerances are required. The practice of using the next higher table value is followed. A lot of 8 units is required.

Table	Description	Time	
16.2-S	Setup	.35	hr
16.3-1	Handle major part, $L + W + H = 69$	.61	min
16.3-2	Handle secondary part, $L + W + H = 27.3$	.55	
16.3-4	Spotweld 23 times	1.68	
	Unit estimate	2.84	min
	Lot estimate	.73	hr
	Shop estimate	21	pc/hr

B. Estimate base cost for Example A above.

Item	Description	Cost
16.3	Setup subtotal	$ 4.04
16.3	Cycle constant	$ 5.20
16.3	Primary part, $69 \times .063$	4.35
16.3	Secondary part, $27.3 \times .302$	8.25
16.3	23 spots, 23×1.18	27.14
	$/100 units subtotal	$45.02
	Lot estimate	$ 7.64

TABLE 16.3   RESISTANCE SPOT WELDING MACHINES

Setup hr

Components	1, 2, or 3	4 or 5	6 and up
$L + W + H < 60$	.30	.35	.40
$L + W + H \geq 60$	.35	.40	.50

Operation elements in estimating minutes

1. Load major part and unload welded assembly

$L + W + H$	Min	$L + W + H$	Min
3.0	.34	100.6	.70
7.5	.36	110.0	.74
12.3	.37	119.8	.78
17.3	.39	130.2	.82
22.5	.41	141.1	.86
28.0	.43	152.5	.90
33.8	.45	164.5	.94
39.8	.48	177.1	.99
46.2	.50	190.3	1.04
52.9	.53	204.2	1.09
59.9	.55	218.8	1.15
67.2	.58	234.1	1.21
75.0	.61	250.2	1.27
83.1	.64	267.0	1.33
91.6	.67	Add'l	.004

2. Load each component part, position with fixture, clamp to major part

L + W + H	Min	L + W + H	Min
3.0	.07	20.0	.38
3.4	.08	22.2	.41
3.9	.09	24.5	.45
4.4	.10	27.1	.50
4.9	.11	29.9	.55
5.6	.12	33.0	.60
6.2	.13	36.4	.67
7.0	.14	40.2	.73
7.8	.16	44.3	.80
8.7	.18	48.9	.89
9.7	.19	53.9	.97
10.8	.21	59.4	1.07
12.0	.23	65.4	1.18
13.3	.26	72.1	1.30
14.7	.28	79.4	1.43
16.3	.31	87.5	1.57
18.1	.34	Add'l	.016

3. Repositioning part during spotwelding

L + W + H	90°	180°	End-for-end
15	.07	.08	.08
35	.08	.09	.11
55	.09	.10	.14
75	.10	.12	.16
95	.12	.13	.19
115	.13	.14	.21
135	.14	.15	.24
155	.16	.17	.27
Add'l	.001	.001	.001

4. Spotweld, reposition for next spotweld, and occasional clean tip

No. spots	Aluminum	Steel	No. spots	Aluminum	Steel
1	.09		15	1.02	.95
2	.16		16	1.08	1.02
3	.22	.07	17	1.15	1.09
4	.29	.14	18	1.21	1.17
5	.36	.22	19	1.28	1.24
6	.42	.29	20	1.35	1.31
7	.49	.36	22	1.48	1.46
8	.55	.44	25	1.68	1.68
9	.62	.51	28	1.87	1.90
10	.69	.58	30	2.01	2.04
11	.75	.66	35	2.34	2.41
12	.82	.73	40	2.67	2.77
13	.88	.80	45	3.00	3.14
14	.95	.88	Add'l	.06	.07

16.4 Torch, Dip, or Furnace Brazing Processes

DESCRIPTION

Brazing and soldering are processes which unite metals. This is accomplished by using a third joining metal, which is introduced into the joint in a liquid state before it solidifies. Brazing and soldering have a filler metal with a melting point higher and lower than 800°F respectively. The filler metal is drawn into the joint by capillary attraction. In these applications, heat is applied to the parts to be joined. It is not applied directly to the filler material alone. Various heat sources can be used as flames, molten salt, or radiant energy. If gas flames are used, it is called torch brazing. Similarly, dip brazing would involve molten salt.

The torch is handheld. The soldering iron is not evaluated here. An oxyacetylene or oxyhydrogen torch applies heat locally, and the filler metal, applied in wire rod, is melted into the joint. Fluxes are applied by pastes or are included as a part of a coated filler metal. Some filler metal is prepared in the forms of rings, washers, or special shapes to fit the joint. If a protective atmosphere or environment is provided during the brazing, a flux may not be required.

A pot-type furnace is shown in Figure 16.4. These pots can be fuel-fired or electrically heated. In addition to dip brazing, they can be used for carburizing, hardening, melting, salt-bath drawing, tempering, and tinning. The pot in Figure 16.4 is 16-in. OD and has a 20-in. depth, with a capacity of 1.89 cu ft. Larger units have a capacity to 5.5 cu ft.

ESTIMATING DATA DISCUSSION

The setup differs with respect to whether jigging is available. There are four operation elements. In the first element, a preassembled assembly is available, and there is no assembly by the operator. If the parts can be held together by friction or gravity, the jig is considered "positioning." If clamping or holding of some sort is required, a holding jig time is selected. For sheet metal parts, five or more components, or when close tolerances are specified, an aligning jig value is picked for the estimate.

In torch brazing, Element 4, three conditions are available for selection. Simple linear inches are the time driver for no-jig or jig conditions. If two or more diameters are joined, the diameter, as is, is selected for the time driver. The time driver is based upon total joint or seam length. For instance, for a cap joint, use the total outside seam length. Either a handheld rod or special filler is used.

Depending upon the atmosphere or containment for brazing, a flux may or may not be needed. With a molten-salt pot, for example, it may be unnecessary to require a flux. Most often a jig is unlikely for dip brazing.

For furnace brazing and soldering, the confinement may range from a protective atmosphere oven to a large furnace. However, the handling time to load and unload is covered in Element 5. It does not include process time. The entry variable is squat area. Only one layer of parts on the sled or of the furnace or oven is considered.

In assembly aside, Element 7, the $L + W$ time driver is the two greatest dimensions of the assembly. Packaging is average time for pack and unpack using wrap, bag, pads, paper, etc. Greater detail can be found in the packaging estimating data.

There is an alternate method to estimating time. Costs may be estimated directly using Item 16.4 of Section IV. These data are a reduction of Table 16.4. The $/100 units depend upon the entry variables of number of seams, torch linear inches of

FIGURE 16.4 A pot-type gas-fired furnace that is used for dip brazing. *(Sunbeam Equipment Corporation)*

brazing, squat area for furnace brazing, and dip area. The constant cost is always used. The estimator, in knowing the operation, will select loading of the braze wire as related to the number of seams. Or, the estimator will select torch brazing as related to the linear length of weld, or furnace loading as related to the squat area as required for a furnace sled.

EXAMPLES

A. A small mechanical assembly, weighing less than 3 lb, is to be torch brazed. Lot quantities are indeterminate. An aligning jig is required because of critical tolerances. The joints are lap. Linear length of the lap joint is 13.25 in. Determine the unit time and hr/100 units.

Table	Description	Time
16.4-1	Aligning jig	1.64 min
16.4-2	Torch braze 13.25 in. × 3.28	4.70
16.4-7	Assembly aside	.77
	Unit estimate	7.11 min
	hr/100 units	11.850

B. An assembly is to be dipped brazed. Parts are clean, and a flux is not required. Metal-to-metal sliding fit and gravity keeps the parts together. The four parts, which slip together, are previously bench assembled, and now are to be brazed with a filler metal. The part area is 21.25 sq in. and has two separate seams. Find a lot estimate for 625 units and the shop estimate.

Table	Description	Time
16.4-S	No jig setup	.15 hr
16.4-1	Preassembled parts	.05 min
16.4-3	Load braze wire to 2 seams and area, 21.25 sq in.	.48
16.4-6	Dip braze	.38
16.4-7	Assembly aside	.05
	Unit estimate	.96 min
	Lot estimate	10.15 hr
	Shop estimate	63 pc/hr

C. Re-estimate Example B above using a base-cost approach. The information is found in Section IV.

Item	Description	Cost
16.4	Setup subtotal	$ 2.02
16.4	Cycle constant	$ 9.30
16.4	Load braze wire, 2 × 2.22	4.44
16.4	Dip braze, 21.25 × .334	7.10
	$/100 units subtotal	$ 20.84
	Lot estimate	$132.27

TABLE 16.4   TORCH, DIP, OR FURNACE BRAZING

Setup

no jig	.15 hr
jig	.20 hr

Operation elements in estimating minutes

1. Load parts to welding bench and position

Preassembled, no jig	.05
Positioning jig for machined parts	.17
Holding jig for 4 or less components, or tolerances not close or simple assembly	.53
Aligning jig for sheet metal parts, or 5 or more components, or close tolerances, or complex assembly	1.64

2. Apply flux to seam

Brush L	Syringe L	Min		Brush L	Syringe L	Min
1.0	2.7	.10		7.8	17.4	.24
1.5	3.8	.11		9.0	19.9	.27
2.1	5.0	.13		10.3	22.7	.30
2.7	6.3	.14		11.8	25.8	.33
3.3	7.7	.15		13.3	29.2	.36
4.1	9.3	.17		15.1	32.9	.39
4.9	11.0	.18		17.0	37.0	.43
5.8	12.9	.20		Add'l		.02
6.8	15.0	.22			Add'l	.01

3. Load bare wire to assembly

Part area	No. separate seams							
	1	2	3	4	5	6	7	8
2	.28	.41	.54	.69	.82	.95	1.08	1.21
19	.31	.44	.58	.71	.84	.97	1.10	1.23
45	.34	.48	.61	.74	.87	1.00	1.13	1.27
70	.38	.51	.64	.77	.90	1.03	1.18	1.31

Add'l seam   .13
Add'l area   .0014

4. Torch braze or solder

No jig in.	Dia. in.	Jig in.	Min		No jig in.	Dia. in.	Jig in.	Min
	.26	.7	.36		15.3	1.92	6.1	2.19
	.29	.8	.39		17.2	2.11	6.8	2.41
	.33	.9	.43		19.2	2.33	7.5	2.65
1.1	.37	1.1	.48		21.4	2.57	8.3	2.92
1.5	.41	1.2	.52		23.8	2.84	9.1	3.21
2.0	.46	1.3	.58		26.4	3.13	10.1	3.53
2.4	.51	1.5	.63		29.4	3.45	11.1	3.88
3.0	.57	1.7	.70		32.6	3.80	12.3	4.27
3.6	.63	1.9	.77		36.1	4.18	13.6	4.70
4.2	.70	2.1	.85		40.0	4.61	14.9	5.17
4.9	.78	2.4	.93		44.3	5.07	16.5	5.68
5.7	.86	2.7	1.02				18.2	6.25
6.5	.95	3.0	1.12				20.0	6.88
7.4	1.05	3.3	1.24				22.0	7.57
8.5	1.17	3.7	1.36				24.3	8.32
9.6	1.29	4.1	1.50				26.8	9.16
10.8	1.42	4.5	1.65		Add'l			.13
12.2	1.57	5.0	1.80			Add'l		1.12
13.7	1.74	5.5	1.99				Add'l	.34

5. Furnace braze

Area	Min	Area	Min	Area	Min	Area	Min
1.0	.03	4.2	.13	7.3	.23	21.3	.66
1.4	.04	4.5	.14	7.7	.24	24.5	.76
1.7	.05	4.9	.15	8.0	.25	28.5	.88
2.1	.06	5.2	.16	9.2	.29	32.4	1.01
2.4	.07	5.6	.17	10.6	.33	37.3	1.16
2.8	.08	5.9	.18	12.2	.33	42.9	1.34
3.1	.09	6.3	.19	14.1	.44	49.3	1.54
3.5	.11	6.6	.20	16.2	.50	56.6	1.77
3.8	.12	7.0	.22	18.6	.58	Add'l	.03

6. Dip braze

Area	Min	Area	Min	Area	Min
3.0	.005	8.6	.11	17.7	.29
3.6	.01	9.2	.12	19.1	.31
4.1	.02	9.8	.13	20.8	.35
4.7	.03	10.5	.15	22.5	.38
5.3	.05	11.2	.16	24.5	.42
5.8	.06	12.1	.18	26.7	.46
6.4	.07	13.0	.20	29.0	.51
7.0	.08	14.0	.22	31.7	.56
7.5	.09	15.1	.24	34.7	.61
8.1	.10	16.3	.26	Add'l	.02

7. Assembly aside
   No jig   .05
   Remove from jig
      $L + W < 6$ in.   .33
      $L + W \geq 6$ in.   .77

8. Package for protection   .15

17.1 Heat Treat Furnaces

DESCRIPTION

Heat treatment is the operation of heating and cooling a metal part in its solid state to change physical properties. While a variety of hardening, tempering, annealing, and normalizing operations can be identified, these estimating data are concerned with furnace loading and unloading. The specific heat-treating operation is immaterial; though operator variations certainly affect how material is handled, these variations have been averaged by the analysis.

Furnaces considered by these estimating data are heavy duty, gas tight, and a production-section pusher. Often there is an unheated pre-heat section followed by a high temperature section. Both ends are equipped with a manual-lift vertical door with protective flame curtains. The operating temperature may be as high as 1800°F. A typical furnace is shown in Figure 17.1. The tunnel cross section of Figure 17.1 is 12-in. wide × 8 in.-high and 7-ft long.

FIGURE 17.1 Manual pusher, atmospheric-tight, electric furnace. (*Pereny Equipment Company, Inc.*)

ESTIMATING DATA DISCUSSION

The setup of .10 hr includes the usual chores, but does not include waiting for furnace warmup or cooldown.

Element 1 is for loading and unloading parts onto a sled, tray, basket, or brick outside of the furnace proper, or on these flat surfaces within the cool chamber. The entry variable is rough-box volume, or cu in., of the part. The volume does not include the sled, tray, etc. For a fixtured part, the volume does include the fixture. For multiple part fixtures, the total volume is prorated over the number of parts. No furnace wait time is included.

Loading and unloading the part onto a fixture for distortion prevention is provided by Element 2. Flat, ring, or conical-shaped parts are the configurations provided. Entry variable is the part width of fixture.

Element 3 deals with putting on, taking off gloves, open and close one furnace door, and load and unload one part (which may weigh up to 30 lb.). It does not include any furnace time.

An alternate to a Table 17.1 approach is given by Item 17.1 of Section IV. The use of this item leads to an estimate expressed in base $/100 units. The entry information is similar for Table 17.1 and Item 17.1. One or both items may be possible for a fixture and furnace loading operation.

EXAMPLES

A. A beryllium copper part, previously formed in a sheet metal operation, is to be precipitation hardened in a furnace operation. The part is reasonably flat, even though it is formed. To avoid distortion, the part is loaded into a multiple unit fixture and then heat treated. Find the unit time if the part size is $1/16 \times 2.025 \times 3.0$ in.

Table	Description	Time
17.2-2	Load flat-shaped part onto fixture	.23 min
17.1-1	Load and unload fixtured part, net volume prorated over units = 3.1 cu in.	.21
	Unit estimate	.44 min

B. An aluminum casting in "O" condition is to be stabilized with a furnace operation. Part volume = 23 cu in. Determine the shop estimate for direct-labor production.

Table	Description	Time
17.1-1	Load and unload part in furnace	.26 min
	Shop estimate	250 pc/hr

C. Estimate base $/100 units for Example A above using Section IV information.

Item	Description	Cost
17.1	Cycle constant for fixture	$ .31
17.1	Width factor, 2.025×1.51	3.06
17.1	Cycle constant for furnace	1.08
17.1	Furnace factor, $.063 \times 2.025 \times 3 \times .314$	.12
	$/100 units	$5.30

TABLE 17.1 HEAT TREAT FURNACES

Setup .10 hr

Operation elements in estimating minutes

1. Load and unload part in furnace

Volume	Min	Volume	Min	Volume	Min	Volume	Min
1.0	.20	26.9	.24	58.4	.29	97	.35
7.0	.21	34.2	.25	67.3	.31	108	.37
13.3	.22	41.9	.26	76.6	.32	119	.39
20.0	.23	50.0	.28	86	.34	131	.41

Volume	Min	Volume	Min	Volume	Min	Volume	Min
143	.43	250	.60	401	.85	964	1.77
156	.45	269	.63	427	.89	1073	1.95
170	.47	288	.67	454	.94	1192	2.14
185	.50	308	.70	621	1.21	1323	2.36
200	.52	330	.73	695	1.33	1467	2.59
216	.55	352	.77	776	1.46	1626	2.85
233	.58	376	.81	866	1.61	Add'l	.002

2. Load and unload part on fixture

Flat shape

Part W	Min	Part W	Min	Part W	Min
0.5	.10	1.8	.21	4.7	.44
0.6	.11	2.1	.23	5.2	.49
0.7	.12	2.4	.25	5.8	.54
0.9	.13	2.7	.28	6.5	.59
1.0	.14	3.0	.30	7.2	.65
1.2	.16	3.4	.33	8.0	.71
1.4	.17	3.8	.37	8.8	.78
1.6	.19	4.2	.40	Add'l	.08

Rings or conical shape

Dia	Min	Dia	Min
.5	.23	2.5	.46
.8	.26	3.1	.52
1.1	.30	3.8	.60
1.5	.35	4.5	.69
2.0	.40	Add'l	.12

3. Load and unload 1 part to furnace   .80

4. Put on and remove asbestos gloves   .18

DEBURRING

18.1 Drill Press Machine Deburring

DESCRIPTION

These data provide for hole or edge burr removal times using floor or bench-mounted drill press machines. The operation of deburring can be processed many ways—notably by machines, portable tools, hand methods, or tumbling. The data here, however, are limited to drill presses only. A variety of spindle-mounted bits can be assumed, and a few are given.

Figure 18.1 is a 10 × 14-in. (tilt-table) 15-in. drill press, where spindle drive is variable in the 500–4000 rpm range. Discussion, typical estimates, and data for the general class of drill press deburring machines follow.

ESTIMATING DATA DISCUSSION

Handling is provided for three categories of parts, flat-like, box-like, and machined. The maximum length plus width, $L + W$, is the entry variable for sheet metal. The smallest box dimensions, or girth, $L + W + H$, is the entry for box structures. A qualitative description for ease or difficulty of handling is the entry variable for machined parts. This handling includes both pickup and aside. It also includes the initial position of the drill-press tool. But if special handling requirements are necessary for tweezers, pliers, etc., add 25%. If a fixture is used, apply the drill-press data.

It should be noted that some parts may fit any of these descriptions, but consistency for a class is necessary to maintain long-term application of the data for best results.

Deburring, or machine time, covers hole-to-hole positioning of the parts and break edges for metals. For nonmetals, such as plastics, other tables are used. The deburr is done with spindle-mounted tools such as drill, countersink, tap, reamer, wire brush, router-bit, sanding disks or sanding drums, grinding burrs, etc.

In Element 3 the hole depths are shallow, thus qualitative judgment of adding 25% per time for four-thread depths, is advised in re-tapping.

FIGURE 18.1 A 15-in. floor drill press with variable spindle rpm. (*Clausing Corporation Machine Tool Group*)

If the holes are to be deburred on both sides, double the hole count.

Item 18.1 of Section IV gives a different approach to estimating drill press machine deburring. Setup and operation costs are listed to permit the finding of unit cost, lot cost, or $/100 units. Many of the methods shown in Table 18.1 are provided.

The constant cost is always used. Additional handling cost is provided by the second term, and the estimating variable depends upon box girth or $L + W + H$. A rehandle cost is available if a flip or end-for-end reposition is necessary. Deburring holes, wire brushing, and wheel buffing are available methods.

EXAMPLES

A. A small machine part, which is difficult to handle, has two side holes to be deburred. The part, bagged, is a lot of 1500. Estimate lot time to deburr using a drill press tooled with a countersink. The holes are on opposite sides.

Table	Description	Time
18.1-S	Setup	.05 hr
18.1-1	Very small, difficult to handle, and stack	.05 min
18.1-2	Reposition	.02
18.1-3	Deburr two holes	.07
18.1-4	Pack and unpack, 2 × .09	.18
	Unit estimate	.32 min
	Lot estimate	8.05 hr

B. A lot of 32 sheet metal parts, which have been braked into a U-shape, have 32 holes accessible to drill press deburring. The holes are to be deburred on both sides. The girth measurements are 40 = 10 + 20 + 10 in. The holes are in 3 planes, but on both surfaces. Find the unit estimate.

Table	Description	Time
18.1-1	Box-like handling	.38 min
18.1-2	Reposition to present 5 planes for deburring	
	Original plane in Element 1, 5 × .15	.75
18.1-3	32 holes, both sides, 1.07 × 2	2.14
18.1-4	Cardboard layer for skid, but layer covers 5 parts, 2 × .05/5	.02
	Unit estimate	3.29 min

C. Re-estimate Example A above using a base-cost approach.

Item	Description	Cost
18.1	Setup subtotal	$ .36
18.1	Cycle constant	$ 1.21
18.1	Small machine part (use rehandle if $L + W + H$ is unknown	1.83
18.1	Deburr two holes, 2 × .414	.83
Estimate	Unpack and pack	1.00
	$/100 units subtotal	$ 4.87
	Lot estimate	$73.38

TABLE 18.1 DRILL PRESS MACHINE DEBURRING

Setup .05 hr

Operation elements in estimating minutes

1. Position and aside

Flat or sheet, extrusion, aluminum and steel, .020–.050 in.

L + W	Min	L + W	Min
9.0	.14	64.6	.31
15.4	.16	79.3	.36
22.7	.18	96.2	.42
31.1	.21	115.7	.48
40.7	.24	138.0	.55
51.8	.27	163.7	.63

Box-like parts

L + W + H	Min	L + W + H	Min	L + W + H	Min
15.0	.07	29.5	.22	72.8	.66
16.5	.09	33.9	.27	85.8	.70
18.2	.11	39.1	.32	101.4	.95
20.3	.13	45.4	.38	120.2	1.14
22.8	.15	52.9	.46	Add'l	.01
25.9	.18	61.9	.55	Hoist	1.78

Very small, pickup, difficult to control, drop	.03
Small in pan, or box, pickup and drop	.02
Medium, under 3 lb, easy to handle, drop	.03
Large, from bench, under 8 lb, pickup and drop	.06
Very small, pickup, and stack	.05
Small, pickup, and stack	.04
Medium, pickup, and stack	.05
Large, from bench, pickup, and stack	.08

2. Reposition to present new surface, edge, plane

Very small, small, medium	.02
Large	.04

Sheet metal

L + W	6	12	24	48	72	96	120
Min	.03	.04	.06	.09	.13	.18	.24

Box-like parts

L + W + H	16	21	35	50	75
Min	.03	.05	.09	.15	.22

Hoist	.58

3. Deburr

Holes with drill, re-ream, re-tap, chamfer

Holes	Min	Holes	Min	Holes	Min	Holes	Min
1	.03	11	.37	21	.70	31	1.04
2	.07	12	.40	22	.74	32	1.07
3	.10	13	.44	23	.77	33	1.11
4	.13	14	.47	24	.81	34	1.14
5	.17	15	.50	25	.84	35	1.17
6	.20	16	.54	26	.87	36	1.21
7	.23	17	.57	27	.91	37	1.24
8	.27	18	.60	28	.94	38	1.27
9	.30	19	.64	29	.97	39	1.31
10	.34	20	.67	30	1.01	Add'l	.034

Wire brush—horizontally turning, spindle mounted

$L + W$	1.1	2.5	4.2	7.2
Min	.13	.29	.49	.80

Wheel buff, spindle mounted

Sq in.	.3	1	3.7	6.3	10
Min	.10	.34	1.26	2.14	3.39

Router tool, spindle-mounted

L	4	9	14	19	24	29
Min	.22	.28	.34	.40	.45	.51

4. Blowing off

Pickup, aside air hose	.04
Blow out bottom hole	.06
Blow off deburring chips	.01/hole
Pack or unpack	
Sheet metal cardboard layer	.05
Envelope, bag, box	.09

18.2 Abrasive Belt Machine Deburring

DESCRIPTION

The conveyorized abrasive belt deburring machine has a traveling belt which passes under an abrasive belt. The part is pulled through and is surface sanded. Small machines handle parts up to 2 1/2-in. thick at a conveyor feed of 20 ft/min. Larger machines with abrasive belts to 60-in. wide have a conveyor feed of 20–60 ft/min. Top and bottom abrasive heads permit single-pass deburring. Belt selection with 120–220 grit with oil lubrication will also produce a satin finish. But 80–120-grit belts are required for deburring operations. Figure 18.2 is an example of conveyorized deburring machine with a height opening of 0–6 in.

Some abrasive belt operations are for box-like structures having parallel planar surfaces to the moving abrasive belt. The box-like part is cross fed

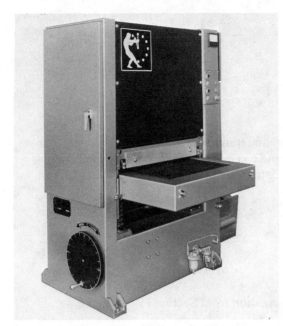

FIGURE 18.2 Abrasive belt deburring and finishing machine. *(Timesavers, Inc.)*

at a right angle to the belt. The operator depresses the belt down over the entire area. Or the operator can localize the pressure for spot surface deburring. Spot or surfacing deburring is on the top only.

The vertical abrasive belt machine has a belt exposed which travels at a relatively low speed. In the smaller sizes, the machines are portable, and they can be mounted on any bench. A table allows resting of flat parts during edge burring.

The following data are for the family of abrasive belt machines.

ESTIMATING DATA DISCUSSION

The setup allows for a belt change along with the customary chore tasks. The sheet metal parts can be gathered and relocated next to the conveyor or belt machine for deburring.

Handling elements vary with the machine and whether handling is already included in the process time or if it is for one or two operators.

Element 3 is for laying on traveling belt or inserting in opening of conveyor. Note that this element does not include the part aside; the entry variable is length plus width $(L + W)$.

Box-like parts are loaded on a machine table over which the overhead belt travels. The table, sometimes pulled out away from the belt, is crossfed under the moving abrasive belt. For box-like parts, the time does not include aside.

For machine parts, there are several circumstances. The pickup and drop or stack depend upon ease of handling. The nature of abrasive belt machining excludes heavy parts from using this method. The reposition element is for parts that use the 1-in. or 4-in. belt, which are normally vertical.

In conveyor deburring, Element 5, the part entry is length (L). Small and medium refer to the size of the machine, or 4 in. for small machines and 18 in. and 30 in. for medium machines. This machine sands the entire surface and top periphery. The conveyor pulls the part through the machine. The times are total as nominally a small conveyor uses one loader while a medium conveyor uses a loader and unloader operator. In the small conveyor, the parts continue to stack off to the side of the belt.

The entry variable for Element 5 is length (L) and 12- or 16-gage aluminum. The moving belt is pressed down onto the surface of the part, and the part is sanded. Either local or total area can be sanded and belt widths vary. Spot welds, indentations, and some welds may be sanded. Though deburring is the original purpose, some surface preparation for a paint coat may be achieved. The entry variable is usually in the direction of the belt movement.

Element 5 also is deburr edges, holes, and cutoffs, thus has the entry variable of deburred length. The parts are handheld during the deburring process. Flat parts can be rested upon a table and the edge pressed into the abrasive belt.

Because of the operation similarity to abrasive belt conveyor deburring, a roll edge, Element 6, is used for sheet metal parts after a shear, notch, or pierce operation. Handling is included in the time. The edge is rolled over slightly by mechanical action and no abrasive sanding occurs. The time is for one side only.

While Table 18.2 provides a time approach, Item 18.2 of Section IV can provide a cost value for abrasive belt operations. Item 18.2 is expressed in $/100 units. Entry variables are similar for Item 18.2 and Table 18.2. The constant cost is always used. Either conveyor or moveable table is selected and the pass length multiplies the cost factor.

EXAMPLES

A. A sheet metal part, previously blanked, pierced and notched from both sides, is to be deburred. The part, 9 × 27.25 in., is clean and a large lot is available. Estimate the unit time.

Table	Description	Time
18.2-1	Turn machine on, off	0 min
18.2-2	Go through stack every 10 pieces	.015
18.2-5	Conveyor sand first side	.17
18.2-2	Carry stack to front	.010
18.2-5	Conveyor sand second side	.17
	Unit estimate	.365 min

B. A small easy-to-handle machine part is to have two circumferences deburred. A 1-in. belt, nonbacked, is available. The diameter is 1.305 in., and can be handled by one hand, although part presentation to the belt is two-handed. Estimate the unit time.

Table	Description	Time
18.2-3	Small part pickup, drop	.03 min
18.2-5	Deburr circumference, 4.1 in.	.14
18.2-4	Turn end-for-end	.02
18.2-5	Deburr second end	.14
	Unit estimate	.33 min

C. Estimate the base cost of Example A above using information from Section IV.

Item	Description	Cost
18.2	Cycle constant	$3.88
18.2	Conveyor sand, $2 \times 21.25 \times .137$	5.82
	$/100 units	$9.70

TABLE 18.2   ABRASIVE BELT MACHINE DEBURRING

Setup   **.1 hr**

Operation elements in estimating minutes

1. Start and stop machine   .04

2. Gather stack
    Several pieces   .15
    Armfull   .25
    Carry stack to front of machine   .10

3. Lay on traveling belt, flat parts (aside not required)

L + W	Min	L + W	Min
2.2	.05	55.6	.12
11.1	.06	64.5	.13
20.0	.07	73.4	.14
28.9	.08	82.3	.15
37.8	.09	91.2	.16
46.7	.10	Add'l	.001

Lay on machine table, box-like part, remove to skid

L + W + H	Min	L + W + H	Min	L + W + H	Min
15.0	.07	29.5	.22	72.8	.66
16.5	.09	33.9	.27	85.8	.79
18.2	.11	39.1	.32	101.4	.95
20.3	.13	45.4	.38	120.4	1.14
22.8	.15	52.9	.46	Add'l	.01
25.9	.18	61.9	.55	Hoist	1.78

Pickup, position to belt, part aside
Very small pickup, difficult to handle, drop ... .03
Small pickup in pan or box, drop ... .02
Medium pickup, under 3 lb, easy to handle, drop ... .03
Large pickup from bench, under 8 lb, drop ... .06
Very small, pickup and stack ... .05
Small, pickup and stack ... .04
Medium, pickup and stack ... .05
Large, pickup and stack ... .08

4. Reposition to present new edge, plane, hole, slot, etc.
    Very small, small, medium ... .02
    Large ... .04

5. Abrasive belt deburr

Conveyor or traveling belt, flat parts, deburr surface

Small L	Medium L	Min		Medium L	Min
1.0		.02		13.6	.12
2.4	1.3	.03		15.1	.13
3.9	2.8	.04		16.6	.14
5.3	4.3	.05		18.2	.15
6.7	5.9	.06		19.7	.16
8.1	7.4	.07		21.3	.17
9.6	9.0	.08		23.9	.18
11.0	10.5	.09		25.3	.19
12.4	12.0	.11		Add'l	.007

Moveable table, horizontal overhead belt, heavy deburring, box-like structures,
deburr surface

12-ga Al L	16-ga Al L	Min		12-ga Al L	16-ga Al L	Min
8.7	10.8	.47		16.4	21.9	1.34
9.5	11.9	.55		17.2	23.0	1.43
10.2	13.0	.64		18.0	24.1	1.52
11.0	14.1	.73		20.6	28.0	1.82
11.8	15.2	.82		23.9	32.6	2.18
12.5	16.3	.90		27.7	38.1	2.62
13.3	17.5	.99		32.3	44.8	3.14
14.1	18.6	1.08		Add'l		.11
14.9	19.7	1.17			Add'l	.08
15.6	20.8	1.25		Steel		.024/sq in.

Vertical abrasive belt, deburr edges, cutoffs, excess material

1-in. belt, nonbacked L	Min		4-in. belt backed L	Min		4-in. belt backed L	Min
.1	.07		.1	.07		14.6	1.91
.9	.08		.5	.50		17.2	2.10
1.8	.10		1.0	.89		20.0	2.31
2.8	.12		2.2	.98		23.0	2.54
4.1	.14		3.5	1.08		26.4	2.79
5.7	.17		4.9	1.18		30.2	3.07
7.6	.20		6.5	1.30		34.3	3.38
9.8	.24		8.3	1.43		38.8	3.71
12.5	.29		10.2	1.58		43.8	4.09
Add'l	.018		12.3	1.73		Add'l	.07

6. Roll edges mechanically

L	Min	L	Min
4.0	.03	24.2	.08
7.5	.04	32.7	.10
11.9	.05	43.4	.12
17.3	.06	56.8	.15

7. Blow off part, once
   - Machine part .10
   - Sheet metal .13
   - Box-like part .25

18.3 Pedestal-Machine Deburring and Finishing

DESCRIPTION

These estimating data are for low- and high-velocity sanding or wire and cloth brushing processes with pedestal machines. The purpose of these machines may be metal preparation or deburring, and oftentimes polishing and buffing. An operator will sit or stand and manipulate the part against the rotating surface.

Removal of weld beads flush to the parent surface plane, dishing-out of spot-weld projections, descaling, blending of dents, deburring holes or surfaces, feathering, and imbedding a special scratch pattern are some of the operations.

The pedestal machine uses a rotary aluminum-oxide grit (or other material) belt grinder over high-speed pulleys. A typical universal belt grinder is shown in Figure 18.3. This machine has a 132-in. long belt with a width of 3 in. Contact area of the belt with the part varies with the diameter of the pulley and width of the belt. The larger diameters have greater flat-surface contact. In the figure, the diameter is 12 in., but contact wheel diameters range from 1 to 16 in. With a 12-in. pulley, the abrasive belt speed is 5500 fpm.

ESTIMATING DATA DISCUSSION

The elements are sensitive to the quality requirements for deburring and finishing. Where fine-deburring and primary metal surface preparation are separated is a moot point, since sometimes these operations are consolidated. Polishing can be achieved on pedestal machines and is also considered here. Most polishing operations are intended to

obtain luster. Overall, these processes are used to remove welds, blend corners or edges, deburr, and as a primary surface preparation before painting, anodizing, or as a moderate-lot solution for a polishing operation.

The handling element includes the pickup-and-aside. Turnover and rehandling to expose other sur-

FIGURE 18.3 Universal abrasive belt grinder with a 12-in. head. (Hammond Machinery Builders)

faces or planes are not covered. Should the part entry variable exceed the maximum girth as provided by Element 1, the difference in size multiplied by .001 min and added to .93 min gives the handling time. If the part is flat sheet metal rather than box-like, add length plus width, as thickness seldom affects girth. For convenience, the estimator may wish to use the next higher table value rather than interpolate.

The rotary-belt sanding Element, 3, uses a fixed-machine location, and the part is positioned against the belt. The belt may range in width, from 1 to 4 in. or more, and has a surface velocity sufficient to categorize the operation as near metal-removal. But in this context, the purpose is the blending of weld beads, or the removal of detrimental-appearing spot weld indentations, or burrs. Parts that can be manipulated would be used with this machine. If the parts are awkward and exposure of the bead to the weld is difficult, a portable tool is possible. With this rotary belt element, the entry variable is length. Remember that the width of a manual pass against the belt is restricted to belt width, for instance 4-in.

Element 4 is for buffing or descaling of discoloration, rust, hard carbon, or metal etching. The first time is for a threshold of 25 sq in. Additional areas above 25 sq in. are indicated as per 1 sq in.

Metal polishing can be described as the process of producing a uniform surface of specific characteristics. In most instances, metal polishing is preceded by machining operations and followed by a buffing operation. The two, buffing and polishing, are sometimes separated, but not in these data. Metal polishing removes metal and corrects surface imperfections, but is not used to generate or retain geometric or dimensional accuracy. The wheels in this application are flexible cloth and vary in hardness, to which the desired abrasive is cemented. Flap-wheels can be considered also. Oftentimes in lot production, metal polishing is termed an art form, but estimating data are provided in Element 5. Area, sq in., is the entry variable.

A fast approach to estimating pedestal-machine deburring is given in Item 18.3 of Section IV. Similar to Table 18.3, the item provides setup and $/100 units. The first term provides for handling and uses the entry variable of box girth or $L + W + H$. A rehandle cost is available for each major reposition. Three deburring methods, belt grinding, wire brushing, and buff and polish, are listed, and their entry variables are length, width, and area.

EXAMPLES

A. A sheet metal chassis having maximum box dimensions of 59.5 in. has 24 in. of gas metal-arc welding bead, and it is necessary to blend the bead to the basic metal surface. The pedestal belt grinder with a suitable grit belt is used to do this job. Find the lot estimate for 20 parts.

Table	Description	Time
18.3-S	Setup	.1 hr
18.3-1	Start, stop machine	.04 min
18.3-2	Handle	.58
18.3-3	24 in. of weld bead	.72
	Unit estimate	1.34 min
	Lot estimate	.55 hr

B. A forging can be handheld and has a light rust over the surface. The irregular dimension, when boxed for girth dimensions, is 17.1 in. The surface area is 36 in. Find the unit estimate.

Table	Description	Time
18.2-2	Handle	.10 min
18.2-4	Remove light rust, .27 + .01 (36−25)	.38
18.2-2	Reposition 5 times, 5 × .05	.25
	Unit estimate	.73 min

C. Estimate the unit cost of Example A above using information from Section IV.

Item	Description	Cost
18.3	Setup subtotal	$ 1.08
18.3	Box factor, 59.5 × .184	$10.95
18.3	Belt grind, 24 × .540	12.96
	$/100 units	$24.99
	Lot cost	$ 6.08
	Unit cost including effects of setup	$ .30

TABLE 18.3 PEDESTAL-MACHINE DEBURRING AND FINISHING

Setup .... **.1 hr**

Operation elements in estimating minutes

1. Start, stop machine .... .04

2. Handling

L + W + H	Min	L + W + H	Min	L + W + H	Min
15.0	.07	25.0	.18	48.0	.41
15.5	.08	26.7	.19	53.0	.46
16.1	.09	28.6	.21	58.7	.52
17.4	.10	30.7	.23	65.1	.58
18.2	.11	33.0	.26	72.3	.65
19.8	.12	35.6	.28	80.3	.74
20.7	.13	38.3	.31	89.4	.83
21.7	.14	41.4	.34	99.6	.93
22.7	.15	44.8	.38	Add'l	.001

Reposition side, edge, turnover, each time .... .05

3. Belt grinding

L	Min	L	Min	L	Min	L	Min
1.0	.04	5.3	.16	10.8	.30	28.8	.79
1.4	.05	5.8	.17	11.9	.33	31.7	.87
1.9	.06	6.2	.18	13.2	.37	35.0	.95
2.3	.08	6.7	.19	14.5	.40	38.5	1.05
2.7	.09	7.1	.20	16.0	.44	42.4	1.15
3.2	.10	7.5	.22	17.7	.49	46.7	1.27
3.6	.11	8.0	.23	19.5	.54	51.5	1.39
4.0	.12	8.4	.24	21.5	.59	56.6	1.53
4.5	.13	8.8	.25	23.7	.65	62.4	1.69
4.9	.15	9.8	.28	26.1	.72	Add'l	.03

4. Wire brush or deburr with wire wheel

Remove surface discoloration, up to 25 sq in	.15
Add'l sq in	.005
Remove light rust or corrosion, up to 25 sq in	.27
Add'l sq in	.02
Remove heavy rust or corrosion, up to 25 sq in	.44
Add'l sq in	.03
Remove hard carbon, metal etching, up to 25 sq in	.68
Add'l sq in	.03

5. Buff or polish with cloth wheel

Area	Min	Area	Min	Area	Min
1.2	.42	2.6	.91	5.6	1.94
1.3	.47	2.9	1.00	6.1	2.14
1.5	.51	3.1	1.10	6.7	2.35
1.6	.56	3.5	1.21	7.4	2.59
1.8	.62	3.8	1.33	8.1	2.85
1.9	.68	4.2	1.46	9.0	3.13
2.1	.75	4.6	1.61	9.8	3.45
2.4	.82	5.1	1.77	Add'l	.35

18.4 Handheld Portable-Tool Deburring

DESCRIPTION

There is a variety of portable tools on the market for deburring. Powered by air, electricity, cable, and hydraulic motor, their description is familiar. Portable-tool deburring methods are popular because of the operator mobility and the low cost of equipment. Sometimes these tools are bench-located; in other situations, the deburring operator will have access to drill presses, pedestal machines, etc., and the portable tools extend the capacity to deburr a wide range of metal parts.

ESTIMATING DATA DISCUSSION

The handling elements include both the pickup, aside, and occasional reposition or turnover to expose various internal or external surfaces, edges, slots, holes, weld beads, spot-weld indentations, scratches, and burrs. With portable-powered tools, one hand can hold the tool while the other simultaneously can reposition the part. Of course, size and difficulty of work may restrict the reposition opportunity.

If the work is awkward, and a turnover or reposition is necessary to expose a new burr, then a lay-down and pickup of the tool, as found in Element 2, is collaterally required. Because of the mobility of the operator, he or she may position the tool and body in different positions relative to the workpiece.

Element 3 uses the air-motor drill, usually with a countersink or bit. The element includes hole-to-hole time and burr for accessible location. If the location is internal, and a reposition is not planned or very difficult to achieve, the hole-to-hole-and-deburr is increased to .15 min. The hole count is for one side. If the number of holes exceeds that which is given, the estimator may add combinations of holes to estimate the number.

For retap or reream metal, or an air-tap of a sheet metal, Element 4 may be used.

Element 5 uses the air-driven rotary flat sander with an abrasive aluminum oxide grit of 50, and a disk usually of 5-in. diameter. As a high-speed surface sander, the element may be used to reduce the crest of the weld bead, blend spot weld indentations, or round sharp corners. Cutouts or holes which may be burred are another application. The tool is held with both hands. Similar remarks apply for Element 6, where the entry variable is length.

Element 7 uses a dual-action sander, i.e., oscillating motion in both the *x-y* direction that is air-driven with a 3-in. wide × 6 in.-long 60–80 grit aluminum oxide paper. The tool may be gripped by one hand. The process may follow a rough-sanding operation. It scratches in a mixed direction and is usually not intended as a basic stock-removal tool, but it does benefit in deburring edges. The pass length suggests that a zone area is sanded.

Single action sanding, Element 7, is for an air-driven portable tool with the scratch action coincident to the long direction of the tool. The data are for 100-grit aluminum oxide. The primary entry variable is surface area, sq in.

Changing of sanding disks or pads is often required on a part basis, especially if the part is large. Otherwise for weld-bead blending, the ratio of one change to 40 in. is appropriate.

Table 18.4 is used to estimate time. Alternately, cost for portable-tool deburring can be found by applying Item 18.4 of Section IV. The constant for the cost equation is always included. Handling cost depends upon box girth ($L + W + H$). If a major rehandle is anticipated, a cost factor is available. Five methods are open to selection. Of course, not all methods are used for each operation.

EXAMPLES

A. A sheet metal chassis having minimum girth dimensions of $L + W + H = 59.5$ in., has 24 in. of gas metal-arc welding length. Portable rotary tool sanding is required to blend the weld bead with the sheet metal surface. Lot quantity is 20.

Table	Description	Time	
18.4-S	Setup	.1	hr
18.4-1	Handle	.58	min
18.4-5	24-in. weld length	5.31	
18.4-2	Replace 2 rotary sanding disks	.28	
	Unit estimate	6.17	min
	Lot estimate	2.157	hr

B. A sheet metal bracket subassembly having a girth $L + W + H = 59.5$ in., has 30 in. of weld bead to sand down, 38 in. of length for dual-action sanding to blend the area, and 825 sq in. of total surface area sanding. Size of lot is 20.

Table	Description	Time	
18.4-S	Setup	.1	hr
18.4-1	Handle	.58	min
18.4-5	38 in. of weld length	8.30	
18.4-7	38 in. of dual-action sanding	.55	
18.4-7	825 sq in. of surface area, $= .95 + (825-336.8) .0019 =$	1.88	
18.4-2	Change 3 pads	.42	
	Unit estimate	11.73	min
	Lot estimate	4.009	hr

C. Find base cost for Example B above using Section IV information.

Item	Description	Cost
18.4	Setup subtotal	$ .73
18.4	Cycle constant	$ .49
18.4	Box factor, $59.5 \times .124$	7.38
18.4	Weld rotary sand, 24×2.79	66.96
	$/100 units subtotal	$74.83
	Lot cost	$15.70

TABLE 18.4 HANDHELD PORTABLE-TOOL DEBURRING

Setup .1 hr

Operation elements in estimating minutes

1. Handling and occasional reposition

L + W + H	Min	L + W + H	Min	L + W + H	Min
15.0	.07	25.0	.18	48.0	.41
15.5	.08	26.7	.19	53.0	.46
16.1	.09	28.6	.21	58.7	.52
17.4	.10	30.7	.23	65.1	.58
18.2	.11	33.0	.26	72.3	.65
19.8	.12	35.6	.28	80.3	.74
20.7	.13	38.3	.31	89.4	.83
21.7	.14	41.4	.34	99.6	.93
22.7	.15	44.8	.38	Add'l	.001

Special reposition, turnover, each time .05

2. Tool handling

Pickup and aside tool from bench	.03
Pickup and aside tool from hook	.04
Pickup and aside tool from suspended spring hanger	.02
Replace portable sanding paper	.14
Open and close goggles	.06

3. Deburr; easy location, air motor

Holes	Min	Holes	Min	Holes	Min	Holes	Min
1	.04	8	.35	15	.65	22	.95
2	.09	9	.39	16	.69	23	.99
3	.13	10	.43	17	.73	24	1.04
4	.17	11	.47	18	.78	25	1.08
5	.22	12	.52	19	.82	26	1.12
6	.26	13	.56	20	.86	27	1.16
7	.30	14	.60	21	.91	Add'l	.043

Difficult location, each hole .15

4. Tap sheet metal, or re-tap, re-ream with air motor

Holes	Min	Holes	Min	Holes	Min	Holes	Min
1	.09	6	.52	11	.96	16	1.40
2	.17	7	.61	12	1.05	17	1.49
3	.26	8	.70	13	1.14	18	1.57
4	.35	9	.79	14	1.22	19	1.66
5	.44	10	.87	15	1.31	Add'l	.087

5. Rotary sand, 5, 7-in. disk, air motor

L	Min	L	Min	L	Min
1.1	.15	3.7	.71	15.9	3.40
1.3	.19	4.5	.89	19.7	4.25
1.5	.23	5.5	1.11	24.5	5.31
1.8	.29	6.8	1.39	30.5	6.64
2.1	.36	8.3	1.74	38.0	8.30
2.5	.46	10.3	2.18	47.4	10.37
3.0	.57	12.8	2.72	Add'l	.23

Rotary sand, 2, 3-in. disk, air motor

L	Min	L	Min	L	Min
1.0	.77	1.8	1.40	3.2	2.30
1.3	1.00	2.0	1.50	3.3	2.50
1.4	1.10	2.2	1.70	3.7	2.80
1.6	1.20	2.5	1.90	4.1	3.10
1.7	1.30	2.8	2.10	Add'l	.77

6. Grinding wheel, electric motor

L	Min	L	Min	L	Min
1.0	.06	6.0	.16	18.3	.39
1.7	.08	7.6	.19	22.4	.47
2.5	.09	9.6	.23	27.4	.56
3.4	.11	12.0	.27	33.3	.67
4.6	.13	14.9	.32	Add'l	.019

7. Dual-action sanding with air sander, or 5-in. drum

Pass Length	Min	Pass Length	Min	Pass Length	Min
2.0	.37	38.9	.55	92.9	.80
10.0	.41	50.5	.60	110.0	.88
18.7	.45	63.3	.66	128.7	.97
28.3	.50	77.4	.73	Add'l	.005

Single-action sanding with air sander

Area	Min.	Area	Min	Area	Min
25.0	.37	115.5	.54	248.7	.79
44.6	.40	144.4	.59	290.6	.87
66.1	.45	175.9	.65	336.8	.95
89.8	.49	210.6	.72	Add'l	.002

18.5 Hand Deburring

DESCRIPTION

This kind of deburring consists of manual elements, as there are no motorized, air, electrical, etc., devices that the operator is using. The operator is using countersinks, burrs, scrapers, files and other simple contrivances that are operated manually.

ESTIMATING DATA DISCUSSION

Hand operations usually imply the absence of cranes, hoists, etc., and handling is for pickup and aside, load on bench, from pan, skid, etc. With hand deburring, some repositioning by the operator on the part during deburring is possible. If a part has to be turned over, then the tool is set aside, and the special reposition is included. A tool rehandle may be colaterally included.

Element 3 has two tables for deburring holes of 1/2-in. diameter and smaller using a countersink bit. Also, holes larger than 1/2 in. are categorized in Element 3 and may use a larger countersink or special tool.

If the material is aluminum and is an edge, as distinguished from a hole, use Element 4. For steel deburring of edges, use Element 4.

For gear tooth deburring, Element 5, allow a reposition for every five teeth. Hand sandpaper, see Element 8, is for a 1-in. pass width.

Item 18.5 of Section IV can be used to estimate direct-labor cost for hand deburring. The constant operational cost is always included along with one or more of the other costs. A cost can be included for each major rehandling, each hole or gear tooth, and breaking of linear edges.

EXAMPLES

A. A small aluminum assembly, $L + W + H = 17.5$ in., has 2 square punched holes of 4 in. length each, 3 elongated holes with burr length of 1.6 in. each, and 14 internal holes less than 1/2 in. diameter. For this small lot, determine the unit estimate.

Table	Description	Time
18.5-1	Handle	.11 min
18.5-2	Pickup, aside scraper	.03
18.5-4	Scrape square holes, 2 × .14	.28
18.5-4	Scrape elongated holes, 2 × .10	.20
18.5-2	Pickup, aside countersink	.03
18.5-3	Deburr 14 holes	.69
	Unit estimate	1.34 min

B. A steel casting has a machine flange with a burr on the inside, irregular opening and on the bolt-circle of 6 1/2-in. ID holes. The casting can be handled and minimum box dimensions for girth are 31.0 in. The irregular opening has a dimension 10.67 in. in length. Using hand labor, estimate the unit time. The forging is medium hardness.

Table	Description	Time
18.5-1	Handle	.26 min
18.5-2	Tool handling for file	.03
18.5-4	File inside burr	.31
18.5-2	Countersink handle	.03
18.5-3	Deburr 6 holes	.29
	Unit estimate	.92 min

C. Determine a unit cost for Example A above. The base-cost approach of Section IV is to be used.

Item	Description	Cost
18.5	Cycle constant	$ 1.70
18.5	2 square holes, break edges 2 × 4 × .240	1.92
18.5	Elongated holes, 3 × 1.6 × .240	1.15
18.5	Elongated holes, 14 × .792	11.09
	$/100 units	$15.86

TABLE 18.5   HAND DEBURRING

Setup   .05 hr

Operation elements in estimating minutes

1. Handling and occasional reposition

L + W + H	Min	L + W + H	Min	L + W + H	Min
15.0	.07	25.0	.18	48.0	.41
15.5	.08	26.7	.19	53.0	.46
16.1	.09	28.6	.21	58.7	.52
17.4	.10	30.7	.23	65.1	.58
18.2	.11	33.0	.26	72.3	.65
19.8	.12	35.6	.28	80.3	.74
20.7	.13	38.3	.31	89.4	.83
21.7	.14	41.4	.34	99.6	.93
22.7	.15	44.8	.38	Add'l	.001

Special reposition, turnover, end-for-end   .05

2. Tool handling

Pickup and aside tool from bench   .03
Pickup and aside tool from hook   .04
Pickup and aside tool from suspended spring hanger   .02

3. Deburr holes

Holes 1/2-in. diameter and under with countersink

Holes	Min	Holes	Min	Holes	Min
1	.05	6	.29	11	.54
2	.10	7	.34	12	.59
3	.15	8	.39	13	.64
4	.19	9	.44	14	.69
5	.24	10	.49	Add'l	.049

Holes over 1/2-in. diameter using large diameter scraper

Holes	Min	Holes	Min	Holes	Min
1	.08	4	.32	7	.57
2	.16	5	.41	8	.65
3	.24	6	.49	Add'l	.08

4. Break edges

Break edge with scraper, file on aluminum

L	Min	L	Min	L	Min
1.0	.08	5.0	.14	19.1	.35
1.5	.09	6.9	.17	24.0	.42
2.1	.10	9.2	.20	29.7	.50
2.8	.11	11.9	.24	36.1	.60
3.5	.12	15.1	.29	Add'l	.015

Break edge with scraper, file on steel

Soft L	Medium L	Hard L	Min
1.0	.4		.07
1.4	.8	.2	.08
1.8	1.2	.5	.09
2.3	1.6	.9	.10
2.8	2.1	1.3	.11
3.4	2.6	1.7	.12
4.0	3.1	2.2	.13
4.7	3.8	2.8	.14
5.5	4.4	3.3	.16
6.3	5.2	4.0	.17
7.3	6.0	4.7	.19
8.3	6.9	5.5	.21
9.4	7.9	6.3	.23
10.7	9.0	7.3	.25

Soft L	Medium L	Hard L	Min
12.0	10.2	8.3	.28
13.5	11.6	9.4	.31
15.2	13.0	10.7	.34
17.0	14.6	12.1	.37
19.0	16.4	13.6	.41
21.1	18.4	15.3	.45
23.6	20.5	17.1	.49
26.2	22.8	19.1	.54
29.1	25.4	21.3	.60
32.3	28.3	23.8	.65
35.8	31.4	26.5	.72
Add'l			.019
	Add'l		.021
		Add'l	.024

5. File gear-teeth edges

Gear diametral pitch	11+	6–10	3–5	1,2
Min per tooth	.07	09	.09	.12

6. Blowoff, get and aside air hose included
   Bottom hole   .10
       4-in. part, to 5 lb   .10
       8-in. part, 5–15 lb   .17
       12-in. part, 15–40 lb   .26

7. Chase thread with hand tap   .40/in.

8. Sand using sandpaper

1-in. pass L	2.0	2.4	2.9	3.5	4.3	6.5	9.8	Add'l
Min	.28	.34	.41	.49	.61	.91	1.37	.14

9. Straighten part

   $L + W$ over 60 in.   4.00
   $L + W$ under 60 in.   2.00

10. Assemble and disassemble to deburr
    Handling per component   .30
    Bolt or screw   .60

18.6 Plastic Material Deburring

DESCRIPTION

These data are grouped for plastic materials that are produced by thermoplastic injection, thermosetting plastic, and bench molding. Plastics usually deburr easier than metals. Although plastics themselves vary greatly as to deburring properties, they are categorized jointly as "plastics."

A variety of deburring elements are used, and their descriptions are given in the next section. No new machines, processes, or manual work descriptions are given beyond those already described in the other deburring of metals sections.

ESTIMATING DATA DISCUSSION

The handling of the molded unit may start with several units to be handled as one. Following separation by degating Element 3, the parts are individually stacked, dropped, or tossed. In a degating operation, the work starts with a pattern of several pieces which are eventually separated. The .07 and .21 min are inadequate in this case; therefore, a "dispose smaller piece" time is available.

Handcutting involves the use of the knife and the cutting action. The time is for each gate cut. A bandsaw can be used for degating, as found in Element 4. Trimming, Element 5, is with a bandsaw or by hand and depends either upon girth or in. Hole deburring may be with a drill press or punch. In prick-punching, Element 6, the pickup of the hammer and point is included in the first hole.

In Element 7, thread deflashing, a tap or die is used for handchasing. Surface or edge preparation involves a file, sandpaper, or scraper, and time is given.

Sand blasting is within a hood and a directed air-grit stream from a gun can be used to prepare surfaces.

Costs can be estimated using Item 18.6 of Section IV. The estimator applies the constant cost and then makes a selection of other deburring requirements.

EXAMPLES

A. A molded plastic cluster of 10 parts per shot is to be degated by hand, and 10 holes have a slight flash. Estimate the unit time.

Table	Description	Time
18.6-1	Handle, .07/10	.007 min
18.6-1	Reposition 20 times for gates and holes, 20 × .023/10	.046
18.6-2	Pick up two tools	.06
18.6-3	Hand degate runner	.11
18.6-6	Open hole by deburring	.05
18.6-1	Toss each piece aside	.03
	Unit estimate	.30 min

B. A phenolic thermosetting resin is molded as a single unit with two inserts. The exposed part of the inserts is about $1/2 \times 1/2 \times 3/8$-in. overall, but is covered by a thin coating. Additionally, 2 gates need to be removed. Find the time per unit.

Table	Description	Time
18.6-1	Bench to bench	.07 min
18.6-3	Saw off gate	.04
18.6-8	Scrape area, area about 1 in.	.25
18.6-8	File edges, about 1.5-in. long, 1.5 × .32	.48
18.6-2	Pick up 2 tools	.06
	Unit estimate	.93 min

C. Find the base-cost of Example A above using Item 18.6 of Section IV.

Item	Description	Cost
18.6	Cost constant	$1.58
18.6	Hand degate runner	2.07
18.6	Deburr 1 hole per part	.73
	$/100 units	$4.38

TABLE 18.6   PLASTIC MATERIAL DEBURRING

Setup	**.05 hr**

Operation elements in estimating minutes

1. Handle (per pc or molded unit)	
Bench to bench, pickup and aside	.07
Skid to skid, pickup and aside	.21
Dispose small pc	.03
Reposition, turn 45° or more to give new surface	.023
Pack or unpack small part, hand held	.06

2. Pick up tool	.03
3. Handcut gate or runner	
⅜ in. or more	.23/ea
Under ⅜ in.	.11/ea
4. Saw off gate or runner	.02/ea
5. Trim flash with saw	.02/in.
Trim flash by hand	
$L + W + H$ over 12 in.	.56/pc
$L + W + H$ under 12 in.	.11/in.
6. Deburr hole with drill or countersink	.06/ea
Open hole with punch	.02/ea
Prick punch with point and hammer	.12/first hole
Add'l hole	.04/ea
7. Deflash threads	.11/in.
8. File or sand edges	.32/in.
Scrape area	.28/sq in.
Hand-sand area	.17/sq in.
9. Sand blast	.02/sq in.
10. Clean	.56/sq in.
Wash with cleaning fluid	.45/sq in.
Wipe part	
Blow off	.23/sq in.
Plug open end	.65/end

18.7 Loose-Abrasive Deburring Processes

DESCRIPTION

Loose-abrasive deburring is also called tumbling and is a controlled method to remove burrs, scale, flash, oxides, as well as to improve surface finish. Parts to be deburred are placed in a rotating barrel or vibrating tub with an abrasive media, water or oil, and perhaps some chemical compound. As the barrel or tub rotates or vibrates, sliding motions of the media cause an abrading action.

Abrasives are usually aluminum oxide and silicon carbide and exist in a preform geometry. A preform size and geometry are available for the particular part. Cleaners are usually alkaline or acid. Alkaline cleaners must be chemically formulated to avoid part rusting. The cleaners are formulated to do certain things; remove rust, suspend oils, etc. In self-tumbling situations, media are oftentimes not used.

Figure 18.7 shows a horizontal-barrel finishing process with two compartments and an 13.8 cu ft volume capacity. The tumbling velocity is variable, ranging from 6 to 30 rpm.

ESTIMATING DATA DISCUSSION

The basic setup value is given for no media change. If media changes can be anticipated by the estimator, the setup is related to the approximate volume of the compartment or tub.

The entry value is volume, meaning box volume of the part. This minimizes volume calculations. For

FIGURE 18.7 Horizontal tumbling barrel with two compartments, 30 x 16-in. in size and 13.8 cu ft capacity. *(Almco Division, King-Seeley Thermos Co)*

The handle, magnet disposing, and pick disposing columns provide the basic handling time. During actual tumbling time, the operator is doing other work. No tumbling or operator waiting time is covered by any of the elements. If a wash or oil dip or both elements are required, they are added to the basic handling value. Wash and oil dip are a function of material corrosion, sensitivity, and pre- or post-operations.

Parts that stick in the screen or flat parts that are difficult to separate from the stones may be pick-disposed where the part is removed, separated, and stacked. Ferrous parts that do not easily screen may be magnet-separated.

If the parts are tumbled without any stones, or a strainer is used to separate the parts, reduce the basic deburr time by one-fourth. For parts with an impingement-damage problem, double the time. For small parts (terminals, nuts, etc.) that are batch loaded and unloaded, a special time of .0005 min is given.

Labor cost can be estimated directly using item 18.7 of Section IV. This cost, expressed in terms of a base, has dimensions of $/100 units. Item 18.7 has entry variables similar to Table 18.7. Box volume, or the least x–y–z coordinate axis dimensions that will envelope the part, is used as a multiplier. The multiplier includes handling, washing, and oil dip.

example, box volume of a turned part is length $\times$ diameter $\times$ diameter *(L $\times$ Dia $\times$ Dia)*. To minimize cost estimating effort, the estimator may wish to follow the policy of using the next higher tabular entry.

TYPICAL ESTIMATES

A. A machined part having box dimensions of $3/8 \times 1\,1/4 \times 1/2$ in. is to be tumbled, washed, and oil dipped. No exceptional problems are forseen. Determine the unit estimate.

Table	Description	Time
18.7-S	Setup	.1 hr
18.7-1	Volume = .23, deburr	.008 min
18.7-1	Wash	.001
18.7-1	Oil dip	.002
	Unit estimate	.011 min

B. A part having box dimensions of $6\,1/2 \times 3 \times 2.125$ in. is to be tumbled. Impingement problems are deburring only.

Table	Description	Time
18.7-1	Volume = 41.4 cu in, and for damage prevention, increase time by 2, 2 $\times$ .22	.44 min
	Unit estimate	.44 min

C. Find base-cost of Example A above using information from Section IV.

Item	Description	Cost
18.7	Box volume = .23, .23 $\times$ .414	$.095
	$/100 units	$.095

TABLE 18.7 LOOSE-ABRASIVE DEBURRING PROCESSES

Setup

No media change	.1 hr
3 cu ft media change	.3 hr
10 cu ft media change	.4 hr
20 cu ft media change	.5 hr

Operation elements in estimating minutes

1. Loose abrasive deburring

Part cu in.	Handle	Wash	Oil dip	Handle magnet-disposing	Handle pick-disposing
.01	.0007	.00003	.0007		.02
.03	.001	.0001	.0008		.02
.05	.002	.0002	.0009		.02
.1	.003	.0003	.001		.03
.2	.006	.0007	.001	.007	.03
.3	.008	.001	.002	.010	.03
.4	.01	.001	.002	.014	.03
.5	.01	.002	.002	.02	.03
1	.03	.003	.004	.04	.04
2	.05	.007	.007	.07	.06
3	.08	.01	.01	.11	.07
7	.13	.02	.02		
22	.19	.03	.03		
54	.22	.05	.04		
104	.24	.05	.04		
171	.28	.06	.05		
238	.32	.07	.06		
305	.35	.07	.06		
405	.41	.09	.07		
709	.58	.12	.10		
920	.69	.14	.12		
1170	.83	.17	.14		
1472	1.00	.20	.17		
1873	1.22	.25	.20		
2376	1.49	.30	.25		
2878	1.77	.36	.29		
3380	2.05	.41	.34		
4133	2.46	.50	.41		
Add'l	.0006	.0001	.0001		

Rivets, pins, terminals	.0005
Printed circuit board	.15

18.8 Abrasive-Media Flow Deburring Machines

DESCRIPTION

Abrasive-media flow deburring machines deburr internal edges or surfaces by a controlled force flow of an abrasive laden semi-solid grinding media. The deburring machines hold the workpiece and tooling in a position relative to the media. Fixtures can hold the workpiece in a position and contain, direct, or restrict the media flow to areas of the workpiece where abrasion is desired. In application, the number of holes or surface area does not necessarily influence the cycle time. Abrasion occurs in areas where media flow is restricted.

Abrasive-media flow machines will deburr a hidden or secondary burr and improve internal surface finish. These machines remove burrs that are inconvenient (or impossible) to reach by manual deburring methods. The deburring also will result in a smoother and brighter finish.

The flow of the media is three dimensional. The media is forced up through a fixture and the workpiece into a top cylinder. After a predetermined volume of media or time has been achieved, the media returns from the top cylinder back through the workpiece and fixture to the bottom cylinder. Different media may be selected for different surface finish and burr removal. The media cylinder diameter and pressure can vary depending on the machine. Also, hydraulic force is used to clamp the workpiece and also to give the desired media pressure. The fixtures, depending on the size and shape of the part, may hold one or several workpieces.

Figure 18.8 is a sketch of an abrasive-media flow deburring machines. Media pressures range from 100 to 3000 psi. Delivery rates of more than 100 gallons per minute are possible.

ESTIMATING DATA DISCUSSION

The setup allows for the time to obtain fixture and parts and to study the blueprints. The setup time also includes adding media, installing the fixture on the machine, one cycle of the machine for running the first part, and its inspection. If the water cooler needs attention, the setup time is increased.

Element 1 deals with loading and unloading parts in a fixture. Time is determined by knowing the number of parts. Because the fixture guides the abrasive media throughout and around the part, it is usual to load a part into a fixture.

The weight of the fixture and part(s) is used for finding the load and unload time of the fixture and parts onto the machine table. The element includes removing a top plate, removing excess media from the fixture and part(s), loading the fixture on the bottom plate, and loading the fixture on machine.

Brinell hardness (Bhn) is used to give an indication of the deburring time. The relationship shows that harder materials require less time. The deburring of holes, size of burr, or surface area is not a factor in this element. Deburring time is shown in Element 3.

The estimator may prefer to estimate costs rather than time. Item 18.8 of Section IV can be applied for these approximate values. The costs relate to a base which represents a national norm Productive Hour Cost (PHC). These operational costs are found by always including the constant cost and multiplying the number of pieces loaded in the fixture by the cost $/100 ($ per 100) unit factor, and multiplying the weight of the fixture and parts by its factor.

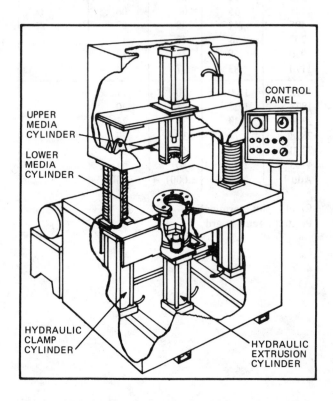

FIGURE 18.8 An abrasive-media flow deburring machine. (Extrude Hone Corp.)

EXAMPLES

A. Internal cavities of a part are inconvenient for manual deburring methods. An abrasive-media flow deburring machine is selected to remove primary and secondary burrs. A fixture is designed for three parts, and total weight is 40 lb. The part has a hardness of 240 Bhn. Find the cycle and unit estimate.

Table	Description	Time
18.8-1	Load part in fixture	1.58 min
18.8-2	Load fixture, unload from machine	1.33
18.8-3	Deburr, 240 Bhn	4.00
	Cycle estimate	6.91 min
	Unit estimate	2.30 min

B. A nickel alloy is used for an airfoil surface. The operation is planned to remove traces of the original casting process. Two 8-lb parts are loaded in a 36-lb fixture. A lot of 500 is to be surfaced finished. Find the unit estimate, hr/100 units, and lot estimate.

Table	Description	Time
18.8-S	Setup	.55 hr
18.8-1	Load and unload part to fixture	1.58 min
18.8-2	Load and unload 52-lb fixture and parts	1.92
18.8-3	Deburr (Hardness of alloy is unknown, use maximum time.)	4.4
	Cycle estimate	7.90 min
	Unit estimate	2.63 min
	Hr/100 units	4.384
	Lot estimate	22.47 hr

C. A tool steel extrusion die is produced by electrical discharge machining. The external surfaces of three T-shaped internal slots must be polished. Each die weighs 14 lb and the fixture weighs 26 lb. Quantity is 1600 dies. Four separate setups are planned for the year. Find the unit estimate, hr/100, lot, and annual hourly requirements.

Table	Description	Time
18.8-S	Setup	.55 hr
18.8-S	Water-cooler	.85 hr
18.8-1	Load and unload one part	.83 min
18.8-2	Fixture and part, 40 lb	1.33
18.8-3	Deburr	2.8
	Unit estimate	4.96 min
	Hr/100 units	8.267
	Lot estimate for 1600 parts	34.47 hr
	Annual time requirement	137.87 hr

D. Re-estimate Example A above using a base-cost approach given in Section IV. This calculation provides direct labor costs based upon a national norm productive hour.

Item	Description	Cost
18.8	Cycle constant cost	$62.90
18.8	Load 3 parts in fixture, 3 × .624	1.87
18.8	Part and fixture weighs 40 lb., 40 × .713	28.50
	Cycle $/300 units	$93.29
	$/100 units	31.10

E. Find the direct-labor cost for Example B above. Use Item 18.8. Two 8-lb parts are loaded in a 36-1b fixture. The lot quantity is 500.

Item	Description	Cost
18.8	Setup cost total	$ 7.23
18.8	Cycle constant	62.90
18.8	Two parts per fixture, 2 × 6.02	12.04
18.8	Weight, 52 × .713	37.08
	$/200 units	$112.02
	$/100 units	$ 56.01
	Lot cost	$287.28

TABLE 18.8 ABRASIVE-MEDIA FLOW DEBURRING MACHINES

Setup

Basic setup	.55 hr
Water-cooler attention	.85 hr

Operation elements in estimating minutes

1. Load and unload parts into fixture

No.	Min	No.	Min
1	.83	7	3.08
2	1.20	8	3.45
3	1.58	9	3.83
4	1.95	10	4.20
5	2.33	11	4.57
6	2.70	12	4.95

2. Load and unload parts and fixture onto machine

Parts and fixtures, lb	Min	Parts and fixtures, lb	Min
14.0	.09	37.2	1.11
18.0	.26	42.2	1.33
22.5	.46	48.2	1.60
25.1	.58	51.7	1.75
28.5	.73	55.4	1.92
30.0	.79	64.0	2.31
33.0	.93	74.4	2.77

3. Abrasive-media flow deburring

Bhn	Min	Bhn	Min
225	4.4	280	3.2
240	4.0	290	3.0
270	3.4	300	2.8

19.1 Chemical Machining and Printed Circuit Board Fabrication

DESCRIPTION

Chemical machining, a process for the removal of metal by chemical action, is suited for production of flat, relatively thin parts having difficult configurations, and for designs requiring area, point, or line removal of metal. Metal is removed from desired areas by etching or chemically converting it into a metallic salt which is carried away by the etchant. Chemical machining produces nameplates, blanks, and printed circuit boards. It is a means to selectively remove metal for weight reduction. While the chemical blanking techniques are appropriate for small- and medium-run quantities and thicknesses less than 3/32 in., it is also suitable for hard-to-work metals such as beryllium copper, and thin materials where the finished product cannot have a burr edge as produced by a blanking die. For printed circuit production, chemical machining is an obvious and popular method.

The artwork and negatives used in chemical machining are the "tooling" for the process. The artwork is drawn oversized and reduced in scale for production. When a large number of parts are to be chemically machined, it is necessary to have multiple images on the same film after photographic reduction. Two transparencies, if opposite-side machining is required, are placed together and registered. The process continues with metal preparation, image printing, etching and resist removal, and postfabrication of parts from a multiple-unit panel. Figure 19.1 is a single-chamber etch machine with a variable velocity conveyor. In the etcher,

oscillating nozzles spray both sides of the metal. Areas of the metal not protected by a photo resist are dissolved, leaving only the finished part. Quantities of small parts are usually held together by metal tabs incorporated into the original artwork, or by an adhesive or plastic-laminated backing. When etching is complete, photo resist may or may not be removed. The various units of the process can be arranged for separated batchwork, or continuous wet-processing systems are available.

ESTIMATING DATA DISCUSSION

These data deal with electroless etching or subtractive etching using chemicals. The volume of work to be handled depends on whether the shop is producing for its own needs or as a vendor to outside customers. Generally, job shops do not have high-volume runs but handle short to medium quantity runs of many types of work with a few of the larger shops handling high-volume production for commercial or industrial application.

The data are for a noncontinuous process and the estimator selects the appropriate operations to produce the design. Batching is the usual mode. Times are selected from five major parts of Table 19.1: (1) artwork and negative preparation, (2) metal preparation, (3) image processing and masking, (4) etching and post etching processes, and (5) fabrication processes.

The data deal with three types of chemical ma-

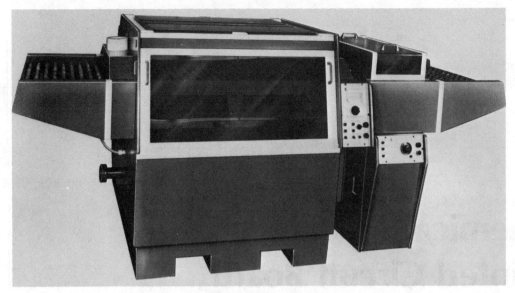

FIGURE 19.1 Conveyorized chemical etching machine. *(Chemcut Corporation)*

chining problems: blanking of small thin parts, production of printed circuit boards, and etching of work for weight reduction or other design purposes. Costs resulting from yield and scrap, and chemical supplies, are not provided, and are usually obtained from a historical analysis of the shop's data. As direct-labor time is influenced by many factors, these average data are for a shop using standard and noncontinuous processing equipment. Complexity of design is a factor averaged out in the data. Raw material, while it can vary, is reasonable as to weight, size, girth, etc., and is not heavy. For instance, printed circuit stock material may arrive in 36 × 48 in. sheets, with copper 1.4 mil thick, either one or both sizes, to panels perhaps 12 × 18 in. in size. The data to follow use a 12 × 18-in. panel as typical, although many other sizes are possible. Data are not too sensitive to panel size although it is sensitive to units on the panel. Chemical blanking may start in the sheet, strip, or roll stock. Material for etching and weight reduction may start out as sheet or strip.

A panel is composed of one or many units of the same design. Thus, panel time is ultimately divided by the number of parts placed on the panel.

EXAMPLES

A. Estimate a 2-in. square printed circuit switch having nickel-gold-rhodium fingers, 28 close-tolerance holes, plating on one side, and 1-oz copper-board two-sided. Raw material is a 12 × 15-in. panel. The desired quantity is 500 switches. Allowing for border and inner-part spacing, there are 5 columns and 8 rows or 40 switches per panel. The number of panels is 13, allowing a 4% scrap loss.

Table	Description	Setup	Operation
19.1-1	Preparation of image	20.0 hr	
19.1-1	Reduction	1.0	
19.1-1	Step and repeat	1.0	
19.1-1	Negative envelope, 13 panels × 10 min	2.17	
19.1-2	Shear panel from raw stock	.15	.14 min
19.1-2	Pierce holes	.10	.18
19.1-2	Degrease	.10	.45
19.1-2	Liquid hone, 12 × 18 × .007	.10	1.51
19.1-2	Apply resist	.10	.35
19.1-2	Load rack	.10	1.00
19.1-3	Expose	.30	2.58

Table	Description	Setup	Operation
19.1-3	Develop	.10 hr	.23 min
	Nickel-gold plate jig	.10	2.62
	Silk-screen mask for rhodium	.10	1.32
	Rhodium plate	.10	2.13
19.1-4	Strip mask and resist, .29 × 40	.10	.76
19.1-4	Etch, cupric chloride	.30	2.10
19.1-5	Pierce one-sized holes		
	.31 + .017 × 28 × 40	.28	19.35
	(Note: Preparation of hole templet not included in setup. See drill press setup table.)		
19.1-5	Shear strip columns, .15 + .092 × 6 hits	.10	.70
	(Note: Remove 2 margins also)		
19.1-5	Shear blank rows, .05 + .065 × 10	.10	.70
19.1-5	Roll burnish edge, 1 edge, .02 × 2	.10	.04
	Total estimate for lot = 26.50 + (13 × 36.16) ÷ 60 = 34.33 hr	26.50 hr	36.16 min
	Unit estimate = 34.33 ÷ 500 = .069 hr		

B. Estimate a 1.75-diameter ring electrical contact, .020-in. thk copper alloy. Raw stock available in 12 × 48-in. strips. Adopting a 12 × 12-in. panel, there are 6 columns and 6 rows allowing inner-part and border space. The number of finished parts is 1800 requiring 50 panels and allowing a 4% scrap, 52 panels will be made.

Table	Description	Setup	Operation
19.1-1	Preparation of image	8.0 hr	
19.1-1	Reduction	1.0	
19.1-1	Step and repeat	1.0	
19.1-1	Negative envelope, 8 × 52 ÷ 60	6.93	
19.1-2	Shear panel from stock	.15	.14 min
19.1-5	Pierce holes	.10	.18
19.1-2	String, clean	.10	.45
19.1-2	Apply resist	.10	.35
19.1-2	Dry	.10	.50
19.1-3	Expose	.30	2.58
19.1-3	Develop	.10	.23
19.1-4	Etch	.30	7.61
19.1-4	Strip resist	.10	.86
19.1-5	Detab, .36 × 36	.10	12.96
	Total estimate for lot = 18.38 + (52 × 25.76) ÷ 60 = 40.71 hr	18.38	25.76 min
	Unit estimate = 40.71 ÷ 1800 = .023 hr		

C. Estimate the time to alkaline-etch an aluminum panel, 3/16 in.-thk, where the panel is 14 × 14 in. Each panel is composed of 2 parts, and raw stock is 14 × 14 in. The lot size is 20. Artwork and negative preparation are considered as overhead.

Table	Description	Setup	Operation
19.1-2	Pierce holes along top border	.10 hr	.18 min
	String and vat clean	.10	.45
19.1-2	Apply resist	.10	.35
19.1-3	Expose	.30	2.58
19.1-3	Develop	.10	.23
19.1-4	Etch	.30	.50
19.1-4	Strip resist	.10	1.32
19.1-2	Deburr sharp edges, 42-in. perimeter, 2 (.59 + (42−30) .02)	.10	1.66
	Total estimate for lot = 20 + (10 × 7.27) ÷ 60 = 2.42 hr	1.20 hr	7.27 min
	Unit estimate = 2.42 ÷ 20 = .121 hr		

TABLE 19.1 CHEMICAL MACHINING AND PRINTED CIRCUIT BOARD FABRICATION

Setup operations in estimating hours

1. Artwork and negative preparation

Preparation of image of part	8–40 hr
Artwork reduced to 1/1 photographically by camera	1 hr
Step and repeat processing of image on one large film for multiple images on blank	1 hr

2. Metal preparation

Shear panel from sheet	.2 hr
Deburr edges of panel by hand-file perimeter	.1 hr
Clean	.1 hr
Pierce hanging holes	.1 hr
Photo-resist vat	
Dip and hang for draining, manual	.1 hr
Dry film application	estimate req'd
Load rack in oven or air dry	.1 hr

3. Image processing and masking

Load photosensitive panel in negative envelope, load into vacuum printer, expose, unload, manual	.3 hr
Develop in solvent spray	.1 hr
Dye	.1 hr
Brush touch up, manual	.1 hr
Silk-screen printing	See Table 4.2

4. Etching and post-etching processes

Etch, load and unload	.3 hr
Conveyor operation for 1-oz circuit panel	.3 hr
Strip resist	.1 hr

5. Fabrication processes

Pierce holes in printed circuit panel	.22 + .06 (no. stations)
Pierce holes with pierce die	2.0 hr
Size holes by drill press	See Table 11.2
Remove piece from panel by clipping tabs, manual	.1 hr
Shear strips from panel	.1 hr
Shear blanks from strip	.1 hr
Roll burnishing	.1 hr
Route, engrave, or slot	.1 hr
Protective coating for intermediate operations	.1 hr

Operation elements in estimating minutes

1. Artwork and negative preparation

Multiple-part negative and its mirror image are registered for alignment and secured together for a negative envelope to accept sensitized metal panel, per panel	8–12

2. Metal preparation

Shear panel from sheet

3 × 3	.07
12 × 18	.14
18 × 24	.21

Deburr edges of panel by hand-file perimeter

In.	6	30	add'l
Min	.16	.59	.02

Clean area

Sq in.	3 × 3	15 × 15	Add'l
Scrub	.12	3.11	.014
Liquid hone	.06	1.56	.007

Degrease	.45/panel
Pierce hanging holes	.18/panel
Photo-resist vat	
Dip and hang for draining, manual	.35/panel
(Note: No drain time included)	
Dry film application	estimate required
Load rack in oven or air dry	
Load several panels at once, unload	3.00
Single load, unload	1.00
(Note: No dry time included)	

3. Image processing and masking

Load photosensitive panel in negative envelope, load into vacuum printer, expose, unload, manual	2.58/panel
Develop in solvent spray	.23/panel
Dye	.77/panel

Brush touch up, manual

L + W	1	3	5	8	Add'l
Min	.90	1.04	1.38	.175	.13

Silk-screen printing	See Table 4.2

4. Etching and post-etching processes

Manual, blanking	7.61/panel
Manual printed circuit	3.33/panel
String and take down (no wait time)	.51/panel
Alkali etch of aluminum panel	

Thickness	Width			
0+ −⅛	0+ to 8	8+ to 14		Min/Panel
⅛+ −¼			8+ to 16	
Length	0+ to 16+			.26
		0+ to 16		.40
			0+ to 16	.38

Conveyor operation for 1-oz printed circuit panel	Min/Panel
Cupric chloride	2.10
Ferric chloride	1.37
Alkaline	1.40
Ammonium persulfate	1.63
Chromic sulfuric	1.75
High speed cupric	1.30
Strip resist	.75/panel
Strip mask for printed circuit tabs	.29/panel
Strip resist, aluminum etching	1.32/panel

5. Fabrication processes

Pierce holes in printed circuit panel	
Load and unload	.31
Rotate turret and pierce first hole of each size in part (turret punching machine)	.07 (no. sizes)
Change punch and die of each hole size	.56 (no. sizes)
(Note: Single-station punching machine)	

Pierce remaining holes		.017 ea
Pierce holes with pierce die		.35/panel
Size holes by drill press		See Table 11.2
Remove piece from panel by clipping tabs, manual		.36 ea
Shear strips from panel		(.15 + .02 × no. hits)/panel units
Shear blanks from strip		(.05 + .065 × no. hits)/strip units
Roll burnishing		.02 (linear in.)
Route, engrave, or slot		
Carbide		.09 (perimeter in.)
Diamond		.07 (perimeter in.)
Protective coating for intermediate operations		

	Printed circuit part	Alum. etching part, chem. blank part
Apply	.32/panel	.58/unit
Wash off	.35/unit	.12/unit

19.2 Electrical Discharge Machining

DESCRIPTION

The conventional electrical discharge machine (EDM) cuts metals by means of electrical discharge or "spark erosion" between the metal to be cut (negative charge) and an electrode (positive charge). This cutting takes place in a nonconductive fluid known as dielectric.

The process fills the tank with the dielectric fluid and submerges the metal inside connected to a negative charge. An electrode is chosen depending on the shape of the cut needed. It is positioned on the top of the workpiece leaving a small gap between.

After connecting the electrode to a positive charge, spark erosion takes place and it causes a "miniature thunderstorm" between the two metals. Flashes of lightning take place in rapid succession. Each one produces a tiny crater in the surface of the two metals. Metal evaporation occurs where the flash strikes.

Equal amounts of material are not removed from both plates. By an appropriate choice of materials (e.g. electrode of copper, workpiece of steel) and a skillful selection of the opening and closing times of the automatic switch, more material is removed from the steel than from the copper.

During the process the dielectric constantly flows through the tank requiring filtration. Also erosion creates heat, so the dielectic has to be cooled. The capacity of work of the conventional EDM machine is measured by the rate of material removal, cu in./min.

ESTIMATING DATA DISCUSSION

The setup element is given in hours. The basic setup includes the time to get the first electrode, unload the old electrode, and load the new one. Also the setup includes the time required to get the fixture (which will hold the workpiece) to the tank, bolt it down, plus the time needed to place and indicate the fixture in two directions. Additionally, it includes the time to install the first workpiece on the fixture and fill the tank with the dielectric fluid.

The operation elements are given in estimating minutes and are arranged into handling and machining catagories. The handling consists of loading and unloading the workpieces and changing the electrode. This time is constant for all operations.

The machining time includes filling the tank and the time for the spindle to go up and down. This time is also constant for all operations. The machining time also includes cutting time, which varies from one operation to another depending on the type of material and the volume of cut. Distinction is made between soft material (notably plain carbon steels) and hard materials (or alloys).

EXAMPLES

A. A .215-in. hole with a .375-in. length of cut is to be done in a low carbon steel. A 3/16-cu in. tube electrode is to be used. A 6 cu mm/min rate of removal is applied in this case. One operator will operate the machine. Find unit estimate.

Table	Description	Time
19.2-1	Unload and load	.91 min
19.2-2	Fill tank to level	.52

19.2-3	Spindle down and up	.58
19.2-4	Cut time, .014 cu in.	9.90
19.2-5	Change electrode (every 10 pieces)	.12
	Unit estimate	12.02 min

B. A lot of 50 pieces of low carbon steel is to be machined. A hole .197 in. with .235 in. of length is cut. One operator will operate the machine. Find the unit and lot estimates.

Table	Description	Time
19.2-S	Setup	.30 hr
19.2-1	Unload and load	.91 min
19.2-2	Fill tank to level	.52
19.2-3	Spindle down and up	.58
19.2-4	Change electrode (every 15 pieces)	.08
	Unit estimate	8.59 min
	Lot estimate	7.47 hr

C. A lot of 30 pieces of high carbon alloy steel is to be machined. A volume of .020 cu in. will be removed. Find the unit and lot estimate.

Table	Description	Time
19.2-S	Setup	.30 hr
19.2-1	Unload and load	.91 min
19.2-2	Fill tank to level	.52
19.2-3	Cut time, .02 cu in.	18.80
19.2-5	Change electrode (every 17 pieces)	.07
	Unit estimate	20.88 min
	Lot estimate	10.76 hr

D. Re-estimate Example C using Item 19.2 of Section IV. This kind of estimate provides direct labor cost for setup and run time.

Item	Description	Cost
19.2	Setup subtotal	$3.75
19.2	Constant for cycle	$44.38
19.2	Cutting, 0.020 × 18,700	$374.00
	$/100 units	$418.38
	Setup cost	$3.75
	Lot cost for 30 pieces	$129.26

TABLE 19.2 ELECTRICAL DISCHARGE MACHINING

Setup	**.30 hr**

Operation elements in estimating minutes

1. Unload and load	.91
2. Fill tank to level	.52
3. Spindle down and up	.58

4. Cut time,
   Soft materials:

Vol. cut	.003	.006	.009	.012	.015	.018	.021
Cut time	3.1	4.8	6.5	8.2	9.9	11.6	13.3

Hard material:

Vol. cut	.003	.006	.009	.012	.015	.018	.021
Cut time	5.2	7.5	9.7	12.0	14.2	16.5	18.8

5. Change electrodes   1.18

19.3 Traveling Wire Electrical Discharge Machining

DESCRIPTION

Traveling wire electrical discharge machining (EDM), a metal cutting process that removes metal with an electrical discharge, is suited for production of parts having extraordinary workpiece configurations, close tolerances, the need of high repeatability, and hard to work metals. Wire EDMing produces a variety of parts such as gears, tools, dies, rotors, turbine blades, etc. It is appropriate for small to medium batch quantities. Actual machining times may vary from a half hour to twenty hours. It uses the heat of an electrical spark to vaporize material, thus essentially no cutting forces are involved and parts can be machined with fragile or complex geometries. The sparks are generated one at a time in rapid succession (pulses) between the electrode (wire) and the workpiece. The sparks must have a medium in which to travel, thus a flushing fluid (water) is used to separate the wire and workpiece. Hence the one requirement is that the workpiece must be electrically conductive. A vertically oriented wire is fed into the workpiece continuously traveling from a supply spool to a take-up spool so that it is constantly renewed.

A power supply provides a voltage between wire and workpiece. By means of an adjustable setting one can determine the pulse amplitude and pulse duration—in other words, the on and off times (microseconds). On time refers to metal removal; off time is the period during which the gap is swept clear of removed metal via flushing. So both the intensity of the spark and the time it flows determine the energy expended and consequently the amount of material removed per unit time.

ESTIMATING DATA DISCUSSION

In traveling wire EDM, setup for different parts remain essentially constant. The setup may be reduced when running consecutive batches of parts with similar geometric configurations but with different dimensions. The manual setup elements are constant. The setup values can be found in Table 19.3 and are given in hours. If machining is over 50 hours, add setup time to change wire spool. Similarly, a coolant flush is necessary for each 35 hours of machining.

The operational elements are listed as: handling, first cut constant, additional cut constant, multiple stack piece part run, and machining. Element 1, part handling, is to be allowed once per piece on a constant basis. The element stone and burr is adjusted for parts according to finish requirements and complexity. The value given is base requirement only per piece. Inspection is usually not included because it may be done internally to the long machining cycles, but will be added at least once per batch. Element 2, first cut constant, is allowed once per piece on the first cut made on the piece. Element 3, additional start cut constant, is to be used once for each additional start cut required. Do not use this element if only one cut is being made—i.e., one cut allow 0X, two cuts allow 1X, three cuts allow 2X. When trim cuts are required use only Element 3, one time per trim cut. Surface requirements determine the number of trims needed. The number of start cuts and trim cuts will be determined from the operational sketch. Element 4, multiple stack piece part run constant, is to be used once for each additional part in excess of one on a multiple basis—i.e., two pieces cut at one time allow 1X, three pieces allow 2X, etc.

The actual cutting cycle on traveling wire EDM is computer controlled and has a high degree of variability. Therefore the cutting cycle requires little operator attention time, which allows the operator to run additional machines. If this is the case, when costing the process divide the total cost by the number of machines attended. Wire EDMing is an unconventional machining process which has some peculiar characteristics. The cutting speed is measured as the length of cut times the workpiece thickness per unit time. Also involved is workpiece material and the physical properties of the wire electrode. Surprisingly, the thicker the workpiece the faster will be the cut in square surface area units per unit of time. This may be explained as follows. In EDM not every pulse generated by the electrode produces a spark; but, the longer length of wire electrode in a thicker workpiece provides more opportunities for the spark to occur, i.e., more

sparks jump from electrode to workpiece. Hence, this makes the progress more efficient in thicker workpieces.

The machine time is to be calculated as length of cut per feed rate, where feed is a direct function of workpiece thickness, material, and electrode wire. Element 5 is used by determining the required wire electrode diameter and material being cut, as well as part dimensions, length, and depth of cut, from the design. Using the appropriate data, determine machine time in minutes per 1 inch of cut. Once the time per 1 inch has been determined, multiply by the length of cut and the total machine time is estimated. The values of Element 5 are of first rough-cut passes. If trim passes are required use a feed of ½ inch per minute, then divide the length of cut by this feed. This gives trim time and should be added to first cut time to obtain the total machine time. The estimator should note that the feeds used in determining these times are for maximum accuracy and not maximum speed.

EXAMPLES

A. Estimate the time required to EDM a small die with a cut length of 6.3 in. The part has a nominal thickness of 1.8 in., and its material is cold work tool steel (D2). Surface finish requires only one rough cut. Inspection will be included. Wire used is 0.010-in. brass. Find unit estimate.

Table	Description	Time	
19.3-1	Supply piece, wash and blow dry	.84	min
19.3-1	Stone and burr piece	.84	
19.3-1	Load and unload	1.00	
19.3-2	Punch data, wait for head to move to start position	.91	
19.3-2	Thread, tie wire, close shield	.96	
19.3-2	Punch data, wait for head to move down, start cycle	.42	
19.3-3	Machine time: time = 6.3×28.14	177.28	
19.3-2	Raise shield, punch data, break wire	.56	
19.3-1	After unloading, inspect	2.30	
	Unit estimate	185.11	min

B. Estimate the time required to produce five progressive dies made of D2 tool steel. Three holes of ⅜-in. diameter are required. The thickness of the dies is 1.12 in. No finish cuts are needed. Wire use will be .010-in. brass. Setup and inspection are required. Length of cut = (⅜ in.) × 3 = 3.53 in.

Table	Description	Time	
19.3-S	Setup	1.40	hr
19.3-1	Part handling	4.98	min
19.3-2	First cut	2.85	
19.3-3	Additional start cut (2×)	4.72	
19.3-5	Machine		
	Rough (1×)	55.60	
	Total hrs = (55.6)5/60 = 4.63 < 38	.00	
	No need to change filters or wire spool		
	Unit estimate	68.15	min
	Hr/1 unit	1.14	
	Lot estimate	7.08	hr

C. A lot of 110 aviation pump rotors are to be machined. Material is D2 tool steel quality, length of cut and depth of cut are 2.27 in. and .600 in. respectively, as determined from the design. Two slots with a surface finish requiring two trim cuts per slot are being machined. The slots have equal dimensions. Inspection is required and so is setup for lot. The wire will be .010-in. brass. Find the unit and lot estimates.

Table	Description	Time	
19.3-S	Setup	1.40	hr
19.3-S	Change wire spool, 122.36/47 = 2.6, (3×)	.60	hr
19.3-S	Change coolant filters, 122.36/38 = 3.22, (3×)	1.64	hr
19.3-1	Part handling	4.98	min
19.3-2	First cut	2.85	
19.3-3	Additional start cut (1×)	2.36	
19.3-3	Trim cut (4×)	1.68	
19.3-4	Machine		
	Rough cut (2×)		
	$T = 2.27$ in. $\times 10.70 = 24.29$	48.58	
	Trim cut (4×)		
	$T = 2.27$ in./.5 in./min = 4.54	18.16	
	Total hr = (48.58 + 18.16) × 110/60 = 122.36 hr > 50		
	Unit estimate	78.61	min
	Setup subtotal	3.64	
	Hr/100 units	131.28	hr
	Lot estimate	148.05	hr

D. Estimate the lot time required to produce six complex gear forms made of a material similar to D2 tool steel. Thickness of each gear is ⅛ in. Wire will be .008-in. brass. Length of cut is 22.4 in. The first gear will be cut by itself with inspection. The remaining five will be cut on a multiple basis. Do not consider setup and no stoning or burring is necessary.

Table	Description	Time	
19.3-1	Part handling, supply	.84	min
19.3-1	Load and unload	1.00	
19.3-1	Inspection	2.30	
19.3-2	First cut constant	2.85	
19.3-4	Machine (thickness = 5 × .125 = .625 in.)	320.32	
	$T = (22.4 \times 14.30)$		
19.3-4	Multiple piece constant, (4 × .84)	3.36	
	Floor-to-floor for 6 gears	500.9	min
	Unit estimate for 1 gear	83.48	min
	Lot estimate for 6 gears	8.35	hr

E. Estimate the time needed to produce 1000 carbide pump liners requiring 4 holes of .252-in. diameter and 1 slot with a length of .84 in. Thickness of each liner is .0160 in. They will be run on a multiple basis of 100. Wire will be .010-in. brass. Setup is required. Carbide is a hard material.

Table	Description	Time	
19.3-S	Setup	1.40	hr
19.3-1	Handling (no inspection)	2.68	min
19.3-2	First cut	2.85	
19.3-3	Additional start cut	9.44	
19.3-4	Machine, rough,		
	$T = 4.01 (45.46) = 182.30$, Total time = (182.3) 10/60 = 30.4 hr		
	≈ 30 hr (No need to change filter.)		
19.3-4	Multiple stack piece,		
	$T = .84 \times 100 = 84.0$	84.0	min

Floor-to-floor for 100 units	281.27	min
Unit estimate	2.81	min
Hr/100 units		
Lot estimate		
Hr/100 units	4.693	
Lot Estimate	48.33	hr

F. Re-estimate Example A given above by the cost equation given as Item 19.3. Material is tool steel. Length of cut = 6.3 in. Thickness is 1.8 in. Find lot estimate for 5 units.

Item	Description	Cost
19.3	Setup	$ 18.37
19.3	Constant handling	$ 245.00
19.3	Cut length of 6.3 in.,	
	Cost equation $= 134.75 \, (97)^{-25.4x}$	
	$x = 1.8$ in. thickness	
	$134.75 \, (.97)^{-25.4(1.8)} \times 6.3$	$3417.16
	$/100 units	$3662.16
	Unit cycle cost	$ 36.62
	Lot cost for 5 units	$ 201.48

TABLE 19.3 TRAVELING WIRE ELECTRICAL DISCHARGE MACHINING

Setup	**1.40**	**hr**
Change wire spool	.30	hr
Change coolant filters	.55	hr

Operation elements in estimating minutes

1. Part handling	.84
Supply piece wash and blow dry	.84
Stone and burr piece as required	
Rating factor: fine finish ($\times$ 2.0)	
Load and unload to and from fixture	1.00
Inspection	2.30
2. First cut start constant	2.85
Punch data to move head to start position,	
wait for head to reposition	.91
Thread, tie wire, close shield	.96
Punch data for head to move down, wait, start cycle	.42
Raise shield, punch data to move head, break wire	.56
3. Additional start cut constant	2.36
Raise shield, punch reposition data, break wire	.56
Relocate part, unclamp and clamp	.47
Thread, tie wire, change weight, close shield	.91
Punch data for head to move down, wait,	
start cycle	.42
Note: Use for trim cut only.	
4. Multiple stack piece part run constant	1.68
Supply piece wash and blow dry	.84
Stone and burr piece	.84
5. Machining, min/in. (where in. is traverse length)	

Thickness In.	Material		
	Tool steel		
	.008-in. B	.010-in. B	.012-in. B
.083	7.08	6.39	7.73
.125	7.39	6.60	7.90

Thickness In.	Material		
	Tool steel		
	.008-in.B	.010-in.B	.012-in.B
.25	8.42	7.27	8.42
.50	10.91	8.82	9.57
.75	14.13	10.70	10.88
1.00	18.31	12.98	12.37
1.25	23.73	15.75	14.07
1.50	30.76	19.11	15.99
1.75	—	23.19	18.18
2.00	—	28.14	20.67
2.25	—	34.14	23.50
2.50	—	41.43	26.72
2.75	—	—	30.38
3.00	—	—	34.53

Thickness In.	Material		
	Carbide	Graphite	Copper
	.010-in. B	.010-in. B	.010-in. B
.083	—	—	4.03
.125	19.75	7.69	4.30
.25	21.05	8.76	5.23
.50	23.94	11.35	7.75
.75	27.21	14.71	11.48
1.00	30.94	19.06	17.01
1.25	35.17	24.70	25.20
1.50	39.98	—	—
1.75	45.46	—	—
2.00	51.68	—	—
2.25	58.75	—	—
2.50	66.80	—	—
2.75	75.94	—	—
3.00	86.33	—	—

20.1 Mask and Unmask Bench

DISCUSSION

Masking is used to protect surfaces against overspray, for lining, and for cutting-in different paints or colors. Large areas can be protected by paper secured with self-adhesive tape or with gummed strip. For cutting-in or lining with spray-paint operations, thin cellulose tape can be positioned over marking lines, against edges or other parts, and to reduce the tendency to build up a thick edge. Trimming fixtures are sometimes attached to the part, and a tape is added to reduce runs onto the part.

Two operations are involved as masking precedes painting while unmasking is done following painting. The masking considered in these estimating data is "bench" work, although masking can be by spraying or dipping processes as well.

ESTIMATING DATA DISCUSSION

Adhesive masking tape and brown Kraft paper are assumed to be available near the masking station, and thus the setup is for typical lot chores.

The position and aside is for flat or boxlike parts. Because there are repositions during the taping time, consideration for reposition is unnecessary. The process of taping causes the part to be repositioned. The $L + W$ or $L + W + H$ are part dimensions.

Element 2 is for the application of paper and tape for flatlike parts. The entry variables are length and width of the masked area, not the part, and the time is per side.

If the part is boxlike, and paper and tape are substantially over three or more of the six surfaces, Element 3 is used. The entry variable is $2L + 2W$, which is the periphery, and the height. Thus, for one unit of $2L + 2W$, .15 min can be added to, or subtracted from, table values. Similarly, for one unit length of height, .06 min is added to, or subtracted from, table values.

If tape is exclusively used, Element 4 is chosen. The width across the top is tape width and lengths are under each dimension. This element is for taping an area, and tolerance requirements are not critical.

When a trimming fixture is used to reduce taping costs, it may be necessary to use Element 5. The entry variable of length is the laid-in tape distance. It secures the part to the fixture.

For dimensions that are closely held, and trim work with a knife or razor blade is anticipated, and the tape is worked-in along the edge, Element 6 is employed. The entry variable is length, meaning tape length.

Spot cover or plugs can be estimated using Element 7.

Masking material, if it is to be brushed, is estimated using Element 8. The area is the brushed-masked area, not part area. The length is the mask-edge length. For instance, if a circular section surrounded by another color is to be masked, then the edge length is the circumference. If any of the mask is against a corner, another part, or braked-edge, then the edge length does not include that distance, because operator-care with brush strokes is not as critical.

For the unmasking operation, Elements 1, 9, 10, or 11 would be selected as needed. The entry variable for 9 is length plus width for the masked material.

Item 20.1 of Section IV will estimate mask and unmasking costs for setup and operation. Item 20.1 is similar to Table 20.1 as to the information required. Entry information for handling depends upon the object: If it is flat or boxlike, the entry variable is $L + W$ or $L + W + H$. To apply paper and tape, the estimator determines whether the object is more flatlike or boxlike. The entry information is $L + W$ or perimeter ($2L + 2W$) and height (H) for flat or box materials. The entry variables are different for handling and apply-paper-tape. If tape is used only, multiply the cost factor by $L \times W$. There is a listed cost for applying spot or plugs. Similarly, this cost would be used again for removal. The unmasking depends upon $L + W$ of the affected area, and handling would be considered again.

EXAMPLES

A. A flat part 7.75×21.2 in. overall has a 6×11.5-in. section masked. Estimate the unit time.

Table	Description	Time
20.1-1	Position and aside	.24 min
20.1-2	Apply paper and tape, $1.96 - (11.5-9).19 - (9-6).11$	1.16
	Unit estimate	1.40 min

B. A boxlike part is to be wrapped for overspray protection. Two plugs in taped holes are necessary. The handling dimensions are $L = 6.5$ in., $W = 7.2$ in., and $H = 2$ in. One surface, the top, is to be sprayed. Find the pc/hr.

Table	Description	Time
20.1-1	Handle, $L + W + H = 16.2$	.09 min
20.1-3	$2L + 2W = 27.4, H = 2$	4.28
20.1-7	2 plugs	.26
	Unit estimate	4.63 min
	Shop estimate	12.9 pc/hr

C. A critical machine part has several dimensions that are taped, and an internal area that is liquid masked. Use dimensions from Example B above plus the tape is 2 and 4 in. $\times$ 7.5 in. long, and one tape is aligned, trimmed, and placed along a circular feature. Estimate the unit time.

Table	Description	Time
20.1-1	Handle	.09 min
20.1-4	Tape area 2 in. tape $\times$ 7.5 in. long	.20
20.1-6	Length of exact edge is about 15 in., $.57 + (15-13.6).05$	.64
20.1-4	Tape area 4 in. $\times$ 7.5 in. long	.39
20.1-8	Internal area of 17 in. and an edge length of 5.4 in., $4.35 + (5.4-4).11 + (17-11).28$	6.18
	Unit estimate	7.50 min

D. Estimate the unit time to unmask the part described in Example B above.

Table	Description	Time
20.1-1	Handle	.09 min
20.1-10	Remove plugs	.38
20.1-9	Remove tape, approximately $30 = L + W$	1.01
	Unit estimate	1.48 min

E. Estimate the unit base-cost of Example B above using Item 20.1 of Section IV.

Item	Description	Cost
		Cost
20.1	Cycle constant	$ 1.82
20.1	Box, 16.2 × .185	3.00
20.1	Box perimeter 2.72 × 27.4 + 2 × 1.09	76.71
20.1	Plugs, 2 × 2.17	4.34
	$/100 units	$85.87

TABLE 20.1   MASK AND UNMASK BENCH

Setup   **.05 hr**

Operation elements in estimating minutes

1. Position and aside, occasional reposition

$L + W$	9.0	22.7	40.7	64.6	96.2	138	Add'l
Min	.14	.18	.24	.31	.42	.55	.003

Box parts

$L + W + H$	16.5	20.3	25.9	33.9	45.4	61.9	85.8	120.2	Add'l
Min	.09	.13	.18	.27	.38	.55	.79	1.14	.010

2. Apply paper and tape to flat parts

Length (L)	Width (W)				
	9	*12*	*18*	*24*	*36*
9	1.96				
12	2.49	2.85			
18	3.58	3.95	4.69		
24	4.66	5.03	5.77	6.51	
36	6.83	7.19	7.93	7.93	10.15
48	8.98	9.35	10.10	10.84	12.32
72	13.31	13.68	14.42	15.16	16.64

Add'l length   .19
Add'l width   .11

3. Apply paper and tape to box parts

$2L + 2W$	Height (H)			
	5	*10*	*15*	*25*
10	1.27	1.56		
20	2.78	3.06	3.34	
30	4.28	4.56	4.86	5.42
40	5.78	6.08	6.36	6.94

Add'l $2L + 2W$ .15
Add'l H .06

4. Tape area

Length (L)	Width (W)				Min
	2	4	6	8	
	6.0				.15
	6.4	4.7			.16
	6.9	4.9			.18
	7.4	5.2	4.2		.20
	8.0	5.5	4.4		.22
	8.6	5.8	4.6		.24
	9.3	6.1	4.9		.26
	10.1	6.5	5.1	4.9	.29
	10.9	6.9	5.4	5.1	.32
	11.9	7.4	5.7	5.3	.35
	12.9	7.9	6.0	5.6	.39
	14.0	8.4	6.4	5.8	.43
	15.3	9.0	6.8	6.1	.47
	16.6	9.7	7.3	6.5	.52
	19.6	11.2	8.2	7.2	.62
	23.2	12.9	9.4	8.1	.74
	27.5	15.0	10.8	9.1	.89
	32.7	17.6	12.5	10.4	1.07
	38.9	20.6	14.5	11.9	1.28
	46.3	24.3	17.0	13.7	1.54
	55.2	28.7	19.9	15.3	1.85
	Add'l				.03
		Add'l			.07
			Add'l		.11
				Add'l	.14

5. Tape and trim edges for trimming fixture

L	1.0	5.6	10.6	16.2	22.3	29.0	36.3	44.5	Add'l
Min	.65	.72	.79	.87	.96	1.05	1.16	1.27	.015

6. Align tape along edge, trim

L	4.0	4.5	5.0	5.7	6.5	7.4	8.6	10.0	11.6	13.6	Add'l
Min	.11	.13	.16	.19	.23	.28	.33	.40	4.8	.57	.05

7. Apply spots or plugs

Spots	Min		Plugs	Min		Spots	Min		Plugs	Min
1	.14		1	.32		8	.98		8	.65
2	.26		2	.37		9	1.10		9	.70
3	.38		3	.41		10	1.22		10	.75
4	.50		4	.46		11	1.34		11	.79
5	.62		5	.51		12	1.46		12	.84
6	.74		6	.56		13	1.58		13	.89
7	.86		7	.60		Add'l	.13		Add'l	.05

8. Handbrushing of liquid mask or adherent coat

	Area						
Length	1	2	3	4	6	8	11
0	1.13	1.40	1.69	1.96	2.51	3.07	3.90
.5	1.18	1.46	1.74	2.01	2.57	3.13	3.96
1.5	1.29	1.57	1.85	2.13	2.68	3.24	4.07
3.5	1.40	1.79	2.07	2.35	2.90	3.46	4.29
4	1.57	1.85	2.13	2.41	2.96	3.52	4.35
6.5	1.85	2.13	2.41	2.68	3.24	3.80	4.63
12	2.47	2.74	3.02	3.30	3.85	4.41	5.24
20	3.36	3.64	3.51	4.19	4.75	5.30	6.13
28	4.25	4.53	4.81	5.08	5.64	6.19	4.25
35	5.03	5.31	5.59	5.87	6.42	6.98	7.81

Add'l length   .11
Add'l area   .28

9. Remove paper and tape or tape from area

L + W	2.0	2.8	3.8	5.0	6.5	8.2	10.3	12.8	15.8	19.4	23.7
Min	.11	.14	.16	.20	.23	.28	.34	.41	.49	.58	.70

L + W	28.9	35.1	42.5	51.4	62.2	75.0	90.5	109.0	131.3	157.9	Add'l
Min	.84	1.01	1.21	1.45	1.74	2.09	2.51	3.02	3.62	4.34	.03

10. Remove spots or plugs

Spots	1	2	3	4	5	6	7	8	9	10	Add'l
Min	.09	.18	.27	.36	.45	.54	.63	.72	.81	.90	.10

Plug	1	2	3	4	5	6	7	8	9	10	Add'l
Min	.19	.38	.57	.76	.95	1.14	1.33	1.52	1.71	1.90	.21

11. Strip liquid or adherent-coating mask   .02/sq in

20.2 Booth, Conveyor and Dip Painting, and Conversion Processes

DESCRIPTION

For industrial painting operations, spray painting is a commonly used method. In spray painting, paint is forced into the spray gun by pressure or suction and then atomized at the discharge end or nozzle of the gun. A spray-painting system may include a compressed air supply, pistol-type spray gun, air and fluid lines, material container, stirrers or agitators, pressure regulators, air filters, and a spray booth or conveyor—and clean-air exhaust. Baking in an oven is more common than air drying.

One system is shown in Figure 20.2A, which shows two operators spraying a conveyorized panel.

Electrostatic spraying processes use the attraction of paint droplets by an electrode in an electrostatic field. The material can be applied using a conveyor, with and without manual application, or by dipping. The airless-type spraying processes coat articles that are carried about a loop in a conveyor, at the center of which is located a disk-type atomizer. Paint is pumped to the disk and centrifugally released from the periphery as a spray of fine particles that carry the same charge as the disk, but are attracted to the parts. The disk also has reciprocal motion in order to spray large surfaces. Figure 20.2B illustrates this disk.

Dip coating is a means to cover all areas, and is normally confined to smaller parts.

The application of paint may be fully manual, semi-, or fully automatic, although some kind of part loading and unloading is usually found. Brush painting is not considered in this guide.

Several types of finishing materials are provided. Provision is given for conversion coatings or prime coat. Wrinkle, enamel, and plastic resins are evaluated. Additionally, other materials can be used with a conveyor, booth, or dipping methods. Liquid masks which can be sprayed are another finish considered.

ESTIMATING DATA DISCUSSION

Several kinds of operations have been grouped within these data. It depends upon the local condi-

FIGURE 20.2B Electrostatic coating disk. *(Ransburg Corporation)*

tions that the estimator is assuming. Conversion and painting can be processed by conveyor, dip, booth, or bench methods. One to several operators may be necessary, and the work may be operator-controlled, semiautomatic, or fully automatic.

For handling, a variety of circumstances dictate which element is preferred. For the ordinary load and unload, a part to be finished, say on a turntable or stand, or in a booth, Element 1 with the entry variable of girth is chosen. The booth may have one or two doors and be a walk-in, or in the smaller situation, a bench booth is possible. Power hoist, dolly, or fork truck are other means of handling where a load and unload of a single part is implied.

Rack or tray parts handling, Element 2, is provided for a variety of purposes. The data are for a typical rack or tray 15 × 35 in. in size. Flat parts (on one surface at least) are laid on the tray spaced with minimum spacing. Racks may have hanging hooks and may vary from 1 to 150 hooks. The entry variable is the number of pieces placed on the tray or rack. Tray loading is for parts that are automatically or operator sprayed. Racks with hooks can be used for dipping as well as operator spraying. Automatic painting of rack-held parts is another possibility. The five conditions for Element 2 are described by the column headings.

Element 3 deals with basket parts, where a typical basket is 18 × 14 × 18 in. in size and is perforated. The basket can be hand-dipped, or be dipped by automatic means. The element includes

FIGURE 20.2A Industrial spray operation. *(DeVilbiss)*

no painting—only handling. While the volume of this basket is 2.5 cu ft., conversions to other sizes can be on the basis of parts per basket, as the only variable is number of parts per basket and the type of loading and unloading. Stacking in a basket is vertical while stacking out of the basket can be horizontal.

The use of single-strand, endless-chain conveyors is found frequently in moderate- to high-production volume shops. Even job shops use this method if the part family is consistent in size. The part is often hooked to the chain by operators, then sprayed or dipped and thru-oven baked (or air dried) and unhooked. Roller coating processes can use these estimating data as they are conveyor controlled. The table entry variables for Element 4 are part spacing center-to-center, expressed in in., and conveyor velocity expressed in feet per minute (fpm). Element 4 time is for one operator. The selected time must be multiplied by the number of operators to man the conveyor for the part being estimated no matter what the lot size. Consider the example where the line velocity is 8 fpm and the chain has hook eyes every 2 ft. A flat part 20×30 in. (with holes in the four edges) can be hooked with the 30-in. dimension horizontally and requires two eyes for two hooks and a free chain-eye in between parts for spray control. In this case the part spacing would be 6 ft. The part could also be hung with the 20-in. dimension parallel to the chain axis, but two chain-eyes are still required for the hooks, but because the long 30-in. dimension is the vertical dimension, open distance between parts is adequate, and the part-spacing center distance is 4 ft.

At 8 fpm and a spacing of 6 ft, the time value is .75 min, but the crew necessary to support this part at this velocity, for example, are 4 spray painting operators, 2 hangers, and 1 relief or swing operator. Thus, the .75 min is multiplied by 7 for an estimate giving 5.25 min/each or .088 hr/unit. Furthermore, if the conveyor is used for part dipping, spraying operators would be unnecessary. Local shop circumstances dictate how Element 4 is to be used. The times in Element 4 can be added or subtracted to give different conveyor velocities.

In spray-booth painting, Element 5, the equipment essentials are the air supply, spray gun, spraying technique, booth, and the paint. Element 5 involves manual cold spraying with a single gun and the booth may be on a bench or in a room with either a dry back or water wash for ventilation. The data are for priming, wrinkle, enamel, and spray mask. Auxiliary work such as wipe clean, say with a dustless rag, or blow off the article are also given because this work is sometimes done prior or subsequent to spraying. The estimator may wish to make a qualitative extension of the data if the booth involves automatic spraying, and the operator is not involved, or the operator is a tender in the case of semiautomatic spraying. Entry data are total area to be sprayed (which means the sum of inside and outside area if both sides are covered). This work is for one piece at a time.

Parts can be rack-hung, dipped, and suspended for baking. After drying, the parts are packed or dumped into containers. A typical hand rack is 12 in. long, has five hooks 3 in. apart for a maximum of 5 parts per rack and 15 per cycle, and the operator is sometimes able to manage three racks at once (note Element 6).

Using parts that have been racked and placed on the drying truck, Element 7 is for painting and replacing the rack on the truck, which is followed by air or oven dry and eventually a pack for protection. Air-pressure or electrostatic methods of spraying are possible, but operators are assumed.

For Element 7, rack spraying using a drying truck with oven or an air dry, part handling was done in Element 2, and Element 7 considers operator spraying where the entry variable is the number of pieces loaded on the rack. Three conditions are specified.

If the rack is conveyorized to the oven, Element 8 is used. Handling to load and unload the rack is given in Element 2.

Element 9 deals with the filling of engraving which involves cleaning, painting, removing excess paint, and touchup. The work is done on a bench, and the entry variable for the element is the length of area, where area is a 2-in. wide path. The area encompasses the engraved characters. In the case of a dial, it equals the mean circumference of the engraved characters times width. A single isolated letter or a small word requires the threshold time for 1 in. Handling, such as Element 1, must be added to Element 9.

Element 10 involves the unpacking and packing of small items, and is abbreviated from Table 24.1.

Another approach to estimating may be found in Item 20.2 of Section IV. Similar to Table 20.2, Item 20.2 provides base setup cost and $/100 units. With your plant productivity assigned to the overall estimate, the value is adjusted for wages and speed. Conveyorized work is estimated knowing conveyor speed, fpm, and one part spacing. The conveyor cost is per worker. The load and unload to spray booth or bench requires a knowledge of the maximum $L + W + H$ of the part. Heavy handling assumes hoist or fork truck, etc. The cost for rack and unload, and basket load and stack out, are related to the number of units on the rack or in the basket. As the number increases, the cost declines. Notice that for this evaluation, there is a negative cost based upon the number of units. If a negative cost would result, use Table 20.2 instead. A number of paint and prime finishes are required, and remember to include the constant. When using fill-engraving, the entry variable is the length of the area to be filled, remembering that the tools are a brush to fill and a rag to wipe off.

EXAMPLES

A. A part is painted white on a 2-ft separated-hook chaineye conveyor. Two parts are hooked on each eye, the second part being hooked to a lower hole in the upper part. Conveyor velocity is 6 fpm to facilitate oven drying. Five operators will man the line. Estimate the unit time.

Table	Description	Time
20.2-4	Line load, spray, unload, at line speed of 6 fpm and part spacing of 2 ft, $.33 \times \frac{1}{2} \times 5$	.83 min
	Unit estimate	.83 min

B. A plexiglass object, 2×3 in. in size, is to have the letters A and B and the word *MODE*, and a 2-in. line filled. The letters are in different spots and are isolated. The plexiglass has a protective strip on both sides, and one strip must be removed. Find the unit time.

Table	Description	Time
20.2-S	Setup for fill engraving operation	.05 hr
20.2-1	Load and unload part	.08 min
20.2-10	Strip masking from top surface	.14
20.2-9	Fill letter A	.30
20.2-9	Fill letter B	.30
20.2-9	Fill word *MODE*, $\frac{1}{2}$-in length	.30
20.2-9	Fill 2-in. hairline	.47
	Unit estimate	1.59 min

C. A top chassis cover is to receive automatic electrostatic spray. Hooks are 18 in. apart. The part designed hook supports two parts. Conveyor velocity is 6 fpm, and two operators tend the conveyor line. Determine the unit estimate and hr/100 units.

Table	Description	Time
20.2-4	Load and unload part, 2 operators at conveyor velocity 6 fpm, 18-in. spacing, $2 (.17 + .01 \times 6)$	.46 min
20.2-4	Spray	0
	Unit estimate	.46 min
	hr/100 units	.77 hr

D. As a preliminary to painting for protection from corrosion and to aid the bond between metal and the paint coating, a zinc phosphate coating is planned. The application is to be applied by immersion methods. The parts are to be racked, dipped manually, and unloaded. The operator, with racks, can handle 10 parts. Find the unit estimate.

Table	Description	Time
20.2-S	Setup racks for existing dip-line	.20 hr
20.2-6	Rack parts, 10 units, and dip	.09 min
20.2-6	Unload and pack (or stack)	.09
	Unit estimate	.18 min

E. A welded steel base is to be zinc chromate sprayed in a booth. The part is to be loaded with a fork truck and placed upon a pedestal for turning. Following the spray work, it is loaded into an oven and subsequently hand sprayed for enamel. Provide the unit time for these two operations. Spray area total = 1721 sq in.

Table	Description		Time	
20.2-S	Setup racks for existing dip-line		.2	hr
20.2-S	Setup second operation		.2	hr
20.2-1	Load and unload weldment in and out of booth from general area			
	and finally to oven, 2 operations		6.00	min
20.2-5	Wipe clean, 1721 sq in., 2 operations		.94	
20.2-5	Blow clean, 2 operations		.34	
20.2-5	Conversion coating		.82	
20.2-5	Enamel		3.65	
	Unit estimate		11.75	min

F. Estimate Example A above using a base-cost approach using information from Section IV.

Item	Description	Cost
20.2	Line speed at 6 fpm and part spacing of 2 ft, 2 part-stack, 5 operators for a 2-part stack	
	$1.51 \times 24 \div 6 \times \frac{1}{2} \times 5$ and for 5 operators	$15.10
	$/100 units for 5 operators	$15.10

G. Find the base cost for Example B above.

Item	Description	Cost
20.2	Handle, $L + W + H = 5+$, $5 \times .218$	$ 1.09
20.1	Unmask, $5 \times .544$	2.72
20.2	Fill 4 areas, 4×9.63	38.52
	$/100 units	$42.33

H. Re-estimate Example D above; however, use a base-cost technique.

Item	Description	Cost
20.2	Rack, hand dip, unload, constant	$ 6.75
20.2	10 units, $10 \times .403$ deduction	−4.03
	$/100 units	$ 2.72

TABLE 20.2   BOOTH, CONVEYOR AND DIP PAINTING, AND CONVERSION PROCESSES

Setup

Conveyor	0 hr
Dip	.20 hr
Booth	.20 hr
Bench	.05 hr
Fill engraving	.05 hr

Operation elements in estimating minutes

1. Handle part to spray booth or bench

$L + W + H$	Min	$L + W + H$	Min	$L + W + H$	Min
15.8	.08	25.0	.17	33.1	.37
16.6	.09	26.8	.19	35.6	.41
17.5	.10	28.7	.21	38.4	.45
18.5	.11	30.8	.23	41.5	.50
19.5	.12	33.1	.25	44.9	.54
20.7	.13	35.6	.28	48.6	.60
22.0	.14	38.4	.31	52.7	.66
23.5	.16	41.5	.34	Add'l	.01

Load and unload part to spray booth or bench (con't)
    Power hoist, hand traverse   1.08
    Dolly   .58
    Fork truck   3.00

2. Load rack or tray parts

No. pc	Rack, place rack on dolly	Rack, place rack on conveyor	Turnover	Unload	Unload, paper wrap, pack
1	.30	.27	.07		.60
2	.15	.14	.06		.39
3	.13	.11	.06		.30
4	.11	.10	.05		.27
5	.10	.09	.04	.06	.23
8	.08	.07	.04	.05	.18
10	.07	.06	.04	.05	.17
12	.06	.05	.03	.05	.15
15	.05	.05	.02	.05	.13
20	.05	.04	.02	.04	.11
25	.04	.04	.01	.04	.10
30	.04	.03	.01	.03	
50	.04	.03	.01	.02	
75	.03	.03	.01	.01	
100	.03	.03	.01	.01	
150	.03	.02	.01	.01	
200	.03	.02	.01	.01	

3. Load basket parts

No. pc	Drop parts in and out of basket	Stack parts in basket, dump out	Stack parts in basket, stack out
2		.72	.72
5		.27	.27
8		.15	.16
10		.14	.15
12		.12	.14
15		.09	.12
20		.08	.11
25		.07	.11
30	.05	.07	.10
40	.04	.06	.10
50	.03	.05	.09
75	.02	.05	.07
100	.02	.04	.06
150	.02	.04	.05
200	.02	.03	
250	.01	.03	
300	.01		
400	.01		

4. Conveyor-line loading, spraying, unloading, min/pc for 1 operator[1]

Conveyor speed, fpm	Part spacing centers, in.									
	3	5	7	12	24	36	48	72	120	Add'l
2	.13	.21	.29	.50	1.00	1.50	2.00	3.00	5.00	.04
3	.08	.14	.19	.33	.67	1.00	1.33	2.00	3.33	.03
4	.06	.10	.15	.25	.50	.75	1.00	1.50	2.50	.02
5	.05	.08	.12	.20	.40	.60	.80	1.20	2.00	.02
6	.04	.07	.10	.17	.33	.50	.67	1.00	1.67	.01
7	.04	.06	.08	.14	.29	.43	.57	.86	1.43	.01
8	.03	.05	.07	.13	.25	.38	.50	.75	1.25	.01
9	.03	.05	.06	.11	.22	.33	.44	.67	1.11	.009
10	.03	.04	.06	.10	.20	.30	.40	.60	1.00	.009
11	.02	.04	.05	.09	.18	.27	.36	.55	.91	.008
12	.02	.03	.05	.08	.17	.25	.33	.50	.83	.007
13	.02	.03	.04	.08	.15	.23	.31	.46	.77	.007
14	.018	.03	.04	.07	.14	.21	.29	.43	.71	.006
15	.017	.03	.04	.07	.13	.20	.27	.40	.67	.006
16	.016	.03	.04	.06	.13	.19	.25	.38	.63	.005
Add'l	.001	.002	.002	.004	.007	.01	.01	.02	.04	

[1] Multiply by number of operators on the line.

5. Prime, paint, or finish in booth

Area, sq in.	Prime or conversion coating	Wrinkle	Enamel	Epoxide resin	Mask	Wipe clean	Blow clean
24	.12	.34	.15	.53	.04		
32	.14	.37	.20	.55	.05		
50	.16	.40	.25	.57	.07		
58	.17	.41	.28	.58	.08	.13	
69	.18	.44	.32	.59	.10	.14	
83	.20	.47	.36	.61	.12	.14	
100	.22	.51	.42	.63	.14	.14	
115	.23	.55	.46	.65	.17	.14	
132	.25	.59	.51	.67	.19	.15	.04
152	.26	.63	.57	.70	.22	.15	.05
175	.28	.69	.63	.73	.25	.16	.05
201	.30	.75	.70	.76	.29	.16	.05
231	.32	.82	.77	.80	.33	.17	.05
266	.34	.90	.86	.84	.38	.17	.05
306	.36	.99	.95	.89	.44	.18	.06
352	.38	1.10	1.06	.95	.50	.19	.06
405	.41	1.22	1.17	1.02	.58	.20	.06
465	.44	1.36	1.30	1.10	.67	.21	.07
535	.46	1.53	1.44	1.19	.77	.22	.07
615	.49	1.71	1.60	1.29	.88	.24	.08
708	.53	1.93	1.77	1.41	1.01	.25	.09
814	.56	2.18	1.97	1.54	1.17	.27	.09
937	.60	2.46	2.18	1.70		.29	.10
1078	.64	2.79	2.42	1.88		.32	.11

Area, sq in.	Prime or conversion coating	Wrinkle	Enamel	Epoxide resin	Mask	Wipe clean	Blow clean
1240	.68	3.17	2.69			.35	.12
1428	.72	3.61	2.98			.38	.14
1640	.77	4.10	3.30			.42	.15
1800	.82	4.66	3.65			.47	.17
2170	.87	5.34	4.06			.52	.19
2500	.93	6.10	4.51			.58	.21
Add'l	.0002	.0023	.0017	.0013	.0014	.0002	.0001

6. Rack and hand dip, manual

No. pc	Rack and dip	Unload and pack	Dump
1	.54	.36	
2	.28	.20	
3	.21	.12	.02
5	.12	.12	.02
6	.12	.09	.02
10	.09	.09	.02
15	.08	.09	.02

7. Rack spraying with drying dolly, oven or air dry

No. pc	Spray one side flat parts	Turn part and spray other side	Spray inside, turn over, spray outside
1	.48	.90	1.08
2	.26	.48	.57
3	.18	.30	.36
4	.11	.25	.27
5	.08	.22	.25
8	.06	.18	.20
10	.05	.15	.17
12	.05	.13	.16
15	.05	.10	.14
20	.04	.07	.11
25	.03	.06	.09
30	.03	.05	.08
50	.02		
75	.01		
100	.01		
150	.01		
200	.01		

8. Rack spraying with rack loaded to conveyor and oven

No. pc	Spray one side flat parts	Turn part and spray other side	Spray inside, turn over, spray outside
1	.42	.84	.96
2	.23	.45	.51
3	.14	.30	.34
4	.10	.21	.30
5	.07	.18	.27
8	.05	.13	.19
10	.05	.11	.16
12	.04	.09	.13
15	.04	.08	.11
20	.03	.06	.09
25	.03	.05	.07
30	.03	.05	.06
50	.02	.04	.05
75	.02		
100	.01		
150	.01		
200	.01		

9. Fill engraving

L of area	Min	L of area	Min	L of area	Min
Word or					
1.0	.30	3.2	1.16	7.1	3.47
2.0	.47	3.6	1.40	8.3	4.17
2.2	.56	4.1	1.67	9.7	5.00
2.3	.67	4.6	2.01	11.4	6.00
2.6	.81	5.3	2.41	13.4	7.20
2.9	.97	6.1	2.89	Add'l	.59

10. Pack and unpack

Box	.12
Envelope	.18
Brown paper	.18
Strip 1 pc of mask	.14

20.3 Metal Chemical Cleaning Processes

DESCRIPTION

Chemical cleaning depends upon a solvent and/or chemical action between the basis material and the dirt, oil, grease, etc. The cleaning solvents con-sidered here are the chlorinated solvents or the vapor degreasers. The cleaning media may be tri-chlorethylene, perchlorethylene, and methylene

FIGURE 20.3 Gas-heated 8 x 8 x 8-ft vapor degreaser. *(Phillips Manufacturing Company)*

chloride. The chemical actions are the bright dip and the chromatic dips. In the bright dip for copper and copper alloys, the medium is sulphuric nitric acid. For aluminum materials, the medium is chromate. While not a chemical cleaning method, estimates for steam cleaning are provided.

The means of production can be manual or automatic, in tanks, submerged or above floor, or in small containers. The parts are lowered into a tank in which the solvent has been heated to its boiling point causing the solvent to vaporize. As the hot vapors meet the cold parts, the vapors condense and dissolve the dirt. The basic degreasing methods of vapor, liquid vapor, spray vapor, and ultrasonic liquid vapor can be utilized with a manually-generated or conveyor system degreaser. Figure 20.3 shows a manually-operated model.

ESTIMATING DATA DISCUSSION

The data are consolidated, that is, each type of chemical cleaning has the required handling, tank-to-tank movement, and delay for the cleaning. Entry variables are girth. For flat parts, girth is usually taken to mean length plus width ($L + W$). For cylindrical parts, girth is defined to the maximum diameter times two plus length (max diameter $\times 2 + L$). Box-type parts are computed as the maximum sum of the dimensions in the X-Y-Z planes.

Degreasing elements are separated on the basis of single or multiple-item degreasing. For bright and chromate dip, the part configuration, whether it is more flat-like, box-like, or cylindrical-like, is another governing entry variable.

Element 5 deals with the process time for steam cleaning using a direct nozzle against a rack, or individual part or basket of parts. A typical rack would have six hooks. The quantity of parts loaded into the basket must be determined by the estimator. Other loading estimates can be found in other tables.

Basket, barrel, tank or pan distinctions are not provided for these data.

Costs can be estimated directly using Item 20.3 of Section IV. This information requires knowledge of the girth cost driver, $L + W + H$.

EXAMPLES

A. A part has a 1.5-in. dia and is 4-in. long. A chromatic dip for this aluminum material is planned for appearance and protection sake. Find the unit estimate.

Table	Description	Time
20.3-4	$L + W + H = 4 + 2 \times 1.5 = 7$	.16 min
	Unit estimate	.16 min

408

B. A part, box-shaped, with $L + W + H = 19.3$ in., and can be multiple degreased. Find the shop estimate.

Table	Description		Time	
20.3-2	For $L + W + H = 19.3$		<u>.055</u>	min
	Unit estimate		.055	min
	Shop estimate		1090	pc/hr

C. Using Item 20.3 of Section IV re-estimate Example B above and find base cost/unit.

Item	Description		Cost	
20.3	$L + W + H = 19.3$, $19.3 \times .051$		<u>$.98</u>	
	$/100 units		$.98	
	Base cost/unit		$.01	

TABLE 20.3   METAL CHEMICAL CLEANING PROCESSES

Setup   **0 hr**

Operation elements in estimating minutes

1. Degrease one part

$L + W + H$	Min	$L + W + H$	Min	$L + W + H$	Min
.2	.01	11	.14	53	.37
.5	.02	13	.15	59	.39
.8	.03	16	.17	63	.41
1.5	.04	18	.19	66	.42
2.5	.05	21	.20	70	.44
3.1	.06	22	.21	75	.46
3.7	.07	25	.23	80	.48
4.4	.08	30	.25	85	.49
5.5	.09	31	.26	95	.53
6.7	.10	37	.29	100	.55
9.5	.12	40	.31	115	.60

2. Degrease many parts simultaneously

$L + W + H$	Min	$L + W + H$	Min	$L + W + H$	Min
.2	.0003	11	.03	53	.15
.5	.0009	13	.035	59	.17
.8	.0015	16	.04	63	.18
1.5	.003	18	.05	66	.19
2.5	.005	21	.055	70	.21
3.1	.007	22	.06	75	.22
3.7	.008	25	.07	80	.24
4.4	.01	30	.08	85	.26
5.5	.015	31	.085	95	.29
6.7	.02	37	.10	100	.31
9.5	.025	40	.11	115	.34

3. Bright dip

Flat	Box	Cylindrical	Min
L + W + H			
6.5	2.3	4.0	.006
6.7	2.4	4.1	.008
6.8	2.5	4.2	.010
7.0			.014
7.4	2.6	4.5	.020
7.5	2.8	4.6	.022
8.0	3.0	4.8	.029
		5.0	.035
9.1	3.5		.047
10.1	3.9	6.0	.063
	4.7	7.0	.092
33	5.2	7.6	.11

Flat	Box	Cylindrical	Min
L + W + H			
16	6.5	9.2	.16
18	7.4	10.5	.19
26	11	15	.33
30.5	13	17.5	.39
35	15	20	.47
41.5	17.5	23	.57
48.5	21	27	.68
57	24.5	32	.82
67	29	37.5	.98
79.5	34	44	1.18
94	41	52	1.41
111	48	62	1.69

4. Chromatic dip

Flat	Box	Cylindrical	Min
L + W + H			
7.6	2.2	3.7	.002
7.7	2.3	3.8	.007
7.8		3.9	.011
		4.0	.014
8.0			.016
	2.5		.018
8.5		4.5	.037
	3.0		.049
9.0		5.0	.056
9.5	3.5		.075
10	4.0	6.0	.099
10.5			.11
11	4.6	6.8	.14
12	5.1	7.4	.16

Flat	Box	Cylindrical	Min
L + W + H			
13	5.7	8.2	.20
	6.4	9.1	.24
15	7.3	10	.28
	8.3	11	.34
18	9.5	13	.41
20	11	15	.49
23	13	17	.59
26	15	20	.70
30	18	23	.84
34	21	27	1.01
39	24	32	1.21
46	29	37	1.46
53	34	44	1.75
63	40	52	2.10

5. Steam clean parts

Rack of parts	3.84
Medium part	1.03
Large part	2.68
Basket of parts to 8 x 18 x 60 in.	2.80
Basket of parts to 2 x 4 x 4 ft	3.80

20.4 Blast-Cleaning Machines

DESCRIPTION

Blast cleaning in one of its various forms cleans by the tumbling action of castings, weldments, etc., on one another as the mill rotates. The machine consists of a cleaning barrel, which is formed by an endless apron conveyor. The work is tumbled beneath a blasting unit located above the load, and

FIGURE 20.4 Tumbler blaster using metallic shot. Vibratory conveyor unloads parts after cleaning into hopper. *(Wheelabrator-Frye, Inc.)*

metallic shot is blasted onto the objects. A tumbler blaster is shown in Figure 20.4.

A variety of blast-cleaning machine configurations exists. Compartmentalized tables which allow separated handling during cleaning of other compartments is available. Swing-out doors which have rotating tables and allow for handling during cleaning, are also available. Double-door arrangements allow loading during cleaning. Conveyorized methods permit loading and unloading on hooks.

ESTIMATING DATA DISCUSSION

The selection of the handling element depends upon the machine type that is assumed and the size of the article that is being blast-cleaned. For the ordinary load and unload, an operator will handle the part from the floor or a table and the entry variable is

weight. Hoists, crane, fork truck, or rail insertion are modifications of the operator load and unload. The loading may be to a turn table, or ring, or arbor. The larger parts are obviously set upon a flat surface. A turnover operation, if required, assumes 75% of the basic load and unload time.

Bulk load assumes a dump into the hopper and undumping into a tote box. The entry variable is the expected number of units to be dumped. If automatic unloading is expected, remove 25%. In some cases, a rack is used having hooks and the part is hooked. The rack has multiple hooks and for smaller parts, the entry variable is the number of hooks on the rack.

If semiautomatic operation is used, the start and stop element is required. For swing-out door blasting units, times are given.

The time for shot blasting and tumbling is given

by Element 3. It depends upon the machine configuration and nature of object blasted. In the tumbling blasting method, the entry for gray iron castings is batch number which relates to the capacity of the tumbling unit. Similarly, for a spinner-hanger, the cleaning time is related to the number of units connected to the eyehook within a compartment. If a monorail is used, the time per unit depends on the hook spacing as the conveyor travel speed is 3 ft/min.

Item 20.4 of Section IV can be used to estimate blast cleaning costs for setup and cycle. A constant cycle cost is always required. Three methods of handling are indicated. For individual load and unload, a cost for 100 units is related to the weight. For bulk and rack load and unload, power equations are provided. The number of units handled in bulk, or the number of units loaded to the designed rack is the cost driver. The exponents for the two equations are different. Not all methods given in Table 20.4 are covered by Item 20.4.

EXAMPLES

A. A gray sand casting weighing 36 lb is received in boxes from the shake-out table. Some sand inclusions remain. A spin-hanger cabinet is used, and 3 parts are suspended on the hanger. The parts are loaded, and then the unit is revolved, allowing the parts to be blasted during loading. Determine the prorated unit time for a lot of 200 castings.

Table	Description	Time	
20.4-S	Setup	.2	hr
20.4-1	Load 3 parts from floor, $1 \times .31$	.31	min
20.4-3	Blast clean using spinner-hanger cabinet, $2 \div 3$	.66	
Remark	Use max of blast cleaning time (blast cleaning requires more time than loading unit)		
	Unit estimate	.66	min
	Prorated unit estimate	.012	hr

B. Steel castings, weighing 14 tons, are loaded on a revolving table, which is guided by tracks for blasting in a car-type room. Two castings are stacked on the table. A turnover is required. Find the unit time.

Table	Description	Time	
20.4-1	Bay crane loading on table, ea	15	min
20.4-3	Blast steel casting, $14/30 \times 20$	9.3	
20.4-1	Turnover, $3/4 \times 15$	11.25	
20.4-3	Blast steel casting	9.3	
	Unit estimate	44.85	min

C. Cores and rims of industrial casterwheels are shot blasted prior to the bonding of rubber to surfaces. Ten units are loaded on a rod. Simultaneously, other wheels are being cleaned on other quadrants of the multi-table compartment machine. Find the hours per 1000 units (hr/1000 units) to clean off welding flux and splatter.

Table	Description	Time	
20.4-1	2-lb units loaded on spindle	.07	min
20.4-3	Clean 50 in. of area, $.004 \times 50$	.20	
Remark	Cleaning exceeds loading		
	Unit estimate	.20	min
	hr/1000 units	3.333	

D. A 2-lb casting is tumble blasted. Find $/100 units and lot cost for 90 units.

Item	Description	Cost
20.4	Setup subtotal	$2.04
20.4	Cycle constant	$3.10
20.4	Individual load, $2 \times .086$	.17
20.4	Tumble blast, $2 \times .256$	.51
	$/100 units	$3.78
	Lot cost	$5.44

TABLE 20.4 BLAST-CLEANING MACHINES

Setup

Batch or lot of parts	.2 hr
Conveyor, automatic	0 hr

Operation elements in estimating minutes

1. Handling

Load and unload one part, lb

From table	From floor	Min		From table	From floor	Min
3.6		.07		46.5	19.3	.21
5.3		.08		52.5	24.0	.24
7.3		.09			29.1	.26
9.4		.10			34.7	.28
11.7		.11			40.9	.31
14.3		.12			47.7	.34
17.1	1.7	.13			55.2	.38
20.2	4.6	.15		Add'l		.004
23.6	7.7	.16			Add'l	.005
27.4	11.2	.18		Electric hoist		1.12
31.5	15.1	.19		Hand double chain hoist		4
36.0	19.3	.21		Bay crane		5–20
41.0	24.0	.24		Fork truck		2–10
				Rail		10–30

Bulk load and unload into machine

No. pc	Min		No. pc	Min
30	.05		75	.02
40	.04		250	.01
50	.03		500	.005

Automatic load and unload — no time

Place parts on rack, unrack

No. pc	Min		No. pc	Min
1	.33		10	.11
2	.20		12	.10
3	.17		20	.08
4	.16		30	.07
5	.15		50	.06
8	.12		75	.04

2. Machine operation

Start and stop	.10
Close and open doors	
Large	1.50
Small	.75

3. Blast cleaning

Tumbling-blasting	
Furnace-hardening steel scale	.003–.01/lb
Steel castings	.005–.02/lb
Gray iron castings (sand inclusions)	15/batch
Compression molded plastic (defashing)	4/batch

Swing-out, rotating-table cabinet
 Weldments (rust, mill scale, and welding flux, small splatter)   4/side
 (Prorate by number of units loaded on table)

Multi-table
 Welded pieces (mill scale, welding fluxes, spatter)   .004/sq in.
 (Prorate by number of units loaded)
Drums   .3/ea

Spinner-hanger cabinet
 Gray iron castings   2/hook
 (Prorate by number of parts on hook)
Car-type room
 Bulk steel castings to 30 tons   5–20/ea

Monorail, overhead

Hook spacing	3	5	7	12	24	36	48
Min (for one operator)	.08	.14	.19	.33	.67	1.00	1.33

Roller, horizontal
Steel beams, angle plate, trusses, girders   4/ea

20.5 Metal Electroplating and Oxide Coating Processes

DESCRIPTION

Electroplating is a means of applying decorative and protective coatings to metals. In commercial plating, the object to be plated is placed in a tank containing a suitable electrolyte. The anode consists of a plate of pure metal while the part is the cathode. The tank contains a solution of salts of the metal to be applied. A dc current is required. When the current is flowing, metal from the anode replenishes the electrolyte solution while ions of the dissolved metal are deposited on the workpiece in a solid state. Oxide coating, i.e., anodizing for aluminum, involves an electrolyte of sulphuric, oxalic, or chromic acid with the part to be anodized as the anode. Since the coating is produced by oxidation, it is permanent and an integral part of the basis material. The coating is porous, which enables organic coatings and dyes to be applied to the surface of alumi-

num. Electroforming is not considered in these data. Conversion coatings are covered in Table 20.3, while other metal preparation and cleaning is given in Table 20.4.

As it affects direct labor time and cost, the tanks, barrels, baskets, hoists, racks, and timers or other controls are the important time drivers. For instance, open-surface or hooded tanks affect the time and style of loading. The racks are critical for loading, as the smallest tank in the line sets the dimension and ultimately the number handled per load. Rack configurations are numerous—rings, box, quad-point, and various designs can be easily constructed to suit special parts. Work-holder contacts such as pressure-type, hook and loose-hole, wire or strip, and nut and screw are possibilities.

Plating can be manual, semi-, and fully auto-

FIGURE 20.5 Horizontal oscillating barrel and hoist assembly for programmed hoist barrel electroplating line. *(Udylite Equipment Systems Division of Oxy Metal Industries Corporation)*

matic. Bath time, however, is restricted to specification, which in turn depends upon dc density, part packing, etc.

Figure 20.5 is an example of a polypropylene barrel and hoist assembly installed in a row programmed-hoist barrel electroplating line for zinc and chromate coating of fasteners.

ESTIMATING DATA DISCUSSION

These estimating data may be for one or several operations and are combined. The estimator may wish to organize the estimate collectively or separately. For instance, the operation string-up/take-down may be by operators other than electroplaters.

Setup is separated for pre-plating operations such as string-up/take-down, rack, and barrel, or steel plate.

The string-up/take-down element, while it can be separated into two different operations, is combined here. The string-up is 70% of the total time. In

oxide coating processes, it may be necessary to use aluminum strip for anodizing instead of wire, and the entry variable is panel $L + W$ size, and hanging length. The variable hanging length means the vertical distance the part will hang.

Cleaning elements are given in number 2. Blow off seams using manual methods have the length of seam as the entry variable. Liquid hone starts with the small parts in the booth, start machine, blast part, stop, and spray to rinse. The small parts could be in a basket, and the load would be blast. Medium parts are those which are individually worked, and the entry variable is $L + W + H$.

Electroplating is divided into manually-controlled and automatic. In manually-controlled, the entry variable for electroplating estimating data, Element 4, is based upon part configuration, girth $L + W + H$, and the type of plate. The three part-type geometries are box-like, cylinder-like, and flat-like. This selection is due to part packing within the container or rack. The girth is the minimum X-Y-Z box container that will fit the three configurations. For cylinders, it is $L + 2D$, where D is the part maximum diameters. Usually, thickness of flat parts does not affect the entry value chosen.

There are many specifications in the field of electrodeposition. In silver plating, for instance, the tank density, basis material, and thickness are only a few of the specifications which affect the estimate. Even so, the many specifications are provided in a composite estimate. Element 4 is for multiple parts for small- and moderate-lot production where racks and baskets are common. Typical baskets are hexagonal with 17-in. flats and 36-in. flat-to-flat, circular with 10-in. *Dia* and 8-in. *H,* rectangular style 48 × 28 in. and 28-in. *H.* Racks with about 150 hooks on a 36 × 52-in. base to a single-hook with manual hoist control. Tanks, of course, are suitably sized to match these requirements, but tank sizes do differ.

The estimate is affected by the number to be plated. If barrel plating is to be used, multiply the table value by .75. To find the manual time for a quantity of one, the data are extended this way. The time for 40, 40, and 50 table entry values found in Element 4 are multiplied by a factor.

Process	Factor
Cadmium plate steel	4
Copper plate copper	2
Gold plate aluminum	7
Gold plate copper	4
Nickel plate copper	3
Nickel-rhodium plate copper	4*
Passivate stainless steel	4
Silver plate aluminum	5
Silver plate copper	3
Tin plate aluminum	7
Tin plate copper	2

*Use nickel value.

Thus, the one-unit time considers the process of

metal cleaning, rinse, acid or alkaline dip, rinse, metal plate, rinse, etc. according to various commercial and federal specifications. On the basis of manual batch time, other estimate values can be constructed for differing batch size, or rack or basket loading.

Elements 4 and 5 are helpful if ease is desired. Many parts can be smaller than the minimum entry values listed. In this case, the estimator will use the threshold value, as the typical estimates point out.

The above discussion is for manually dipped parts, i.e., by hand or hoist, and requires that the part be wired, clipped, or somehow loaded to the rack or basket.

Whenever automatic plating is used and manual racking and unracking are required, Element 6 is used. Entry variables are maximum dimension and weight. While there could be a contradiction as the two may not agree for a part, the better choice would be to adopt the larger time value. The racks have 25 hooks, and the operator presents the part to hook in a way to hang it through a port hole.

It is possible that parts will be unracked or disposed to a package operation directly after the electroplating. The estimator may want to use Table 24.1 for these operations.

Costs can be estimated using an approach given in Item 20.5 of Section IV. For string-up and takedown, the cost driver is the hanging height. For electroplating, anodize, and metal preparation, the cost driver is girth, or $L + W + H$. There is a negative constant cost for all the examples. It will be possible for parts smaller than $L + W + H = 4$ to have the final computed cost as negative. Whenever this happens it will be necessary to use Table 20.5. Threshold times from Table 20.5 are used for very small $L + W + H$ values.

EXAMPLES

A. A steel stamping, similar to a scissor half, is to be cadmium plated using still-plating methods. Part dimensions are 4.5 in. (*L*), 1.2 in. (*W*), and ⅛ in. (max thk). The finger hole is easily available for hooking. Lot size is 1750. Find the unit estimate for several operations.

Table	Description	Time
20.5-S	Racking	.05 hr
20.5-S	Still plating	.10 hr
20.5-1	Hang part in its hole	.09 min
20.5-4	Cadmium plate, 5.8-in. flat part, and using the threshold value	.018
	Unit estimate	.108 min

B. Estimate A above if the object is to be barrel plated.

Table	Description	Time
20.5-S	Setup the barrel plate	.20 hr
20.5-4	Cadmium barrel plate, .75 × .018	.014 min
	Unit estimate	.014 min

C. Re-estimate Example A above in terms of base cost using Item 20.5 of Section IV.

Item	Description	Cost
20.5	Hang part in hole, unhang	$1.76
20.5	Cad plate — 4.92 + 1.03 × 5.8	1.05
	$/100 units	$2.81
	Base cost/unit	$ .028

TABLE 20.5 METAL ELECTROPLATING AND OXIDE COATING PROCESSES

Setup

String-up/take-down, racking	.05 hr
Still plating	.10
Barrel plating	.20
Automatic-conveyor line	1–8 hr

Operation elements in estimating minutes

1. String-up, take-down

Wire

Hanging L	.5	1.0	1.5	2.0	2.5	3.0	3.5	5
Min	.14	.16	.17	.19	.20	.22	.23	.28

Hanging L	6	7	8	9	10	13	15
Min	.31	.34	.37	.40	.43	.52	.58

Aluminum strip

L	L + W 0–4 in.	4+–12 in.	12+
.2	.16		
.6	.17		
1.2	.18	.29	
1.9	.19	.32	
2.5	.20	.35	
3.0	.21	.37	
3.5		.40	
4.0		.42	
4.5		.44	
5.5		.49	
10		.70	.63
15			.82
20			1.00

Alligator clip	.08
Hang part in hole on rack, and unhang Maximum single dimension to 3 in.	.06

Maximum single dimension, 3+ to 9 in.   .09
Maximum single dimension, 9+ to 20 in.   .16
Longest dimension, 20+ in.   .35

2. Clean

Blow off seams

L	.5	1	2	4	Add'l
Min	.50	.55	.63	.81	.09

Liquid hone

L + W + H	1	2	4	8	16	32	Add'l
Min	.52	.59	.73	1.01	1.34	2.32	.07

3. Strip liquid mask

L + W + H	1	2	4	6	Add'l
Min	.01	.02	.08	.13	.03

Install robber wire   .48
Remove robber wire   .27

4. Electroplating, min/pc

Box	L + W + H Cylinder	Flat	Bright Alloy	Cadmium	Copper	Gold
2	3	6			.028	
		7	.004	.018	.068	.012
		8	.020	.044	.11	.022
3	4	9	.037	.069	.15	.057
	5	10	.062	.11	.21	.10
	6	12	.099	.17	.30	.16
4	7	14	.14	.22	.40	.22
5	8	16	.18	.30	.51	.30
6	9	18	.23	.37	.62	.38
7	10	20	.27	.44	.74	.45
8	12	23	.34	.54	.90	.57
9	14	26	.40	.65	1.07	.68
11	16	30	.49	.79	1.29	.83
16	20	35	.67	1.06	1.73	1.13
18	23		.76	1.20	1.94	1.28
20	26		.84	1.33	2.16	1.42
24	30	40	.98	1.54	2.49	1.65
40	40	50	1.46	2.28	3.68	2.46
Add'l			.075	.078	.12	.085
	Add'l		.061	.062	.10	.068
		Add'l	.053	.036	.057	.038

4. Electroplating, min/unit

L + W + H						
Box	Cylinder	Flat	Nickel	Rhodium	Silver	Tin
2	3	6		.014		.014
		7	.015	.029	.023	.049
		8	.044	.057	.057	.085
3	4	9	.072	.086	.092	.12
	5	10	.12	.13	.15	.18
	6	12	.18	.20	.22	.26
4	7	14	.24	.26	.30	.34
5	8	16	.32	.34	.40	.44
6	9	18	.40	.42	.49	.54
7	10	20	.48	.50	.59	.64
8	12	23	.60	.62	.73	.78
9	14	26	.71	.74	.87	.93
11	16	30	.87	.90	1.06	1.13
16	20	35	1.18	1.21	1.43	1.52
18	23		1.32	1.36	1.62	1.71
20	26		1.48	1.52	1.80	1.90
24	30	40	1.71	1.75	2.08	2.19
40	40	50	2.54	2.60	3.09	3.24
Add'l			.088	.089	.11	.11
	Add'l		.070	.072	.085	.088
		Add'l	.039	.040	.048	.050

5. Oxide coating and other processes, min/unit

L + W + H					Chemical	
Box	Cylinder	Flat	Anodize	Blacken	Polish	Passivate
2	3	6	.018			
		7	.043	.004	.010	
		8	.069	.020	.030	
3	4	9	.095	.037	.050	.005
	5	10	.13	.062	.081	.028
	6	12	.19	.099	.13	.063
4	7	14	.25	.14	.17	.10
5	8	16	.32	.18	.23	.14
6	9	18	.40	.23	.28	.18
7	10	20	.47	.27	.34	.22
8	12	23	.57	.34	.42	.29
9	14	26	.68	.40	.50	.35
11	16	30	.82	.49	.61	.43
16	20	35	1.10	.67	.82	.59
18	23		1.23	.76	.93	.67
20	26		1.37	.84	1.03	.75
24	30	40	1.58	.98	1.20	.87
40	40	50	2.34	1.46	1.78	1.31
Add'l			.080	.051	.061	.046
	Add'l		.064	.040	.049	.036
		Add'l	.036	.023	.027	.022

6. Rack and unrack part on hook

Max Dim	Weight	No. pc/rack									
		1	3	5	8	10	12	15	18	20	25
0 < Dim ≤ 3 in.	0 < Wt ≤ .2 lb							.07	.07	.06	.06
3 < Dim ≤ 9	.2 < Wt ≤ 3					.11	.09	.08	.07	.06	.06
9 < Dim ≤ 20	3 < Wt ≤ 8		.33	.21	.12	.12	.10	.09			
20 < Dim ≤ 36	8 < Wt ≤ 12	.90	.35	.24	.13	.13					

ASSEMBLY

21.1 Bench Assembly

DESCRIPTION

The estimating data in this section are for general bench assembly. They are listed with the purpose of the work element to be done, and not on the basis of fundamental motions. No machines are involved in bench assembly, although a range of hand or powered-hand tools is included. The data are also not associated with a reach or move distance, as this information may be unavailable at the time of estimating.

The type of work done on the bench is too vast to attempt to provide extensive description. Instead, we have chosen to identify key elements that are versatile and broadly usable.

ESTIMATING DATA DISCUSSION

No setup is allowed for bench assembly. Throughout the data, reference is made to part size. While ambiguity is difficult to prevent, the part size is identified as very small, small, medium, large, and very large. These descriptions are not classified relative to a specific machine but to manual handling characteristics. The parts classification is included in the following table.

It should be understood that "very large" is in the context of bench assembly. This description is unacceptable for the other processes and machines described in this estimating guide.

The data are expressed in min/occurrence and

Part Size	Remarks
Very small	When handled individually, the parts are difficult to control, though they can be handled easily in handfuls. Tweezers are sometimes used.
Small	Small parts are easy to manage by handfuls or with fingers. No dimension exceeds 3 in. and weight does not exceed ¼ lb.
Medium	Medium-sized parts are sometimes handled by double handfuls. Their maximum dimension and weight are 9 in. and 3 lb.
Large	Each large part is handled separately, and a large part requires the use of two hands. The maximum dimension and weight are 20 in. and 8 lb.
Very large	A very large part has a maximum dimension and weight of 36 in. and 12 lb.

are three-place decimals under .10 min. As the data are multiplied by the frequency of occurrence, rounding off of these elements leads to errors.

Elements 3 and 4 are concerned with the same part. For each different part, Element 3 is first used. For each subsequent part, Element 4 is applied. Other elements are self-explanatory.

EXAMPLE

A. A frame has several components attached using screws, nuts, and washer. Stack bins and ordinary hand tools are laid out for the job. Estimate the job, as described below.

Table	Description	Time
21.1-1	Get and aside basic part	.045 min
21.1-3	Get small component, place on restricted frame, .027 + .015	.042
21.1-7	Get screw and washer, place, 7 times, 7 × .099	.69
21.1-7	Get nut, start, 7 times, 7 × .083	.58
21.1-7	Spintite 6 threads, 7 times, 7 × .045 + 7 × .015 × 5	.84
21.1-3	Get very small component	.03
21.1-4	Get and place 3 more components into 3 very small holes, 3 × .045	.14
21.1-7	Get screw, nut, and washer, 8 times, and place and start, 8 × .083 + 8 × .024	.86
21.1-7	Spintite 6 threads, 8 times, 8 × .045 + 8 × .015 × 5	.96
21.1-9	Air clean, medium	.063
21.1-9	Rubber stamp	.13
	Unit estimate	4.38

TABLE 21.1   BENCH ASSEMBLY

Setup   **0**

Operation elements in estimating minutes

1. Handle basic part

Part Size	Type of Handling			
	Toss	Place	Stack	Conveyor
Very small	.027	.039	.042	
Small	.021	.036	.039	
Medium	.030	.042	.045	.042
Large	.078	.084	.090	.054
Very large		.13	.14	.090

2. Tumble or turn parts

Part size	0°–90°	90°–180°
Very small	.009	.018
Small	.012	.024
Medium	.015	.030
Large	.030	.060
Very large	.039	.078

	Part size	On open bench	Into angle or vee	Into formed nest	Over 1 pin or into hole	Over 2 pins or 1 pin nested	Add for close tol or care	Add for other part aligned
3. Place and position part	Very small	.018	.024	.033	.040	.045	.018	.018
	Small	.021	.027	.030	.027	.039	.015	.012
	Medium	.024	.030	.036	.033	.051	.015	.018
	Large	.051	.060	.066	.063	.084	.021	.030
	Very large	.063	.075	.084	.078	.11	.030	.036
4. Get and place add'l part	Very small	.036	.042	.048	.045	.060	.018	.018
	Small	.027	.036	.042	.039	.054	.015	.012
	Medium	.042	.048	.057	.054	.069	.015	.018
	Large	.078	.087	.093	.090	.11	.021	.030
	Very large	.11	.12	.13	.12	.14	.030	.040

Part size	On open bench	Into angle or vee	Into formed nest	Over 1 pin or into hole	Over 2 pins or 1 pin nested	Add for close tol or care	Add for other part aligned
5. Get and place multiple part (multiple get)							
Very small	.024	.033	.042	.036	.048	.018	.018
Small	.024	.033	.045	.036	.048	.015	.012
Medium	.033	.045	.051	.048	.057	.015	.018

6. Handle tool
    Simple grasp   .036
    Difficult grasp   .048

7. Fasteners
    Get screw or nut and place (multiple get)   .024
    Get screw and washer, place   .099
    Get screw, 2 washers, place   .15
    Get screw or nut, start 1½ threads   .083
    Get screw, washer, start   .13
    Get screw, place on split or magnetic screwdriver, and start or get nut, place,
        start with spin tight   .11
    Get screw, washer, place on driver and start   .15
    Get screw, 2 washers, place on driver, start   .19
    Add for starting sheet metal or self tapping screws   .096
  Run screw or nut down
    Hand, each thread   .015
    Hand tool, 1 standard thread   .045
        Ea add'l   .015
  Power driver, 1st 10 threads   .024
    Ea add'l 10 threads   .009
  Open end wrench, ea thread   .060

8. Fixture handling and clamping
    Close and open toggle clamp   .042
    Close and open cam acting lever clamp   .051
    Close and open swing or slide clamp   .030
    Tighten and loosen thumb or wing nut   .084
    Tighten and loosen nut or bolt with wrench   .24
    Place and remove holding pin   .06
    Place and remove locating arbor or nest   .14
    Place and remove clamping plate   .054
    Tap part in and out of fixture   .072
    Pry part out of fixutre   .092
    Operate air clamp   .015
    Index fixture one station   .042
    Place clamp or spacer on part   .060
    Remove clamp or spacer from part   .030

9. Miscellaneous elements
    Drill and pin with roll pin, 1st hole   1.40
        Add'l hole   .68
    Chase one piece, 1st hole   .16
        Add'l hole   .07
    Install helicoil spring   .52
    Rubber stamp once   .13
    Air clean
        Small   .048
        Medium   .063
        Large   .093
        Very large   .13

21.2 Riveting and Assembly Machines

DESCRIPTION

In riveting, a one-piece fastener consisting of a head and body is passed through an aligned hole of two or more pieces. It is then clinched, or a second head is formed on the body end. While the rivets have a variety of materials, sizes, and shapes for various purposes, our concerns are for the machines which do this operation.

Riveting machines may be floor mounted, bench mounted, or even hand held. Whether they are manual or automatic, the rivet is fed from the hopper to a track or manually loaded that drops it, shank down, in the center of the upper jaws. A driver action pushes the rivet onto a spring-mounted plunger on the lower arm of the machine. A lower die clinches the rivet. The power to drive the rivet may be pneumatic or electric.

Hardware can mean a number of things. For instance, standoffs, terminals, pemnuts, press nuts, springs, clips, eyelets, bushing, tubes, or anything that is pressed-in and is multiple-carried by one hand is considered hardware.

Assembly machines are specially designed, and one is shown in Figure 21.2. The direct-labor costs vary with the machine design requirements.

ESTIMATING DATA DISCUSSION

A setup depends on whether the operation is the first light-mechanical assembly or not. Following setups require less time.

The handling element deals only with parts. It involves the handling of any rivet, screw, etc. The entry variable is location (from a skid or a bench).

FIGURE 21.2 A specially designed machine for automatic syringe assembly. (*Hill Rockford*)

Obviously, the larger part is on the skid. Additional parts location can be from either a skid or bench, as well. In light-mechanical assembly, a hoist is unlikely, and the weight of the part is within operator safety limits. The times for one are total.

Element 2 includes get hardware, position hardware, position part, and cycle (or press). Element 3, "rivet," represents a rivet, stake, roll, flare, or spin type of a machine element. It includes position part and machine cycle. The entry variable is the number of cycles.

Several special fixture handling and clamping elements in 4 are given. These are associated with light-mechanical assembly. Similarly, Element 5 lists some miscellaneous machine times. Specially designed assembly machines depend upon cycle time designed for the unit. They may or may not require operator attendance for work such as filling tubs with parts and watching.

Item 21.2 of Section IV can be used to estimate riveting or assembly machines directly. The constant cost is for the basic part and is always used. A cost is provided for each minor part that may be used. A rivet cost is specified for each cycle.

EXAMPLES

A. A major part, located in a skid, has 2 large skid-located parts, and 8 minor tote-box parts to be assembled by riveting. For hardware-mounting there are 27 holes into which rivets are inserted and pressed. Once the hardware is attached, 15 rivets are rolled. Determine the unit time and the hr/100 units.

Table	Description	Time
21.2-S	Setup, first operation	.25 hr
21.2-1	Get basic part and two skid-mounted parts	.50 min
21.2-1	Get 8 minor parts	.31
21.2-2	Hardware mounting, 27 cycles	1.90
21.2-3	Rivet, 15 cycles	.70
21.2-1	Assembly aside to skid	.13
	Unit estimate	3.54 min
	Hr/100 units	5.90

B. Re-estimate Example A above using a base-cost approach. The information is found in Section IV.

Item	Description	Cost
21.2	Setup subtotal	$ 1.93
21.2	Cycle constant	$ 2.50
21.2	10 minor parts, 10 × 1.74	17.40
21.2	42 cycles, 42 × .957	40.19
	$/100 units	$60.17

TABLE 21.2   RIVETING AND ASSEMBLY MACHINES

Setup

First operation	.25 hr
Additional operations	.10 hr

Operation elements in estimating minutes

1. Handling

Major and minor parts		From skid	From bench
Get basic part		.13	.03
Get minor part no.	1	.31	.07
	2	.50	.10
	3	.68	.14
	4	.86	.17
	5	1.05	.21
	6	1.23	.24
	7	1.42	.28

Major and minor parts	From skid	From bench
8	1.60	.31
9	1.79	.35
10	1.97	.38
Add'l.	.18	.035

Aside to skid   .13
Aside to bench   .03

2. Press in hardware

No. Cycles	Min	No. Cycles	Min	No. Cycles	Min	No. Cycles	Min
1	.06	11	.77	21	1.48	31	2.19
2	.13	12	.84	22	1.55	32	2.26
3	.20	13	.91	23	1.62	33	2.33
4	.27	14	.98	24	1.69	34	2.40
5	.34	15	1.05	25	1.76	35	2.47
6	.41	16	1.12	26	1.83	36	2.54
7	.48	17	1.19	27	1.90	37	2.62
8	.55	18	1.27	28	1.98	37	2.69
9	.63	19	1.34	29	2.05	39	2.67
10	.70	20	1.41	30	2.12	Add'l	.071

3. Rivet

No. Cycles	Min	No. Cycles	Min	No. Cycles	Min	No. Cycles	Min
1	.06	11	.52	21	.97	31	1.43
2	.11	12	.56	22	1.02	32	1.48
3	.15	13	.61	23	1.07	33	1.52
4	.20	14	.65	24	1.11	34	1.57
5	.24	15	.70	25	1.16	35	1.61
6	.29	16	.75	26	1.20	36	1.66
7	.33	17	.79	27	1.25	37	1.71
8	.38	18	.84	28	1.29	38	1.75
9	.43	19	.88	29	1.34	39	1.80
10	.47	20	.93	30	1.38	Add'l	.046

4. Special fixture handling and clamping
    Place and remove locating pin or arbor   .09
    Open and close toggle clamp   .14
    Open and close cam acting lever   .04
    Open and close swing or slide clamp   .05
    Tighten and loosen thumb screw or wing nut   .03
    Tighten and loosen nut or bolt with wrench   .08
    Operate air clamp   .24
    Pry part out of fixture   .02
    Pry part into fixture   .10
    Tap part in and out of fixture   .07

5. Miscellaneous machine times
    Arbor press with lever   .03
    Arbor press with wheel or small hydraulic press   .04
    Hopper feed screw setters   .03
    Small bench welder   .06

6. Miscellaneous light-mechanical assembly
    Centerpunch   .07
    Helicoil insert in predrilled hole   .48

21.3 Robot Machines

DESCRIPTION

Industrial robots are machines that load, process, transfer, position, and unload. These data deal with all these elements, with the exception of processing. (Consult other tables for processing.)

Industrial robots consist of the manipulator (or mechanical unit), which actually performs the functions; controller, which stores data and directs the movements of the manipulator; and the power supply. The manipulator is a series of mechanical linkages and joints that allows movement in various directions. These mechanisms are driven by actuators, which may be pneumatic or hydraulic cylinders, hydraulic rotary actuators, or electric motors. The actuators my be coupled directly to the mechanical links or joints or, they may drive indirectly through gears, chains, or ball screws. Feedback devices are installed to sense the positions of the various links and joints and to transmit this information to the controller. The feedback devices may be limit switches or position measuring devices such as encoders, potentiometers or resolvers, or tachometers.

Figure 21.3 is a robot handling two die cast ma-

chines. The die cast machines are 800-ton units and have 21-ft 6-in. centers.

ESTIMATING DATA DISCUSSION

Most robot applications use more than two independent axes. To estimate the traverse time required for each axis, which may involve the working-tip attitude and path, and then calculating the time for the longest motion, would be unnecessarily laborious, as velocities (wrist movements, etc.) are nominally expressed in degrees/second (deg/sec). Or, in-out reach (radial travel) is expressed by robot manufacturers in terms of in./sec

Element 1 deals with moving from a rest position to the proximity of the first area of processing. Similarly, it offers an estimate for retracting from processing to the rest position. The robot tool can be any choice, but its weight should be known. The extension distance is also necessary to know.

After positioning to the work area, adjusting the robot tool attitude to be normal to the metal is given by Element 2. Any minor zone change, where a

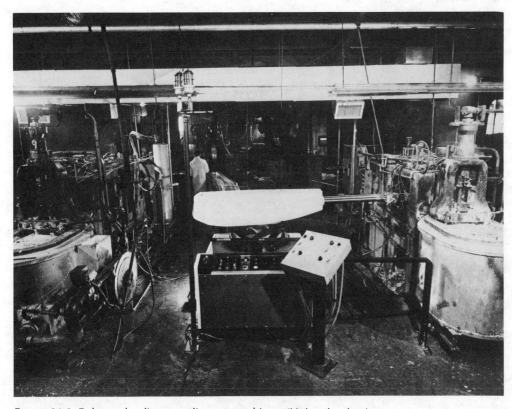

FIGURE 21.3 Robot unloading two die cast machines. *(Unimation Inc.)*

robot tool attitude change is required, Element 2 is required. "Simple" implies no interference.

Element 3 is used for a group of sequential skips in which the distance is small and no significant change in the attitude of the gun is required.

If the tool spins, to dry or centrifuge, etc., a spin estimate value is given.

Table 21.3 provides estimates for robot tool movement. (Use other tables for processing values.)

Item 21.3 of Section IV can be used for quick estimating where the information is expressed in $/100 units. The constant value is always used. For each robot tool zone, after the initial one, an additional cost can be provided to the estimate. If the robot tool moves point to point, a cost value can be selected. Obviously, if the robot machines is unattended by a direct-labor operator, there is neither direct-labor cost nor time consumption.

EXAMPLES

A. A body side and roof rail are spot welded using a robot machine. The side and rail have 29 and 28 spots. A spot-welding gun is 35 lb, and a maximum reach gives 750 in.-lb. Spot weld separation is 2 in. for wheel well and 1.5 in. for the roof rail. Obstructions exist between the weld zones, which require complex convolute paths for the robot gun tip. Clamps are necessary within the welding zones, and inner movement is necessary. Movements for the gun from rest to the workpiece are complex. Find the unit estimate and the hr/10,000 units. It is pointed out that if the robot is unattended, direct labor does not exist, and a direct labor estimate is unnecessary. The cost of the robot is then "overhead".

Table	Description	Time
21.3-1	Approach to weld zone, 750 in.-lb., complex movement	.081 min
21.3-2	Position to work area	.025
	Weld 29 times, 29 × .01, steel material	.29
21.3-3	Point-to-point tool movement, 2 in., 29 × .009	.261
21.3-2	Position tool to roof rail, 750 in.-lb.	.025
	Weld 28 times, 28 × .01	.28
21.3-3	Point-to-point tool movement, 1.5, 28 × .008	.224
21.3-1	Retract tool to rest position, 750 in.-lb	.081
	Unit estimate	1.267 min
	Hr/10,000 units	211.167

B. Re-estimate the direct labor for the robot cost only for Example A. Use information from Section IV. Assume that the robot is attended by one direct operator.

Item	Description	Cost
21.3	Cycle constant	$ 3.38
21.3	To tool zone	.53
21.3	Point to point, 57 × .181	10.32
21.3	To roof zone	.53
21.3	Return to rest	.53
	$/100 units	$15.29

TABLE 21.3   ROBOT MACHINES

Setup   **0**

Operation elements in estimating minutes

1. Approach or retract robot tool to work

In.-lb	250	500	750	1000	2000	3000
Simple	.049	.052	.056	.059	.073	.087
Complex	.072	.077	.081	.086	.104	.122

2. Positioning of robot tool to work area, ea area

In.-lb	250	500	750	1000	2000	3000
Simple	.013	.015	.017	.019	.027	
Complex	.023	.024	.025	.026	.027	.032

3. Point-to-point movement of robot tool without processing, ea time

Distance	.5	1.0	1.5	2.0	2.5	3.0
Min	.006	.007	.008	.009	.011	.012

4. Spin   .01/rev

5. Processing, spot welding, drill, mill, paint, die cast, cut, mold, etc.   See other tables

FOR PRODUCTION WORKERS ONLY 22.1
"   INSPECTION   "   "   22.2

22.1 Machine, Process, and Bench Inspection

DESCRIPTION

These data are for production workers checking their work. It is unlike the data labeled *Inspection Tables and Machines* which is for receiving, tool, source, or final inspection customarily done by inspectors.

A variety of measuring instruments are used, such as direct-reading, angular, and plane instruments. Principles for the readings may be mechanical, optical, electronic/electrical, and pneumatic. The gages can be read as direct, digital, analog, comparative, or projecting. Furthermore, gages can be classified into master, inspection, and manufacturing, which deal with their truth of measurement.

It is the manufacturing gages, located on or about the machine, process, or bench, that are considered here. There are many types too numerous to mention, but they are listed in Table 22.1. Other gages, notably master and inspection grade, are not process or machine based, and they are found in Table 22.2.

ESTIMATING DATA DISCUSSION

There is no setup for Table 22.1 since it is provided by other machine, process, or bench data.

Two categories are evaluated. In the first, the workpiece is checked following completion. The inspection occurs during an automatic cycle of a following part and time required for checking is less than the automatic element.

In the second category, the work is mounted on the machine or process and inspection occurs during an interruption of the cycle, or during the process without elemental interruption. This is called in-processing inspection.

The key to the calculation of inspection time is whether or not the interruption increases direct-labor time for the unit estimate. If there is an interruption, the possibility exists for an inspection time to be added to the unit estimate, given the time for the inspection and the frequency of inspection to the number of parts is significant when compared to the unit cycle estimate. The work is done by production workers, or by inspectors at the work stations, and cycle time is interrupted.

The times include pickup of the measuring device, adjust to dimension, read dimension, and lay aside. The times do not include part handling. If that is necessary, then the machine or process data are used.

Element 3 lists the measuring devices and the times for various total dimensional tolerances.

The following table, gaging frequency, relates total dimensional tolerance to gaging frequency. As expected, the frequency is inversely proportional to the functional dimensional tolerance. For example, a .005-in. tolerance would require two checks per one part while a .010-in. tolerance would require one check per 25 parts. These ratios are judgmental, although they are comparative to typical company practices.

Item 22.1 of Section IV can be used to find typical base costs for a production inspection that

Total dimensional tolerance	Gaging frequency per no. of parts or occurrences
−.0002	3/1
.0003−.0005	2/1
.0006−.001	1/1
.002 −.005	1/5
.006 −.010	1/25
.011 −.030	1/50
Fraction	1/50
Feature	1/100

← ADJUSTMENT FACTOR

Frequency to get this dimension

interrupts the production cycle. The information is $/100 occurrences. An occurrence may happen, for instance, once or twice, etc. for a part or not at all. The cost driver is the tolerance. Knowledge of a specific device for inspection is not required. Gaging frequency is figured in the cost. Examples of the use of this item are provided in many other locations in addition to Example D.

EXAMPLES

A. A steel casting weighing 700 lb is drilled, counterbored, and tapped on an NC machining center. Although there are 37 holes, only several are critical, and they are listed in the schedule below. Tape control is stopped pending inspection for specified dimensions using the ratio identified in Element 4. Find the unit estimate of inspection time that would be added to the direct-labor NC machine-center production estimate.

Table	Description	Time
22.1-3	Vernier caliper .005-in. ID of bore, .13/5, where 5 is gaging frequency	.026 min
22.1-3	Vernier caliper fractional step, .10/50	.002
22.1-3	Plug gage 3 bores with go/no-go, each .002 in. total tolerance, 3 × .08/5	.048
22.1-3	Machinist micrometer check of five .001-in. ID, 5 × .16/1	.80
22.1-3	Depth check step with depth micrometer for .005-in. total tolerance, .29/5	.058
	Unit estimate	.934 min

B. A radial drill machines a forging having 2 center-to-center locating dimension, and a five-internal thread is also checked. Work is done subsequent to production and during the boring of 2 holes. What time will the unit estimate require? The schedule of inspection is given below. (Note that gaging frequency is shown in the table in the Estimating Data Discussion above.)

Table	Description	Time
22.1-3	Plug gage 2 bores, .005-in. tolerance, 2 × .15/5	.060 min
22.1-3	Mike 2 depths, .010-in. tolerance, 2 × .29/25	.023
22.1-3	Go/no-go gage check of 2 bores simultaneously, .002-in., .22/5	.044
	Unit estimate	.13 min

C. A part is drilled, reamed, and tapped in a box jig. Inspection is done following production of the part. Evelute the unit estimate. As the work is handled by a sensitive drill press, the time is added to the estimate.

Table	Description	Time
22.1-3	Plug gages, 2 at .002-in. tolerance, 2 × .16/5	.064 min
22.1-3	Snap thread gage, 1 occurrence at .010 pitch tolerance, .17/25	.007
	Unit estimate	.071 min

D. Estimate the base cost of Example B above using Item 22.1 of Section IV. This cost would be added to the direct-labor operation cost.

Item	Description	Cost
22.1	2−.005 in. tolerances, 2 × .615	$1.23
22.1	2−.010 in. tolerance, 2 × .615	1.23
22.1	2−.002 in. tolerance, 2 × 3.72	7.44
	$/100 units	$9.90

TABLE 22.1 MACHINE, PROCESS, AND BENCH INSPECTION (PRODUCTION OPERATOR)

Setup   **0**

Operation elements in estimating minutes

1. Handling   See other machine, process, or bench tables.

2. Machining, processing, or benchwork   See other machine, process, or bench tables.

3. Inspection

	Total dimensional tolerance					
Measuring device	Fraction	.005	.001	.0005	.0002	Feature
Scale	.11					
Scale-square	.10					
Vernier caliper	.10	.13				
Plug gage, end	.06	.07	.08	.09		
Go/no-go, 2 end	.11	.15	.16	.17	.20	
Machinist micrometer, inside		.16	.16			
Machinist micrometer, outside		.14	.16	.29		
Dial indicator and surface reference		.10	.11	.24		
Snap gages		.07	.09	.11		
Thread snap gages			.17			
Thread gage, plug or ring			.30			
Depth micrometer			.29			
Dial bore gage			.17	.18		
Visual						.05
Pneumatic bore gage		.18	.19	.20		
Transfer caliper, ID	.25					
Transfer caliper, OD	.14					
Pin and surface inspection gage		.5	.5	.6		
Go/no-go templet	.22	.22				
Machine-mounted electronic gages, internal and readout dimension		.06	.06	.06	.06	
Machine-mounted electronic gages, external and readout dimension		.05	.05	.05	.05	
Radius gage	.06					.06
Thickness gage	.10					.10
Protractor	.10	.13				
Dial indicator, plug member		.5	.5	.6		
Gears over pins	.15	.20	.4	.6		

Values are adjusted by gaging frequency.

22.2 Inspection Table and Machines

DESCRIPTION

Inspection is either a direct- or indirect-labor operation. Where it is classed as indirect, the usual procedure is to charge appropriate expenses and eventually determine inspection labor costs as overhead. For indirect inspection labor these estimating data are not usually considered. When inspection is classified as direct, and planning operations stipulate the nature of work, these estimating data can be used.

Inspection operations are found in receiving and final areas, as well as patrol, departmental, or conveyor-line functions. The inspection may correspond to a sampling plan, 100% of all parts, proof-test for a tool, or as an approval of a part from a setup, thus allowing the machine operator to continue on with production.

These data are for an inspection table, booth, or room where the equipment is available. Roving inspection for occasional part inspection to determine changing dimensions or attribute quality is not evaluated.

A coordinate measuring machine is useful where production quantity is low to medium, and usually in one setup manages to check hole locations on different faces from plane-to-plane dimensions. The part to be measured is placed on the work table and aligned. A probe is moved to a reference point and then moved to various points to be checked. Electronic readout or computer printout options are available. Figure 22.2 is typical.

ESTIMATING DATA DISCUSSION

All parts, whether sampled or 100% fully inspected, are handled, and are allotted time for a primary handle. Contrariwise, subsequent repositioning or tumbling, or turning over, are specifically excluded, as that time is excluded in the application of the inspection of tools and equipment while the part is being inspected.

In random selection of a part, a time of .1 is allowed which permits several styles for random-part picking.

FIGURE 22.2 Coordinate measuring machine. (*Boice Division, Mechanical Technology Inc.*)

In many of the inspection elements, the entry variables are the number of similar dimensions and sample size. As the data are sensitive to two variables, the procedure is to first select the row specifying the sample size or next lower value and to move horizontally across to the number of dimensions. Values for additional dimensions or sample units are provided. Because the data are two-variable linear, some tables do not show values for the lower ranges of sample size and dimensions, as these values would be negative because of the negative intercept. For those tabular cells which show no time value, the preferred procedure is to choose a threshold value. A reverse procedure will lead to a different threshold or minimum value.

The minimum value is for handling the instrument, gage, etc., and the part simultaneously to measurement. Many tables show additional time for dimensions and sample unit. An overall average time for inspection is also listed, and is called "expected."

Element 3 is for thimble and barrel micrometers, including inside, outside, blade, telescope, depth, etc. If eight different mikes are used, then the entry variable is "8." Plug gaging is for go/no-go and includes checking of both go and no-go. Element 3, visual check, is for feature appearance and surface defects. In Element 13, either a device for teeth counting or manual counting is permitted. Elements 15 through 18 allow for a variety of setups to mechanically verify dimensions.

Table 22.2 is for inspection only. It does not consider the time to correct defective material. Gaging frequency, implying the smaller the tolerance the more frequent dimensional checks, is handled by specifying sample size per sampling plan.

Machine inspection, as provided by Element 19, is able to check hole locations on different faces, plane-to-plane dimensions, concentricities, etc., and checks out a part in much the same way as an NC machine makes it. This elemental time is per dimension checked.

Item 22.2 of Section IV can be used to estimate base costs in terms of $/100 dimension-units. One unit may have several dimensions, or a sample of several units may have one dimension. Each entry cost expressing dimension-units is multiplied by the product of dimension-units. The sample cost may be prorated over the lot. The entry variable is the type of measurement device, not the tolerance.

EXAMPLES

A. A lot of 60 turned parts is randomly sampled for three units. Eight dimensions are critically checked, two features are visually inspected, and eight dimensions are minor but necessitate scale or vernier caliper confirmation. Determine unit time for inspected parts, prorated time per unit, and find lot time. The schedule of the inspected dimensions are below. All work is for table.

Table	Description	Time
22.2-S	Bench setup	.05 hr
22.2-1	Load, unload part, very large turning	.2 min
22.2-2	Random selection	.1
22.2-3	5 miked dimensions, 3 external and 2 internal, 4.6/3	1.5
22.2-4	1 dimension that is plug-checked, .6/3	.2
22.2-10	Thread gaging, 1.4/3	.5
22.2-16	Bench center, runout check, 4.7/3	1.6
22.2-8	Visual check of 2 features, .2/2	.1
22.2-9	Vernier check of 8 dimensions, 2.6/3	.9
	Inspected unit estimate	5.1 min
	Prorated time to inspect work	.26 min
	Lot time	.31 hr

B. First-part or proof inspection is required of a stamped part to assure die performance. Inspection is mechanical table, and the optical comparator is used for difficult dimensions. All print dimensions are verified. Find the time for first-part inspection.

Table	Description	Time
22.2-S	Table setup	.05 hr
22.2-4	Plug gage, 4 holes	.3 min
22.2-6	Radius check, 2 corners	.1
22.2-9	Caliper check length and width, 3 notches for 5 dimensions	1.5

Table	Description	Time
22.2-12	Compare 4 center and 3 hole-to-hole lengths for 7 dimension	7.6
22.1-8	Visually check 3 features	.1
22.2-3	Mike thickness of sheet stock	1.5
	Unit estimate	11.1 min
	Proof inspection	.24 hr

C. A casting classed as critical is 100% inspected for major dimensions. Other dimensions and features can be sampled following military procedures. These include minor, not-mating tolerances, and surface roughness. The lot is 40 units, and sampling tables indicate the sample size is 7. The feature and dimension schedule are given in the description below. All work is bench. Part size is medium.

Table	Description	Time
22.2-S	Table inspection. Sample-work considered first.	.05 hr
22.2-1	Load and unload part	.1 min
22.2-2	Random selection	.1
22.2-3	Micrometer check, blade, OD, ID, and depth types, 9 dimensions, 11.0 + 2 × .15 = 12.0, 7 units	1.7
22.2-4	2 dimensions are plug checked, 2.5 − 3 × .5 = 1.0, 7 units	.1
22.2-5	Scale 4 pads, 8 dimensions, 3.1 + 3 × .8 + 2 × .3 = 6.1, 7 units	.9
22.2-7	Counterbore is thickness checked, 1.5 + 2 × .4 = 2.3, 7 units	.3
22.2-9	Caliper check of 5 dimensions, 2.2 + 2 × .2 = 2.6, 7 units	.4
	Estimate surface roughness, 2 areas	.4
	Sample unit inspection subtotal	4.0 min
	100% unit inspection. All parts are reloaded and unloaded	
22.1-1	Load and unload part	.1 min
22.1-3	ID check of bore, 13.3 + 15 (.5) = 20.8, 40 units	.5
22.2-4	Plug check of 2-line bored holes	
22.2-17	Bolt circle of 4 tapped holes, 14.7 + 15 (.5) = 22.20, 40 units	.6
22.2-15	Flat plate, dial indicator for parallel surface, 6.8 + 15 (2.1) = 38.3, 40 units	1.0
22.2-17	Dial indicate to plug on flat plate, 14.7 + 15 (.5) = 22.5, 40 units	.6
	100% sampled-part unit estimate	2.8 min
	100% lot inspection estimate	1.87 hr
	100% lot inspection and sample inspection	2.38 hr

D. Find the base cost for Example A above. Assume that a cost estimate is desired for an inspector operation even though the inspection program is considered indirect. Some dimensions are check for one unit, while others have different numbers of units.

Item	Description	Cost
22.2	Mike, 3 units × 5 dimensions, 3 × 5 × 3.97	$ 59.55
22.2	Plug, 3 × 1 × 2.05	6.15
22.2	Thread, 3 × 1 × 5.22 (use plug gage)	15.66
22.2	Bench center, 3 × 1 × 15.5 (use comparator)	46.50
22.2	Visual, 3 × 2 × .806	4.84
22.2	8 units for vernier check, 8 × 1.61	12.88
	$/100 units inspected	$145.58

TABLE 22.2   INSPECTION TABLE AND MACHINES

Setup

Table	.05 hr
Machine	.25 hr

Operation elements in estimating minutes

1. Handle one at a time; medium, large	.1
One at a time very large	.2
Bulk, very small to small	.0005–.05

2. Miscellaneous elements
   Random part selections .1
   Stamp part with rubber stamp,
      1st part .1
      Each 3 add'l parts .1
   Air clean .1
   Wipe with shop cloth,
      1st surface .1
      5 add'l surfaces .1
   Remove part from envelope, return .1
   Wrap, unwrap with Kraft paper .2
   Tagging lot or part .1
   Write signature, minor statements .1

3. Micrometer gaging

Sample size	No. of miked dimensions / part									
	1	2	3	4	5	6	7	8	9	10
1					1.5	3.1	4.7	6.3	7.9	9.5
2				.7	2.3	3.9	5.5	7.1	8.7	10.3
3				1.4	4.6	5.4	6.2	7.8	9.4	11.0
5			1.3	2.9	4.5	6.1	7.7	9.4	11.0	12.6
10	1.9	3.5	5.1	6.7	8.3	9.9	11.5	13.1	14.7	16.4
15	5.7	7.3	8.9	10.5	12.1	13.7	15.3	16.9	18.5	20.1
25	13.3	14.9	16.5	18.1	19.7	21.3	22.9	24.5	26.1	27.7

   Add'l sample unit .5
   Expected time to mike 1 dimension/unit .2

4. Plug gaging

Sample size	No. of dimensions / part									
	1	2	3	4	5	6	7	8	9	10
1					.3	1.1	1.9	2.7	3.4	4.2
2				.1	.8	1.6	2.4	3.2	3.9	4.7
3				.6	1.3	2.1	2.9	3.7	4.4	5.2
5			.8	1.6	2.3	3.1	3.9	4.7	5.4	6.2
10	1.7	2.5	3.3	4.1	4.8	5.6	6.4	7.1	7.9	8.7
15	4.2	5.0	5.8	6.6	7.3	8.1	8.9	9.6	10.4	11.2
25	9.2	10.0	10.8	11.5	12.3	13.1	13.9	14.6	15.4	16.2

   Add'l dimension .8
   Add'l sample unit .5
   Expected time to plug 1 dimension/unit .1

5. Scale and snap gage

Sample size	No. of like dimensions / part				
	1	2	3	4	5
1			.3	1.1	1.9
2			.5	1.4	2.2
3			.8	1.7	2.5
5		.6	1.4	2.2	3.1
10	1.2	2.0	2.8	3.7	4.5
15	2.6	3.4	4.2	5.1	5.9
25	5.4	6.2	7.1	7.9	8.7

   Add'l dimension .8
   Add'l sample unit .3
   Expected time to measure 1 dimension/unit .1

6. Radius gage

Sample size	No. of like dimensions / part				
	1	2	3	4	5
1			.1	.3	.5
2		.1	.2	.4	.6
3		.2	.3	.5	.7
5	.2	.4	.6	.7	.9
10	.8	.9	1.1	1.3	1.5

Add'l dimension	.2
Add'l sample unit	.1
Expected time to measure 1 radius/unit	.04

7. Thickness gage

Sample size	No. of like dimensions / part				
	1	2	3	4	5
1		.3	.8	1.4	1.9
2	.1	.7	1.3	1.8	2.4
3	.6	1.2	1.7	2.3	2.8
5	1.5	2.1	2.6	3.2	3.7
10	3.7	4.3	4.9	5.4	6.0

Add'l dimension	.6
Add'l sample unit	.4
Expected time to measure 1 dimension/unit	.18

8. Visual check

Sample size	No. of like dimensions / part				
	1	2	3	4	5
1			.1	.3	.5
2			.2	.4	.6
3		.2	.4	.5	.7
5	.2	.4	.6	.8	1.0
10	.9	1.1	1.3	1.5	1.7

Add'l dimension	.2
Add'l sample unit	.1
Expected time to visually check 1 dimension/unit	.04

9. Vernier caliper and protractor

Sample size	No. of like dimensions / part									
	1	2	3	4	5	6	7	8	9	10
1	.2	.6	.9	1.2	1.5	1.8	2.1	2.5	2.8	3.1
2	.4	.7	1.1	1.4	1.7	2.0	2.3	2.6	2.9	3.3
3	.6	.9	1.2	1.6	1.9	2.2	2.5	2.8	3.1	3.4
5	1.0	1.3	1.6	1.9	2.2	2.5	2.9	3.2	3.5	3.8
10	1.9	2.2	2.5	2.8	3.1	3.4	3.8	4.1	4.4	4.7
15	2.8	3.1	3.4	3.7	4.0	4.4	4.7	5.0	5.3	5.6

Add'l dimension	.3
Add'l sample unit	.2
Expected time to measure 1 dimension/unit	.08

438

10. Plug and ring thread gaging

Sample size	No. of like dimensions/part									
	1	2	3	4	5	6	7	8	9	10
1					1.0	3.1	5.3	7.4	9.5	11.6
2				.1	2.2	4.4	6.5	8.6	10.7	12.8
3				1.4	3.5	5.6	7.7	9.8	12.0	14.1
5			1.7	3.8	5.9	8.1	10.2	12.3	14.4	16.5
10	3.6	5.7	7.8	10.0	12.1	14.2	16.3	18.4	20.6	22.7
15	9.7	11.9	14.0	16.1	18.2	20.3	22.5	24.6	26.7	28.8
25	22.0	24.2	26.3	28.4	30.5	32.6	34.8	36.9	39.0	41.1

Add'l dimension 2.1
Add'l sample unit 1.2
Expected time to thread gage 1 dimension/unit .26

11. Ring gage

Sample size	No. of like dimensions/part									
	1	2	3	4	5	6	7	8	9	10
1				.2	.7	1.1	1.6	2.0	2.5	2.9
2				.4	.9	1.3	1.8	2.2	2.7	3.1
3			.2	.6	1.1	1.5	2.0	2.4	2.8	3.3
5		.1	.5	1.0	1.4	1.9	2.3	2.8	3.2	3.7
10	.6	1.0	1.5	1.9	2.4	2.8	3.3	3.7	4.1	4.6
15	1.5	2.0	2.4	2.8	3.3	3.7	4.2	4.6	5.1	5.5

Add'l dimension .4
Add'l sample unit .2
Expected time to measure 1 dimension/unit .06

12. Optical comparator

Sample size	No. of like dimensions/part									
	1	2	3	4	5	6	7	8	9	10
1				.9	3.1	5.4	7.6	9.9	12.1	14.4
2		.6	2.8	5.1	7.3	9.6	11.8	14.1	16.3	18.6
3	2.5	4.8	7.0	9.3	11.5	13.8	16.0	18.3	20.5	22.8
5	11.0	13.2	15.5	17.7	20.0	22.2	24.5	26.7	29.0	31.2
10	32.0	34.3	36.5	38.8	41.0	43.3	45.5	47.8	50.0	52.3
15	53.1	55.3	57.6	59.8	62.1	64.3	66.6	68.8	71.1	73.3
25	95.2	97.4	99.7	102	104	106	109	111	113	115

Add'l dimension 2.2
Add'l sample unit 4.2
Expected time to measure 1 dimension/unit .77

13. Counting teeth

Sample size	No. of teeth/part									
	10	20	40	60	80	100	120	140	160	200
1				.3	.9	1.6	2.2	2.8	3.5	4.7
2			.5	1.1	1.7	2.4	3.0	3.6	4.2	5.5
3	.3	.6	1.3	1.9	2.5	3.1	3.8	4.4	5.0	6.3
5	1.9	2.2	2.8	3.4	4.1	4.7	5.3	6.0	6.6	7.8

Add'l teeth .03
Add'l sample unit .78

14. Mike gears over wires

Sample size	1	2	3	5	10	15	25	Add'l
Min	2.3	3.0	3.7	5.1	8.6	12.2	19.3	.7

15. Bench micrometer, flat plate

Sample size	1	2	3	5	10	15	25	Add'l
Min	2.3	2.5	2.7	3.0	4.0	4.9	6.8	2.1

16. Bench center and dial indicator

Sample size	1	2	3	5	10	15	25	Add'l
Min	3.9	4.3	4.7	5.5	7.4	9.3	13.3	3.6

17. Bench centers, dial indicator, plug member

Sample size	1	2	3	5	10	15	25	Add'l
Min	3.1	3.6	3.8	4.8	7.3	9.7	14.7	.5

18. V-Block, dial indicator, and flat plate

Sample size	1	2	3	5	10	15	25	Add'l
Min	2.3	2.7	3.0	3.8	5.7	7.6	11.4	.4

19. Coordinate measuring machine   .75/dimension

ELECTRONIC FABRICATION

23.1 Component Sequencing Machines

DESCRIPTION

The electrical component sequencer is a computer-controlled machine which selects electrical components, i.e. resistors, capacitors, diodes, etc., and places them on a tape in a specific order. The tape is used by other automatic machines (see Tables 23.2 and 23.3 for examples) which place these components onto circuit boards at high rates of speed. The sequencer has the capability of sequencing any series of standard components. The number of components in a certain sequence may be from ten components to over a hundred components. The lot or run may consist of any desired amount of these sequences. A "sequence" is the terminology used to mean one printed circuit board. The operator initiates the computer program to operate the machine in the desired manner according to instructions. The operation of the sequencer is fully automatic and only requires periodic adjustments and corrections (replacing missing components, adjusting alignment, clearing scrap, etc.). The number of input reels which have only one type of electrical component vary according to need. Activation of operating mechanisms, such as the heads which align and cut off component leads, is powered pneumatically. A machine may have the ability to stop feed automatically when a component is missing from a sequence when indicated by an optical sensor. The computer also indicates which part is missing. Figure 23.1 is an example of an axial lead component sequencer with loading rates to 25,000 components per hour.

ESTIMATING DATA DISCUSSION

The term "head change" means loading a particular component part reel and placing the tape of identical components in the head, which will cut off and place the component onto the conveyor. There are a number of these heads available, which allows for a sequence of different kinds of ordered components. The setup is performed by two operators and is reflected in the time. The head is either removed from the mounting by loosening a nut or the head is supplied with a quick release and snap-on mechanism. The number of head changes depends on the setup of the previous run and the needs of the sequence to be performed. Each head change is multiplied by the value. A printed circuit board may require ten components, which may be the same as the previous run. The number of head changes presents a confusing choice if the estimator is unaware of how the boards are to be scheduled. For purpose of our examples, we have adopted the rule that 50% of the heads need to be changed. The estimator will need to consider his or her experience and be guided by that.

Element 1, "sequence," represents the actual start and run of the machine. The feed is constant but is interrupted by various adjustments which must be made to ensure the quality of the output sequence. These interruptions are included within the data.

The estimating method selects the time needed to produce one sequence (which will be components on one circuit board) and use the number of sequences as the lot. The unit estimate is the complete sequence rather than a single electronic component. Total time for the run is the number of sequences desired multiplied by the unit estimate.

Element 1 is an extensive listing of a constant time. It was prepared as a listing to aid estimating convenience. If the number of components falls between two table values, use the higher value as little error is

FIGURE 23.1 Universal Instruments Model 2596 Axial Lead Component Sequencer.

introduced. Note that there is only one table, as the handling and other irregular work elements have been consolidated into this one element.

The estimator may wish to estimate direct labor cost rather than time. This can be done by using the information in Section IV. Item 23.1 of Section IV allows cost determination directly using the Productive Hour Cost of a base area.

EXAMPLES

A. A printed circuit board will use 91 components. The 91 components are arranged in sequence, and 650 sequences are required for the lot. Assume that 32 head changes are necessary. Find the unit, hr/100 units, and the lot estimate.

Table	Description		Time	
23.1-S	Head changes, 32 × .05		1.60	hr
23-1-1	91 components in sequence		1.00	min
	Unit estimate		1.00	min
	Hr/100 units		1.667	
	Lot estimate		12.44	hr

B. A printed circuit card has a bill of material listing of 182 components. Two hundred and fifty sequences are needed. We anticipated that 18 head changes are required. Find the unit, hr/100 units, lot estimates, and the shop value (pc/hr).

Table	Description		Time	
23.1-S	Head changes, 18 × .05		.90	hr
23.1-1	182 components in sequence		2.00	min
	Unit estimate		2.00	min
	Hr/100 units		3.34	
	Lot estimate		9.25	hr
	Pc/hr		30	

C. Use Table 23.1 to estimate a card type of 36 components. There are 55 cards necessary. Assume that five head changes are necessary. Find the unit, hr/100 units, and lot estimates.

Table	Description		Time	
23.1-S	Head changes, 5 × .05		.25	hr
23.1-1	36 components		.40	min
	Unit estimate		.40	min
	Hr/100 units		.668	
	Lot estimate		.62	hr

442

D. Re-estimate Example A using an operational cost approach. The rule-of-thumb information is provided by Item 23.1 of Section IV. This information expresses setup in terms of dollars per occurrence and cycle as $/100 units. Find the Productive Hour Cost (PHC) of the lot for 650 printed circuit cards.

Item	Description	Cost
23.1	Setup cost, subtotal	$ .52
23.1	91 components, 91 × .190	17.05
	$/100 units	$ 17.05
	Lot estimate for 65 printed circuit cards	$111.36

TABLE 23.1   COMPONENT SEQUENCING MACHINES

Setup, each head change   **.05 hr**

Operation elements in estimating minutes

1. Sequence

Components	Min	Components	Min	Components	Min
10	.11	42	.45	132	1.40
11	.12	47	.50	141	1.50
12	.13	52	.55	150	1.60
13	.14	56	.60	160	1.70
14	.15	61	.65	169	1.80
15	.16	66	.70	179	1.90
16	.17	71	.75	188	2.0
17	.18	75	.80	282	3.0
18	.19	80	.85	376	4.0
19	.20	85	.90	470	5.0
20	.21	89	.95	564	6.0
21	.22	94	1.00	650	7.0
22	.23	99	1.05	752	8.0
23	.24	103	1.10	847	9.0
24	.25	108	1.15	941	10.0
28	.30	113	1.20	1035	11.0
33	.35	118	1.25	1129	12.0
38	.40	122	1.30	Add'l	.011

23.2 Component Insertion Machines

DESCRIPTION

The following estimating data are for component inserting machines used in the circuit board industry. The machine is used for inserting micro-chips that have been packaged in a certain size case (usually .3-in. or .6-in. wide). The packages can have any number of leads but usually have 8, 16, or 32. The machine can be powered mechanically or hydraulically. Figure 23.2 is an example of a dual inline package inserting machine.

Small clamps hold a board to a table. The table moves in an x-y plane, positioning the board for insertion of the package. Next, a head lowers in the z-

FIGURE 23.2 Universal Instruments Model 6772A Multi-Module Dip Inserter.

direction inserting the correct package into the printed circuit (PC) holes while cutting the leads underneath and crimping either with an outside or inside crimp at varying angles. The head can place any size package according to its size. Packages are chosen above the machine, where they are held in tubes. The tables can hold from one to several boards depending on the sizes of the table and designs.

ESTIMATING DATA DISCUSSION

Setup of the machine requires that a computer program be loaded into memory. The computer controls the movement of the table in the x-y plane, movement of the package loading head in the z direction, and the correct choice of package corresponding to its position on the circuit board. The operator loads the tubes and containers which are within easy reach.

With setup completed, the next step is to begin the process. Elements are relatively simple. Element 1 includes picking up an empty board, placing it on the machine, removing the completed board, and placing it in a stack. If the table is holding two or more boards it is often possible for the operator to perform this task while the machine works on other boards.

The entry for Element 2 is the number of components. It may be convenient to use a higher value on the table if the exact number is not shown.

The estimator may wish to find the productive hour cost for this operation. This PHC reflects a base area wage that is national U.S. norm data.

Item 23.2 of Section IV is used to show the direct labor cost. Setup cost is provided. Cycle cost is composed of a constant and a variable. The constant cost is used without adjustment. The number of packages is multiplied by the factor. The total of the constant and machine insertion effort gives the $/100 units.

EXAMPLES

A. A board must have 10 chips mounted. Table loading will accommodate three boards, but loading of two boards is internal to the machine automatic cycle of inserting components. The job consists of 50 boards. Find the unit estimate to process one board.

Table	Description	Time	
23.2-S	Basic setup	.1	hr
23.2-S	Fill containers, small	.1	
23.2-S	Load program, manual	.3	
	Setup subtotal	.5	hr
23.2-1	Load 1 board	.24	min
	Load 2 boards, internal to automatic cycle	0.0	
	Insert 30 chips	.48	
	Total cycle time	.72	min
	Unit estimate	.24	min

B. A board must be manufactued one-by-one for a quantity of 1000. Each board will have 90 chips. Program loading to the machine is with satellite link. Find the setup and unit estimate and hr/100 units for the job.

Table	Description	Time	
23.2-S	Basic setup	.1	hr
23.2-S	Fill containers	.2	
23.2-S	Load program, satellite	.2	
	Setup subtotal	.5	hr
23.2-1	Load 1 board	.24	min
	Insert 90 chips	1.44	
	Unit estimate	1.68	min
	Hr/100 units	2.800	

C. Five hundred boards having 55 chips each are to be made on a machine table which allows side-by-side processing of two boards. The machine stops to load each board; however, this machine action is really no different than single-board processing. The program is centrally loaded. The inserting head is also scheduled for a change. Find the lot time.

Table	Description	Time	
23.2-S	Basic setup	.1	hr
23.2-S	Fill containers, 2 times, large	.4	
23.2-S	Load computer	.1	
	Total setup	.6	hr
23.2-1	Handle	.24	min
23.2-2	Insert components, 55	.88	
	Unit estimate	1.12	min
	Hr/100 units	1.867	
	Lot estimate	9.93	hr

F. Find the productive hour cost of direct labor for Example A above. Use Item 23.2 of Section IV. Express the result as a setup cost, $/100 units, and lot cost.

Item	Description	Cost
23.2	Setup subtotal	$5.21
23.2	Cycle constant	$4.17
23.2	10 chips, 10 × .281	2.81
	$/100 units	$6.98
	Lot cost for 50 boards	$8.70

TABLE 23.2 COMPONENT INSERTION MACHINES

Setup

Basic	.1 hr
Fill containers with material:	
small job	.1 hr
large job	.2 hr
Change head for different width of package	.1 hr

Operation elements in estimating minutes

1. Handling, combined	.24
Pick up board	.04
Place on table and secure	.10
Remove from table	.05
Place in stack	.05

2. Insert components

No. of components	5	8	10	15	18	20	25
Min	.08	.13	.16	.24	.29	.32	.40

No. of components	28	30	35	40	45	50	55
Min	.45	.48	.56	.64	.72	.80	.88

No. of components	60	65	70	75	80	90	100
Min	.96	1.04	1.12	1.20	1.28	1.44	1.60

23.3 Axial-Lead Component Insertion Machines

DESCRIPTION

Axial-lead component insertion machines automatically insert axial-shaped electrical components into printed circuit board (PC) holes. Raw materials for the machine are a printed circuit board and a reel or tape. The components are previously sequenced and placed on the tape. The components are axial-shaped, such as resistors, and have two wires or leads extending from the ends of the resistor. The wire diameters are about .015 to .037 in. depending upon the machine or design. The body length of the resistor may vary. The variable distance that is programmed is from center-to-center of the form leads. The rolls will have many sequences. One sequence may have sufficient numbers for the axial-shape components as required by the PC board. The machines considered here are numerically controlled, which directs table positioning and machine head motion. Figure 23.3 is an example of a single-head variable center distance axial-component insertion machine.

The components have been previously sequenced into a roll via a sequence machine which is considered by Table 23.1. The roll of ordered components is mounted on the insertion machine and the components are fed onto the upper machine head.

Printed circuit boards are loaded into a fixture mounted upon a movable table. The boards are located in the fixture using pins and are clamped. A variety of fixture holding devices are possible with one or more boards or x-y fixtures.

The machine process is as follows. The table moves to a designated position over the PC board as commanded by the NC control. The upper-machine head cuts the component from the roll of tape and inserts it into the two holes. A lower-machine head raises and cuts the leads to length and bends them to either 90° or 45°. The heads retract and the table moves to a new position. The process of insertion continues.

The operator can override an automatic stop to

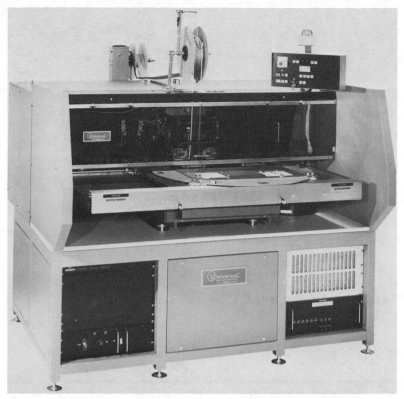

FIGURE 23.3 Universal Instruments Model 6287A Variable Center Distance Insertion Machine.

insert more than one board without restarting the machine.

ESTIMATING DATA DISCUSSION

The basic setup time, given in hours, includes getting the computer tape and instruction manual, reading the tape into the computer, getting the lot of boards to be inserted and the sequenced roll of components, examining the manual, and adjusting the fixture. Time may be added to the basic time for a fixture change.

The operation elements include the loading and unloading of a board, start, and the insertion of components into one board. If more than one board can be loaded into a fixture and there is a delay in the cycle time, additional handling may be considered. Usually, the unload and load time will be used once since loading of multiple boards occurs internal to the machine cycle. If an x-y fixture is used, the insertion time should only be used once since the times are for a completely inserted board. If the number of components is less than 35, the handling time should be added for as many boards per fixture since the operator does not have enough time to remove them internal to the automatic cycle of inserting components.

It is also possible to estimate the operation costs. Item 23.3 of Section IV can provide the direct labor cost where the productive hour cost (PHC) serves as the base value. The method is straightforward. The constant cost is always used, and the factor multiplies the number of components. The sum of these two provide the $/100 units. A setup cost is also provided. Lot costs can be found using the formula $SU + N(\$/unit)$.

EXAMPLES

A. Insert 380 components into a 36×24-in. printed circuit board. Order size is 50 boards. The fixture holds one board and the operation requires a special fixture. Determine setup and the unit estimate.

Table	Description	Time
23.3-S	Setup, basic	.45 hr
23.3-S	Fixture	.05
	Total setup	.50 hr

Table	Description	Time	
23.3-1	Unload, load, and start machine	.31	min
23.3-2	Insert components	2.40	
	Unit estimate	2.71	min

B. Insert 210 components into a 12 × 8-in. printed circuit board. The order size is 100 boards. The fixture holds two boards. Determine the hr/100 units.

Table	Description	Time	
23.3-S	Setup	.45	hr
23.3-1	Unload, load, start machine	.31	min
23.3-2	Insert components	1.38	
23.3-2	Insert second board	1.38	
	Total cycle time	3.07	min
	Unit estimate	1.54	min
	Hr/100 units	2.567	

C. Insert 180 components into a 12 × 8-in. printed circuit board. The fixture is an *x-y* fixture.

Table	Description	Time	
23.3-S	Setup	.45	hr
23.3-S	Fixture	.05	hr
	Total setup	.50	hr
23.3-1	Unload, load, start machine	.31	min
23.3-2	Insertion of components	1.20	
	Unit estimate	1.51	min
	Hr/100 units	2.517	
	Lot estimate	1.00	hr

D. Insert 25 components into a 12 × 6-in. printed circuit board. The order size is 220 boards. The fixture holds three boards. No new fixture is needed. Determine the unit estimate.

Table	Description	Time	
23.3-S	Setup	.45	hr
23.3-1	Unload, load, start machine,	.31	min
	Handling of 2nd board	.31	
23.3-1	Handling of 3rd board	.31	
23.3-2	Insert components	.26	
23.3-2	Insert 2nd board	.26	
23.3-2	Insert 3rd board	.26	
	Cycle time	1.71	min
	Unit estimate	.57	min

E. Insert 30 components into a 12 × 8-in. printed circuit board. The fixture holds two boards. Determine the cycle time and unit estimate.

Table	Description	Time	
23.3-S	Setup	.45	hr
23.3-1	Unload, load, start machine	.31	min
23.3-1	Handling 2nd board	.31	
23.3-2	Insert components	.26	
23.3-2	Insert 2nd board	.26	
	Cycle time	1.14	min
	Unit estimate	.57	min

F. Re-estimate Example A above using Item 23.3 of Section IV. Find the $/100 units and the cost for one board, where the operation is to insert 380 components.

Item	Description	Cost
23.3	Setup subtotal	$ 4.89
23.3	Constant for cycle	5.41
23.3	Variable portion, 380 $\times$ .099	37.62
	$/100 units	$43.03
	$/1 unit	$ 4.30

TABLE 23.3 AXIAL-LEAD COMPONENT INSERTION MACHINES

Setup

Basic	.45 hr
Fixture additional	.05 hr

Operation elements in estimating minutes

1. Load, unload, start machine .31

2. Insert components for one board

No. of components	Min
30	.26
36	.29
43	.34
53	.39
62	.45
73	.52
86	.60
102	.67
118	.79
139	.91
162	1.04
188	1.20
218	1.38
252	1.58
292	1.82
337	2.09
390	2.40
450	2.76
519	3.18
Add'l	.0006

23.4 Printed Circuit Board Stuffing

DESCRIPTION

The estimating is for a manual bench assembly. The data are not associated with fundamental motions, and no machines are used in the process, but a few hand tools are available when needed. A worker completes an entire printed circuit (PC) board completely; that is, there is no conveyor line. The worker starts by adding each element to the PC board one at a time. Every element is carefully checked for its identification number. After the element is in place on the board, it is soldered to the board. One or more parts may be soldered to the board at the same time.

Once all of the parts are attached to the board, the worker cleans it by brushing it with alcohol. The board is then dried with an air hose. Next the PC board is sent to the inspector where it must pass an inspection. If any errors are found, they are immediately fixed and it is reinspected. When the board has passed the inspection it is chemically sealed with hysol.

Those factors not considered are the drying time of the chemical seal, an overall final inspection, and electronic and environment testing.

Every item on the bench is easily accessible. The only times the worker needs to move from the desk is when hysoling, cleaning, or taking a PC board to the inspector.

ESTIMATING DATA DISCUSSION

In these data a setup time is not allowed.

Because of the high quality of a board, a handle is needed for each part placed on the board. The parts (i.e., chips, resistors, electronic components, etc.) are carefully inspected for their identification number so that it matches the one given on the blueprint. The parts used in the PC board stuffing can be broken into two categories: components and chips. The data treats these as identical parts. The data separate the parts by the number of pins or wires (called electronic parts in this discussion) being soldered to the board. Separating the electronic parts in this fashion eliminates the problem of separating these by part size.

The data are given in minutes per occurrence. As the data are multiplied by the frequency of occurrence, rounding-off errors may result.

EXAMPLES

A. A PC board has five 2-pin elements, twelve 6-pin elements, a connector with 36 pins, a cleaning, and a single inspection. Determine a unit estimate. Assume only one board is to be fabricated for the lot.

Table	Description	Time
23.4-1	Handle and inspect parts, 17 × .40	6.80 min
23.4-2	Adjust part to holes	
	2 pin, 5 × .40	2.00
	6 pin, 12 × .54	6.48
23.4-3	Solder and flux	
	2 pin, 5 × .44	2.20
	6 pin, 12 × .75	9.00
23.4-5	Insert and solder connectors, 36 pin	3.94
23.4-6	Screw on connectors	1.86
23.4-4	Cleaning and drying	.73
23.4-7	Inspection, one board only	28.13
	Unit estimate	61.31 min

B. Twenty PC boards will be made with the following: three 2-pin parts, five 4-pin parts, two 10-pin parts, three connectors with 12, 14, and 26 pins respectively, soldering done after all parts connected, a single cleaning, inspection, hysoling, and another inspection. Determine the unit estimate for this process. Find the lot estimate. The work will be done on a pass-along assembly line. Element 1 of Table 23.4 is not used in this case. Only the first board receives a full inspection.

Table	Description	Time
23.4-2	Adjust part to holes	
	2 pin, 3 × .40	1.20 min
	4 pin, 5 × .44	2.20
	10 pin, 2 × .65	1.30
23.4-3	Solder and flux, 2 (3) + 4 (5) + 10 (2) = 41 locations	4.28
23.4-5	Insert and solder connectors	
	12 pin	2.96
	14 pin	2.96
	26 pin	3.58
23.4-6	Screw on connectors 3 × 1.86	5.58
23.4-4	Cleaning and drying	.73
23.4-7	Inspection. First board prorated over 20, 28.3/20	1.42
	Each additional board	5.40
23.4-8	Hysoling	2.32
	Unit estimate	33.93 min

C. A board is planned to have the following elements: nineteen 2-pin, twenty-six 3-pin, and seventeen 8-pin. A cleaning is to be done after each set of pins is attached to the board. A connector is then added (36 pins) with another cleaning. This is followed by an inspection and hysoling. Find the unit estimate. A lot of 30 boards is needed.

Table	Description	Time
23.4-1	Handle and inspect 62 parts, 62 × .40	24.80 min
23.4-2	Adjust part to holes	
	2 pin, 19 × .40	7.60
	3 pin, 26 × .44	11.44
	8 pin, 17 × .59	10.03
23.4-3	Solder and flux	
	2 pin, 19 × .44	8.36
	3 pin, 26 × .48	12.48
	8 pin, 17 × .94	15.98
23.4-5	Insert and solder connectors, 36 pin	3.94
23.4-6	Screw on connectors	1.855
23.4-4	Cleaning and drying, 4 × .73	2.92
23.4-7	Inspection, 28.3/80, first part	.35
	Each subsequent board	5.40
23.4-8	Hysoling	2.32
	Unit estimate	105.58 min

D. Re-estimate Example A above using Item 23.4 of Section IV. This calculation finds the base cost. It is a faster estimation.

Item	Description	Cost
23.4	Constant	$ 493.00
23.4	17 component elements, 17 × 16.2	275.40
23.4	Total number of pins, 5 × 2 + 6 × 12 = 82 pins. 82 × 1.92	157.44
23.4	One cleaning	11.80
23.4	One connector	67.20
	$/100 units	$1004.84

E. Use Item 23.4 given in Section IV and re-estimate Example B above.

Item	Description	Cost
23.4	Constant	$493.00
23.4	10 component elements, 10×16.2	162.00
23.4	46 total pins, 46×1.93	88.78
23.4	1 cleaning	11.80
23.4	3 connectors, 3×67.2	201.60
23.4	1 inspection, $1 \times 87.03/20$	4.35
	$/100 units	$961.53

TABLE 23.4 PRINTED CIRCUIT BOARD STUFFING

Setup

Operation elements in estimating minutes

1. Handle and inspect a part   .40

2. Adjust an electronic element for a hole and insert in board

No. of pins	Min
2	.40
4	.44
5	.49
7	.54
9	.59
11	.65
13	.71

3. Solder and flux an element to board

No. of pins	Min
2	.44
3	.48
4	.59
5	.71
6	.78
7	.86
8	.94
9	1.04
10	1.14
12	1.26
13	1.38
14	1.52
16	1.67
Average	.104 each

4. Clean and air dry board   .73

5. Insert and solder connectors

No. of pins	Min
15	2.96
22	3.26
30	3.58
38	3.94
47	4.33
57	4.78

6. Connector to the board with screws   1.86
7. Inspect board
   First time   28.3
   each additional   5.4

8. Hysol the board   2.32

23.5 Printed Circuit Board Drilling Machines

DESCRIPTION

The printed circuit board (PCB) drill machine is a paper-tape programmable drilling tool used to production drill, rework, or modify multi-layer printed circuit boards. The drill consists of the x and y axes machine movement and programmable controller. Spindles on these machines may range from one to four.

The x and y axes machine movement has overall travel of 14 in. and 18 in. under each spindle. The z-axis stroke is 0.8 in. Repeatable positioning is provided with an accuracy of $\pm$ .0005 in. over the full range of travel.

The programmable controller consists of a keyboard, CRT, and a paper tape punch. Individual program control of all axes is provided with rates selectable from 10 to 300 in. per min. Coordinates may be specified from a programmable zero reference located anywhere in the working volume or incrementally from the last location. Programs are stored on paper tape.

Spindle speed is variable from 6,000 to 54,000 rpm. The spindle chuck accepts sizes from .013 in. to .25 in. in diameter.

ESTIMATING DATA DISCUSSION

Setup elements are in hours. The basic setup includes cleaning the reading mechanism of the paper tape unit, loading the paper tape into the reading unit, and ad-justment of the traversing table to a standard starting position. The operator views a mark on the table under a set of cross hairs and makes manual adjustments until the mark is aligned. Setup Element 2 includes selection of the bit, cleaning of the bit and chuck, and the chucking of the bit. Element 3 checks and adjusts the depth of the hole to match production requirements. This procedure is done for each spindle. Element 4 is a routine to make minor adjustments in the coordinates and depth of the holes, and a final check to ensure all positions are correct before production. This element is variable based on the number of spindles used.

In a typical cycle, two boards are mounted to a fixture that traverses under a spindle. The board position at the back of the fixture is referred to as board 1. The board position at the front of the fixture is called board 2. Each board is drilled on both sides. One side is completed in board position 1, and the other side is completed in board position 2. Eight cycle elements are involved in a typical production run to produce one complete board. Element 1 describes the loading of board 1. This involves the unloading and aside of the previous board, pick up and placement of the new board, and the securing of the new board to the fixture. Element 2 deals with the machine traverse to the position of the first hole in board 2. Since the traverse is rapid, Element 2 is constant. Element 3 consists of the sequence of drilling and repositioning involved in completing board 2. This element is variable with respect to the number of holes drilled. Element 4 is the machine traverse to the position of hole 1 in board 1. It will be considered constant. Element 5 deals with the sequence of drilling and repositioning to complete board 1. This element is variable with respect to the number of holes drilled. Element 6 is the machine traverse back to the original position to reload board 1. It is considered constant. Element 7 is the reload of board 2. This element has the same components as Element 1. Element 7 is done while Element 5 is being completed by the machine, so it is only included in the estimate when Element 5 is less than Element 7. Element 8 deals with the visual in-spection of each card. A templet is used to speed location of the holes, and a hand magnifying glass is used to inspect small diameter holes. Element 8 may be completed as the cards are removed from board position 2, or it may be done as a separate operation at the end of the cycle or by another worker. Examples of all these cases will follow.

The operation cost estimating relationship may be used instead of the tables to make cost estimates. These cost facts are found in Section IV under Item 23.5 and apply to a typical production run in which Elements 7 and 8 are completed during the machine cycle. The result of the equations will yield $/100 units.

EXAMPLES

A. A 6 × 8-in. printed circuit board is to have 13 holes drilled on each side at given locations. One spindle is used. The paper tape is provided. Loading of the second board, and visual inspection of the boards are completed during the machine cycle. There are 150 boards in the lot. Find the hr/lot including setup.

Table	Description	Time
23.5-S	Setup	.25 hr
23.5-1	Reload board position 1	.10 min
23.5-2	Traverse to hole 1, board 2	.08
23.5-3	Drill 13 holes, board 2	.16
23.5-4	Traverse to hole 1, board 1	.04
23.5-5	Drill 13 holes, board 1	.14
23.5-6	Traverse to original position	.12
	Unit estimate	.64 min
	Lot estimate	1.85 hr

B. A printed circuit board requires 20 holes drilled on each side. One spindle is used. Reload of board 2 is during the machine cycle, but visual inspection is done by the operator at the end of each cycle. Find the unit estimate for the cycle.

Table	Description	Time
23.5-1	Reload board position 1	.10 min
23.5-2	Traverse to hole 1, board 2	.08
23.5-3	Drill 20 holes, board 2	.29
23.5-4	Traverse to hole 1, board 1	.04
23.5-5	Drill 20 holes, board 1	.29
23.5-6	Traverse to original position	.12
23.5-8	Visual inspection	.17
	Unit estimate	1.09 min

C. A large printed circuit board must have 26 holes drilled per side. The lot size is 200 cards and 3 spindles will be used. Reloading board 2 and visual inspection is done during machine cycle. Calculate the lot time and the hours per 100 units.

Table	Description	Time	
23.5-S	Setup	.52	hr
23.5-1	Reload board position 1	.10	min
23.5-2	Traverse to hole 1, board 2	.08	
23.5-3	Drill 26 holes, board 2	.44	
23.5-4	Traverse to hole 1, board 1	.04	
23.5-5	Drill 26 holes, board 1	.45	
23.5-6	Traverse to original position	.12	
	Unit estimate	1.23	min
	Hr/100 units	2.050	hr
	Lot estimate	4.620	

D. Five hundred printed circuit boards are drilled with 18 holes. Two spindles are used. Reload of board 2 is during the machine cycle. Find the unit and lot estimates.

Table	Description	Time	
23.5-S	Setup	.39	hr
23.5-1	Reload board position 1	.10	min
23.5-2	Traverse to hole 1, board 2	.08	
23.5-3	Drill 18 holes, board 2	.29	
23.5-4	Traverse to hole 1, board 1	.04	
23.5-5	Drill 18 holes, board 1	.29	
23.5-6	Traverse to original position	.12	
	Unit estimate	.92	min
	Lot estimate	8.072	hr

E. Repeat Example A using Item 23.5 of Section IV. There is one spindle.

Item	Description	Cost
23.5	Setup subtotal	$ 2.48
23.5	Constant	$ 2.22
23.5	13 holes, 13 × .842	10.95
	$/100 units	$13.17

TABLE 23.5 PRINTED CIRCUIT BOARD DRILLING MACHINES

Setup in estimating hours

1. Basic .05 hr
2. Change drill bits .02 /spindle
3. Check and adjust hole depth .05 /spindle
4. Adjust offset and final check

No. of spindles	1	2	3	4
Hours	.13	.20	.26	.33

Operation elements in estimating minute

1. Load board position 1 .10
2. Traverse to hole 1 position in board 2 .08
3. Reposition and drill holes in board 2

No. holes/side	13	16	20	24	28	Add'l
Min	.16	.21	.29	.36	.44	.02

4. Traverse to hole 1 position in board 1 .042

5. Reposition and drill holes in board 1

No. holes / side	13	16	20	24	28	Add'l
Min	.14	.21	.29	.37	.45	.021

6. Traverse to original position   .12
7. Reload board position 2   .08
8. Visual inspection of holes   .17

23.6 Wave Soldering Machines

DESCRIPTION

A wave soldering machine applies a layer of molten solder to a printed circuit board. Solidification of the metal electrically secures the inserted components into place. The machine consists of a conveyor that mechanically transports the circuit boards through the system. Machines do vary, but a typical process for the board is:

1. Flux, which applies a liquid layer to remove surface oxides and to give the filler metal the fluidity to wet the joint surfaces completely;
2. Heating elements, which raise the temperature for proper solder adhesion;
3. Air knives, used to remove excess flux;
4. A pass-over the crest of the liquid solder wave at a set height and;
5. The washing cycle, which may vary from a series of washes, rinses and air knives to a simple dishwasher.

The machines are able to solder different sizes of boards at variable rates of speed. Maximum and minimum rates are determined by the design of the machine and the application limitations. One or two operators may perform the loading and unloading operations, which is important in time estimating. Machine types are variable. Smaller machines, used for smaller lot quantities, make use of conveyor racks which can be adjusted to different board sizes. Larger machines have adjustable width conveyors and are used for large lots. Sometimes they run continuously for one or two shifts.

Figure 23.6A is a sketch of a large unit that is intended for a large quantity of the same size boards. Two operators are required. Figure 23.6B is a sketch of a semiautomatic wave soldering machine intended for short runs or occasional use. It uses either one or two operators. It handles variable sized boards, which are first inserted into fixtures or racks. The racks are returned on a return carriage. A dishwasher may be used for cleaning and flux removal. Figure 23.6C is a photograph of a unit that can solder various sized boards, fine lines, large lands, and multilayer boards. A return conveyor system is also available.

ESTIMATING DATA DISCUSSION

These estimating data cover the wave soldering operation of a continuously operating automatic self-washing machine and semiautomatic machine. These data describe the limits of wave soldering machines, so time estimates should be possible for a variety of applications.

The setup elements are given in hours. Element 1 includes the time required to fill the flux tank, check the level, and ensure that the foamer is working properly. The height must be within limits, and this is also included.

Some wave soldering machines use racks which hold the board and transport it along the conveyor. Element 2 lists the time required to adjust each rack to the correct width of the board. The time must be multiplied by the number of conveyor racks that will be used.

A setup accounts for the time to adjust the width of the conveyor for board width. This may require a few fine adjustments and these have been included in the value. To ensure that the board is being accurately soldered, it is moved over the solder wave manually and then inspected. Then it is run automatically to ensure that the belt speed is producing a good solder finish. Elements 5 and 6 give these values. The height of the solder must be adjusted in relation to the board, and this is done after both the normal manual automatic test runs. Element 5 considers the different adjustment techniques.

Element 6 is the time required to add solder and to remove the waste, called dross, from the solder pot. This is done before each run and may be repeated again during the process and is included as often as necessary.

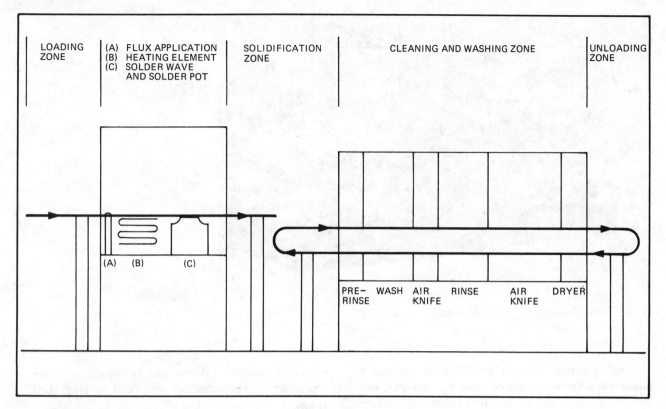

FIGURE 23.6A Automatic wave soldering machine, variable board sizes and speed rates.

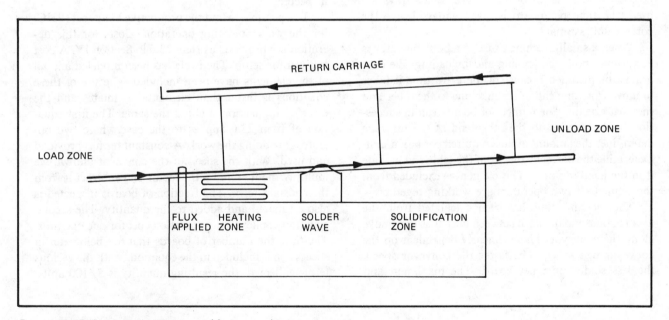

FIGURE 23.6B Semiautomatic wave soldering machine.

FIGURE 23.6C Electrovert Ultrapak Wavesolder System.

The operation elements are listed in estimating minutes and are arranged into handling, machine, and inspection categories. The handling consists of loading and unloading elements, which vary depending on the type of machine that is used. Element 1, gathering the boards, includes the time to walk to and from the position where the lot of boards are. When trays are used, the time per board is given and will give the correct unit estimate.

When a small machine is used and one operator is performing both the loading and unloading, Element 5 must be included because of the extra time it takes to move from one end of the machine to the other and then back again. The number of boards run in succession before moving to the other end of the machine determines the amount of time required per board unit. Determine the correct value from the table and include it in the handling time. This element is excluded from the estimate if two operators are working together.

The machine time has been calculated from the average time and distance between boards as they move along the conveyor. This is linearly dependent on the conveyor belt speed. The faster the conveyor speed, the less solder time per board. The maximum and minimum speeds are determined by the design of the solder wave. The estimator will need to know belt speed.

The time to visually inspect the soldered circuit board is given in Element 11. This time should be multiplied by the fraction of boards soldered that are inspected.

It is possible to find the productive hour cost (PHC) for the wave soldering operation. Costs for this operation are provided as Item 23.6 in Section IV. A cost is given for setup. The cycle has been modeled and all of the elements have been included. The use of these equations is faster than elemental estimates and the error of application is about the same. The first equation of Item 23.6 applies to the case where two operators are doing the work. A constant term is provided and used. With the speed of the conveyor known, we multiply the ft/min by the factor and subtract it from the constant term. The fraction of boards inspected is also estimated and added to the quantity. The second equation applies to the operation cost for one operator. The time the number of boards that are being run in succession is included in the equation. With the various terms collected, the resulting quantity is $/100 units.

EXAMPLES

A. A lot of 72 circuit boards is to be soldered. A machine using conveyor racks will be used and will be run at a rate of 4 ft per min. One operator will load and unload so four conveyor racks will be used. Each board will be inspected. This will be the only lot of the day so the setup is extensive. Find unit and lot estimates.

Table	Description	Time
23.6-S2	Adjust conveyor racks to correct board width, 4 boards × .01	.04 hr
23.6-S1	Fill flux tank	.12
23.6-S5	Run first board manually	.06
23.6-S7	Adjust height of solder wave, table leg adjust	.07
23.6-S6	Run second board automatically	.03
	Setup total	.32 hr
23.6-1	Gather tray of boards	.13 min
23.6-2	Position board in conveyor rack	.09
23.6-3	Place rack on conveyor	.04
23.6-5	Operator moves to opposite end (4 boards run in succession)	.07
23.6-6	Remove rack from conveyor, remove board	.03
23.6-7	Place rack on return carriage	.05
23.6-9	Place board on tray	.04
23.6-10	Machine time (4 feet per minute)	.49
23.6-11	Inspection, visual; each board	.06
	Unit estimate	1.00 min
	Lot estimate	1.52 hr

B. Using an automatic wave soldering machine, 1100 circuit boards will be soldered. Two operators are required and this will be included in the handling time needed in the estimate. Assume this will be the first run of the day and the setup will be extensive. Conveyor speed is 9 ft per min and one out of 25 boards will be inspected. Find the unit and lot estimates.

Table	Description	Time
23.6-S1	Fill flux tank	.12 hr
23.6-S4	Fill automatic washers with soap	.03
23.6-S8	Add solder (4-five pound bars)	.15
	Clean dross from solder pot	
	Adjust solder temperature	
23.6-S3	Adjust conveyor to correct board width	.04
23.6-S5	Run first board manually	.06
23.6-S6	Run second board automatically	.03
23.6-S7	Adjust height of solder wave, crank adjustment	.03
	Setup total	.46 hr
23.6-1	Gather stack of boards, tray	.13 min
23.6-4	Place and position boards on conveyor	.07
23.6-8	Unload board from conveyor	.02
23.6-9	Place board on tray	.04
23.6-10	Machine time (9 ft per min)	.34
23.6-11	Inspection, visual; one out of 25 boards	.002
	Unit estimate	.602 min
	Lot estimate	11.56 hr

C. A wave soldering machine that uses conveyor racks has a small lot to run. There are 20 boards of one size, six of another, and then two of a small size. The conveyor speed is set at 5 ft per min, and 5 racks will be run in succession. Two operators will be used to load and unload the boards. This is not the first lot run of the day so setup will be average.

Table	Description	Time
23.6-S	Adjust conveyor racks to correct board width, 5 × .01, three times	.15 hr
23.6-S	Run first board manually	.06
23.6-S	Run second board automatically	.03
23.6-S	Adjust height of solder (table leg adjustment)	.07
23.6-S	Clean dross from solder pot	.05
	Setup total	.36 hr

23.6-1	Gather stock, one board at a time	.19	min
23.6-2	Position board in conveyor rack, tighten	.09	
23.6-3	Place rack in conveyor	.04	
23.6-6	Remove rack from conveyor, remove board	.03	
23.6-7	Place rack on return carriage	.05	
23.6-9	Place board on tray	.04	
23.6-10	Machine time, 5 ft per min	.45	
23.6-11	Inspection, visual one out of two boards	.03	
	Unit estimate	1.02	min
	Lot estimate	.936	hr

D. A lot of 750 circuit boards is to be soldered, and an automatic wave soldering machine is used. The rate of the conveyor is 7 ft per min, and one out of every ten boards is inspected during the operation. The second shift will begin with this lot so the setup will include most elements. Find the unit and lot estimates.

Table	Description	Time	
23.6-S	Setup total	.46	hr
23.6-1	Gather stack, tray of boards	.13	min
23.6-4	Place and position board on conveyor	.07	
23.6-8	Unload board from conveyor	.02	
23.6-9	Place board on tray	.04	
23.6-10	Machine time, 7 ft per min	.39	
23.6-11	Inspection, one out of ten boards	.006	
	Unit estimate	.656	min
	Lot estimate	8.66	hr

E. One operator will run the weekly lot of circuit boards for a small company. There are 65 boards of one size and 47 of another that must be soldered. Conveyor racks are used on this type of machine and the belt speed is set at 4.5 ft per min. The operator will perform all of the loading and unloading, plus the setup. Three conveyor racks are run in succession before the operator moves to the opposite end. Find the lot estimate and pc/hr.

Table	Description	Time	
23.6-1	Gather stack, tray of boards	.13	min
23.6-2	Position board in conveyor rack	.09	
23.6-3	Place rack on conveyor	.04	
23.6-5	Operator moves to opposite end (3 boards run in succession)	.09	
23.6-6	Remove rack from conveyor, remove board	.03	
23.6-7	Place rack on return carriage	.05	
23.6-9	Place board on tray	.04	
23.6-10	Machine time, 4.5 ft/min	.45	
23.6-11	Inspection, one out of two boards	.03	
	Unit estimate	.95	min
	Lot estimate	2.26	hr
	Pc/hr	63	

F. Re-estimate Example A using the operation estimate for one operator. Refer to Item 23.6 of Section IV. Find the $/100 units and lot estimate.

Item	Description	Cost
23.6	Setup subtotal	$4.15
23.6	One-person operation cost constant	$24.59
23.6	Velocity of conveyor, 4 ft/min, 4×1.27	−12.85
23.6	Inspection, each board	−3.28
	$/100 units	$8.46
	Lot cost for 72 boards	$10.24

G. Find the productive hour cost for Example C where two operators are used. Find lot cost.

Item	Description	Cost
23.6	Setup subtotal	$4.15
23.6	Constant requirement	$22.04
23.6	Velocity reduction, 5 ft/min, 5 × 1.27	−6.35
23.6	Inspection, 50%	.50
	$/100 units	$16.19
	Lot cost	$8.68

TABLE 23.6 WAVE SOLDERING MACHINES

Setup

1. Fill flux tank and check specific gravity	.12 hr
2. Adjust conveyor racks to correct width, per rack	.01
Adjust conveyor to correct board width	.04
3. Fill automatic washers with soap	.03
4. Run first board manually	.06
Run second board automatically	.03
5. Adjust height of solder wave:	
crank adjustment	.03
table leg adjustment	.07
6. Add solder, clean dross, and adjust temperature	.15

Operation elements in estimating minutes

1. Gather stack, move to machine:	
one board at a time	.19
tray of boards	.13
2. Position board in conveyor rack, tighten	.09
3. Place rack on conveyor	.04
4. Place and position board on conveyor	.07

5. Operator moves to opposite end of conveyor and then back again, for one operator loading and unloading the boards

Boards run in succession	1	2	3	4	5
Time per board, min	.14	.11	.09	.07	.06

6. Remove rack from conveyor, remove board	.03
7. Place rack on return carriage	.05
8. Unload board from conveyor	.02
9. Place board on tray	.04
10. Wave solder	

Ft. per min	1	2	3	4	5	6	7	8	9	10
Solder time per board, min	.64	.58	.53	.49	.45	.42	.39	.36	.34	.32

11. Inspect (visual), time per inspection	.06

23.7 Wire Harness Bench Assembly

DESCRIPTION

Assembly of a harness is performed at the bench having a board with an attached harness layout. Nails or pins are located along the track and benches. These pins confine the loose wires within the layout. Associated with the laying of the wires is lacing or strapping, which requires a roll of lacing cord or plastic straps. These cords or straps are secured around the bundle with a special strapping tool. Other common elements are the cutting of the wire to an exact length per the layout, which strips insulation from the end of the wire to a predetermined length, and crimping lugs to the ends of the wires. Each of the elements requires a tool.

Wires that interconnect various electrical and electronic components are often routed together. This group of wires, tied into a neat bundle, is known as a wire harness or cable. A wire harness may be prefabricated on a jig or bench and, sometimes, in a chassis. A wire harness is similar to multiple-wire cable. However, a wire harness is not usually a linear cable, but provides for the branching of individual wires throughout its length as required by the circuits associated with the electrical circuitry. In the production of the harness, a wire harness ends at a terminal board or at a cable connector.

Harnesses vary in length a few inches to many feet. The intent of these data is to present data that represents the size that will be assembled on a bench-style station. Automatic assembly methods are not considered. Figure 23.7 is a sample of a harness. Other terms refer to this operation as "cabling."

ESTIMATING DATA DISCUSSION

Spot ties are individual ties produced with linear lacing cord or with nylon lacing tape. Various knots such as the square knot secure the tie. Cable lacing is the term applied to the production of many ties with a single length of lacing cord or tape. In the lacing of the cable, care is exercised to have each tie as snug and self-locking; otherwise, the lacing is inefficient. Nylon cable ties are small belts or straps used to bind a wire harness individually. The spacing between adjacent ties of a wire harness is ½ in. or more, but the maximum spacing is determined by the diameter of the harness. A harness should be neat and orderly with all wires running parallel to each other. Wires should not weave in and out as illustrated by the dark wire in Fig. 23.7. All spot tying and lacing should also be uniform. A harness that leans against a sharp corner or abrasive surface should be protected against abrasion. A plastic sleeving is placed around the harness and held in place with spot ties.

A great variety of cable connectors are encountered in electronics manufacture. Their elaboration is found in other locations of the *Estimator*.

Setup is provided for loading bundles of wires into a wire rack and also deals with the usual chores of starting a new job.

Cycle data assume a harness board with nails along the pattern to guide the assembler. Each end of the pattern has a spring holding device to hold the wire. Identification of harness branches are provided on the layout. A written instruction is available to aid where each wire is laid.

The operation elements are provided as a consolidated grouping or as single elements. The consolidated elements are a group of several individual elements, which are also provided. The consolidated elements do not require grouping and selection. On the other hand, an estimator may separately identify those elements

and build up an estimate. Both opportunities are available. Our discussion first describes the individual elements, as these are the items that are grouped for a consolidated element.

Element 1 includes several items. Get a wire includes obtaining a wire from a predetermined location in a wire rack and a move of the wire to the harness board. It assumes that locations are memorized. Start a wire begins with wire at the harness board and moves an end of the wire to a starting point, place in holding device, and regrasp wire preparatory to laying wire. The holding device is pressure type such as a spring. Lay a wire on a harness board begins with grasp of a loose end of wire, and lay wire on the harness board between pins along a directed route to a termination point of the wire. End the lay in wire (time also included start of a wire) involves the wire at the end of the trunk or branch and place end of wire into a holding device and hand releases wire. The consolidated element involves a get, start, lay, and end wire.

In Element 2, the operator assembles a pre-wired connector to board and end-run wires. It also includes obtaining a pre-wired connector from a bench and placing it on a harness board between posts. Get back wire, and lay on board between pins along described path to the termination point on the bench is also included. It concludes with the placement of the wire end into the holding device.

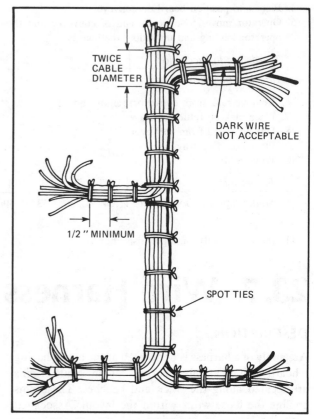

FIGURE 23.7 The spacing between spot ties should be at least ½ in., and the ties should be snug and self-locking.

462

Element 3, lacing a harness, is described by the following work. It involves manually securing the harness with cord prior to removing the harness from the board. The steps are start and tie. Starting and ending ties are combined since one always involves the other. The value also includes time to varnish two ties and changing the position of the board for ease of lacing. A lock stitch is an element between the ties that secures the body of the harness. Each stitch is spaced three inches. Congestion of these elements is possible due to branches and pins on the board. A dress and remove element separates and straightens the wires of the harness for a neat-appearing harness. A time is provided to remove the completed harness from the harness board and place the harness aside.

Strapping of a harness or branch is identified as Element 4. It may be more economical to strap instead of lacing, and sometimes strapping is used in addition to lacing. Strapping involves placing a strap around the harness every three inches. The time includes getting and placing strap and tightening. A tool is used. Congestion may occur because of branches in the harness or interfering pins on the board. The action of dressing and removing is used to separate and straighten end compressed wires for a neater finished appearance.

Element 5 consists of consolidated work and single elements. This element is collectively referred to cut, strip, and lug. Usually some, if not all of the wire end, need to be cut and stripped to a prescribed length. Sometimes stripping is eliminated which prevents fraying of wire ends. Lugging, when required, is usually over a stripped end, although not always. This action is determined by the type of lug. Cut wire includes getting the cutter and placing aside. Each additional cut time value is without the get and aside cutter. The cut dimension is determined by a mark on the harness board for each wire. Similar instructions are noted for stripping. Lugging the first end involves a get and aside of a lugging tool. Additional lugged ends are without this tool time. Labeling effort includes placing and securing a marker on the harness. Time is indicated for removing the harness from the board. Observe that time is associated with the number of branches. The time allows for care to ensure that lugs and connections are disengaged.

Miscellaneous elements are identified in Element 6. The end of a shielded wire is taped, which includes obtaining a roll of tape, start taping and wrapping to a specific location, cutting tape, replacing wire harness into position, and dropping of tape. A length may be taped, and the length of run is indicated. It includes the usual get and aside of the tape. A tube, which is pre-split along the length, is forced over the harness and includes the tieing. A tube may be guided over several wires by sliding the tube to a location. The time is determined by the length of sleeving.

If the estimator wishes to use rule-of-thumb methods, he or she is referred to the Operation Costs, Section IV. These data are related to the base area which uses a national norm productive hour cost. The cost drivers for Item 23.7 is the number of wires and the total length of the main trunk and branches. The estimator multiplies the number of wires by the total length, which is again multiplied by the factor given in Item 23.7.

EXAMPLES

A. A 24-in. long harness having three branches is to be estimated for a lot of 10 units. Branch 1, 2, 3, 4 and 5 have 12, 6, 4, 10, and 4 ends which are cut and stripped. The harness has 18 wires. The main trunk is laced and branches 2, 3, and 4 are spot tied. The main trunk is 24 in., and branches 2, 3, and 5 are 6, 18, and 8 in.

Table	Description	Time	
23.7-S	Setup	.05	hr
23.7-1	Lay 16 24-in.,	3.23	min
	212-in.	.38	
23.7-7	Lace 24 in. of main trunk	1.84	
23.7-4	Spot tie 13 places, branches 2, 3, and 5; 13 × .36	4.68	
23.7-5	Cut 36 ends; .78 + 11 × .03	1.11	
23.7-5	Strip 36 ends of wires; 1.03 + 11 × .04	1.47	
23.7-5	Remove harness from board, use 6 branches	.70	
	Unit estimate	13.41	min
	Hr/100 units	22.35	
	Lot estimate	2.205	hr

B. A harness is to be produced on a board. Features of the harness are as follows: There are 26 wires, one main trunk, four branches, and one branch less than 3 in. There is one connector with 10 wires having two mounting holes. Pins and nails are positioned on the board according to drawing specifications. The wires are cut to indicated drawing length, and the ends are stripped $\frac{1}{4}$ in. The main trunk and branch 2 is laced per specification. Branch 4 is spot tied. Branches 1, 3, and 5 are strapped tied per specification. One end has a crimped lug. Wires are numbered for identification. A lot of 27 harnesses is to be estimated. Find the unit estimate, hours/100 units, and lot time.

Table	Description	Time	
23.7-S	Setup	.05	hr
23.7-2	Load pre-wired connector, lay in 10 wires, and distance is 30 in.	1.50	min
23.7-1	Lay in 16 wires with average length of 24 in., 4.05 + .23	4.28	
23.7-3	Lace main branch, 30 in.	2.05	
23.7-3	Lace branch 2, 18 in.	1.63	
23.7-4	Spot-tie branch 4	.36	
23.7-4	Strap tie branches 1, 3, 5		
	Branch 1 is 12 in.	.91	
	Branch 3 is 8 in.	.91	
	Branch 5 is 10 in.	.91	
23.7-4	Cut 42 wires to length, .78 + 17 × .03	1.29	
23.7-4	Strip 42 wires, $\frac{1}{4}$ in., 1.03 + 17 × .04	1.71	
23.7-4	Lug 1 wire	.24	
23.7-4	Remove harness, 7 branches	.80	
23.7-4	Label cable with marker	.24	
	Unit estimate	16.91	min
	Hr/100 units	28.184	
	Lot time	7.660	hr

C. A harness is to be bench assembled. The harness has 48 wires, and 24 are pre-assembled to a connector. The main branch is 60-in. long. Branches 2, 3, 4, 6, 7, and 8 are 12 in., 12 in., 10 in., 8 in., 15 in., and 10 in. in length. All ends are cut and stripped. Six ends are lugged. The main branch is laced every three inches and the branch is strapped. Branches 2, 3, 4, 6, and 7 are spot tied. The harness is taped at a bend near branch 3 and is 3-in. long. Find the unit and shop estimate.

Table	Description	Time	
23.7-S	Setup	0.05	hr
23.7-2	Assemble pre-wire connector to board, 24 wires with average length of 60 in., 3.98 + 4 × .18	4.70	min
23.7-1	Lay wires, 10 are 60 in.,	2.40	
	10 are 36 in.,	2.10	
	4 are 24 in.	.80	
23.7-3	Lace 60 in.	3.10	
23.7-4	Spot tie 24 locations, 24 × .36	8.64	
23.7-4	Strap 3 places for 6 in., use minimum	.91	
23.7-6	Tape 3-in. long	1.26	
23.7-5	Cut 72 ends, .78 + 47 × .03	1.41	
23.7-5	Strip 72 ends 1.03 + 47 × .04	1.88	
23.7-5	Lug 6 ends, .48 + .06	.54	
23.7-5	Remove harness from board	.90	
	Unit estimate	28.64	min
	Pc/hr	2.1	
	Hr/100 units	47.734	

D. Re-estimate Example A above using Item 23.7 in Section V. The factor multiplies the number wires in the length times the length of the main and branch harness. For Example A, the harness has 18 wires. The lengths are 24 + 6 + 18 + 8 = 56 in. Find the setup, $/100 units, and lot cost.

Item	Description	Cost
23.7	Setup cost subtotal	$ .48
23.7	18 wires, 56-in. length, 18 × 56 × .106	$106.85

464

Item	Description	Cost
	$/100 units	$106.85
	Unit cost	$ 20.69
	Lot cost for 10 units	$ 11.17

TABLE 23.7 WIRE HARNESS BENCH ASSEMBLY

Setup   **.05 hr**

Operation elements in estimating minutes

1. Get wire, start, lay, and end wire

No. of Wires	Distance					
	12	24	36	48	60	72
1	.19	.20	.21	.22	.24	.26
2	.38	.40	.42	.44	.48	.52
3	.57	.60	.63	.66	.72	.78
4	.76	.80	.84	.88	.96	1.04
5	.95	1.00	1.05	1.10	1.20	1.30
6	1.14	1.20	1.26	1.32	1.44	1.56
7	1.33	1.40	1.47	1.54	1.68	1.82
8	1.52	1.60	1.68	1.76	1.92	2.08
9	1.71	1.80	1.89	1.98	2.16	2.34
10	1.90	2.00	2.10	2.20	2.40	2.60
12	2.28	2.40	2.52	2.64	2.88	3.12
15	2.85	3.00	3.15	3.30	3.60	3.90
20	3.80	4.00	4.20	4.40	4.80	5.20
25	4.75	5.00	5.25	5.50	6.00	6.50
28	5.32	5.60	5.88	6.16	6.72	7.28
30	5.70	6.00	6.30	6.60	7.20	7.80
40	7.50	8.00	8.40	8.80	9.60	10.40
50	9.50	10.00	10.50	11.00	12.00	13.00
75	14.25	15.00	15.75	16.50	18.00	19.50
100	19.00	20.00	21.00	22.00	24.00	26.00
Add'l wire	.22	.23	.24	.25	.27	.29

Get wire from holder, per wire	.04
Start wire and end run, per wire	.09
Run wire in cable, per wire	.08

2. Assemble pre-wired connector to board, lay and end wire

No. of Wires	Distance					
	12	24	36	48	60	72
1	.46	.48	.50	.53	.56	.59
2	.54	.58	.62	.68	.74	.80
3	.62	.68	.74	.83	.92	1.01
4	.70	.78	.86	.98	1.10	1.22
5	.78	.88	.98	1.13	1.28	1.43
6	.86	.98	1.10	1.28	1.46	1.64
7	.94	1.08	1.22	1.43	1.64	1.85
8	1.02	1.18	1.34	1.58	1.82	2.06
9	1.10	1.28	1.46	1.73	2.00	2.27
10	1.18	1.38	1.58	1.88	2.18	2.48
20	1.98	2.38	2.78	3.38	3.98	4.58
25	2.38	2.88	3.38	4.13	4.88	5.63
30	2.78	3.38	3.98	4.88	5.78	6.68

No. of Wires	Distance					
	12	24	36	48	60	72
40	3.58	4.38	5.18	6.38	7.58	8.78
50	4.38	5.38	6.38	7.88	9.38	10.88
75	6.38	7.88	9.38	11.63	13.88	16.13
100	8.38	10.38	12.38	15.38	18.38	21.38
Add'l wire	.08	.10	.12	.15	.18	.21

Assemble pre-wired connector to cable board	.38
Lay wire, each	.08
End wire, each	.04
Mount wired connector to holding fixture	1.29
Mount wiring plug to plate with mounted plug	1.01

3. Lacing of harness trunk or branch

Distance	12	18	24	30	36	42	48
Min	1.42	1.63	1.84	2.05	2.26	2.47	2.68

Distance	54	60	66	72	Add'l ft
Min	2.89	3.10	3.31	3.52	.42

Start and end tie	1.09
Lock stitch every 3 in.	.09
Correct for congestion of cable every 12 in.	.04
Dress harness, every 12 in.	.02

4. Strapping of harness trunk or branch

Distance	12	18	24	30	36	42
Strapping min	.85	1.19	1.70	2.89	4.08	4.42
Congestion min	.04	.06	.08	.10	.12	.12
Dressing min	.02	.03	.04	.05	.06	.07
Consolidated	.91	1.28	1.82	3.04	4.26	4.61

Distance	48	54	60	66	72	Add'l ft
Strapping min	4.76	5.10	5.44	5.78	6.12	.68
Congestion min	.16	.18	.20	.22	.24	.04
Dressing min	.08	.09	.10	.11	.12	.02
Consolidated	5.00	5.37	5.74	6.11	6.48	.74

Strapping a bundle with plastic tie wrap every 3 in.	.17
Correct for congestion of interference with posts or branch per ft	.04
Dress trunk or branch every 12 in.	.02
Spot tie for branch from trunk, per tie	.36
Spot tie for branch from trunk with varnish	.42

5. Cut, strip, and lug wires

	Wires								
	1	2	3	4	5	10	15	25	Add'l
Cut	.06	.09	.12	.15	.18	.33	.48	.78	.03
Strip	.07	.11	.15	.19	.23	.43	.63	1.03	.04
Lug	.24	.30	.36	.42	.48	.78	1.08	1.68	.06

Cut wire,	.06 for first,	.03/add'l
Strip wire,	.07 for first,	.04/add'l
Lug wire,	.24 for first,	.06/add'l

Label harness with marker   .24

Remove harness from board	6	7	8	9	10	Add'l
Min	.70	.80	.90	1.00	1.10	.10

6. Miscellaneous

Tape ends of shielded wire	1	2
Min	.40	.80

Tape start and finish length	2	3	4	5	6	7	8	Add'l
Min	.42	1.26	1.68	2.10	2.52	2.94	3.36	.42

Roll tape around harness, per in.   .22

Taping around branch, each	1	2	3	4	5	Add'l
Min	.27	.54	.81	1.08	1.35	.27

Split tubing, lay over harness, tie tubing	1	2	3	4	5	Add'l
Min	.74	1.48	2.22	2.96	3.70	.74

Sleeve over several wires	1	2	3	4	5	Add'l
Min	.39	.78	1.17	1.56	1.95	.39

Route wire through aparture
    Easy (no force required) up to 5 in. of wire   .03
    Difficult (force required) up to 5 in. of wire   .06
    Each additional 5 in. of wire   .01

23.8 Flat Cable Connector Assembly

DESCRIPTION

Growing industrial acceptance of flat ribbon cable has led to increased production. The demand has resulted from advantages of faster insulation stripping and mass termination on conductors offered by the connectors. In utilizing these machines, production rate improves over hand labor requirements. Connectors are assembled to flat ribbon cable leading to reduced costs and improved quality.

Early development of connector/flat ribbon cable was initiated about 1960. This concept was based on the "U" shape contact principle, which strips insulation from round conductors during mating. Later, the U-contact principle was applied to develop a connector/flat ribbon cable system with characteristics demanded by the electronic industry. The design solved a number of problems including elimination of wiring errors and simplification of harness assembly. The U-contacts are formed with parallel legs which displace insulation as the conductor is forced into the slot. Deflection of these legs during termination results in a permanent, gas-tight grip on the cable conductor.

The mass termination machines are simple and accurate. We consider three types of equipment: manual press, pneumatic press, and semi-automatic machine.

The assembly procedures utilizing the first two types of equipment are as follows: The assembler begins by removing a connector cover from the transfer adhesive strip. The cover snaps down against the adjacent cover, breaking it from the liner. The cover is pulled laterally away from the strip, leaving the adhesive with a smooth clean edge. The cable is placed on the cover with the ribbed cable contour matching. The cable and cover subassembly are next placed in a steel locator plate, and the mating connector body is positioned over them. The press is operated to force U-contacts over the flat cable conductors ensuring a reliable electrical connection. This is the standard assembly procedure for all mass termination connectors. Only the locator plate need be changed to accommodate differences in connector format.

The following is the assembly procedure utilizing the semi-automatic machine for manufacturing mass termination flat cables: The feed followers are removed, the channel widths are adjusted to connector size, the connector covers are placed into the channel, and pressure sensitive tape is removed. The width of feed follower is adjusted by sliding a spring loaded adjustable rail to appropriate connector width. The above steps should be repeated for connector. Cable is fed through the magazine until it hits the stop. The foot pedal is depressed.

Inasmuch as this operation is relatively simple, the estimator may want to find the cost for 100 terminations directly by using the operational cost data provided by Section IV, Item 23.8.

EXAMPLES

A. A cable assembly consists of 6 in. of cable and two connectors. Find the unit estimate for the manual press operation to terminate the cable with two connectors for both ends. Also find the estimated time for a lot of 25 cables.

Table	Description	Time
23.8-S	Setup	.02 hr
23.8-1	Remove top covers, 2 × .05	.10 min
23.8-1	Place cover on cables, 2 × .07	.14
23.8-1	Place cover-cables in locator plate, 2 × .03	.06
23.8-1	Remove connectors, 2 × .01	.02
23.8-1	Place connectors in locator plates, 2 × .06	.12
23.8-1	Press down, 2 × .04	.08
23.8-1	Remove the assembly	.04
	Unit estimate	.56 min
	Lot estimate	.25 hr

B. Repeat Example A utilizing pneumatic press.

Table	Description	Time
23.8-S	Setup	.02 hr
23.8-2	Remove top covers, 2 × .05	.10 min
23.8-2	Place covers on cables, 2 × .07	.14
23.8-2	Place cover cables in locator plate, 2 × .03	.06
23.8-2	Remove connectors, 2 × .01	.02
23.8-2	Place connectors in locator plates, 2 × .06	.12
23.8-2	Press down, 2 × .02	.04
23.8-2	Remove the assemblies	.04
	Unit estimate	.52 min
	Lot estimate	.25 hr

C. Repeat Example A utilizing semi-automatic machine.

Table	Description	Time
23.8-S	Setup	.03 hr
23.8-3	Feed cable, 2 × .01	.02 min
23.8-3	Terminate cable, 2 × .01	.02
23.8-3	Remove cable, 2 × .01	.02
	Unit estimate	.06 min
	Lot estimate	.05 hr

D. Repeat Example A above using the data of Section IV.

Item	Description	Cost
23.8	Setup subtotal	$ .98
23.8	Connectors for two ends, 2 × 4.52	9.04
	$/100 units	$9.04

Item	Description	Cost
	$/unit	$ .90
	Lot cost for 25 cables	$3.24

23.8 FLAT CABLE CONNECTOR ASSEMBLY

Setup

Manual or pneumatic press	.01 hr
Semiautomatic	.03 hr

Operation elements in estimating minutes

1. Manual press

Remove top cover	.05
Place cover on cable	.07
Place cover cable assembly in locator plate	.03
Remove connector	.01
Place connector in locator plate	.06
Press down	.04
Remove the assembly	.02

2. Pneumatic press

Remove top cover	.05
Place cover on cable	.07
Place cover cable assembly in locator plate	.03
Remove connector	.01
Place connector in locator plate	.06
Press down	.02
Remove the assembly	.02

3. Semiautomatic

Feed cable	.01
Terminate cable	.01
Remove cable	.01

23.9 D-Subminiature Connector Assembly

DESCRIPTION

D-subminiature connectors are designed to accommodate cable-to-panel and cable-to-cable applications. These are pin and socket devices which employ contacts encased in a molded dielectric insert surrounded by D-shaped shells for polarization. These connectors are designed for applications where space and weight are prime considerations. These high-contact density connectors are especially suited for connecting a computer to a terminal or a printer. Other applications include circuit-termination, computers, and computer peripheral equipment, data terminal, telecommunica-

tions systems, medical equipment, military systems, instrumentation, and cable assemblies.

Four sizes of D-subminiature connectors are considered here. These are 9, 15, 25, and 37 contacts. The most popular of these connectors are the 25 and 37 positions. The 25 position is called RS232, and the 37 position is called RS449. These connectors are used as communication input/output connecting devices. Four types of D-subminiature connectors are discussed: insulation displacing (discrete wires), solder, solder with linear, and crimp-contact type.

Only operation time for 25 and 37 positions are

provided. For operation data, mass termination and the manufacturing procedure on mass termination, see the flat cable section, Table 23.8.

ESTIMATING DATA DISCUSSION

After mass termination, the operation of terminating D-subminiature connectors is a cost-effective method. Using a semi-automatic machine, two wires are simultaneously inserted in connectors' contacts. The wire is pierced and cut.

Solder types of connectors are terminated by hand stripping the wires, pre-soldering connector contacts, and soldering the wires to one side of connector and then to the other side. A vise is used to hold the connector.

A fixture is used to terminate a solder with linear connector. All the wires are selected, inserted, and soldered to one side of the connector. Then the other side is terminated.

The method of crimp contacts is described as follows: First the contacts are crimped to the wires. Then the contacted wires are inserted into the connector. The advantage of this type of connector is significant when few wires are terminated.

EXAMPLES

A. Estimate the time for RS232 cable assembly connecting a computer terminal to a printer. All the 25 contacts of D-subminiature connector are to be wired. A lot quantity of 50 cables will be manufactured. Use the method of insulation displacing connector.

Table	Description	Time	
23.9-S	Setup cables and load connectors	.03	hr
23.9-1	Place connector in the nest	.03	min
23.9-2	Spread and fan wires	.11	
23.9-3	Connectorizing 25 pins	.68	
23.9-4	Remove connector	.03	
	Unit estimate	.85	min
	Lot estimate	.73	hr

B. Find unit time, hr/100 units, and lot estimates using solder connector for the problem described above. Now assume a quantity of 500 cable assemblies.

Table	Description	Time	
23.9-S	Setup	.05	hr
23.9-5	Strip wires, 25 wires $\times$ .03 min/wires	.75	min
23.9-6	Place the connector in the vise	.42	
23.9-7	Get solder iron, fill solder cup, .06 $\times$ 25 contacts	1.50	
23.9-7	Solder wires to the connector, .07 min/wire $\times$ 25 wires	1.75	
23.9-8	Turn the connector in the vise	.42	
23.9-9	Remove cable and connector	.09	
	Unit estimate	5.28	min
	Hr/100 units	8.800	
	Lot estimate	44.05	hr

C. Find unit time using solder linear connector for the problem described above. The production quantity is 2000 cable assemblies.

Table	Description	Time	
23.9-S	Setup	.03	hr
23.9-10	Place wires	.14	min
23.9-11	Insert wires into fixtures	.01	
23.9-11	Strip and cut	.03	
23.9-12	Handle solder iron and solder pins	.87	
23.9-13	Turn connector and release cable	.02	
	Unit estimate	1.15	min
	Hr/100 units	1.197	
	Lot estimate	23.97	hr

TABLE 23.9 D-SUBMINIATURE CONNECTOR ASSEMBLY

Setup

Insulation displacing	.03 hr
Solder	.05 hr
Solder linear	.03 hr

Operation elements in estimating minutes

1. Place connector in the nest   .03

2. Spread and fan wires   .11

3. Select and insert wires

Pair	Min		Pair	Min
1st	.080		8th	.046
2nd	.074		9th	.041
3rd	.071		10th	.038
4th	.068		11th	.034
5th	.062		12th	.034
6th	.057		13th	.031
7th	.052		Total	.688

Selecting paired wires out of 13th pair cable to connectorize 25 pin connector

Wires in pair	Min		Wires in pair	Min
1st	.08		1st–8th	.51
1st + 2nd	.15		1st–9th	.55
1st + 2nd + 3rd	.22		1st–10th	.58
1st–4th	.29		1st–11th	.62
1st–5th	.35		1st–12th	.65
1st–6th	.41		1st–13th	.68
1st–7th	.46			

Selecting paired wires out of 19th pair cable to connectorize 37 pin connector

Wires in pair	Min		Wires in pair	Min
1st	.083		11th	.049
2nd	.080		12th	.046
3rd	.077		13th	.043
4th	.074		14th	.041
5th	.071		15th	.039
6th	.068		16th	.038
7th	.062		17th	.034
8th	.060		18th	.034
9th	.057		19th	.031
10th	.052			

Selecting paired wires out of 19th pair cable to connectorize 37 pin connector

Wires in pair	Min		Wires in pair	Min
1st	.08		1st–8th	.57
1st + 2nd	.16		1st–9th	.63
1st + 2nd + 3rd	.24		1st–10th	.68
1st–4th	.31		1st–11th	.72
1st–5th	.38		1st–12th	.77
1st–6th	.45		1st–13th	.81
1st–7th	.51		1st–14th	.85

Wires in pair	Min		Wires in pair	Min
1st–15th	.89		1st–18th	1.00
1st–16th	.93		1st–19th	1.03
1st–17th	.96			

4. Remove connector .03

5. Strip wires, solder method .03 ea

6. Place the connector in the vise .42

7. Get solder iron .30
   Fill solder cup with solder .06 ea contact
   Solder wires to the connector .07 ea wire

8. Turn the connector in the vise .42

9. Remove the cable and connector .09

10. Place wires, solder linear method .14

11. Insert wire into fixture, solder linear method .01
    Strip and cut, solder linear method .03

12. Handle solder iron and solder, solder linear method:
    25 pins .87
    37 pins 1.26

13. Turn connectors, solder linear method .02

14. Release .08

23.10 Single-Wire Termination Machines

DESCRIPTION

Wire terminal applicator machines apply strip terminals used in the manufacture of electrical connections on cables, jumpers, and related assemblies. Most machines will accommodate a range of wire gages and specify a necessary crimp height for each size. The crimp height refers to the thickness of the terminal at the crimp location after crimping (see Figure 23.10 A).

The applicator machines power a vertical action ram which drives the crimping die. The die performs three specific functions:

1. It crimps the terminal at two locations, folding the terminal ears around the wire insulation and crimping the terminal barrel around the bare wire;

2. It cuts the terminal from its carrier strip and;

3. It advances the carrier strip, placing the next terminal in the crimping area.

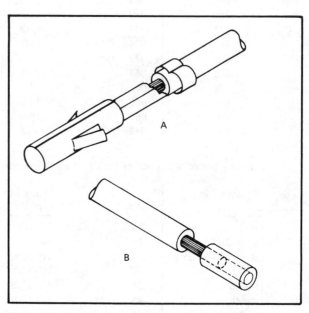

FIGURE 23.10 (A) Crimp height; (B) pre-cut insulation.

472

The terminal carrier strip is fed to the left side of the crimping die from a reel mounted on top of the machine. Termination is accomplished by inserting a stripped wire end into a terminal on the crimping anvil of the die and actuating the ram with a foot switch. Operation is simple and specially trained operators are not required.

ESTIMATING DATA DISCUSSION

Basic setup elements for single wire termination include locating wires near the machine, cleaning the feed track to remove the metal cut from between the terminals, and testing the machine's operations. The operation test involves terminating a few wires, inspecting the crimp, and measuring the crimp height with a micrometer. Two setup elements, changing the terminal reel and adjusting the die, are not necessarily performed each time with the basic elements. For example, the machine is often equipped with sufficient correct terminals and does not require adjustment, in which case one should not include these elements in the setup time.

There are six general operation elements. Certain elements are always included in the cycle time while others are only included in special instances. Element 1 involves securing a handful of wire from the workbench and turning to face the machine. This element is constant.

Element 2 involves turning the wires end for end to organize common ends. This element should only be included when the two ends of the wire are stripped different lengths or a terminal is already attached to one end.

When the wires are supplied with pre-cut insulation (see Figure 23.10B), so that the insulation piece may be removed by hand, Element 3 should be included.

Element 4 involves placing the stripped wire end into the crimping die, actuating the crimping mechanism with a foot switch, and removing the terminated wire. This element is constant.

Element 5 includes brief inspection of the handful of termination wires and placing them on the table. This inspection is a quick check to make sure that all the terminals are securely fastened to the wires. Bad wires are set aside.

Element 6 involves sorting the finished wires into piles of 100 and taping them into bundles to be sent for final inspection.

Note that the handling times for Elements 2, 5, and 6 are a function of wire length. This is a result of increased handling difficulty for the longer wires due to the tangling and increased bulk.

It is recommended that the following three rules be used to obtain values from the estimating table.

1. If the value of the time driver (in our case wire length) is less than the minimum table value then use the smallest value given.

2. If the time driver value falls between values in the table use the largest value.

3. If the time driver value is greater than the maximum table value use the maximum value.

Preliminary estimates may be obtained using the aggregate cost estimating relationship. The cost relationship is merely a linear correlation between cycle time and wire length. This relationship is given as Item 23.10 in Section IV. The cycle cost units are $/100 wires. Setup is given as an aggregate value of all the possible setup elements and is expressed in dollars per occurrence.

EXAMPLES

A. A lot of 6-in., 18-gage wires are to be terminated on one end. The wires are supplied with the insulation on each end pre-cut to different lengths. The machine is already equipped with a reel of the correct terminals and the die does not require adjustment. Lot size is 5000 wires. Estimate the unit and lot times.

Table	Description	Time
23.10-1S	Locate wires near machine	.04 hr
23.10-S3	Clean feed track	.01
23.10-S5	Test operation	.06 hr
	Setup subtotal	.11 hr
23.10-1	Grab wires	.003 min
23.10-2	Arrange wires	.006
23.10-3	Remove insulation	.010
23.10-4	Terminate	.028
23.10-5	Inspect and place aside	.005
23.10-6	Count and bundle	.009
	Unit estimate	.061 min
	Lot estimate	5.19 hr

B. A lot of 16-gage wires are to be terminated. The wires are 17-in. long, and both ends have the insulation pre-cut the same length. The machine requires a reel change and adjustments along with the other setup elements. The lot consists of 8000 wires. Find the unit and lot estimates.

Table	Description	Time	
23.10-S1	Locate wires near machine	.04	hr
23.10-S2	Change terminal reel	.05	
23.10-S3	Clean feed track	.01	
23.10-S4	Adjust die	.02	
23.10-S5	Test operation	.06	
	Setup subtotal	.18	hr
23.10-1	Grab wires	.003	min
23.10-3	Remove insulation	.010	
23.10-4	Terminate	.028	
23.10-5	Inspect and place wires aside	.011	
23.10-6	Count and bundle	.016	
	Unit estimate	.068	min
	Lot estimate	9.25	hr

C. A lot of 20-gage wires are to be terminated. The wires are 11-in. long with one end already terminated. All setup elements are required. The lot is 3000 wires. Estimate the unit lot times.

Table	Description	Time	
23.10-S	Setup (1–5)	.18	hr
23.10-1	Grab wires	.003	min
23.10-2	Arrange wires	.009	
23.10-3	Remove insulation	.010	
23.10-4	Terminate	.028	
23.10-5	Inspect and place aside	.008	
23.10-6	Count and bundle	.012	
	Unit estimate	.070	min
	Lot estimate	3.68	hr

D. Re-estimate Example A using the cost estimating relationship given as Item 23.10 in Section IV.

Item	Description	Cost
23.10	Setup	$ 1.74
23.10	Constant cost for cycle	$ .803
23.10	6-in. wire, 6 × .030	.18
	$/100 units	.983
	Lot cost for 5000 wires	$50.89

TABLE 23.10   SINGLE-WIRE TERMINATION MACHINES

Setup   **Hr**

	Hr
1. Locate wires near machine	.04
2. Change terminal reel	.05
3. Clean feed track	.01
4. Adjust die	.02
5. Test operation	.06

Operation Elements in Estimating Minutes

1. Grab handful of wires   .003

2. Arrange wires in hand

In.	6	7	9	11	14	17
Min	.006	.007	.008	.009	.011	.013

3. Remove pre-cut insulation   .010

4. Terminate   .028

5. Inspect and place aside

In.	6	7	9	11	14	17
Min	.005	.006	.007	.008	.010	.011

6. Count and tape in bundles of 100

In.	6	7	9	11	14	17
Min	.009	.009	.011	.012	.014	.016

23.11 Resistance Micro-Spot Welding

DESCRIPTION

Resistance micro-spot welding (RMSW) welds two pieces of metal together by passing a current through the metal. Pressure is necessary at a high amperage. The metal is raised to a temperature sufficient to lightly melt the metal. Two electrodes press the metal together, thus completing the weld. The two electrodes are then removed and the metal returns to room temperature.

There are two types of RMSW considered here. One is a foot-pedal operated press in which an upper electrode is lowered by a foot pedal and brought into contact with the metal. The lower electrode is positioned below the metal. The other setup is a hand-held weld clamp in which the electrodes are mounted to the tips of the C-clamp. Two electrodes bear on the metal by squeezing the clamp. In both setups, the current is actuated by the pressure between the electrodes reaching a pre-set level. The purpose of RMSW is not only in ensuring a reliable spot-weld joint. It is also used in place of other operations such as soldering when the design requires the absence of foreign material.

ESTIMATING DATA DISCUSSION

The setup required for RMSW consists of setting pressure to activate the current, the power level to pass through the metal, and obtain parts. For the weld press, it is necessary to set the gap for the electrodes.

Element 1 consists of loading the parts to be welded into the welding fixture or onto the welding machine. Usually there are several parts loaded before each pair of parts is welded. The independent variable is the number of parts loaded.

Element 2 consists of the actual welding process. The independent variable is the number of welds.

Element 3 is the removal of the part after welding. The time required to perform this element is generally a constant.

The process of data adjustment for different RMSW operations is simply done by counting the number of parts loaded and the number of welds required. There may be several RMSW operations performed before the product is completed and setup time is required for each operation.

These operations can be estimated for the direct labor cost using Item 23.11 of Section IV. A setup cost is listed. The use of the equation is easy, as one need only to multiply the factors by the number of individual parts and separate spot welds. The result of this equation is $/100 units for the run-time.

EXAMPLES

A. To assemble the mandrel, one places two end pieces or caps to each end of a cylindrical sheet of metal. Two identical operations are performed, consisting of placing the tube and one endpiece into a fixture, and then welding using 11 welds around the tube. The weld press is used.

Table	Description	Time
23.11-S	Setup	.15 hr
23.11-1	Load parts	.26 min
23.11-2	Spot weld 11 times	.28

Table	Description	Time
23.11-3	Remove piece	.08
	Repeat 1–3	.62
	Unit estimate	1.24 min
	Shop estimate	48 pc/hr

B. Two small interpieces are welded to two pins. The interpieces are placed into a custom made fixture which holds the header. The fixture is then placed between the electrodes of the weld press. This requires two welds and three parts to be loaded. Find the unit and shop estimate.

Table	Description	Time
23.11-S	Setup	.15 hr
23.11-1	Load parts	.33 min
23.11-2	Spot weld two times	.08
23.11-3	Remove piece	.08
	Unit estimate	.52 min
	Shop estimate	115 pc/hr

C. Use Item 23.11 of Section IV to determine the direct labor cost for Example A. There are 2 parts and 11 spot welds. Find the setup, $/100 cost, and lot cost for 825 units.

Item	Description	Cost
23.11	Setup	$ 1.01
23.11	Constant	$ 2.53
23.11	Handling cost, 2×1	1.00
23.11	Welding cost, $11 \times .439$	4.83
	$/100 units	$ 8.36
	Setup cost	$ 1.01
	Lot cost	$69.97

TABLE 23.11   RESISTANCE MICRO-SPOT WELDING

Setup

1. Machine press		.15 hr
2. C-clamp style		.05 hr

Operation elements in estimating minutes

1. Load parts

No. of parts	Machine press	C-clamp
2	.24	.14
3	.33	.16
4	.42	.18
5	.52	.23
6	.61	.27
8	.80	.32
10	.99	.39

2. Spot weld

No. of welds	Machine press	C-clamp
2	.07	.19
3	.09	.22
4	.11	.25
5	.14	.31
6	.16	.37
7	.18	.46
9	.22	.55
11	.26	.55
14	.32	.67
17	.38	.82

476

No. of welds	Machine press	C-clamp
21	.40	1.00
26	.57	1.23

3. Unload
   Machine press   .07
   C-clamp part   .19

23.12 Coil Winding Machines

DESCRIPTION

A coil winder provides a means to wind different shapes and types of coil quickly. Used in production of electromagnetic devices such as deflection coils, focus coils, inductors, and toroids, etc., the machines are capable of winding coils with segment windings of up to 180° or 360° continuous windings or bobbin windings. Wire used on the machine as reported here is between 16- and 45-gage, and cores up to 1-in. diameter can be accommodated. The winder contains a pre-set electronic counter assembly which controls the number of turns wound on the core. The motor provides a 0-400 rpm output to the winding head assembly. The core holding fixture rotates and the interaction between it and the rotating winding head yields correct winding of the coil. The winding process is semi-automatic, requiring the operator to thread the winding head and the core fixture. Constant supervision of the machine is needed to ensure that there is no disalignment of the shuttle and core. The machine is best suited for small quantity jobs. Now consider the general classification of coil winding machines.

ESTIMATING DATA DISCUSSION

Since the coil winder can produce coils of many different sizes and dimensions, a distinction is made concerning coil type. Distinctions are made in some of the cycle elements between bobbins or toroids. For the toroidal pieces, the setup time is .10 hr. This allows time to mount the winding head, install the shuttle, attach the wire spool and core holding fixture, and the core itself. Cleanup and other chores are included. This basic setup also assumes that the choice of winding head, shuttle size, and core size are all known. Experimentation in fitting shuttle size to core proportions can result in a much longer setup time and is not accounted for here. For the bobbins setup time include time for mounting the chuck, inserting the bobbin, and mounting the thread spool, and cleaning up.

The cycle time for toroids is arranged into six main elements. Element 1 consists of picking up the spool thread, leading it over the wire tension guide, threading it through the shuttle, and securing. The wire is wrapped around once and the free end clipped short.

In Element 2 the process is automatic. The operator initially sets the load/wind switch, the digital footage counter, and the speed control. The speed control regulates the feed rate of the shuttle and is set at approximately 160 rpm. The operator then flips the power switch, and the machine loads the shuttle. This element has both a constant and variable portion to it.

Element 3 consists of mainly wrapping the thread through the core and securing it before the winding process. Occasionally adjustment of the core's position is needed.

Element 4 deals with the actual winding of the toroids by the machine. The number of turns desired and the wire size used are the variable factors in determining the element time. In Element 5 the core and shuttle are removed from the machine and the extra wire is cut from the shuttle. The toroid's wire ends are wrapped around by hand and trimmed. The coil is then inspected for even turns of wire and to ensure that none of the wire insulation has been scraped off in the winding process.

The cycle elements for the production of bobbins are simpler than for a toroid. Element 1 consists of leading the wire over the tension guides and attaching it to the bobbin. The winding time, Element 4, varies with the number of turns required for the bobbin. It includes operator start and stop time. Elements 5 and 6 give the estimating times for removing the bobbin from the holder, clipping the wire, and inspecting for even turns. In Element 4, the correct number of turns is found on the table and the wire gage bracket is located at the table's head. The intersection of that column and row is the elemental time. If any variable is less than the minimum shown in the table, the minimum value listed is chosen. If any variables fall between the listed table values, the next higher value is used. If any exceed the tabular listed value, the maximum of the values is used. These rules aid consistency in estimates.

The estimator may want to find the direct labor cost for the operation. This is possible by Item 23.12 of Section IV. The setup is given in dollars per occurrence. Cycle time is in $/100 units. The cycle cost depends upon a constant and a factor for the number of turns.

EXAMPLES

A. A toroid is needed for a high voltage power supply. It requires 1500 turns of 36-gage wire. The core diameter is small, requiring precise alignment. Find the unit estimate and hr/100 units for the job.

Table	Description	Time	
23.12-S	Setup	.10	hr
23.12-1	Thread shuttle	.50	min
23.12-2	Operator start and stop	.25	
23.12-2	Machine load 40 ft	.32	
23.12-3	Thread wire through core	.57	
23.12-4	Machine wind wire on core	21.96	
23.12-5	Stop, removal of core and shuttle	.78	
23.12-6	Inspect insulation and windings	.60	
	Unit estimate	28.60	min
	Hr/100 units	47.667	

B. An inductor for a low voltage power supply has been ordered. It requires 1000 turns of 41-gage wire. Find the unit and lot estimate if 50 are ordered.

Table	Description	Time	
23.12-S	Setup	.10	hr
23.12-1	Thread shuttle	.50	min
23.12-2	Operator start and stop	.25	
23.12-2	Machine load 30 ft	.24	
23.12-3	Thread wire through core	.57	
23.12-4	Machine wind wire on core	14.88	
23.12-5	Stop, removal of core, shuttle	.78	
23.12-6	Inspect insulation and windings	.60	
	Unit estimate	21.42	min
	Hr/100 units	35.70	
	Lot estimate	17.95	hr

C. A 7/32-in. *Dia* bobbin coil is assembled. It has 400 turns of 38-gage wire. Estimate the unit time and pc/hr.

Table	Description	Time	
23.12-S	Setup	.05	hr
23.12-3	Lead wire over guides, thread bobbin	.25	min
23.12-4	Machine wind thread onto bobbin	.83	
23.12-5	Stop, remove bobbin from chuck	.17	
23.12-6	Inspection of windings	.58	
	Unit estimate	3.03	min
	Pc/hr	19.8	

D. A special toroid requires 478 turns of 38-gage wire. A lot of 400 has been ordered. Find the unit and lot estimate for the job.

Table	Description	Time	
23.12-S	Setup	.10	hr
23.12-1	Thread shuttle	.50	min
23.12-2	Operator start and stop	.25	
23.12-2	Machine load, 20 ft	.16	
23.12-3	Thread wire through core	.57	
23.12-3	Adjust core position with shuttle	.67	
23.12-4	Machine wind the core	5.98	
23.12-5	Stop, removal of core, shuttle	.78	
23.12-6	Inspect windings, insulation	.60	
	Unit estimate	13.11	min

Table	Description	Time
	Hr/100 units	21.850
	Lot estimate	87.500 hr

E. Re-estimate Example A above using Item 23.12 of Section IV to find setup cost and $/100 units. Also find the direct labor cost for one unit. The part is a toroid.

Item	Description	Cost
23.12	Setup subtotal	$ .95
23.12	1500 turns, 1500 × .228	342.00
	$/100 units	$342.00
	$/1 unit	$ 3.42

F. Provide a direct labor cost for the lot of 10 units for Example C. Item Description Cost

Item	Description	Cost
23.12	Setup subtotal	$ .95
23.12	Constant for cycle	$34.87
23.12	400 turns, 400 × .033	13.20
	$/100 units	$48.07
	Lot cost for 10 units	5.76 hr

TABLE 23.12   COIL WINDING MACHINES

Setup

Toroids	.10 hr
Bobbins	.05 hr

Operation elements in estimating minutes

1. Thread wire over guides and through the shuttle   .50

2. Load wire onto shuttle, operator start and stop   .25

Machine loading

Feet	10	15	20	25	30	35	40	45
Min	.08	.12	.16	.20	.24	.28	.32	.36

3. Thread wire through core and secure   .57
   Lead wire over guides and through bobbin   .25
   Adjust core position with shuttle   .67

4. Machine wind

Torrids:

No. of turns	Wire size (gage)		
	24–32	34–36	38–42
300	2.17	2.25	2.42
400	3.78	3.90	4.20
500	5.38	5.56	5.98
600	6.98	7.21	7.76
700	8.59	8.87	9.54
800	10.19	10.52	11.32
900	11.79	12.18	13.10
1000	13.39	13.83	14.88

No. of turns	Wire size (gage)		
	24–32	34–36	38–42
1000	13.39	13.83	14.88
1100	15.00	15.49	16.66
1200	16.60	17.15	18.44

No. of turns	Wire size (gage)		
	24–32	34–36	38–42
1300	18.18	18.78	20.22
1400	19.80	20.46	22.00
1500	21.26	21.96	23.78
1600	23.01	23.77	25.56
1700	24.61	25.42	27.32
1800	26.21	27.08	29.12

Bobbins:

No. of turns	200	300	400	500	600	700	800	900	1000
Min	.42	.63	.83	1.04	1.25	1.46	1.75	1.97	2.19

5. Removal of coil from winder
   Removal of core and shuttle, wire is stripped from shuttle, core wire is wrapped
   and trimmed   .78

   Removal of bobbin from chuck, trim wire ends   .17

6. Inspection
   Toroids, check windings and insulation   .60
   Bobbins, check windings   .58

24.1 Packaging Bench and Machines

DESCRIPTION

These estimating data are intended for temporary or final packaging. The purpose of temporary packaging may be for interim inventory and for protection against corrosion, moisture, abuse, or loss. The intention of final packaging may be for consumer or industrial pack, box, envelope, and/or bag. The materials for packaging are wood, paper, plastic, and metal. Cushioning for transport or stability is also considered. The items to be packaged are industrial and are not normally foodstuffs or pharmaceuticals.

The information is for low- to moderate-lot quantities using bench work. Semi- or fully automatic machines are necessary for moderate-to-large quantities. Individual, multiple, and bulk quantities are factors of choice in using the tables.

Figure 24.1 is a universal wrapping machine for short or long runs. It employs shrink or non-shrink wrapping materials. The product infeed and discharge are on the same end of the machine which allows one operator to feed the product and pack off where higher speeds are not required, which is about 40 units/min.

ESTIMATING DATA DISCUSSION

The data are organized differently than other tables. In addition to the setup, operational elements are associated to (1) handling of one, several, or bulk, (2) order time per occurrence, and (3) a unit time for pack. Thus, the data are pro-rated against the lot, order, or quantity restriction of the container, as well as the unit time for the pack. Single

or multiple packaging must be evaluated. In addition to a unit or lot estimate, we may want to know an order estimate, as the order quantity may be less than the lot quantity.

The description of packaging direct labor can be diverse; it can be bench work only, bench and machine alternately or in some combined way, or machine tending exclusively. Element choice is provided for this job diversity. The final package can consist of a variety of intermediate packages, each with different quantities of the same or different parts.

Order paperwork is optional, but it relates to invoice or billing paper, inventory slips, routings, guarantees, or computer cards added to the order, or marked in accordance with shipping instructions either to an interim internal or external inventory or directly to the customer. Shipping labels and general package instructions are included in this element.

Element 1 is usually independent of the type of pack and the quantity packaged.

Element 2 is manual get and position part for packaging. Conceivably, the part(s) get and position could be from a cart, skid, tote box, hanger, conveyor line, rack, moveable cage, pan, rod, jar, carton, etc. The three entry variables are maximum dimension, weight, and the nature of the arrival of the units. While there may be a contradiction between the maximum dimension and weight range, these suggestions allow for a consistent selection. Simple implies easy reaches, object handlings, and moves underload. Stack implies interference, while several suggest that several can be handled simultaneously. Bulk remove is a containerized transfer and dumping is possible. All manual packaging and many machine packaging operations will include Element 2.

Elements 3 through 16 deal with bench packaging. The estimator should carefully note what the element is "per." Unit differs from units; and bag, package, carton, or box implies one or more than one unit inasmuch as one or more may be jointly packaged in these containers. Some elements give a constant time per the package type plus a time for the part being loaded. Thus the order or lot (and they may differ) quantity is important. Some work would be done for the bag, package, etc., as a finish wrap. The procedure is to find the unit estimate, and multiply by the lot or order (or both) quantity to establish the estimate.

Element 3 constant time is per straw, and the number of parts used with each straw must be determined from the dimensions. The .02 min refers to part loading.

Two types of loading are considered in Element 6. In the nonbulk pack, the entry variable is the smallest X-Y-Z coordinate dimension. With 200+ bulk pack, the time is per the number loaded into the bag. No distinction is made to the bag seal, i.e., fold and staple, heat seal, or pressure close. In Element 7, the bag units are the divisor.

For Element 9, the .83 min covers preparation of the plastic or glass jar, and it is prorated against the number of units placed with the jar. Optional cushion or inner layer time is provided. But each part, singly or bulk, is placed within the jar and is added to the time for this pack. A lid means a turned and pressure cap.

The foam is preslitted in Element 11, and the slit length is the entry variable.

Element 12, or inner wrap, is wrapping material laced between two or more units. Distinctions are made with respect to materials used. Thus, if several units are packaged, the time includes both inner wrap package and minutes per unit (min/unit). Overwrap, Element 13, has the wrapping material around the outside of one or more units. It includes a constant time for material related to the package units and a variable wrapping time related to girth $L + W + H$. A third part of the overwrap is the number of units, and is expressed as a unit time.

Elements 14 and 15 are organized similarly. A container constant plus a unit or bulk load is stated. A final total time is divided by the number of units in the container.

Element 17 is for automatic packaging. Entry variable is the package per minute and units per package. The time is per unit of final product and is labor time for machine watching. If the operator watches more than one machine, the minutes per part is divided by the number of machines.

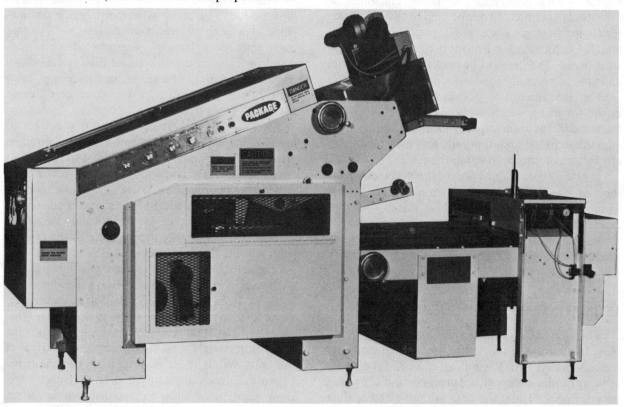

FIGURE 24.1 Universal wrapping machine for size range up to 16 in. length, 9 in. width and 5 in. height. *(Package Machinery Company)*

EXAMPLES

A. Parts that are easily removed from a hook-plating rack are placed into a tote box. Find the unit estimate. No order paperwork is required. Dimension is 4 in.

Table	Description	Time
24.1-2	Unload from rack	.03 min
24.1-5	Place in tote box by stacking	.01
	Unit estimate	.04 min

B. Painted parts that have a girth of $L = 4$, $W = 2$, and $H = 0.6$ in. are innerwrapped. Ten parts are placed in a corrugated paper carton for shipment. The parts are removed from a belt conveyor and the order size is moderate. Find the carton time and the unit estimate. Order paperwork is required for each carton.

Table	Description	Time
24.1-1	Order paperwork, 2.00/10	.20 min
24.1-2	Remove from conveyor, ea	.09
24.1-12	Brown paper innerwrap, and 10 units will have an approximate box dimension of 5 high and 2 across for a 10 x 8 x 10-in. dimension, .37/10	.037
24.1-12	The sum of the two smallest major dimensions is 6	.33
24.1-10	Corrugated carton, 1.51/10	.15
24.1-10	Nonbulk pack	.06
	Unit estimate	.87 min
	Order estimate	8.67 min

C. The part in B is from a lot of 600, 200 of which are packaged as in B above, and the remainder will be Kimpak overwrapped for cartons containing 6 units. Each carton has order-processing. Find the lot estimates for B and C.

Table	Description	Time
24.1-S	Setup	.15 hr
24.1-1	Order processing, 2.00/6	.33 min
24.1-2	Remove from conveyor, ea	.09
24.1-13	Kimpak material, 1.06/6	.18
24.1-13	Package of 6 has $L + W + H = 26$, $.01 \times 26$	.26
24.1-13	Unit time	.04
24.1-10	Corrugated carton, 1.51/6	.25
24.1-10	Nonbulk pack	.06
	Unit estimate	1.18 min
	Order estimate	7.08 min
	Lot estimate, $.15 + 200 \times .87/60 + 400 \times 1.18/60$	10.92 hr

D. Two little parts are inserted into a coin envelope. Ten coin envelopes are placed in a metal-edge paper box. Find the unit estimate.

Table	Description	Time
24.1-S	Setup	.15 hr
24.1-2	Get and position unit	.03 min
24.1-4	Load 2 units in coin envelopes, $.14 + .03 = .17/2$	.09
24.1-15	Metal-edge paper box, $.75/10 \times 2$	.04
24.1-15	Insert envelope and unit is ½ x 3 × 5-in. size, .01/2	.01
	Unit estimate	.17 min

TABLE 24.1 PACKAGING BENCH AND MACHINES

Setup

Bench packaging	.15 hr
Machine packaging	2.0 hr

Operation elements in estimating minutes

1. Order paperwork   2.00

2. Get and position unit, manual

Maximum dimension	Weight range	Simple	Stack	Several	Bulk remove
Difficult grasp less than 3 in.	Under .2 lb	.03 .02	.04 .04	.005 .01	.001–.0005 .001–.0005
3 to 9 in. 9 to 20 in.	Under 3 lb Under 8 lb	.03 .08	.05 .09	.01 .02	.02 .04
20 to 36 in. 36+ in.	Under 12 lb Under hoist load		.14 .25		

3. Soda straw or pipe cleaner   .28 / straw + .02 / unit

4. Coin envelope   .14 / first unit + .03 / add'l unit

5. Metal, wood, plastic tote box
    Dump   .005–.0001
    Stack, place   .01

6. Plastic bag

Non bulk pack

Smallest X, Y, or Z dimension	.1	.5	1	1.5	2	Add'l
Min / unit	.08	.11	.17	.22	.29	.13

Bulk pack

1–200 units	.01 / unit
200 or more units	.58 / bag units

7. Aluminum foil bags

10 or less bags	.97 / bag units
11 or more bags	.85 / bag units

8. Paper sack

Units in sack	1	3	6	9	Add'l	Bulk
Min / sack	.78	.85	.98	1.05	.03	1.05 / sack

9. Jar with lid   .83 / jar units
    Optional tissue cushion   .21 / jar units
    Optional tissue innerlayer

No. of layers / jar	2	3	4	5	Add'l
Min / jar units	.18	.36	.53	.71	.18

Nonbulk pack

L + W + H	1	2	3	4	Add'l
Min / unit	.01	.02	.03	.04	.01

Bulk pack

1–200 units	.01 / unit
200 or more units	.58 / jar units

10. Corrugated paper carton (ctn)
    Optional paper cushion or layer
    Coin envelope, or bag, or sack placed within carton
    Nonbulk pack

    1.51/ctn units
    .22/layer units
    .01/bag
    .06/unit

    Bulk pack

1–200 units	.16/ctn + .01/unit
200 or more units	.58/units

11. Slitted foam   .21/foam units

Slit length in.	1	2	3	4	Add'l
Min/unit	.13	.16	.20	.23	.03

12. Innerwrap

    Brown paper

Largest major dimension	2	7	12	19
Min/innerwrap package (pkg)	.30	.33	.37	.41

    Kimpack   .50/innerwrap pkg
    Tissue   .26/innerwrap pkg

Sum of 2 smallest major unit dimensions	1	2	3	4	Add'l
Min/unit	.05	.07	.08	.10	.02

13. Overwrap
    Brown paper $.87/\text{overwrap pkg} + .02/(\text{pkg } L + W + H)$
    Kimpack $1.06/\text{overwrap pkg} + .01/(\text{pkg } L + W + H)$
    Tissue $.45/\text{overwrap pkg} + .01/(\text{pkg } L + W + H)$
    No. of units/overwrap pkg   .04/unit

14. Plastic tube: .63/tube units + following value

No. of units placed in plastic tube	1	20	80	140
Min/units	.08	1.26	1.33	1.38

    Optional cushion   .16/tube units

15. Metal-edge paper box: .75/box units + following value
    Nonbulk pack

Smallest major dimension of unit placed in box	.1	.3	.8	1.3	Add'l
Min/unit	.01	.02	.03	.04	.02

    Bulk pack

1–200 units	.01/unit
200 or more units	.58/box units

    Optional tissue cushion   .36/box units

16. Miscellaneous bench packaging elements
    Stamp part with rubber stamp   .11
    Apply adhesive label   .26
    Add desiccant   .14

17. Automatic machine packaging, min/part

Units/ pkg	Pkg/min												
	10	20	30	40	50	60	70	80	90	100	150	200	300
1	.10	.05	.03	.03	.02	.02	.01	.01	.01	.01	.007	.005	.003
2	.05	.03	.02	.01	.01	.01	.007	.006	.006	.005	.003	.003	.002
3	.03	.02	.01	.01	.007	.006	.005	.004	.004	.003	.002	.002	.001
4	.03	.01	.01	.006	.005	.004	.004	.003	.003	.003	.003	.001	.001
5	.02	.01	.007	.005	.004	.003	.003	.003	.002	.002	.001	.001	.001
6	.02	.008	.006	.004	.003	.003	.002	.002	.002	.002	.001	.001	.001
8	.01	.007	.004	.003	.003	.002	.002	.002	.001	.001	.001	.001	.0004
10	.01	.006	.003	.003	.002	.002	.002	.001	.001	.001	.001	.001	.0003

24.2 Corrugated-Cardboard Packaging Conveyor-Assembly

DESCRIPTION

These data are for the final packaging of industrial products in corrugated cardboard cartons. The items have a girth which ranges from 75 to 300 and are to be packaged one item per carton. Materials used in the packaging are styrofoam, foam rubber, and polyurethane strapping in addition to the corrugated paper carton elements. Cushioning for the stability and protection of delicate products during transport is also considered.

The packaging assembly uses a mechanical roller conveyor, which is belt driven to transport the unit from final assembly and inspection. There is no power drive through the packaging assembly area, however, allowing the worker to move the product through the work stations at his or her speed. The information provided is for low to moderate lot quantities using bench work for the majority of the elements with machine assistance for some elements.

ESTIMATING DATA DISCUSSION

Setup includes time for punch in and out and to queue the product to be processed at the beginning of the roller conveyor. The setup involves stocking of packaging materials in bins or on shelves, where they are accessible to the worker. This can be done manually where the material is removed from its shipping carton and placed on the shelves, or alternatively the carton may be cut and placed directly on the shelving with a forklift.

Element 1 is the paperwork that may be necessary, including inventory slips, routing, shipping labels, etc. If it is used, the element time is divided by the quantity in the lot.

Element 2 is the manual get, fold, and position of the previously cut corrugated cardboard parts. The parts are located on the shelving and the transport of the work down the conveyor to the next part storage is included. Tabulated data include constant time related to the size of the material and a variable folding time related to the number of folds in each part. Element 2 is included in all manual packaging operations.

Element 3 is the manual get, position, and secure of any styrofoam or foam rubber cushioning materials. As in Element 2, the materials are presumed to be prefabricated to the proper dimensions and transport time is included. The padding may be molded to the product and thus requires fitting or it may be placed loosely on or around the product.

Element 4 is the manual placing of the carton over the completed product or work station. It is assumed that the large dimensions of the product make it easier to place the carton over the product and secure it rather than picking up the product and placing it into a carton with a lid. The relative clearance between the product and the inner packaging and the outer carton is the major time driver for Element 4.

Element 5 is the securing of the carton with polyurethane straps. Strapping can be done either manually or with an automatic strapping machine. If the machine is used, it is assumed that it is integrated directly into the conveyor system, and therefore no special handling is required. Element 5 includes a variable strapping time related to the perimeter of the box encircled by the strap (strap length). Provisions for any special positioning of the carton are also considered. Taping of the strap ends may be required in the case of automatic strapping to prevent the loose ends from catching on other cartons.

Element 6 considers plastic and paper sacks that may be a part of the inner packaging.

For operational estimates, three separate time estimating relationships are given. Note the rule of thumb as given by Item 24.2 of Section IV. The first includes the folding, positioning, and securing of cardboard parts as well as cushioning materials. To find the unit estimate, multiply the number of cardboard parts by the factor, and add it to the constant. If padding is needed, multiply the number of pads by the factor, and add it to the previously obtained value. The second and third relationships are for manual and automatic strapping respectively. The procedure for both relationships is to multiply the number of straps required by the given factor and add the constant. Operational estimating may be selected by the estimator if a productive hour cost value is desired. These values are for direct-labor effort only.

EXAMPLES

A. A unit is to be packaged that uses three separate cardboard parts requiring 4, 8, and 16 folds respectively. The unit is to be padded with two molded styrofoam inserts. The outside box fits tightly over the unit and is to be strapped four times with 180-in. straps. When strapping, it is necessary to rotate the unit 90 degrees for each strap. Find the unit estimate and lot estimate for 55 units.

Table	Description	Time
24.2-S	Setup, manual	.80 hr
24.2-2	Fold 1st box	.08 min
24.2-2	Fold 2nd box	.65
24.2-2	Fold 3rd box	1.73
24.2-3	Cushioning (2 inserts)	.08
24.2-3	Secure inserts	.12
23.2-4	Fit outside carton	2.40
23.2-5	Position carton on strapping machine	.03
23.2-5	Strap with machine (4 straps)	2.00
23.2-5	Rotate 4 times	.24
	Unit estimate	7.33 min
	Lot estimate	7.51 hr

B. A large standing unit is to be rolled into a box requiring 8 folds. Loose padding is placed inside the box. Because of the bulk (250-in. perimeter) and weight, hand strapping is required. Three straps are needed. Find the unit estimate and lot estimate for 15 units.

Table	Description	Time
24.2-S	Setup, manual	.80 hr
24.2-4	Fit outside, moderate clearance	1.05 min
24.2-2	Fold carton	.65
24.2-3	Padding	.06
24.2-5	3 straps, 250 in.	14.28
	Unit estimate	16.04 min
	Lot estimate	4.81 hr

C. Four small boxes (8 folds) are placed in a large carton (8 folds) and are secured with 4 pieces of molded cushioning. Two 120-in. straps are manually secured around the carton. A forklift is used for setup.

Table	Description	Time
24.2-S	Setup	.47 hr
24.2-2	Fold 4 inner boxes	2.60 min
24.2-3	Tape 4 boxes	.24
24.2-3	Position padding	.16
24.2-2	Fold outer carton	.65
24.2-4	Place outside carton over inner pack	.25
24.2-5	Strap manually	5.12
	Unit estimate	9.02 min

D. Repeat Example A, using automated setup and consider order paperwork.

Table	Description	Time
24.2-S	Setup, automated	.47 hr
24.2-1	Order paperwork, 2.00/55	.04 min
24.2-7	Unit estimate from Example A	7.33
	Unit estimate	7.37 min
	Lot estimate	7.23 hr

E. Fold outer carton (6 folds) and place product inside with minimum clearance. Both ends of the carton are taped shut. Find unit estimate.

Table	Description	Time
24.2-2	Fold outer carton	.37 min
24.2-4	Place product in carton	2.40
24.2-3	Secure ends with tape	.12
	Unit estimate	2.89 min

F. Repeat Example A using the operational cost estimating relationship given by Item 24.2 of Section IV. The number of cardboard parts = 4, number of inserts = 2, and perimeter = 180 in. Find the setup cost, hr/100 units, and the lot cost for 55 units.

Item	Description	Cost
24.2	Setup subtotal	$ 5.82
24.2	Cycle constant	$17.69
24.2	Cardboard parts, 4 × 7.87	31.48
24.2	Inserts, 2 × 1.29	2.58
24.2	Perimeter, 180 × .035	6.30
24.2	Automatic strapping constant	.75
	$/100 units	$58.80
	Lot cost	$38.16

G. Find the direct labor cost for 15 units using Item 24.2 of Section IV. From Example B, we note that the number of cardboard inserts = 1, number of cushioning inserts = 1, straps are applied manually, and the perimeter = 250 in.

Item	Description	Cost
24.2	Setup manual	$ 5.82
24.2	Cycle constant	$17.69
24.2	Cardboard inserts	7.87
24.2	Manual application constant	2.67
24.2	Strap perimeter, 250 × .225	56.25
	$/100 units	$84.48
	Lot cost	$18.49

TABLE 24.2   CORRUGATED-CARDBOARD PACKAGING CONVEYOR-ASSEMBLY

Setup

Manual stocking	.80 hr
Stocking with forklift	.47 hr

Operation elements in estimating minutes

1. Order paperwork   2.00

2. Get, fold and position cardboard piece, manual

No. of folds	Min	No. of folds	Min
4	.08	6	.37
5	.24	7	.49

No. of folds	Min	No. of folds	Min
8	.65	14	1.46
9	.78	16	1.73
10	.92	18	2.01
12	1.20	20	2.28

3. Get and secure cushioning materials, manual

Molded fit	.04
Loosely placed	.015
Secure with tape	.06

4. Place carton over unit with inner packaging, manual

Minimum clearance	2.40
Moderate clearance	1.05
Clearance not a factor	.25

5. Secure carton with straps

Automatic strapping machine

Perimeter (in)	Min
80	.25
100	.30
115	.34
130	.37
145	.41
160	.45
180	.50
200	.56

Position carton on machine   .03
Rotate carton 90–180 degrees

Large	.06
Small	.08

Manual strapping, thread strap and crimp metal fastener

Perimeter (in.)	Min
130	2.56
150	2.92
170	3.29
190	3.66
210	4.03
230	4.40
250	4.76

6. Inner package

Plastic bag	.11
Paper sack	.09

24.3 Case Packing Conveyor

DESCRIPTION

The side loading case packer often constitutes the final stage of packaging before shipment. The type of work is continuous, fully automatic packing of boxes in a case. The machine is directly related to the previous operation within a conveyor system. Due to the varied output of the boxing operations, delays in the casing operation take place. The usual operation on this machine is 14 cases per minute, maximum output, and 12 boxes per case. The data, however, allow for other conditions, should they vary from these experiences.

Operations peculiar to this machine are the reloading of empty cases, the monitoring of both the sealer glue, and the ink roller that labels each case. This machine may not require an operator. Now consider the general industrial operation of loading boxes into a case on a conveyor.

ESTIMATING DATA DISCUSSION

The setup time for this machine is considered an overhead cost.

Element 1 of the packing process is the queuing of boxes on the conveyor, or just enough to set off the pressure needle that pushes a load of boxes to Element 2.

Element 2 consists of stacking rows of boxes vertically onto a horizontal plate and inserting them into an opened case. For example, there may be 3 rows of 4 boxes loading into a case.

Element 3 is merely the closing and sealing of the cases. Elements 1 and 2 are internal to the workings of the machine so their times will be 0. Element 3 alone determines the rate at which the machine packs cases. The time provided for Element 3 is the unit time for 1 box which depends upon the number loaded and the conveyor rate of cases per min.

EXAMPLES

A. A lot of 6000 boxes is to be prepared for shipment. Determine the unit and lot estimates for 12 boxes per case and a rate of 5.7 cases per minute.

Table	Description	Time	
24.3-1	Line up boxes on conveyor	0.00	min
24.3-2	Stack boxes and load into case	0.00	
24.3-3	Close and seal case	0.015	
	Unit estimate	0.015	
	Lot estimate	1.5	hr

B. Using a rate of 8 cases per minute and 10 boxes per case, determine the unit estimate, lot estimate, and hr/100 for the casing of 4000 boxes.

Table	Description	Time	
24.3-1	Line up boxes on conveyor	0.00	min
24.3-2	Stack boxes and load into case	0.00	
24.3-3	Close and seal case	0.013	
	Unit estimate	0.013	
	Lot estimate	0.87	hr
	Hr/100	.022	

C. Re-estimate Example A using the aggregated cost estimating relationships given by Item 24.3 in Section IV.

Item	Description	Cost
24.3	Setup	0
24.3	Close and seal, $16.96/(12 \times 5.7)$	.248
	$/100 units	$ .248
	Unit estimate	$ .0025
	Lot cost	$14.88

TABLE 24.3   CASE PACKING CONVEYOR

Setup		0.00

Operation elements in estimating minutes

1. Line up boxes on conveyor	0	
2. Stack boxes and load into case	0	

3. Close and seal cases

No. of boxes	Cases / min						
	2	4	5	5.7	6	8	10
9	.058	.029	.023	.020	.019	.015	.012
10	.053	.026	.021	.018	.018	.013	.011
12	.044	.022	.018	.015	.015	.011	.009
16	.033	.016	.013	.012	.011	.008	.007
20	.026	.013	.011	.009	.009	.007	.005

UNIT ESTIMATE = .036 MIN ⟹ LOOK UP .03 AND ADD .006

NOTE HIS PERCISION RULES

APPENDIX

Conversion Table

Percision comes
From the table

Estimated min/unit	Hr/1	Hr/10	Hr/100	Hr/1000	Hr/10,000	Pc/hr
.0001				.0017	.01667	600,000
.0002				.0033	.03333	300,000
.0003			.001	.0050	.05000	200,000
.0004			.001	.0067	.06667	150,000
.0005			.001	.0083	.08333	120,000
.0006			.001	.0100	.10000	100,000
.0007			.001	.0117	.11667	85,714
.0008			.001	.0133	.13333	75,000
.0009			.002	.0150	.15000	66,667
.001			.002	.0167	.16667	60,000
.002			.003	.0333	.33333	30,000
.003			.005	.0500	.50000	20,000
.004			.007	.0667	.66667	15,000
.005			.008	.0833	.83333	12,000
.006			.010	.1000	1.00000	10,000
.007			.012	.1167	1.16667	8 571
.008			.013	.1333	1.33333	7 500
.009			.015	.1500	1.50000	6 667
.01			.017	.1667	1.66667	6 000
.02			.033	.3333	3.33333	3 000
.03		.01	.050	.5000	5.00000	2 000
.04		.01	.067	.6667	6.66667	1 500
.05		.01	.083	.8333	8.33333	1 200
.06		.01	.100	1.0000	10.00000	1 000
.07		.01	.117	1.1667	11.66667	857
.08		.01	.133	1.3333	13.33333	750
.09		.02	.150	1.5000	15.00000	667

Estimated min/unit	Hr/1	Hr/10	Hr/100	Hr/1000	Hr/10,000	Pc/hr
.10		.02	.167	1.6667	16.66667	600
.11		.02	.183	1.8333	18.33333	545
.12		.02	.200	2.0000	20.00000	500
.13		.02	.217	2.1667	21.66667	462
.14		.02	.233	2.3333	23.33333	429
.15		.03	.250	2.5000	25.00000	400
.16		.03	.267	2.6667	26.66667	375
.17		.03	.283	2.8333	28.33333	353
.18		.03	.300	3.0000	30.00000	333
.19		.03	.317	3.1667	31.66667	316
.20		.03	.333	3.3333	33.33333	300
.21		.04	.350	3.5000	35.00000	286
.22		.04	.367	3.6667	36.66667	273
.23		.04	.383	3.8333	38.33333	261
.24		.04	.400	4.0000	40.00000	250
.25		.04	.417	4.1667	41.66667	240
.26		.04	.433	4.3333	43.33333	231
.27		.05	.450	4.5000	45.00000	222
.28		.05	.467	4.6667	46.66667	214
.29		.05	.483	4.8333	48.33333	207
.30		.05	.500	5.0000	50.00000	200
.31		.05	.517	5.1667	51.66667	194
.32		.05	.533	5.3333	53.33333	188
.33		.06	.550	5.5000	55.00000	182
.34		.06	.567	5.6667	56.66667	176
.35		.06	.583	5.8333	58.33333	171
.36		.06	.600	6.0000	60.00000	167
.37		.06	.617	6.1667	61.66667	162
.38		.06	.633	6.3333	63.33333	158
.39		.07	.650	6.5000	65.00000	154
.40		.07	.667	6.6667	66.66667	150
.41		.07	.683	6.8333	68.33333	146
.42		.07	.700	7.0000	70.00000	143
.43		.07	.717	7.1667	71.66667	140
.44		.07	.733	7.3333	73.33333	136
.45		.08	.750	7.5000	75.00000	133
.46		.08	.767	7.6667	76.66667	130
.47		.08	.783	7.8333	78.33333	128
.48		.08	.800	8.0000	80.00000	125
.49		.08	.817	8.1667	81.66667	122
.50		.08	.833	8.3333	83.33333	120
.51		.09	.850	8.5000	85.00000	118
.52		.09	.867	8.6667	86.66667	115
.53		.09	.883	8.8333	88.33333	113
.54		.09	.900	9.0000	90.00000	111
.55		.09	.917	9.1667	91.66667	109
.56		.09	.933	9.3333	93.33333	107
.57		.10	.950	9.5000	95.00000	105
.58		.10	.967	9.6667	96.66667	103
.59		.10	.983	9.8333	98.33333	102
.60		.10	1.000	10.0000	100.00000	100

Estimated min/unit	Hr/1	Hr/10	Hr/100	Hr/1000	Hr/10,000	Pc/hr
.61		.10	1.017	10.1667		98
.62		.10	1.033	10.3333		97
.63		.11	1.050	10.5000		95
.64		.11	1.067	10.6667		94
.65		.11	1.083	10.8333		92
.66		.11	1.100	11.0000		91
.67		.11	1.117	11.1667		90
.68		.11	1.133	11.3333		88
.69		.12	1.150	11.5000		87
.70		.12	1.167	11.6667		86
.71		.12	1.183	11.8333		85
.72		.12	1.200	12.0000		83
.73		.12	1.217	12.1667		82
.74		.12	1.233	12.3333		81
.75		.13	1.250	12.5000		80
.76		.13	1.267	12.6667		79
.77		.13	1.283	12.8333		78
.78		.13	1.300	13.0000		77
.79		.13	1.317	13.1667		76
.80		.13	1.333	13.3333		75
.81		.14	1.350	13.5000		74
.82		.14	1.367	13.6667		73
.83		.14	1.383	13.8333		72
.84		.14	1.400	14.0000		71
.85		.14	1.417	14.1667		71
.86		.14	1.433	14.3333		70
.87		.15	1.450	14.5000		69
.88		.15	1.467	14.6667		68
.89		.15	1.483	14.8333		67
.90		.15	1.500	15.0000		67
.91		.15	1.517	15.1667		66
.92		.15	1.533	15.3333		65
.93		.16	1.550	15.5000		65
.94		.16	1.567	15.6667		64
.95		.16	1.583	15.8333		63
.96		.16	1.600	16.0000		63
.97		.16	1.617	16.1667		62
.98		.16	1.633	16.3333		61
.99		.17	1.650	16.5000		61
1.00		.17	1.667	16.6667		60
1.01		.17	1.683	16.8333		59
1.02		.17	1.700	17.0000		59
1.03		.17	1.717	17.1667		58
1.04		.17	1.733	17.3333		58
1.05		.18	1.750	17.5000		57
1.06		.18	1.767	17.6667		57
1.07		.18	1.783	17.8333		56
1.08		.18	1.800	18.0000		56
1.09		.18	1.817	18.1667		55
1.10		.18	1.833	18.3333		55
1.11		.19	1.850	18.5000		54

Estimated min/unit	Hr/1	Hr/10	Hr/100	Hr/1000	Hr/10,000	Pc/hr
1.12		.19	1.867	18.6667		54
1.13		.19	1.883	18.8333		53
1.14		.19	1.900	19.0000		53
1.15		.19	1.917	19.1667		52
1.16		.19	1.933	19.3333		52
1.17		.20	1.950	19.5000		51
1.18		.20	1.967	19.6667		51
1.19		.20	1.983	19.8333		50
1.20		.20	2.000	20.0000		50
1.21		.20	2.017	20.1667		50
1.22		.20	2.033	20.3333		49
1.23		.21	2.050	20.5000		49
1.24		.21	2.067	20.6667		48
1.25		.21	2.083	20.8333		48
1.26		.21	2.100	21.0000		48
1.27		.21	2.117	21.1667		47
1.28		.21	2.133	21.3333		47
1.29		.22	2.150	21.5000		47
1.30		.22	2.167	21.6667		46
1.31		.22	2.183	21.8333		46
1.32		.22	2.200	22.0000		45
1.33		.22	2.217	22.1667		45
1.34		.22	2.233	22.3333		45
1.35		.23	2.250	22.5000		44
1.36		.23	2.267	22.6667		44
1.37		.23	2.283	22.8333		44
1.38		.23	2.300	23.0000		43
1.39		.23	2.317	23.1667		43
1.40		.23	2.333	23.3333		43
1.41		.24	2.350	23.5000		43
1.42		.24	2.367	23.6667		42
1.43		.24	2.383	23.8333		42
1.44		.24	2.400	24.0000		42
1.45		.24	2.417	24.1667		41
1.46		.24	2.433	24.3333		41
1.47		.25	2.450	24.5000		41
1.48		.25	2.467	24.6667		41
1.49		.25	2.483	24.8333		40
1.50		.25	2.500	25.0000		40
1.51		.25	2.517	25.1667		40
1.52		.25	2.533	25.3333		39
1.53		.26	2.550	25.5000		39
1.54		.26	2.567	25.6667		39
1.55		.26	2.583	25.8333		39
1.56		.26	2.600	26.0000		38
1.57		.26	2.617	26.1667		38
1.58		.26	2.633	26.3333		38
1.59		.27	2.650	26.5000		38
1.60		.27	2.667	26.6667		38
1.61		.27	2.683	26.8333		37
1.62		.27	2.700	27.0000		37

Estimated min / unit	Hr / 1	Hr / 10	Hr / 100	Hr / 1000	Hr / 10,000	Pc / hr
1.63		.27	2.717	27.1667		37
1.64		.27	2.717	27.3333		37
1.65		.28	2.750	27.5000		36
1.66		.28	2.767	27.6667		36
1.67		.28	2.783	27.8333		36
1.68		.28	2.800	28.0000		36
1.69		.28	2.817	28.1667		36
1.70		.28	2.833	28.3333		35
1.71		.29	2.850	28.5000		35
1.72		.29	2.867	28.6667		35
1.73		.29	2.883	28.8333		35
1.74		.29	2.900	29.0000		34
1.75		.29	2.917	29.1667		34
1.76		.29	2.933	29.3333		34
1.77		.30	2.950	29.5000		34
1.78		.30	2.967	29.6667		34
1.79		.30	2.983	29.8333		34
1.80		.30	3.000	30.0000		33
1.81		.30	3.017	30.1667		33
1.82		.30	3.033	30.3333		33
1.83		.31	3.050	30.5000		33
1.84		.31	3.067	30.6667		33
1.85		.31	3.083	30.8333		32
1.86		.31	3.100	31.0000		32
1.87		.31	3.117	31.1667		32
1.88		.31	3.133	31.3333		32
1.89		.32	3.150	31.5000		32
1.90		.32	3.167	31.6667		32
1.91		.32	3.183	31.8333		31
1.92		.32	3.200	32.0000		31
1.93		.32	3.217	32.1667		31
1.94		.32	3.233	32.3333		31
1.95		.33	3.250	32.5000		31
1.96		.33	3.267	32.6667		31
1.97		.33	3.283	32.8333		30
1.98		.33	3.300	33.0000		30
1.99		.33	3.317	33.1667		30
2.00		.33	3.333	33.3333		30
2.04		.34	3.400	34.000		29
2.06		.34	3.433	34.3333		29
2.08		.35	3.467	34.6667		29
2.10		.35	3.500	35.0000		29
2.12		.35	3.533	35.3333		28
2.14		.36	3.567	35.6667		28
2.16		.36	3.600	36.0000		28
2.18		.36	3.633	36.3333		28
2.20		.37	3.667	36.6667		27
2.22		.37	3.700	37.0000		27
2.24		.37	3.733	37.3333		27
2.26		.38	3.767	37.6667		27
2.28		.38	3.800	38.0000		26

Estimated min/unit	Hr/1	Hr/10	Hr/100	Hr/1000	Hr/10,000	Pc/hr
2.30		.38	3.833	38.3333		26
2.32		.39	3.867	38.6667		26
2.34		.39	3.900	39.0000		26
2.36		.39	3.933	39.3333		25
2.38		.40	3.967	39.6667		25
2.40		.40	4.000	40.0000		25
2.42		.40	4.033	40.3333		25
2.44		.41	4.067	40.6667		25
2.46		.41	4.100	41.0000		24
2.48		.41	4.133	41.3333		24
2.50		.42	4.167	41.6667		24
2.52		.42	4.200	42.0000		24
2.54		.42	4.233	42.3333		24
2.56		.43	4.267	42.6667		23
2.58		.43	4.300	43.0000		23
2.60		.43	4.333	43.3333		23
2.62		.44	4.367	43.6667		23
2.64		.44	4.400	44.0000		23
2.66		.44	4.433	44.3333		23
2.68		.45	4.467	44.6667		22
2.70		.45	4.500	45.0000		22
2.72		.45	4.533	45.3333		22
2.74		.46	4.567	45.6667		22
2.76		.46	4.600	46.0000		22
2.78		.46	4.633	46.3333		22
2.80		.47	4.667	46.6667		21
2.82		.47	4.700	47.0000		21
2.84		.47	4.733	47.3333		21
2.86		.48	4.767	47.6667		21
2.88		.48	4.800	48.0000		21
2.90		.48	4.833	48.3333		21
2.92		.49	4.867	48.6667		21
2.94		.49	4.900	49.0000		20
2.96		.49	4.933	49.3333		20
2.98		.50	4.967	49.6667		20
3.00	.1	.50	5.000	50.0000		20
3.05	.1	.51	5.083	50.8333		19.7
3.10	.1	.52	5.167	51.6667		19.4
3.15	.1	.53	5.250	52.5000		19.0
3.20	.1	.53	5.333	53.5555		18.8
3.25	.1	.54	5.417	54.1667		18.5
3.30	.1	.55	5.500	55.0000		18.2
3.35	.1	.56	5.583	55.8333		17.9
3.40	.1	.57	5.067	56.6667		17.6
3.45	.1	.58	5.750	57.5000		17.4
3.50	.1	.58	5.833	58.3333		17.1
3.55	.1	.59	5.917	59.1667		16.9
3.60	.1	.60	6.000	60.0000		16.7
3.65	.1	.61	6.083	60.8333		16.4
3.70	.1	.62	6.167	61.6667		16.2
3.75	.1	.63	6.250	62.5000		16.0

Estimated min / unit	Hr / 1	Hr / 10	Hr / 100	Hr / 1000	Hr / 10,000	Pc / hr
3.80	.1	.63	6.333	63.3333		15.8
3.85	.1	.64	6.417	64.1667		15.6
3.90	.1	.65	6.500	65.0000		15.4
3.95	.1	.66	6.583	65.8333		15.2
4.00	.1	.67	6.667	66.6667		15.0
4.05	.1	.68	6.750	67.5000		14.8
4.10	.1	.68	6.833	68.3333		14.6
4.15	.1	.69	6.917	69.1667		14.5
4.20	.1	.70	7.000	70.0000		14.3
4.25	.1	.71	7.083	70.8333		14.1
4.30	.1	.72	7.167	71.6667		14.0
4.35	.1	.73	7.250	72.5000		13.8
4.40	.1	.73	7.333	73.3333		13.6
4.45	.1	.74	7.417	74.1667		13.5
4.50	.1	.75	7.500	75.0000		13.3
4.55	.1	.76	7.583	75.8333		13.2
4.60	.1	.77	7.667	76.6667		13.0
4.65	.1	.78	7.750	77.5000		12.9
4.70	.1	.78	7.833	78.3333		12.8
4.75	.1	.79	7.917	79.1667		12.6
4.80	.1	.80	8.000	80.0000		12.5
4.85	.1	.81	8.083	80.8333		12.4
4.90	.1	.82	8.167	81.6667		12.2
4.95	.1	.83	8.250	82.5000		12.1
5.00	.1	.83	8.333	83.3333		12.0
5.10	.1	.85	8.500	85.0000		11.8
5.20	.1	.87	8.667	86.6667		11.5
5.30	.1	.88	8.833	88.3333		11.3
5.40	.1	.90	9.000	90.0000		11.1
5.50	.1	.92	9.167	91.6667		10.9
5.60	.1	.93	9.333	93.3333		10.7
5.70	.1	.95	9.500	95.0000		10.5
5.80	.1	.97	9.667	96.6667		10.3
5.90	.1	.98	9.833	98.3333		10.2
6.00	.1	1.00	10.000	100.0000		10.0
6.20	.1	1.03	10.333			9.7
6.40	.1	1.07	10.667			9.4
6.60	.1	1.10	11.000			9.1
6.80	.1	1.13	11.333			8.8
7.00	.1	1.17	11.667			8.6
7.20	.1	1.20	12.000			8.3
7.40	.1	1.23	12.333			8.1
7.60	.1	1.27	12.667			7.9
7.80	.1	1.30	13.000			7.7
8.00	.1	1.33	13.333			7.5
8.20	.1	1.37	13.667			7.3
8.40	.1	1.40	14.000			7.1
8.60	.1	1.43	14.333			7.0
8.80	.1	1.47	14.667			6.8
9.00	.2	1.50	15.000			6.7
9.20	.2	1.53	15.333			6.5

Estimated min / unit	Hr / 1	Hr / 10	Hr / 100	Hr / 1000	Hr / 10,000	Pc / hr
9.40	.2	1.57	15.667			6.4
9.60	.2	1.60	16.000			6.3
9.80	.2	1.63	16.333			6.1
10.00	.2	1.67	16.667			6.0
11.00	.2	1.83	18.333			5.5
12.00	.2	2.00	20.000			5.0
13.00	.2	2.17	21.667			4.6
14.00	.2	2.33	23.333			4.3
15.00	.3	2.50	25.000			4.0
16.00	.3	2.67	26.667			3.8
17.00	.3	2.83	28.333			3.5
18.00	.3	3.00	30.000			3.3
19.00	.3	3.17	31.667			3.2
20.00	.3	3.33	33.333			3.0
25.00	.4	4.17	41.667			2.4
30.00	.5	5.00	50.000			2.0
35.00	.6	5.83	58.333			1.7
40.00	.7	6.67	66.667			1.5
45.00	.8	7.50	75.000			1.3
50.00	.8	8.33	83.333			1.2
60.00	1.0	10.00	100.000			1.0
70.00	1.2	11.67				0.86
80.00	1.3	13.33				0.75
90.00	1.5	15.00				0.67
100.00	1.7	16.67				0.60

Index

ERRORS IN ESTIMATING:

1. -TRANSPOSING NUMBERS & ERRORS
   USUALLY MORE POSITIVE ERRORS

2. - OMITT ELEMENTS ~~AND~~ OR OPERATIONS

2. ERRORS IN POLICY:
   a) ERROR IN A CONSTANT USED
   b) WRONG PROCCESSES OR ELEMENT SELECTION
   c) WRONG MODEL

3. RISK
   WHY DID THE LOW MAN'S BID HAVE IT THAT LOW?
   ERROR? HIGH PRODUCTIVITY? NEEDS JOB? FITS WELL INTO BUSINESS

   $$\text{CAPTURE RATE} = \frac{\text{ESTIMATES WON}}{\text{ESTIMATES MADE}}$$

TO CALCULATE THE ERROR:

A. $$\frac{\text{ACTUAL} - \text{EST}}{\text{ACTUAL}}$$

B. $$\frac{\text{DETAIL EST} - \text{PRELIM. EST}}{\text{DETAIL EST.}}$$

EX: 100 JOBS
- 30 TECH. REASONS
* PRELIMINARY EST
  -20 ECONOMIC REASONS
* DETAILED EST. ON 50
  GET 15 JOBS
* ACTUAL COST ON 15
  DETERMINE PRODUCTIVITY
  FACTOR FOR YOUR ESTIMATES